OPTIMAL CONTROL OF
ENGINEERING PROCESSES

A BLAISDELL BOOK IN THE PURE AND APPLIED SCIENCES

CONSULTING EDITOR

Leon Lapidus, Princeton University

Optimal Control of Engineering Processes

Leon Lapidus / PRINCETON UNIVERSITY

Rein Luus / UNIVERSITY OF TORONTO

BLAISDELL PUBLISHING COMPANY

A Division of Ginn and Company

WALTHAM, MASSACHUSETTS · TORONTO · LONDON

Library of Congress Catalog Card Number: 67-13055
Printed in the United States of America.

To Bette

Preface

This book is designed as a text for seniors or first-year graduate students in engineering who are interested in optimal control. It provides the student with the basic fundamentals of this important area, which has application to both process control and on-line digital control of systems or processes. Since much of the subject can be treated most simply by the use of vector–matrix methods, part of the first chapter is devoted to acquainting the reader with matrix manipulations. This chapter also presents the fundamental definitions and concepts, both mathematical and physical, to be used in later chapters. Throughout, an effort is made to provide a clear and logical presentation of the subject rather than to merely impart information.

In order to present the material in a unified manner, we have minimized the number of physical systems used to illustrate the conceptual discussions. This has the over-all advantage that the memory of the reader is not overburdened and the different mathematical techniques can be readily compared and understood. Also, we have chosen physical systems that are realistic enough to maintain a continued interest.

The reader will find that a strong background in mathematical techniques and chemical engineering is not essential to understanding this book. We have presented this information as it is required in the development and discussion. Although most of the examples are from chemical engineering, a sufficient background is given so that readers who are not in this field will have no problem in fully understanding the physical systems under consideration and clearly seeing the motivation underlying their solution. Our experience in teaching a number of graduate groups over the last few years confirms this procedure.

The mathematical techniques are introduced gradually, with simple illustrations used wherever possible. This facilitates the absorption of new ideas and illustrates their application to optimal control in an elementary, yet meaningful, manner. At the end of each chapter, more detailed examples are considered and fully explained so that the reader will see the application of the material in an effective way.

The ideas in this book are intended as a solid background for the design of optimal control of engineering systems. Ample references are given at the end of each chapter to allow the reader to pursue his interests further. Throughout the book an effort is made to provide a unified approach to solving practical problems and to bridge the gap between theory and practice.

We have developed the chapters in a systematic manner. After having carefully built the foundation in Chapter 1, we present in Chapter 2 various mathematical procedures which can be used to construct the optimal control for engineering systems. Simple illustrations at this stage acquaint the reader with these methods, presenting both the computational difficulties and the advantages of certain methods over others. In Chapter 3 the methods developed in Chapter 2 are applied to engineering problems that are either linear in nature or linearized. These methods are then extended and applied to nonlinear systems in Chapter 4. In Chapter 5 stability concepts are introduced and applied in control synthesis. The main emphasis in Chapter 6 is on the averaging technique which can be used effectively to analyze two-dimensional, highly nonlinear systems.

We are grateful to Dr. H. Lesser, Dr. T. Jensen, Mr. B. Baker, and numerous other people who furnished some of the computational results presented in this book or helped in the formulation of certain of the concepts discussed. Our thanks also to the National Science Foundation, which supported some of the work quoted under NSF Grant GK-460; computer time for many of the calculations was furnished by Princeton University, supported in part by National Science Foundation Grant NSF GP-579. Finally, financial assistance was gratefully received by one of the authors from Princeton University in the form of a Sloan Postdoctoral fellowship during a substantial period of the development of this book.

L.L.
R.L.

Contents

List of Symbols

a_{ij}	element in the ith row and jth column of $\boldsymbol{A}$ matrix
a	constant; a parameter in Mathieu equation
A	constant
$\boldsymbol{A}$	state coefficient matrix ($n \times n$)
A_i	ith area mapped by the radius in the phase plane
b_j	lower constraint on u_j
b	flow rate; constant
B	constant
$\boldsymbol{B}$	control coefficient matrix ($n \times r$); other matrix
c_j	upper constraint on u_j
c_i	ith element of the constant vector $\mathbf{c}$; cost of ith item
c_p	heat capacity; constant
$\boldsymbol{c}$	constant vector
C_n	class containing all the functions whose derivatives including the nth are continuous
C	total cost; deviation from steady state concentration
$\boldsymbol{C}$	constant matrix
d	constant; distance function
$\boldsymbol{d}_i$	vectors defined specifically for the extraction train
D	domain; differential operator $\equiv d/dx$
D_i	constant
$\boldsymbol{D}$	matrix; a diagonal matrix
e	constant
$\boldsymbol{e}_i$	ith orthogonal unit vector
$\boldsymbol{e}$	error vector; unit vector
$\mathbf{E}$	coefficient matrix for the transformed Riccati equation
f	general function; constant

f_i ith element of the vector $\boldsymbol{f}$
$\boldsymbol{f}$ general vector function (continuous)
F flow rate; force; damping factor
g_p scalar
g general function; positive quantity; constraint function
$\boldsymbol{g}$ some vector function
G flow rate of inert gas stream
$\boldsymbol{G}$ influence (Green's) function
h small deviation; inert liquid holdup on each plate; raffinate holdup; constraint function
$\boldsymbol{h}$ general discrete-time function
H_μ Hurwitz determinant of degree μ
H inert vapor holdup; extract holdup; Hamiltonian; enthalpy
I performance index; current
$\bar{I}$ light intensity
$\boldsymbol{I}$ unit matrix
j Riccati equation variable in scalar form
J indicator of figure of merit; integral of performance index
J_i ith job
$\boldsymbol{J}_{p-k}$ positive semidefinite symmetric matrix
k small deviation; proportional control constant; index for sampling times; restoring force constant
k_i reaction velocity constant
K constant; stroboscopic function
$\boldsymbol{K}$ feedback gain matrix; control variation matrix
$\boldsymbol{K}_{p-k}$ feedback coefficient matrix
$\bar{\boldsymbol{K}}$ time-varying feedback matrix
l constant
L flow rate of inert liquid absorbent; inductance; stroboscopic function
$\boldsymbol{L}$ coefficient matrix for $\boldsymbol{u}^*$
m number of output variables; mass
$\boldsymbol{m}$ transformed control such that $\boldsymbol{m}_e = \boldsymbol{0}$
M constant; contour integral; supremum of H
n number of state variables
N number of discretized levels for a state variable
O order of
p constant
p_{ij} element in ith row and jth column of matrix $\boldsymbol{P}$
P number of sampling intervals or stages; function of x and y; profit
P_2 function of variables of second degree or higher

$\boldsymbol{P}$ weighting matrix; second variation matrix
q constant; flow rate
q_{ij} element in ith row and jth column of matrix $\boldsymbol{Q}$
$\boldsymbol{q}$ slack vector; unknown vector
Q function of x and y; quadratic form; number of discretized levels for control variable
Q_2 function of variables of second degree or higher
$\boldsymbol{Q}$ weighting matrix
r number of control variables; constricting radius
r_i constricting radius for u_i
R scalar; resistance; radius of a hypersphere; function of z; number of time stages
$\boldsymbol{R}$ weighting matrix; second variation matrix
s number of uncontrolled variables; number of hypersurfaces; signature of matrix
$\mathbf{s}$ slack vector; vector expression
S nonoptimal index; smooth surface
$\boldsymbol{S}$ weighting matrix
t time
t_f final time of operation
t_0 initial time (usually taken to be zero)
T sampling time; deviation from steady state temperature
T_i transport delay
T_1 largest term in power series
T_R reactor temperature
$\boldsymbol{T}$ second variation matrix
u_j jth element of control vector $\boldsymbol{u}$
$\boldsymbol{u}$ control vector ($r \times 1$)
$\boldsymbol{u}^*$ modified control vector ($rP \times 1$)
$\boldsymbol{u}^d$ control at desired state
$\boldsymbol{u}^\circ$ optimal control vector
v normalized flow rate; integral expression
$\boldsymbol{v}$ column vector of controllability matrix; transformed $\boldsymbol{y}$ vector; transformed control vector; uncontrolled variable vector
V Liapunov function; trial function; voltage
V_k $(k + 1)$th Liapunov function obtained by iteration
w scalar function; extract solvent flow rate
$\boldsymbol{w}$ orthogonalized column vector of controllability matrix
W scalar function
W_T total quantity of solvent to be distributed

$\boldsymbol{W}$ controllability matrix
x general variable
x_i ith element of the state vector $\boldsymbol{x}$; mole fraction of species i
x_m composition of liquid leaving the mth plate; raffinate composition leaving the mth stage
x^0 extremum point
$\boldsymbol{x}$ state of the system
$\boldsymbol{x}_0$ initial state $= \boldsymbol{x}(0)$
$\boldsymbol{x}_e$ equilibrium state
$\boldsymbol{x}^d$ desired state
y general variable
y_i ith element of the output vector $\boldsymbol{y}$
y_m composition of vapor leaving the mth plate; extract composition leaving the mth stage
y^0 extremum point
$\boldsymbol{y}$ output of the system
z_i ith element of the adjoint vector $\boldsymbol{z}$; transformed variable
$\boldsymbol{z}$ adjoint vector; deviation from steady state
$\boldsymbol{Z}$ matrix
α constant; operator; delay factor; function of $\|\boldsymbol{x}\|$
$-\boldsymbol{\alpha}$ lower bound for $\boldsymbol{u}$
$\boldsymbol{\alpha}^*$ vector of lower bounds $(rP \times 1)$
β delay factor; function of $\|\boldsymbol{x}\|$
$\boldsymbol{\beta}$ upper bound for $\boldsymbol{u}$
$\boldsymbol{\beta}^*$ vector of upper bounds $(rP \times 1)$
γ bound on control; function of $\|\boldsymbol{x}\|$
γ_i bound on u_i
δ increment, for example, δt, $\delta \boldsymbol{u}$, and so on
δ_{ij} Kronecker delta
Δ increment, for example, Δt; forward difference operator; determinant
$\boldsymbol{\Delta}$ control coefficient matrix for discrete systems
ε small parameter
ε_i some constant
η dimensionless temperature
$\boldsymbol{\eta}$ adjoint vector at $t = 0$
θ time
$\boldsymbol{\theta}$ matrix
λ eigenvalue; dummy variable; Lagrange multiplier
$\boldsymbol{\lambda}$ vector of Lagrange multipliers
$\boldsymbol{\Lambda}$ diagonal matrix

μ degree of Hurwitz determinant
ρ square of the radius; stopping relation; density
ξ dimensionless concentration
$\boldsymbol{\xi}$ arbitrary nonzero vector
τ rescaled time; stroboscopic time
τ_i time of execution of ith job
ϕ transformed angle in phase plane; integrand for performance index
$\boldsymbol{\Phi}$ transition matrix; state coefficient matrix for discrete systems
ψ angle measured in the phase plane; additional term in performance index to weight the final state
$\boldsymbol{\psi}$ final state constraint
ω angular frequency

Subscripts

e equilibrium
f final time
i initial condition; index
j index
k index
l index
m index
n index
0 initial condition
ss steady state
A component A
E Euclidean
P relating to stage P
R reactor
S sum of the absolute values
T total
ν size of the determinant B_ν
μ degree of Hurwitz determinant

Superscripts

$*$ specific value; modified quantity
$'$ transpose
generalized inverse
$^\circ$ optimal; specific value
d desired
j iteration step
p pth iteration step

I

Fundamental Definitions and System Structures

Control, in the sense to be used in this book, is concerned with affecting the physical behavior of systems. Control may be achieved by means of mechanical, electrical, electromechanical, electronic, and other devices, which should function without direct human intervention or supervision. The theory and application of control are a complex and immature subject undergoing development and change at present. There are a few simple notions, however, which are at the heart of any control analysis, in whatever form that theory may be explained or to whatever problems it may be applied.

The assumptions which enter into the study of a control problem may be classed into the following four groups.

(1) *Measurement.* What dynamical variables of the system can be measured, how accurate are these measurements, and how fast can they be performed?

(2) *Dynamics.* How does the system change with time, or what will be the future effect of the inputs which are applied at present?

(3) *Performance criteria.* How should the system behave, or when are its outputs considered satisfactory?

(4) *Stability.* How can we assure ourselves that any control which is used does not cause the system to become unstable or "runaway"?

It is relatively simple to illustrate each of these four different groups of assumptions by taking the continuous-stirred-tank reactor (CSTR), which is familiar to chemical engineers, as a simple example.

The measurement problem (1) is concerned with chemical analysis of the input and/or output stream, determination of the temperature inside the reactor, and various flow-rates and concentrations. Usually only a few of these can be measured, due to physical or economic reasons.

The dynamics (2) of the CSTR involve both the molecular mechanisms of chemical reaction and the collective effects of heat transfer, mass transfer, and catalysis. These factors must be described in precise mathematical terms, for instance, by differential equations. The equations do not necessarily have to come from a profound physical theory (although physical understanding of the problem is always helpful); they might be obtained in a purely empirical way by matching the observed behavior of the reactor. The important thing is that the behavior of the equations and of the actual reactor be closely similar, at least in regard to those things one wants to control.

The performance criterion (3) for the control of the CSTR is usually one of maximizing the desired yield of the reaction. Alternatively, one might want to keep the energy requirements low or to increase the throughput without appreciably reducing the yield. In more complex cases, one might wish to change the relative proportion of the end products of the reaction, depending on the sales situation at the moment. Some of these considerations may be contradictory, in which case they must be given relative weights so that a compromise can be made. In any event, some precise specification must be set up which expresses the management's view as to what the desirable mode of operation should be. This is often a very difficult task, but fortunately nowadays management is ably assisted in this by operations researchers, market analysts, sales forecasters, etc. Performance specifications need not be set up in such a way that they can be actually achieved; they merely represent goals that one attempts to reach by means of control.

The stability (4) of CSTR has really two implications. First, there could be more than one steady state at which the reactor can potentially operate. Then, by stability of the reactor one essentially means its stability at a particular desirable steady state. If the system can be kept close to this state under all operational conditions, the CSTR is said to be stable. If, however, the system drifts to another steady state, the CSTR is said to be unstable even if the latter point itself is stable. This brings to mind immediately the concept of "region of stability." The other implication is stability as considered from the physical side. The specifications for the controller should not be so unreasonable as to exceed obvious physical limitations of the equipment. Also the control should not be such that the reactor burns up or creates some equally unwanted situation.

It is a widespread misconception that once the relevant physical variables in a system can be measured, the control of the system is quite trivial. This is sometimes further supported by a well-known theorem in information theory which (quoted out of context) says that no amount of data processing can increase the information already contained in the primary physical measurements.

As every driver knows, merely looking at the white line on the road is not enough to keep the car in the lane. There must be a link between the eye and the steering wheel. By analogy, the principal problem in control theory is to prescribe how to utilize the available information in affecting the free variables of the system. In other words, the problem is to compute the best control action on the basis of measurements.

In the simplest control systems, this is accomplished by making the control signal equal to the error signal (the difference between desired and actual output). This is feedback control in its simplest form. Whenever the control signal is determined from consideration of the actual system output, the control system is called feedback control. Here the output information is fed back through the control signal to the input of the system. Plant parameter uncertainty and drift and subjected disturbances make feedback configuration attractive. In more complicated feedback systems, the error signal is subjected to certain analog computing operations (differentiation, integration, etc.) which result in the control signal. An example of this is the well-known proportional, reset and rate controller. In large-scale control systems built to work with digital computers, much more complicated operations can be performed on the measured data.

These general comments merely serve to point out some of the features involved in the development of control theory and its application to physical systems. It is, of course, necessary to be more explicit in many areas. Thus, this first chapter will be concerned with developing the ground rules for all succeeding chapters in the book, that is, presenting the basic definitions to be used, structuring the necessary mathematical models, defining the control and stability problems to be analyzed, and outlining a number of physical systems to be used as representative examples.

Before starting on this material, however, it is important to briefly address ourselves to the *identification problem*. This concerns the problem of specifying the explicit form of the equations describing a physical process. In this book we shall always assume that these equations can be obtained directly by the application of first principles. In many problems the means of identifying a physical system may be as important, if not more important, than the control itself. However, the complexity and details required for a valid understanding of this feature precludes any further discussion here.

1.1. Fundamental definitions and notation

To present a unified picture throughout this book, we will use certain definitions and consistent notations. Some of these may seem extraneous to the reader, but for purposes of clarity in subsequent discussion it seems worthwhile to briefly develop these items.

Operator. An operator is a symbol for some mathematical procedure which changes one function into another function. Thus, the following are some operators applied to the continuous function $f(x) = x^2 + a$, with $a = \text{const}$. In

Operator operating on $f(x) = x^2 + a$	Resulting function
$c = \text{const}$	$cx^2 + ca$
square root	$(x^2 + a)^{1/2}$
$D = d/dx$	$2x$
$I = \int(\ )\,dx$	$x^3/3 + ax + K$

addition, there are certain operators which apply to discrete functions and for which the independent variable can take on only discrete values, that is, the identification of composition in a series of discrete but connected stages $f(x_n)$, where n indicates a stage number. Listed below are two such discrete operators taken from among a large variety of possible ones [4].*

Operator operating on $f(x_n)$	Resulting function
Δ	$f(x_{n+1}) - f(x_n)$
∇	$f(x_n) - f(x_{n-1})$

Linearity. An operator α is linear if

$$\alpha[f(x) + g(x)] = \alpha f(x) + \alpha g(x).$$

Thus the c operator, the D, I, Δ, and ∇ operators above are all linear. By contrast, an operator which is not linear is called nonlinear, an example being the square-root operator.

It is important to note that a particular mathematical formula may involve not just one but many different operators. Furthermore, some of these may be linear and others nonlinear. As an example, consider the simple ordinary differential equation

$$dy/dx = y^2 + x^2.$$

* Numbers in brackets refer to references listed at the end of each chapter.

This may be written as

$$Dy = f(y, x),$$

where the terminology is taken to mean that the operator D applied to y yields dy/dx.

Vectors and matrices. Since we shall constantly be dealing with systems of many dimensions in many variables, the convenient shorthand notation consistent with vector–matrix terminology will be used. We shall attempt to always use small bold-face italic letters to denote vectors and capital boldface italic letters to denote matrices. Thus $\boldsymbol{x}$ will be a vector and $\boldsymbol{A}$ a matrix. The usual terminology consistent with vector–matrix operations will be assumed [4], but there are certain items which seem important enough to quote here. Thus $\boldsymbol{x}$ will always be taken as a *column* vector and the prime, $\boldsymbol{x}'$, will indicate the *transpose* of either a vector or matrix in which the rows and columns are interchanged. The designation $(m \times n)$ for either a vector or matrix will mean the number of rows (m) and the number of columns (n), respectively:

$$\underset{(n \times 1)}{\boldsymbol{x} = \begin{bmatrix} x_1 \\ x_2 \\ \vdots \\ x_n \end{bmatrix}}, \qquad \underset{(1 \times n)}{\boldsymbol{x}' = [x_1 \quad x_2, \ldots, x_n]},$$

$$\underset{(m \times n)}{\boldsymbol{A} = \begin{bmatrix} a_{11} & a_{12} & \cdots & a_{1n} \\ a_{21} & a_{22} & \cdots & a_{2n} \\ \vdots & & & \vdots \\ a_{m1} & & \cdots & a_{mn} \end{bmatrix}}, \qquad \underset{(n \times m)}{\boldsymbol{A}' = \begin{bmatrix} a_{11} & a_{21} & \cdots & a_{m1} \\ a_{12} & a_{22} & \cdots & a_{m2} \\ \vdots & & & \vdots \\ a_{1n} & & \cdots & a_{mn} \end{bmatrix}}.$$

It is relatively easy to verify

$$(\boldsymbol{A}\boldsymbol{x})' = \boldsymbol{x}'\boldsymbol{A}',$$

in which the transpose of a product yields the inverted transposed products. When a matrix equals its transpose,

$$\boldsymbol{A} = \boldsymbol{A}',$$

the matrix $\boldsymbol{A}$ is called *symmetric*. This cannot occur, of course, unless $\boldsymbol{A}$ is *square*, of size $(n \times n)$. The *inverse* of a square matrix $\boldsymbol{A}$ is denoted by $\boldsymbol{A}^{-1}$, which has the property

$$\boldsymbol{A}^{-1}\boldsymbol{A} = \boldsymbol{A}\boldsymbol{A}^{-1} = \boldsymbol{J},$$

where $\boldsymbol{I}$ is the *identity* matrix. There also exists the *generalized inverse* of a matrix which is not square [31]. It possesses the property that it always exists and satisfies the axioms

$$AA^{\#}A = A, \qquad A^{\#}AA^{\#} = A^{\#}, \qquad (A^{\#}A)' = A^{\#}A, \qquad (AA^{\#})' = AA^{\#},$$

where $A^{\#}$ is the *generalized* or *pseudo-inverse*. The identity matrix fulfills the function in matrix notation that 1 does in scalar notation. Thus if we introduce the *Kronecker delta*, δ_{ij}, defined as

$$\delta_{ij} = \begin{cases} 1, & i = j, \\ 0, & i \neq j, \end{cases}$$

we see that $\boldsymbol{I}$ is a matrix with elements equal to δ_{ij} (i refers to a row and j to a column). It follows that

$$AI = IA = A.$$

Of final interest is the *scalar* or *dot product* of two vectors, $\boldsymbol{x}$ and $\boldsymbol{y}$, defined as

$$\boldsymbol{x}'\boldsymbol{y} = \boldsymbol{y}'\boldsymbol{x} = \sum_{i=1}^{n} x_i y_i = \text{scalar}$$

or as the sum of the products of equivalent elements in $\boldsymbol{x}$ and $\boldsymbol{y}$. Alternatively, we may write in equivalent notation

$$\boldsymbol{x} \cdot \boldsymbol{y} = (\boldsymbol{x}, \boldsymbol{y}) = \boldsymbol{x}'\boldsymbol{y}$$

for the scalar product. When we consider the scalar product of $\boldsymbol{x}'\boldsymbol{x}$ we see that it is the sum of the squares of the elements of $\boldsymbol{x}$, that is,

$$\boldsymbol{x}'\boldsymbol{x} = \sum_{i=1}^{n} x_i^2.$$

Actually, this analysis of the scalar product may be extended by the use of the *quadratic form* (discussed later) defined as a scalar function $V(\boldsymbol{x})$ or $V(\boldsymbol{x}, \boldsymbol{A})$ so that

$$V(\boldsymbol{x}) = V(\boldsymbol{x}, \boldsymbol{A}) = \boldsymbol{x}'\boldsymbol{A}\boldsymbol{x} = \sum_{i,j=1}^{n} x_i a_{ij} x_j,$$

where a_{ij} are the elements of $\boldsymbol{A}$. If we choose $\boldsymbol{A} = \boldsymbol{I}$, we return to the scalar product; when $\boldsymbol{A} \neq \boldsymbol{I}$, the quadratic form is seen to be a weighted sum of squares of the elements x_i by the elements a_{ij}.

Differentiation of a vector. Given the vector

$$\boldsymbol{f}(\boldsymbol{x}) = \begin{bmatrix} f_1 \\ f_2 \\ \vdots \\ f_n \end{bmatrix},$$

we may differentiate this vector with respect to $\boldsymbol{x}$ by first taking the transpose and then

$$\frac{d\boldsymbol{f}'}{d\boldsymbol{x}} = \begin{bmatrix} d/dx_1 \\ \vdots \\ d/dx_n \end{bmatrix} [f_1 f_2 \dots f_n] = \begin{bmatrix} \frac{df_1}{dx_1} & \frac{df_2}{dx_1} & \cdots & \frac{df_n}{dx_1} \\ \vdots & & & \vdots \\ \frac{df_1}{dx_n} & & \cdots & \frac{df_n}{dx_n} \end{bmatrix}.$$

Thus, it also follows that

$$\frac{d\boldsymbol{f}'}{d\boldsymbol{x}} \boldsymbol{z} = \begin{bmatrix} \frac{df_1}{dx_1} & \cdots & \frac{df_n}{dx_1} \\ \vdots & & \vdots \\ \frac{df_1}{dx_n} & \cdots & \frac{df_n}{dx_n} \end{bmatrix} \begin{bmatrix} z_1 \\ z_2 \\ \vdots \\ z_n \end{bmatrix} = \begin{bmatrix} \frac{df_1}{dx_1} z_1 + \cdots + \frac{df_n}{dx_1} z_n \\ \vdots \\ \frac{df_1}{dx_n} z_1 + \cdots + \frac{df_n}{dx_n} z_n \end{bmatrix},$$

which is an $(n \times 1)$ vector each element of which is the sum of n terms. This type of formulation and manipulation will be encountered in Chapter 2, where the so-called adjoint equations are introduced.

Eigenfunctions and Eigenvalues. Consider the relationship

$$\alpha f = \lambda f,$$

where $\lambda = \text{const} \neq 0$ and $\alpha = \text{operator}$. If such a relationship exists, f is called an eigenfunction and λ an eigenvalue. If f is a vector $\boldsymbol{f}$ rather than a scalar then $\boldsymbol{f}$ is called an eigenvector. To illustrate,

$$\boldsymbol{A}\boldsymbol{x} = \lambda \boldsymbol{x} \qquad \text{or} \qquad (\boldsymbol{A} - \lambda \boldsymbol{I})\boldsymbol{x} = \boldsymbol{0}$$

fulfills the necessary conditions. However, it is well known that there can be a unique value for $\boldsymbol{x}$, other than the null vector, only if the determinant of $(\boldsymbol{A} - \lambda \boldsymbol{I})$ denoted by $\det(\boldsymbol{A} - \lambda \boldsymbol{I})$ is zero. This requirement leads to the *characteristic equation* of $\boldsymbol{A}$, which is a polynomial in λ obtained by expanding $\det(\boldsymbol{A} - \lambda \boldsymbol{I}) = 0$.

It is relatively obvious that if $\boldsymbol{A}$, of size $(n \times n)$, yields a polynomial in λ (it will be of degree n), there are a number of different values of λ which will satisfy this polynomial. These roots of the polynomial, $\lambda_1, \lambda_2, \dots, \lambda_n$, are known as the eigenvalues of $\boldsymbol{A}$. Furthermore, for each λ_i there will then be a corresponding $\boldsymbol{x}_i$. These $\boldsymbol{x}_i$, namely $\boldsymbol{x}_1, \boldsymbol{x}_2, \dots, \boldsymbol{x}_n$, are the eigenvectors of $\boldsymbol{A}$. When the eigenvalues λ_i are all distinct $(\lambda_i - \lambda_j \neq 0, i \neq j)$ and $\boldsymbol{A}$ is symmetric, then it can be shown that the eigenvectors are *orthogonal*, that is,

$$\boldsymbol{x}_i' \boldsymbol{x}_j = \delta_{ij} \times \text{const}.$$

The vectors may be converted to a *normalized orthogonal* set by dividing by the constant (determined from the numerical elements in x_j) so that

$$x_i' x_j = \delta_{ij},$$

where δ_{ij} is the Kronecker delta defined previously.

Vector norm. The norm of a vector x denoted by $\|x\|$ may be thought of as a measure of the length of the vector. It is a scalar function which assigns to every vector x in a given Euclidean space a real number denoted by $\|x\|$ such that

(1) $\|x\| > 0$ for all $x \neq 0$,

(2) $\|x\| = 0$ if and only if $x = 0$,

(3) $\|x + y\| \leq \|x\| + \|y\|$ for all x and y,

(4) $\|\lambda x\| = |\lambda| \cdot \|x\|$ for all x and λ a real scalar constant.

The best-known norm is the Euclidean measure of length

$$\|x\|_E = (x'x)^{1/2} = \left(\sum_{i=1}^{n} x_i^2\right)^{1/2}$$

representing the square root of the sum of squares of the elements of x. A more general form of this norm which we shall repeatedly be using in this book is the generalized *Euclidean norm* or *quadratic form*

$$\|x\|_{E,Q}^2 = \|x\|_Q^2 = x'Qx = \left(\sum_{i=1}^{n} \sum_{j=1}^{n} x_i q_{ij} x_j\right), \tag{1.1}$$

where Q is square and positive-definite. This implies that $x'Qx > 0$ for all $x \neq 0$ (see the subsequent discussion). Note that Q may be thought of here as an operator. The subscript E, denoting Euclidean, may be dropped for convenience. Unless otherwise stated this is the norm to be used in all subsequent discussions.

There are, of course, other norms which may be used. For example,

$$\|x\|_M = \max_i \{|x_i|\}$$

and

$$\|x\|_S = \sum_{1}^{n} |x_i|$$

are other norms defined in terms of the maximum element in x or the sum of the absolute values of the elements in x. All the norms here can be shown to satisfy the four previously stated conditions to define a norm.

There is a geometrical interpretation which can be used to describe a norm. Thus, if we consider x to be two-dimensional (two elements), it can be easily verified that for $\|x\|_E = 1.0$ the norm represents a circle of radius 1.0 about the origin, that for $\|x\|_M = 1.0$ the norm represents a square with sides parallel to the axes, and that for $\|x\|_S = 1.0$ the norm is a square around the origin but tipped (a diamond). These simple geometric forms can be changed if desired by introducing suitable weighting functions. Thus,

$$\|\boldsymbol{x}\|_{E,\alpha} = \left(\sum_{i=1}^{n} \alpha_i x_i^2\right)^{1/2} \qquad (\alpha_i = \text{positive scalar constants})$$

can be used to convert the circle to an ellipse.

It is also possible to define the norm of a matrix, that is, if A is any $(n \times n)$ matrix, we say $\|A\|$ is the norm of A if it is a real nonnegative number such that, for any $(n \times 1)$ vector x,

(1) $\|Ax\| \leq \|A\| \cdot \|x\|$,

(2) if $C = AB$, then $\|C\| \leq \|A\| \cdot \|B\|$,

(3) $\|A + B\| \leq \|A\| + \|B\|$,

(4) $\|\lambda A\| = |\lambda| \cdot \|A\|$.

Sign-definite. The scalar function of a vector, $V(x)$, is said to be positive-definite if $V(x) > 0$ for $x \neq \mathbf{0}$ and $V(\mathbf{0}) = 0$ for $x = \mathbf{0}$. The negative of a positive-definite function is called negative-definite.

When the scalar V is a function of a vector and a scalar, $V(x, t)$ where t is implied to mean time, then $V(x, t)$ is positive-definite only when it is possible to find a positive-definite function $W(x)$ such that $V - W > 0$ for $x \neq \mathbf{0}$, and $V(\mathbf{0}, t) = 0$ for $x = \mathbf{0}$.

A quadratic form, $V(x, Q) = x'Qx$, is positive-semidefinite if $V(x, Q) \geq 0$ for all x. If in addition, $V(x, Q) = 0$ implies $x = \mathbf{0}$, then the quadratic form is positive-definite. One says, with a slight abuse of language, that the matrix Q is positive (semi-) definite if $V(x, Q)$ is positive (semi-) definite.

Lipschitz condition. If there is a scalar constant K such that

$$\|\alpha x - \alpha y\| \leq K\|x - y\|,$$

the operator α is said to satisfy a Lipschitz condition. If $K < 1.0$, α is further called a contraction operator.

Differentiation of a quadratic form. Let us consider the *differentiation* of a *quadratic form*

$$V(x, Q) = x'Qx = \sum_{i=1}^{n} \sum_{j=1}^{n} x_i q_{ij} x_j$$

with respect to a scalar x_k. Carrying out the indicated operation yields

$$\frac{dV(x, Q)}{dx_k} = 2q_{kk}x_k + \sum_{\substack{i=1,\\ i\neq k}}^{n} q_{ik}x_i + \sum_{\substack{j=1,\\ j\neq k}}^{n} q_{kj}x_j.$$

This becomes, on grouping back,

$$\frac{dV(\boldsymbol{x}, \boldsymbol{Q})}{dx_k} = \sum_{i=1}^{n} q_{ki}x_i + \sum_{j=1}^{n} q_{jk}x_j = \sum_{i=1}^{n} (q_{ki} + q_{ik})x_i .$$

But this is merely the sum of the kth row of column vectors $\boldsymbol{Qx}$ and $\boldsymbol{Q'x}$, and thus

$$\frac{dV(\boldsymbol{x}, \boldsymbol{Q})}{dx_k} = (\boldsymbol{Qx})_k + (\boldsymbol{Q'x})_k .$$

When the quadratic form is differentiated with respect to the vector $\boldsymbol{x}$ rather than a scalar, the result is essentially the same except that all the rows, and not just the kth, come in. Thus, we have

$$\frac{d}{d\boldsymbol{x}} V(\boldsymbol{x}, \boldsymbol{Q}) = \begin{bmatrix} d/dx_1 \\ d/dx_2 \\ \vdots \\ d/dx_n \end{bmatrix} V(\boldsymbol{x}, \boldsymbol{Q}) = \begin{bmatrix} dV(\boldsymbol{x}, \boldsymbol{Q})/dx_1 \\ dV(\boldsymbol{x}, \boldsymbol{Q})/dx_2 \\ \vdots \\ dV(\boldsymbol{x}, \boldsymbol{Q})/dx_n \end{bmatrix} = \begin{bmatrix} (\boldsymbol{Qx})_1 + (\boldsymbol{Q'x})_1 \\ (\boldsymbol{Qx})_2 + (\boldsymbol{Q'x})_2 \\ \vdots \\ (\boldsymbol{Qx})_n + (\boldsymbol{Q'x})_n \end{bmatrix}.$$

$$\frac{d}{d\boldsymbol{x}} V(\boldsymbol{x}, \boldsymbol{Q}) = \boldsymbol{Qx} + \boldsymbol{Q'x}.$$

We note that if $\boldsymbol{Q}$ is symmetric, then

$$\frac{d}{d\boldsymbol{x}} V(\boldsymbol{x}, \boldsymbol{Q}) = 2\boldsymbol{Qx} \qquad (\boldsymbol{Q} = \text{symmetric}).$$

Linearly independent set of vectors. A set of vectors, $\boldsymbol{x}_1, \boldsymbol{x}_2, \ldots, \boldsymbol{x}_n$, is said to be *linearly independent* if no set of nonzero constants $c_1, c_2, \ldots, c_n$ exists such that

$$c_1\boldsymbol{x}_1 + c_2\boldsymbol{x}_2 + \cdots + c_n\boldsymbol{x}_n = \boldsymbol{0}.$$

Otherwise the vectors are *linearly dependent*. The unit vectors $\boldsymbol{e}_1, \boldsymbol{e}_2, \ldots, \boldsymbol{e}_n$, for example, are linearly independent. Thus,

$$c_1\boldsymbol{e}_1 + c_2\boldsymbol{e}_2 + \cdots + c_n\boldsymbol{e}_n = \boldsymbol{0},$$

and if we take $\boldsymbol{e}_i$ to be a vector of two elements and consider only two terms ($n = 2$),

$$c_1\left[\begin{smallmatrix}1\\0\end{smallmatrix}\right] + c_2\left[\begin{smallmatrix}0\\1\end{smallmatrix}\right] = \boldsymbol{0}$$

or

$$c_1 + 0 = 0, \qquad 0 + c_2 = 0.$$

Only if $c_1 = c_2 = 0$ can the equality be satisfied. If we add a third vector to the set, $\boldsymbol{x}_3 = \left[\begin{smallmatrix}1\\1\end{smallmatrix}\right]$ or $\boldsymbol{x}_3 = \left[\begin{smallmatrix}0\\0\end{smallmatrix}\right] = \boldsymbol{0}$ = null vector, the result is a linearly dependent set. For illustration,

$$c_1\left[\begin{smallmatrix}1\\0\end{smallmatrix}\right] + c_2\left[\begin{smallmatrix}0\\1\end{smallmatrix}\right] + c_3\left[\begin{smallmatrix}1\\1\end{smallmatrix}\right] = \boldsymbol{0},$$

which leads to

$$c_1 + c_3 = 0, \qquad c_2 + c_3 = 0.$$

Finally, we note that the unit vectors $\boldsymbol{e}_1, \boldsymbol{e}_2, \ldots, \boldsymbol{e}_n$ are *orthogonal* to each other and that any vector which can be resolved orthogonal to a set of vectors will be linearly independent of these vectors. Thus it is not necessary that

$$c_1 = c_2 = c_3 = 0,$$

and the set is linearly dependent. If the null vector is added to the set $\boldsymbol{e}_1$ and $\boldsymbol{e}_2$, then it is easy to see that any choice of c_3 will satisfy the conditions. In fact, the null vector cannot be in any linearly independent set of vectors.

Stationary and maxima (minima) points. We shall frequently refer to the terms *stationary* and *maxima* (*minima*) in connection with an optimal control policy. To illustrate here the *unconstrained* meaning of these terms, we first turn to the single variable problem and a corresponding function $f(x)$. If a point x° of a domain D on which the function $f(x)$ is defined has a derivative $[df(x)]/dx|_{x=x^\circ}$ which exists and if

$$\left.\frac{df(x)}{dx}\right|_{x=x^\circ} = 0,$$

then x° is defined to be a *stationary* point. If $[df(x)]/dx|_{x=x^\circ}$ does not exist [at the point there is an instantaneous change in $f(x)$], we can have a *maximum* (*minimum*) which is not stationary. Furthermore, it is possible to have maximum (minimum) points at which $[df(x)]/dx|_{x=x^\circ}$ exists but is not zero, namely, at the end points of the domain.

The point x° is defined as an *absolute* or *global* maximum if

$$f(x) \leq f(x^\circ)$$

and an absolute or global minimum if the inequality sign is reversed. In much the same sense, a *relative* or *local* maximum (minimum) infers that $f(x^\circ)$ is an absolute maximum (minimum) in a subset of points in the domain.

To analyze the stationary point further, we note that a sufficient condition that a point x° be stationary is that $[df(x)]/dx|_{x=x^\circ} = 0$. However, this is only a necessary condition for a variety of subclasses of stationary points, namely, those extreme points which are maxima (minima) and horizontal inflection points which are not maxima (minima) points. As illustrated in Figure 1.1 we note that

at B and D there are maxima,
at C and E there are minima, (all stationary points with $[df(x)]/dx = 0$)
at F there is an inflection,
at G there is a maximum but $[df(x)]/dx$ does not exist,
at A there is a minimum but $[df(x)]/dx \neq 0$.

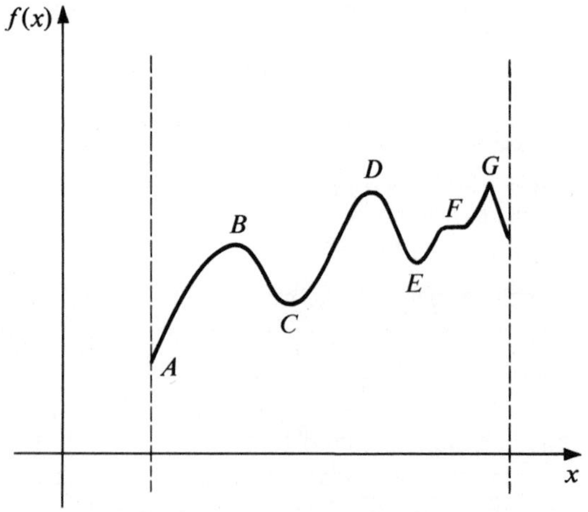

FIGURE 1.1. Various types of extrema

The necessary and sufficient conditions are that $[d^2f(x)]/dx^2 < 0$ for a maximum and $[d^2f(x)]/dx^2 > 0$ for a minimum and, if the first derivative exists, it must vanish at the extremum. Alternatively, to determine the extremum the behavior of the first nonzero derivative can be examined.

To discuss the analogous multidimensional case and the point

$$\boldsymbol{x}^\circ = (x_1^\circ, x_2^\circ, \ldots, x_n^\circ)$$

it is convenient to use the *Taylor series expansion*. If a function $f(x, y)$ of two variables (for convenience) is expanded in the neighborhood of the point (x°, y°), then

$$f(x^\circ + h, y^\circ + k) = f(x^\circ, y^\circ) + \sum_{i=1}^{n} \frac{1}{i!}\left(h\frac{\partial}{\partial x} + k\frac{\partial}{\partial y}\right)^i f(x, y)\Bigg|_{\substack{x=x^\circ\\ y=y^\circ}}$$
$$+ \text{ remainder terms,}$$

where h and k are small deviations from x° and y°, respectively. For the point $f(x^\circ, y^\circ)$ to be a stationary point, it is necessary that

$$\frac{\partial f}{\partial x}\bigg|_{x=x^\circ} = \frac{\partial f}{\partial y}\bigg|_{y=y^\circ} = 0.$$

But once again this condition is not sufficient to assure that (x°, y°) is an extremum. Thus, we add the sufficiency conditions that if

$$\frac{\partial^2 f}{\partial x^2}\frac{\partial^2 f}{\partial y^2} - \left(\frac{\partial^2 f}{\partial x\,\partial y}\right)^2\Bigg|_{\substack{x=x^\circ\\ y=y^\circ}} > 0,$$

we are assured that (x°, y°) is a local maximum (minimum). Furthermore, if

$$\left.\frac{\partial^2 f}{\partial x^2}\right|_{\substack{x=x^\circ\\ y=y^\circ}} < 0, \qquad \left.\frac{\partial^2 f}{\partial y^2}\right|_{\substack{x=x^\circ\\ y=y^\circ}} < 0,$$

then (x°, y°) is a maximum. The reversal of the inequality signs specifies a minimum. In the same sense, if the first condition is less than zero, the stationary point is neither maximum nor a minimum and instead is a saddle point (equivalent to the one-dimensional inflection point).

Obviously, this analysis can be extended to any number of dimensions but the analysis gets more complex. The difficulty in actually evaluating the various conditions is apparent. Furthermore, the analysis does not hold directly when constraints are placed on the parameters. However, this problem is simplified considerably when $f(x_1, x_2, \ldots, x_n)$ has only one extremum. If the single extremum is a maximum, the function, $f(x_1, x_2, \ldots, x_n)$, is called a *concave* surface or a concave function. Conversely, if the single extremum is a minimum the function is called a *convex* surface or a convex function.

Convex functions. Consider a simple two-dimensional region such as a triangle or circle. If we connect any two points in this region with a straight line, all the points on the straight line remain in the region; this is then called a convex region. In more general terms, if we have a region of n dimensions and if $(x_1, \ldots, x_n)$ and $(y_1, \ldots, y_n)$ both belong to the region, then the region is called convex if

$$\alpha x_1 + (1 - \alpha)y_1, \ldots, \alpha x_n + (1 - \alpha)y_n \qquad (0 \le \alpha \le 1)$$

also is in the region. A function of a single variable $f(x)$ is convex on an interval if it satisfies the inequality

$$f\left(\frac{x_1 + x_2}{2}\right) \le \frac{f(x_1) + f(x_2)}{2}$$

for x_1, x_2 as any two points on the interval. This can easily be shown to be equivalent to

$$f[\alpha x_1 + (1 - \alpha)x_2] \le \alpha f(x_1) + (1 - \alpha)f(x_2) \qquad (0 \le \alpha \le 1),$$

and it is immediately apparent that a convex function so defined can have only a single well-defined minimum. It is further noted that if the equality (instead of inequality) holds, the function, f, is *linear*, and then the minimum occurs on the boundary of the region.

Gradient. We shall frequently have recourse to the use of the *gradient* or *gradient vector*. In our terminology we may think of a scalar function $V(\boldsymbol{x})$ for which the gradient of V with respect to $\boldsymbol{x}$ will be a vector denoted as

$$\frac{\partial}{\partial \boldsymbol{x}} V = \nabla_{\boldsymbol{x}} V = \text{grad}_{\boldsymbol{x}}\, V = \begin{bmatrix} \partial V/\partial x_1 \\ \vdots \\ \partial V/\partial x_n \end{bmatrix}, \tag{1.2}$$

where ∇ is the "del" operator. All these forms on the left-hand side c Equation (1.2) are equivalent and may be used in an interchangeable manner. An alternative formulation with a slightly different meaning will also be used,

$$\frac{\partial}{\partial x(i)} V = \nabla_{x(i)} V = \text{grad}_{x(i)}\ V = \begin{bmatrix} \partial V/\partial x(0) \\ \vdots \\ \partial V/\partial x(P-1) \end{bmatrix}, \tag{1.3}$$

where in $x(i)$, $i = 0, 1, \ldots, P-1$.

Class of functions. It frequently turns out that a function $f(x)$ must be classified in some manner or other. A convenient procedure is to analyze the resulting derivatives of $f(x)$. Thus a function $f(x)$ is said to be in *class* C_n in a domain D if all derivatives up to and including $f^{(n)}(x)$ exist and are continuous in D. This may be written as $f(x) \varepsilon C_n$ in D. As a typical illustration, if a function is merely continuous in a domain (x_0, x_1) it is in class C_0. By contrast, if $f(x)$ is continuous and $[df(x)]/dx$ exists and is continuous, the function is in class C_1.

As further detail, we note that if a function is piecewise continuous in (x_0, x_1) but the over-all interval can be divided into a finite number of subintervals in

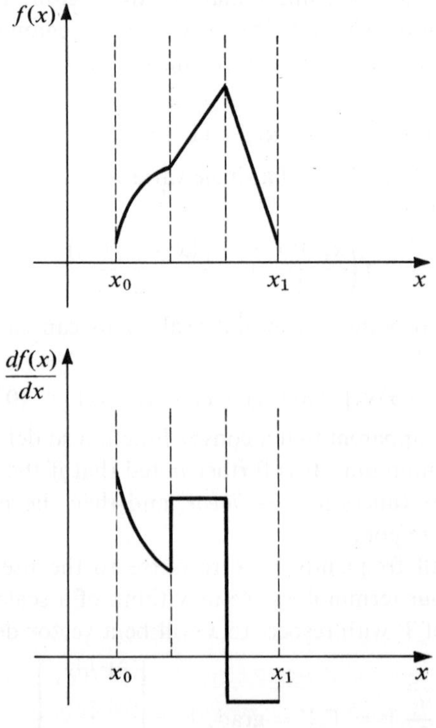

FIGURE 1.2. Typical class C_0 function

each of which $f(x)$ and $[df(x)]/dx$ exist and are continuous, then $f(x)$ is in class C_0. This of course allows $[df(x)]/dx$ to be discontinuous at various points. Figure 1.2 shows a typical class C_0 function. We note further that $[df(x)]/dx$ is still integrable for a class C_0 function and that its integral $f(x)$ is continuous.

1.2. Continuous-time system model

In the major portion of this book, we shall assume that the physical *system*, *plant*, or *process* to be controlled is described mathematically by a set of *deterministic lumped-parameter* equations. Physical considerations may suggest using *distributed-parameter* (partial) differential equations, but these are difficult to handle at our current state of control analysis and therefore are often replaced by a lumped approximation. This corresponds to the idea of lumping together abstractly all the causal factors which have an effect on the future. This abstract quantity is called the *state*. In physical terms, it corresponds to a detailed description of the stored energy in the system. In mathematical terms, the initial conditions which must be specified to solve a differential equation describing the behavior of the system constitute the initial state. The evolution of the system in time can then be described in terms of the changes of this state. Since these changes are usually brought about as a result of external inputs (or control manipulations), we may represent the transformation in state by the transition

$$S(t_0) \xrightarrow{u(t)} S(t_f),$$

taken to read: the state at time t_0 is transformed into the state at time t_f, $t_f > t_0$, by the action of $\boldsymbol{u}(t)$. To illustrate this idea in concrete terms, consider the set of ordinary differential equations corresponding to the general *continuous-time* form,

$$\begin{aligned}
\frac{dx_1}{dt} &= \dot{x}_1(t) = f_1[x_1, x_2, \ldots, x_n, u_1, \ldots, u_r, v_1, \ldots, v_s, t], \\
\frac{dx_2}{dt} &= \dot{x}_2(t) = f_2[x_1, x_2, \ldots, x_n, u_1, \ldots, u_r, v_1, \ldots, v_s, t], \\
&\vdots \\
\frac{dx_n}{dt} &= \dot{x}_n(t) = f_n[x_1, x_2, \ldots, x_n, u_1, \ldots, u_r, v_1, \ldots, v_s, t],
\end{aligned} \tag{1.4}$$

where the x_i, u_i and v_i, $i = 1, 2, \ldots$, are functions of time t. The state at any time t is represented by the vector $\boldsymbol{x}(t)$ with n elements $x_1, x_2, \ldots, x_n$ (the *state variables*); control is exerted through the vector $\boldsymbol{u}(t)$ with r elements $u_1, \ldots, u_r$ (the *control variables*) and $\boldsymbol{v}(t)$ is a vector with s elements $v_1, \ldots, v_s$ (the *uncontrolled variables*).

In vector notation, we may write Equation (1.4) as

$$\dot{\boldsymbol{x}}(t) = \boldsymbol{f}[\boldsymbol{x}(t), \boldsymbol{u}(t), \boldsymbol{v}(t), t], \tag{1.5}$$

where $\boldsymbol{f}$ is a vector with n elements $f_1, f_2, \ldots, f_n$. For the CSTR discussed previously the x_i's might be the concentrations and temperature in the reactor, the u_i's might be the input flow rates or temperatures, and the v_i's might be the ambient temperature or some other uncontrollable effect influencing the behavior of the system.

Alternatively, we might neglect the uncontrollable variables other than in the form of parameter variations and write Equation (1.5) as

$$\dot{\boldsymbol{x}}(t) = \boldsymbol{f}[\boldsymbol{x}(t), \boldsymbol{u}(t), t] \tag{1.6}$$

Associated with the set of differential equations is a corresponding set of initial conditions which we indicate as

$$\boldsymbol{x}(t_0) = \boldsymbol{x}(t = 0) = \boldsymbol{x}(0), \tag{1.7}$$

where we have taken $t_0 = 0$ for convenience.

We shall always assume that the functions f_i are continuous and satisfy a Lipschitz condition for every two points in the domain of interest. This assures us that, given a set of initial conditions and given the values of the control variables, there exists a solution to the differential equations and that the solution is unique. In this way the transformation of state above has a well-defined meaning. The solution will frequently be called a *trajectory* of $\boldsymbol{x}(t)$ which starts at $\boldsymbol{x}(0)$ and passes through n-dimensional space up to $\boldsymbol{x}(t_f)$. The actual determination of such a trajectory may or may not be a simple computational matter. As shown below, only when $\boldsymbol{f}$ is a linear function (the equations are linear) can a closed analytical solution for Equation (1.6) be obtained. When $\boldsymbol{f}$ is nonlinear, it is necessary to turn to numerical techniques to evaluate the trajectory.

When $\boldsymbol{u}(t) = \boldsymbol{0}$ in Equation (1.6) (or 1.5), we shall say that the system is *free* or *unforced*,

$$\dot{\boldsymbol{x}}(t) = \boldsymbol{f}[\boldsymbol{x}(t), t]. \tag{1.8}$$

If

$$\boldsymbol{f}(\boldsymbol{x}(t), \boldsymbol{u}(t), t) = \boldsymbol{f}[\boldsymbol{x}(t), \boldsymbol{u}(t)], \tag{1.9}$$

where $\boldsymbol{f}$ does not contain t explicitly, we call the system *stationary*. Finally, if a system is both free and stationary, we call it *autonomous* (conversely, a system which contains time explicitly is called *nonautonomous*).

A special case of a free or unforced system occurs when

$$\boldsymbol{f}(\boldsymbol{x}_e, t) = \boldsymbol{0} \qquad \text{(for all } t\text{);} \tag{1.10}$$

$\boldsymbol{x}_e$ as defined in this way is called an equilibrium state and implies that a trajectory through such a state remains at the same state for all time. In other words, if the unforced system is started at an equilibrium state, it remains at that state for all time. Actually, of course, outside disturbances influence the behavior of a process at an equilibrium state and a real process may never remain fixed at a single point. A real process cannot be started at the equilibrium state, and therefore a detailed analysis is usually required to ensure the stability of the operation at the desired steady state. It should be pointed out that the equilibrium state, $\boldsymbol{x}_e$, being a special case of steady-state conditions, is also defined as $\dot{\boldsymbol{x}} = \boldsymbol{0}$.

A complementary function which is also of interest is the *desired state* $\boldsymbol{x}^d$. This may represent the desired result of the control in the sense of moving the process from an initial condition to $\boldsymbol{x}^d$. In many problems of interest $\boldsymbol{x}^d = \boldsymbol{x}_e$, and the desired state is an equilibrium state; proceeding further along this line, we see that it also is possible that for $\boldsymbol{x}^d = \boldsymbol{x}_e = \boldsymbol{0}$, the desired state is an equilibrium state corresponding to the origin. This point will be developed in a later section of this chapter.

It is quite possible, if not most probable, that some of the state variables x_i in $\boldsymbol{x}$ are not *directly measurable*. Thus, certain compositions in a reactor may be known to be present but analytical techniques may not be available to measure each individual component. Frequently, however, it is possible to estimate these components by means of alternative equivalent signals. Thus, we shall refer to the *output variables* $y_i(t)$ of the *output vector* $\boldsymbol{y}(t)$ as related to the state variables by an algebraic equation such as

$$\boldsymbol{y}(t) = \boldsymbol{H}\boldsymbol{x}(t), \tag{1.11}$$

where the matrix $\boldsymbol{H}$ maps the state variables into the measurable output variables. Equation (1.11) shows a linear type of relationship ($\boldsymbol{H}$ is a linear operator), but a nonlinear relationship is equally possible. Note that if there are fewer output signals than state variables, $\boldsymbol{H}$ is not square and $\boldsymbol{H}^{-1}$ does not exist.

Of further interest to chemical engineering processes is the fact that *pure transport delays* may occur in the dynamic system. These may result from transmission-line delays or from distributed effects in the process itself. As a first approximation, it is possible to characterize the dynamic system by a pure transport delay in series with the normal system. If the normal system is linear, the principle of superposition can be evoked to frame the control system in much the same form as without the delay factor. For the moment we illustrate these delays as extensions of Equation (1.6) by

$$\dot{\boldsymbol{x}}(t) = \boldsymbol{f}[(\boldsymbol{x}(t), \boldsymbol{u}(t), \boldsymbol{u}(t - T_1), t] \tag{1.12}$$

or

$$\dot{\boldsymbol{x}}(t) = \boldsymbol{f}[\boldsymbol{x}(t), \boldsymbol{x}(t - T_2), \boldsymbol{u}(t), \boldsymbol{u}(t - T_1), t], \tag{1.13}$$

where T_1 is the transport delay in the control variables and T_2 is the transport delay in the state variables.

1.3. Linear continuous-time system models

It would seem apparent that the linear system model is more amenable to analytic considerations than the corresponding nonlinear system model. In fact, there is currently available a considerable amount of information regarding the linear control algorithm, whereas the corresponding nonlinear control algorithm is still in the state of active investigation.

A linear model can, of course, arise in two different ways, (1) when the system itself is linear, and (2) as an approximation to a nonlinear system. The procedure for carrying out the second arrangement is referred to as linearization and can be illustrated rather simply. The basic idea here is to expand the variables in a Taylor series expansion about an equilibrium point $\boldsymbol{x}_e$ and then truncate this series to retain only the corresponding linear terms. For example, consider an equation of the form

$$\frac{dx}{dt} = K - K_1 x - K_2 e^{-K_3/y} x, \tag{1.14}$$

which is frequently encountered in chemical engineering work (this is only a single equation with two variables x and y; obviously, another equation is needed in terms of dy/dt, but for our purposes here this is sufficient). The multivariable Taylor series can be represented in the present sense by

$$f(x_e + h, y_e + k) = f(x_e, y_e) + h \left.\frac{\partial f}{\partial x}\right|_{x_e, y_e} + k \left.\frac{\partial f}{\partial y}\right|_{x_e, y_e} + \text{nonlinear terms}, \tag{1.15}$$

where h and k are the deviations from the equilibrium state defined by

$$x = x_e + h, \qquad y = y_e + k, \tag{1.16}$$

and

$$f(x, y) = K - K_1 x - K_2 e^{-K_3/y} x.$$

The direct application of the expansion given by Equation (1.15) yields

$$\frac{d(x_e + h)}{dt} = (K - K_1 x_e - K_2 e^{-K_3/y_e} x_e) + h[-K_1 - K_2 e^{-K_3/y_e}]$$

$$+ k\left[-\frac{K_2 K_3}{y_e^2} e^{-K_3/y_e} x_e\right]. \tag{1.17}$$

However, since

$$\frac{dx_e}{dt} = K - K_1 x_e - K_2 e^{-K_3/y_e} x_e \equiv 0,$$

Equation (1.17) simplifies to

$$\frac{dh}{dt} = -[K_1 + K_2 e^{-K_3/y_e}]h - \left[K_2 x_e \frac{K_3}{y_e^2} e^{-K_3/y_e}\right]k$$

$$= -\frac{K}{x_e} h - \frac{(K - K_1 x_e)K_3}{y_e^2} k = a_0 h + b_0 k.$$

This equation is now in a linear form, since a_0 and b_0 are merely constants. If a nonlinear term such as x^2 were involved, the Taylor series expansion could be linearized about x_e to yield

$$x^2 = x_e^2 + 2x_e h.$$

Actually, it is not necessary to carry out all the manipulations shown above, since $f(x_e, y_e)$ always drops out. Thus, for the nonlinear equation in the form

$$\dot{\boldsymbol{x}}(t) = \boldsymbol{f}[\boldsymbol{x}(t), \boldsymbol{u}(t)],$$

linearization leads to the linear matrix equation

$$\dot{\boldsymbol{x}}(t) = \boldsymbol{A}(t)\boldsymbol{x}(t) + \boldsymbol{B}(t)\boldsymbol{u}(t), \tag{1.18}$$

where the $(n \times n)$ matrix $\boldsymbol{A}(t)$ has elements $[\partial f_i(t)/\partial x_j]$ and the $(n \times r)$ matrix $\boldsymbol{B}(t)$ has elements $[\partial f_i(t)/\partial u_j]$. If the original nonlinear system is stationary, the linearization leads to the constant matrices $\boldsymbol{A}$ and $\boldsymbol{B}$ and the equation

$$\dot{\boldsymbol{x}}(t) = \boldsymbol{A}\boldsymbol{x}(t) + \boldsymbol{B}\boldsymbol{u}(t). \tag{1.19}$$

Equations (1.18) or (1.19) will represent our standard form of the linear continuous-time model. It will be realized that if these equations come from a nonlinear system, $\boldsymbol{x}(t)$ and $\boldsymbol{u}(t)$ will represent perturbations about equilibrium points $\boldsymbol{x}_e$ and $\boldsymbol{u}_e$.

The solution of Equation (1.19) with $\boldsymbol{A}$ and $\boldsymbol{B}$ as constant matrices can be obtained in analogy to the method used for the scalar equation

$$dx/dt = Ax + Bu$$

by first obtaining the homogeneous solution, then the particular solution, and finally adding both together. The homogeneous form of (1.19) is

$$\dot{\boldsymbol{x}}(t) = \boldsymbol{A}\boldsymbol{x}(t), \qquad \boldsymbol{x}(0) = \boldsymbol{x}(t = 0)^*, \tag{1.20}$$

and a suggested solution would be

$$\boldsymbol{x}(t) = \exp(\boldsymbol{A}t)\boldsymbol{x}(0), \tag{1.21}$$

* In most of the work presented here we start an initial condition at $t = 0$. Some authors prefer the generalized time $t = t_0$, but this only seems to complicate the nomenclature.

where exp $(\boldsymbol{A}t)$ is the exponential function of the matrix $\boldsymbol{A}t$ defined by the Taylor series

$$\exp(\boldsymbol{A}t) = \sum_{i=0}^{\infty} \frac{(\boldsymbol{A}t)^i}{i!}. \tag{1.22}$$

Defining the derivative of a function, we have

$$\frac{d}{dt}\exp(\boldsymbol{A}t) = \lim_{h\to 0}\frac{1}{h}\{\exp[\boldsymbol{A}(t+h)] - \exp(\boldsymbol{A}t)\}$$

$$= \lim_{h\to 0}\frac{\exp(\boldsymbol{A}t)}{h}[\exp(\boldsymbol{A}h) - \boldsymbol{I}].$$

Applying the series expansion for exp $(\boldsymbol{A}h)$ yields

$$\frac{d}{dt}\exp(\boldsymbol{A}t) = \exp(\boldsymbol{A}t)\boldsymbol{A} = (\boldsymbol{A})\exp(\boldsymbol{A}t). \tag{1.23}$$

Thus if the right-hand side of Equation (1.21) is differentiated, there results

$$\frac{d}{dt}[\exp(\boldsymbol{A}t)\boldsymbol{x}(0)] = (\boldsymbol{A})\exp(\boldsymbol{A}t)\boldsymbol{x}(0) = \boldsymbol{A}\boldsymbol{x}(t),$$

and Equation (1.21) is seen to be the homogeneous solution of (1.19).

For purposes of notational simplicity, we shall now write

$$\boldsymbol{\Phi}(t, t_0) = \exp[\boldsymbol{A}(t - t_0)], \tag{1.24}$$

where $\boldsymbol{\Phi}(t, t_0)$ is called the *transition matrix*. In our particular case, $t_0 = 0$, and thus we may write

$$\boldsymbol{\Phi}(t) = \exp(\boldsymbol{A}t)$$

and the homogeneous solution as

$$\boldsymbol{x}(t) = \boldsymbol{\Phi}(t)\boldsymbol{x}(0). \tag{1.25}$$

From the equations derived above, it is relatively easy to show the following properties of the transition matrix:

$$\boldsymbol{\Phi}^{-1}(t) = \boldsymbol{\Phi}(-t), \qquad \boldsymbol{\Phi}(0) = \boldsymbol{I}, \qquad \boldsymbol{\Phi}(t_1)\boldsymbol{\Phi}(t_2) = \boldsymbol{\Phi}(t_1 + t_2).$$

Now we are in a position to obtain the complete solution. We note that

$$\dot{\boldsymbol{\Phi}}(t) = \boldsymbol{A}\boldsymbol{\Phi}(t),$$

and postmultiplying by $\boldsymbol{\Phi}^{-1}(t)$, we obtain

$$\dot{\boldsymbol{\Phi}}(t)\boldsymbol{\Phi}^{-1}(t) = \boldsymbol{A}.$$

Thus, we have

$$\boldsymbol{A} = \dot{\boldsymbol{\Phi}}(t)\boldsymbol{\Phi}^{-1}(t) = \dot{\boldsymbol{\Phi}}(t)\boldsymbol{\Phi}(-t).$$

But noting that $\boldsymbol{\Phi}^{-1}(t)\boldsymbol{\Phi}(t) = \boldsymbol{I}$ and differentiating with respect to t, we also obtain

$$\boldsymbol{A} = -\boldsymbol{\Phi}(t)\dot{\boldsymbol{\Phi}}(-t).$$

Substituting into Equation (1.19), we have

$$\dot{\boldsymbol{x}}(t) = \boldsymbol{A}\boldsymbol{x} + \boldsymbol{B}\boldsymbol{u} = -\boldsymbol{\Phi}(t)\dot{\boldsymbol{\Phi}}(-t)\boldsymbol{x} + \boldsymbol{B}\boldsymbol{u}.$$

Multiplying by $\boldsymbol{\Phi}(-t)$ and noting that $\boldsymbol{\Phi}(-t)\boldsymbol{\Phi}(t) = \boldsymbol{\Phi}(0) = \boldsymbol{I}$ yields

$$\boldsymbol{\Phi}(-t)\dot{\boldsymbol{x}} + \dot{\boldsymbol{\Phi}}(-t)\boldsymbol{x} = \boldsymbol{\Phi}(-t)\boldsymbol{B}\boldsymbol{u}.$$

But the left-hand side is a perfect differential. Therefore,

$$(d/dt)[\boldsymbol{\Phi}(-t)\boldsymbol{x}] = \boldsymbol{\Phi}(-t)\boldsymbol{B}\boldsymbol{u},$$

and integrating gives

$$\boldsymbol{\Phi}(-t)\boldsymbol{x} = \int_0^t \boldsymbol{\Phi}(-\lambda)\boldsymbol{B}\boldsymbol{u}(\lambda)\, d\lambda + \boldsymbol{\Phi}(0)\boldsymbol{x}(0).$$

This can now be premultiplied by $\boldsymbol{\Phi}(t)$ to yield, with $\boldsymbol{\Phi}(0) = \boldsymbol{I}$,

$$\boldsymbol{x}(t) = \boldsymbol{\Phi}(t)\boldsymbol{x}(0) + \int_0^t \boldsymbol{\Phi}(t-\lambda)\boldsymbol{B}\boldsymbol{u}(\lambda)\, d\lambda. \tag{1.26}$$

Equation (1.26) represents the solution of the stationary, linear continuous-time matrix Equation (1.19). It allows one to calculate the state $\boldsymbol{x}(t)$ at any time t, given the initial condition $\boldsymbol{x}(0)$, the control function $\boldsymbol{u}(t)$ and, of course, the matrices $\boldsymbol{A}$ and $\boldsymbol{B}$. When $\boldsymbol{u}(t) = \boldsymbol{0}$, Equation (1.26) simplifies to Equation (1.25).

Actually, Equation (1.26) can be derived by a simpler path using the variation of parameter technique. Thus, we write

$$\boldsymbol{x}(t) = \boldsymbol{\Phi}(t)\boldsymbol{g}(t),$$

where, at the moment, $\boldsymbol{g}(t)$ is some vector function of t to be determined and $\boldsymbol{\Phi}(t)$ is the transition matrix satisfying the differential equation

$$\dot{\boldsymbol{\Phi}}(t) = \boldsymbol{A}\boldsymbol{\Phi}(t).$$

But immediately,

$$\dot{\boldsymbol{x}}(t) = \dot{\boldsymbol{\Phi}}\boldsymbol{g} + \boldsymbol{\Phi}\dot{\boldsymbol{g}} = \boldsymbol{A}\boldsymbol{x} + \boldsymbol{B}\boldsymbol{u}.$$

Substituting $\boldsymbol{x} = \boldsymbol{\Phi}\boldsymbol{g}$ into the last term and canceling, we get

$$\dot{\boldsymbol{g}} = \boldsymbol{\Phi}(-t)\boldsymbol{B}\boldsymbol{u}(t).$$

Thus

$$\boldsymbol{g} = \int_0^t \boldsymbol{\Phi}(-\lambda)\boldsymbol{B}\boldsymbol{u}(\lambda)\, d\lambda + \boldsymbol{c},$$

with $\boldsymbol{c}$ an arbitrary constant vector. But since $\boldsymbol{g} = \boldsymbol{x}(0)$ at $t = 0$,

$$\boldsymbol{g} = \int_0^t \boldsymbol{\Phi}(-\lambda)\boldsymbol{B}\boldsymbol{u}(\lambda)\, d\lambda + \boldsymbol{x}(0),$$

and

$$\boldsymbol{x}(t) = \boldsymbol{\Phi}(t)\boldsymbol{x}(0) + \int_0^t \boldsymbol{\Phi}(t-\lambda)\boldsymbol{B}\boldsymbol{u}(\lambda)\, d\lambda,$$

as before.

There are a number of other points of interest connected with this linear system and the transition matrix. From the relationship $\boldsymbol{\Phi}(0) = \boldsymbol{I}$, we can see that we may write Equation (1.25) as

$$\boldsymbol{x}(0) = \boldsymbol{\Phi}(0)\boldsymbol{x}(0) = \boldsymbol{I}\boldsymbol{x}(0).$$

Thus another way to look at the transition matrix $\boldsymbol{\Phi}(t)$ is to observe that it satisfies the same homogeneous equation as $\boldsymbol{x}(t)$ but with a different initial condition, namely with $\boldsymbol{x}(0)\boldsymbol{x}'(0) = \boldsymbol{I}$.

We have defined the transition matrix $\boldsymbol{\Phi}(t)$ as given by exp $[\boldsymbol{A}t]$ and its infinite series of Equation (1.22). Such a computation requires a considerable amount of matrix multiplications; in Section 1.11 we give some consideration how to truncate the series with the assurance that this calculation is sufficiently accurate to represent the exponential. There does exist an alternative way to evaluate $\boldsymbol{\Phi}(t)$ which involves a transformation in terms of the diagonal matrix

$$\boldsymbol{\Lambda} = \begin{bmatrix} \lambda_1 & \cdots & & 0 \\ & \lambda_2 & & \\ \vdots & & \ddots & \vdots \\ 0 & \cdots & & \lambda_n \end{bmatrix},$$

where $\lambda_1, \lambda_2, \ldots, \lambda_n$ are real and distinct eigenvalues of $\boldsymbol{A}$. If we let $\boldsymbol{Z}$ be the matrix of normalized eigenvectors corresponding to the ordered choice $\lambda_1, \lambda_2, \ldots, \lambda_n$ and define the change of variables

$$\boldsymbol{x} = \boldsymbol{Z}\boldsymbol{y},$$

then it follows from Equation (1.20) that

$$\dot{\boldsymbol{x}}(t) = \boldsymbol{A}\boldsymbol{x}(t) \qquad \text{or} \qquad \boldsymbol{Z}\dot{\boldsymbol{y}}(t) = \boldsymbol{A}\boldsymbol{Z}\boldsymbol{y}(t).$$

But since $\boldsymbol{Z}$ is made up of the normalized eigenvectors (normalized such that $\boldsymbol{x}_i'\,\boldsymbol{x}_j = \delta_{ij}$), it is readily confirmed that $\boldsymbol{Z}'\boldsymbol{Z} = \boldsymbol{I}$, and thus

$$\dot{\boldsymbol{y}}(t) = \boldsymbol{Z}'\boldsymbol{A}\boldsymbol{Z}\boldsymbol{y}(t).$$

But the solution to this equation is

$$\boldsymbol{y}(t) = \exp\,[\boldsymbol{Z}'\boldsymbol{A}\boldsymbol{Z}t]\boldsymbol{y}(0),$$

and if we perform the multiplication of $\boldsymbol{Z}'\boldsymbol{A}\boldsymbol{Z}$, we note that $\boldsymbol{Z}'\boldsymbol{A}\boldsymbol{Z} = \boldsymbol{\Lambda}$. Thus

$$\boldsymbol{y}(t) = \exp[\boldsymbol{\Lambda}t]\boldsymbol{y}(0). \tag{1.27}$$

Expanding $\exp[\boldsymbol{\Lambda}t]$ in the exponential series, we find that

$$\exp[\boldsymbol{\Lambda}t] = \boldsymbol{I} + \begin{bmatrix} \lambda_1 t & \cdots & 0 \\ \vdots & \ddots & \vdots \\ 0 & \cdots & \lambda_n t \end{bmatrix} + \begin{bmatrix} \frac{(\lambda_1 t)^2}{2!} & \cdots & 0 \\ \vdots & \ddots & \vdots \\ 0 & \cdots & \frac{(\lambda_n t)^2}{2!} \end{bmatrix} + \cdots = \begin{bmatrix} e^{\lambda_1 t} & \cdots & 0 \\ \vdots & \ddots & \vdots \\ 0 & \cdots & e^{\lambda_n t} \end{bmatrix}. \tag{1.28}$$

Now we note that if we can calculate the eigenvalues of $\boldsymbol{A}$, Equation (1.28) gives $\exp[\boldsymbol{\Lambda}t]$ in closed form. Returning to the original variables, from Equation (1.27), we now get

$$\boldsymbol{x}(t) = \boldsymbol{Z}[\exp(\boldsymbol{\Lambda}t)]\boldsymbol{Z}'\boldsymbol{x}(0). \tag{1.29}$$

Thus, $\boldsymbol{\Phi}(t) = \boldsymbol{Z}[\exp(\boldsymbol{\Lambda}t)]\boldsymbol{Z}'$, and we may calculate the transition matrix by first calculating the eigenvalues and then the normalized eigenvectors. In the authors' experience, the exponential series seems to be easier to use, and thus only it will be considered in this book.

As a side point, if $A = A(t)$ in the scalar equation, then it follows that

$$x(t) = \exp\left[\int_0^t A(\lambda)\, d\lambda\right] x(0).$$

When $\boldsymbol{A}$ is a function of time in the vector equation (1.20), Equation (1.25) is still a solution; but only when $\boldsymbol{A}(t)$ commutes with $\int_0^t \boldsymbol{A}(\lambda)\, d\lambda$ does it follow that

$$\boldsymbol{\Phi}(t) = \exp\left[\int_0^t \boldsymbol{A}(\lambda)\, d\lambda\right].$$

In following through to the solution of Equation (1.26) we can see that $\boldsymbol{u}(t)$ behaved like a constant. It thus follows immediately that the solution to a simplified linear version of Equation (1.12) (a transport delay in the control vector),

$$\dot{\boldsymbol{x}}(t) = \boldsymbol{A}\boldsymbol{x}(t) + \boldsymbol{B}\boldsymbol{u}(t - T_1),$$

is given by

$$\boldsymbol{x}(t) = \boldsymbol{\Phi}(t)\boldsymbol{x}(0) + \int_0^t \boldsymbol{\Phi}(t-\lambda)\boldsymbol{B}\boldsymbol{u}(\lambda - T_1)\, d\lambda. \tag{1.30}$$

1.4. Discrete-time system models

In addition to, or equivalent to, the continuous-time system models developed in Sections 1.2 and 1.3, it is possible to define discrete-time system models. Such discrete models follow very naturally from some procedures for handling nonlinear systems and (or) the fact that most control algorithms are conveniently implemented on digital computers.

The basic difference to be exploited here between the continuous-time and the discrete-time formulations is simply stated. In the continuous-time domain, all variables such as $\boldsymbol{x}(t)$ and $\boldsymbol{u}(t)$ are continuous in the sense of being specified for all values of the variable t; in the discrete-time domain $\boldsymbol{x}(t)$ and $\boldsymbol{u}(t)$ are assumed to be known or specified only at certain discrete values of t.

To illustrate the manner in which discrete-time system models may arise, consider first the generalized nonlinear equation (1.6)

$$\dot{\boldsymbol{x}}(t) = \boldsymbol{f}[\boldsymbol{x}(t), \boldsymbol{u}(t), t],$$

and think how this equation could be integrated, given $\boldsymbol{x}(0)$ and $\boldsymbol{u}(t)$. Obviously we must, in general, turn to a numerical procedure which can be written in simplest form as

$$\frac{\boldsymbol{x}(t_{k+1}) - \boldsymbol{x}(t_k)}{\Delta t} = \boldsymbol{f}\,[\boldsymbol{x}(t_k), \boldsymbol{u}(t_k), t_k]$$

or, on the rearranging and collecting of terms, as

$$\boldsymbol{x}(t_{k+1}) = \boldsymbol{h}[\boldsymbol{x}(t_k), \boldsymbol{u}(t_k), t_k], \tag{1.31}$$

where $\boldsymbol{h}$ is used to denote the resulting functional relationship. In this last equation $\boldsymbol{x}(t_k)$ and $\boldsymbol{u}(t_k)$ represent the state and control at time $t = t_k$. Thus, insertion of all the terms at time t_k into the right-hand side of Equation (1.31) yields the value of the state $\boldsymbol{x}(t_{k+1})$ at time t_{k+1}. Starting with the known initial condition $\boldsymbol{x}(0)$, a set of discrete values $\boldsymbol{x}(t_1), \boldsymbol{x}(t_2), \ldots$ can be evaluated recursively. If the value of Δt is fixed,

$$t_{k+1} - t_k = \Delta t = T,$$

where T is called the *sampling period* and is constant for any k, then we can write

$$t_k = kT,$$

since t_0 is taken to be zero.

Equation (1.31) can be written in the form

$$\boldsymbol{x}[(k+1)T] = \boldsymbol{h}[\boldsymbol{x}(kT), \boldsymbol{u}(kT), kT].$$

But usually the sampling time is understood and can therefore be dropped to put this into a more convenient form:

$$\boldsymbol{x}(k+1) = \boldsymbol{h}[\boldsymbol{x}(k), \boldsymbol{u}(k), k], \tag{1.32}$$

$$\boldsymbol{x}(0) = \boldsymbol{x}(k=0) \qquad (k = 0, 1, 2, \ldots).$$

Equation (1.32) is the discrete analog of the continuous system model, Equation (1.6).

Consider next the solution of the linear, stationary continuous-time system model as given by Equation (1.26),

$$\boldsymbol{x}(t) = \boldsymbol{\Phi}(t)\boldsymbol{x}(0) + \int_0^t \boldsymbol{\Phi}(t - \lambda)\boldsymbol{B}\boldsymbol{u}(\lambda)\, d\lambda.$$

If $t = T$ and if $\boldsymbol{u}(t)$ is assumed to be held constant and equal to $\boldsymbol{u}(0)$ over the time period $t = 0$ to $t = T$, then it follows that

$$\boldsymbol{x}(T) = \boldsymbol{\Phi}(T)\boldsymbol{x}(0) + \left[\int_0^T \boldsymbol{\Phi}(T - \lambda)\boldsymbol{B}\, d\lambda\right]\boldsymbol{u}(0).$$

But if we call $\boldsymbol{\Delta}(T) = [\int_0^T \boldsymbol{\Phi}(T - \lambda)\, d\lambda]\boldsymbol{B}$, $\boldsymbol{B}$ being constant, then

$$\boldsymbol{x}(T) = \boldsymbol{\Phi}(T)\boldsymbol{x}(0) + \boldsymbol{\Delta}(T)\boldsymbol{u}(0). \tag{1.33}$$

Equation (1.33) thus yields the value of the state variable $\boldsymbol{x}(T)$ at time $t = T$. Let us now repeat the entire procedure but integrate from $t = T$ to $t = 2T$ using a constant value of $\boldsymbol{u}(T)$. But since the time over which we are integrating is the same in length as in the previous time step, we may write

$$\boldsymbol{x}(2T) = \boldsymbol{\Phi}(T)\boldsymbol{x}(T) + \boldsymbol{\Delta}(T)\boldsymbol{u}(T).$$

Continuing the entire process, we obtain

$$\boldsymbol{x}[(k + 1)T] = \boldsymbol{\Phi}(T)\boldsymbol{x}(kT) + \boldsymbol{\Delta}(T)\boldsymbol{u}(kT) \qquad (k = 0, 1, 2, \ldots).$$

In even simpler terms,

$$\boldsymbol{x}(k + 1) = \boldsymbol{\Phi}(T)\boldsymbol{x}(k) + \boldsymbol{\Delta}(T)\boldsymbol{u}(k) \qquad (k = 0, 1, 2, \ldots), \tag{1.34}$$

which is seen to be an explicit form of Equation (1.32). The only problem inherent in the use of Equation (1.34) is the evaluation of

$$\boldsymbol{\Phi}(T) = \exp(\boldsymbol{A}T) \tag{1.35}$$

and

$$\boldsymbol{\Delta}(T) = \left\{\int_0^T \exp[\boldsymbol{A}(T - \lambda)]\, d\lambda\right\}\boldsymbol{B}. \tag{1.36}$$

Later in this Section we shall discuss more fully the connection between t_k and T.

Equation (1.34) may be used recursively to generate $\boldsymbol{x}(1), \boldsymbol{x}(2), \boldsymbol{x}(3), \ldots$. It is interesting to actually carry out this recursive development using the simple nomenclature that $\boldsymbol{\Phi}(T) = \boldsymbol{\Phi} = \text{const}$ and that $\boldsymbol{\Delta}(T) = \boldsymbol{\Delta} = \text{const}$. Thus,

$$\begin{aligned}
\boldsymbol{x}(k + 1) &= \boldsymbol{\Phi}\boldsymbol{x}(k) + \boldsymbol{\Delta}\boldsymbol{u}(k),\\
\boldsymbol{x}(k + 2) &= \boldsymbol{\Phi}\boldsymbol{x}(k + 1) + \boldsymbol{\Delta}\boldsymbol{u}(k + 1)\\
&= \boldsymbol{\Phi}^2\boldsymbol{x}(k) + \boldsymbol{\Phi}\boldsymbol{\Delta}\boldsymbol{u}(k) + \boldsymbol{\Delta}\boldsymbol{u}(k + 1),\\
\boldsymbol{x}(k + 3) &= \boldsymbol{\Phi}^3\boldsymbol{x}(k) + \boldsymbol{\Phi}^2\boldsymbol{\Delta}\boldsymbol{u}(k) + \boldsymbol{\Phi}\boldsymbol{\Delta}\boldsymbol{u}(k + 1) + \boldsymbol{\Delta}\boldsymbol{u}(k + 2),\\
&\ \ \vdots\\
\boldsymbol{x}(k + P) &= \boldsymbol{\Phi}^P\boldsymbol{x}(k) + \sum_{i=0}^{P-1} \boldsymbol{\Phi}^{P-1-i}\boldsymbol{\Delta}\boldsymbol{u}(k + i).
\end{aligned} \tag{1.37}$$

This equation shows how the state $\boldsymbol{x}(k+P)$ after P sampling periods is predicted on the basis of the state $\boldsymbol{x}(k)$ and the sequence of inputs $\boldsymbol{u}(k)$, $\boldsymbol{u}(k+1), \ldots,$ $\boldsymbol{u}(k+P-1)$.

Just as we outlined a number of special cases for the continuous-time system, we may do the same for the present discrete-time system. Thus, using Equation (1.32) to start, we define the *free* system, $\boldsymbol{u}(k) = \boldsymbol{0}$, as

$$\boldsymbol{x}(k+1) = \boldsymbol{h}[\boldsymbol{x}(k), k], \tag{1.38}$$

the *stationary* system as

$$\boldsymbol{x}(k+1) = \boldsymbol{h}[\boldsymbol{x}(k), \boldsymbol{u}(k)], \tag{1.39}$$

and if it is both free and stationary, as *autonomous.* Note that Equation (1.34) is a stationary discrete model. The *equilibrium state* $\boldsymbol{x}_e$ occurs when, for all k,

$$\boldsymbol{x}_e = \boldsymbol{h}(\boldsymbol{x}_e, k). \tag{1.40}$$

The analogies to the *transport delay* continuous systems are given by

$$\boldsymbol{x}(k+1) = \boldsymbol{h}[\boldsymbol{x}(k), \boldsymbol{u}(k), \boldsymbol{u}(k-\alpha), k] \tag{1.41}$$

and

$$\boldsymbol{x}(k+1) = \boldsymbol{h}[\boldsymbol{x}(k), \boldsymbol{x}(k-\beta), \boldsymbol{u}(k), \boldsymbol{u}(k-\alpha), k], \tag{1.42}$$

where α and β represent the delay factors.

Many of the other concepts developed in the linear continuous-time system model also follow. Thus we may *linearize* a nonlinear discrete system to yield an equation equivalent to (1.34),

$$\boldsymbol{x}(k+1) = \boldsymbol{\Phi}(T)\boldsymbol{x}(k) + \boldsymbol{\Delta}(T)\boldsymbol{u}(k),$$

where the elements in $\boldsymbol{\Phi}(T)$ are given by $[\partial h_i/\partial x_j]$ and those in $\boldsymbol{\Delta}(T)$ by $[\partial h_i/\partial u_j]$.

In developing Equation (1.34), use was made of the *sampling period T* and it was implicit that the sampling was periodic with period T. This is equivalent to using a sample-and-hold element to replace the continuous variables. Such a device is the basis of the so-called sampled-data system; it can easily be visualized that if any calculations are carried out on a digital computer, the result is a sampled system since the computer works in discrete time only. Such a periodic sampling, where $t_k = kT$, $T = \text{const} > 0$, is only one special case of a multiplicity of different possible sampling situations. These other procedures have been discussed in detail by Kalman and Bertram [20] and will not be amplified further in this book.

As a final point in this section, we should comment on the fact that we have pointed out that Equation (1.34) or its equivalent with transport delay in the control variables,

$$\boldsymbol{x}(k+1) = \boldsymbol{\Phi}(T)\boldsymbol{x}(k) + \boldsymbol{\Delta}(T)\boldsymbol{u}(k-\alpha) \qquad (k = 0, 1, 2, \ldots), \tag{1.43}$$

is the discrete-time model in the special case of a linear, stationary process and may be used recursively to generate $\boldsymbol{x}(1), \boldsymbol{x}(2), \boldsymbol{x}(3), \ldots$. It is once again interesting to actually carry out this recursive development using the simpler nomenclature that $\boldsymbol{\Phi}(T) = \boldsymbol{\Phi} = \text{const}$ and $\boldsymbol{\Delta}(T) = \boldsymbol{\Delta} = \text{const}$. Thus,

$$\begin{aligned} \boldsymbol{x}(k+1) &= \boldsymbol{\Phi x}(k) + \boldsymbol{\Delta u}(k-\alpha), \\ \boldsymbol{x}(k+2) &= \boldsymbol{\Phi x}(k+1) + \boldsymbol{\Delta u}(k+1-\alpha), \\ &= \boldsymbol{\Phi}^2\boldsymbol{x}(k) + \boldsymbol{\Phi\Delta u}(k-\alpha) + \boldsymbol{\Delta u}(k+1-\alpha), \\ &\vdots \\ \boldsymbol{x}(k+P) &= \boldsymbol{\Phi}^P x(k) + \boldsymbol{\Phi}^{P-1}\boldsymbol{\Delta u}(k-\alpha) + \cdots + \boldsymbol{\Delta u}(k+P-1-\alpha) \end{aligned}$$

or

$$\boldsymbol{x}(k+P) = \boldsymbol{\Phi}^P \boldsymbol{x}(k) + \sum_{i=0}^{P-1} \boldsymbol{\Phi}^{P-1-i}\boldsymbol{\Delta u}(k+i-\alpha). \tag{1.44}$$

This equation shows how the state $\boldsymbol{x}(k+P)$ after P sampling periods is predicted on the basis of the state $\boldsymbol{x}(k)$ and the sequence of inputs $\boldsymbol{u}(k-\alpha), \ldots,$ $\boldsymbol{u}(k+P-1-\alpha)$. The corresponding case of no transport delay is Equation (1.37). In both cases it is necessary that the inverse of $\boldsymbol{\Phi}$ exists.

1.5. Constraints on the state and control vectors

It is relatively obvious that in any physical system there will be some type of constraint on the range of manipulation of the variables. Thus, the amplitude may be bounded in the sense that a valve can only be opened to a maximum position or closed. In the same sense, there may be constraints on the state or output variables with a temperature, as illustration, restricted to an upper and lower bound.

Constraints on the control variables may be conveniently summarized in a rather concise fashion [36]. We illustrate the technique for the discrete-time system with the continuous-time following by replacing summations with integrals. Let us define a norm of $\boldsymbol{u}(k)$ by the formula

$$\|\boldsymbol{u}\| = K^{-1}\left[\sum_{i=0}^{P-1}\sum_{j=1}^{r}|u_j(i)|^q\right]^{1/q}, \tag{1.45}$$

where K is a positive number, q = adjustable const ≥ 1. Furthermore, we assume that the control constraints are given by

$$\|\boldsymbol{u}\| \leq 1.0. \tag{1.46}$$

For q = an integer, Equations (1.45) and (1.46) yield a wide variety of norm constraints. Thus, when $q = 1$, Equations (1.45) and (1.46) yield

$$\sum_{i=0}^{P-1}\sum_{j=1}^{r}|u_j(i)| \leq K, \tag{1.47}$$

called the *total-area constraint*. In other words, $q = 1$ in Equation (1.45) bounds the sum of all the control variables applied over the entire control sequence. If $q = 2$ is used, Equations (1.45) and (1.46) yield

$$\sum_{i=0}^{P-1} \sum_{j=1}^{r} u_j(i)^2 \leq K^2 = M, \tag{1.48}$$

where $K = M^{1/2}$. This is called a *quadratic* or *total-energy constraint* since it limits the total energy of the input. The case of $q = \infty$ is also of interest, but we show the result first for a simpler case, namely for a single control variable such that

$$\|u\| = K^{-1}\left[\sum_{i=0}^{P-1} |u(i)|^q\right]^{1/q} \leq 1.0. \tag{1.49}$$

In this case, it is relatively easy to show that [36]

$$\|u\| = \lim_{q\to\infty} K^{-1}\left[\sum_{i=0}^{P-1} |u(i)|^q\right]^{1/q} = \frac{1}{K} \max_{i=0,1,2,\ldots,P-1} |u(i)|, \tag{1.50}$$

so that a control solution which satisfies Equation (1.49) will guarantee that the *amplitude constraint* $\max_i|u(i)| \leq K$ is satisfied. In other words, no control input in the entire sequence may exceed K in magnitude. The extension to the multiple-control-variable case leads to an equivalent result, namely,

$$\max_i \max_j |u_j(i)| \leq K \qquad (0 \leq i \leq P-1, \qquad 1 \leq j \leq r), \tag{1.51}$$

with the obvious connotation. A control $\boldsymbol{u}$ which satisfies the constraint equation (1.46) for some appropriately chosen norm will be called admissible or allowable. The collection of all admissible controls will be called an admissible set.

There are also a number of other variations possible, such as different constraints on each individual input, but the details will not be given here. Some constraints could also be applied to the state variables to give an admissible state, and even to mixtures of control and state variables, but we shall not go into greater detail here. The next section of this chapter will approach this problem in a similar, yet different, fashion.

1.6. The performance index

To measure the "goodness-of-control" in some meaningful manner, it is necessary to introduce a criterion which specifies how well the system is doing. In alternative terms, we wish to specify how close the control achieves any goal which we set up for it. This is accomplished by means of a *scalar performance index* (however, see Zadeh [40]) which, for example, may be taken as the integrated (or, in the discrete-time case, summed) *error* along the motions of the system. A convenient measure of the error is the difference between the state at any time t, $\boldsymbol{x}(t)$, and the desired state of the system $\boldsymbol{x}^d$ ($\boldsymbol{x}^d$ may in many cases be an equilibrium point). However, it frequently is easier to consider the origin as the desired state; we shall now show that a simple linear transformation can accomplish this result. Consider Equation (1.19) for illustration,

$$\dot{\boldsymbol{x}}(t) = \boldsymbol{A}\boldsymbol{x}(t) + \boldsymbol{B}\boldsymbol{u}(t),$$

with initial condition $\boldsymbol{x}(0)$ and final or desired condition $\boldsymbol{x}^d$. Define a new state vector $\boldsymbol{y}(t) = \boldsymbol{x}(t) - \boldsymbol{x}^d$ and let $\boldsymbol{u}^d$ be the control needed to maintain $\boldsymbol{x}(t)$ in its final state, that is,

$$\boldsymbol{A}\boldsymbol{x}^d + \boldsymbol{B}\boldsymbol{u}^d = \boldsymbol{0}$$

or

$$\boldsymbol{u}^d = -(\boldsymbol{B}'\boldsymbol{B})^{-1}\boldsymbol{B}'\boldsymbol{A}\boldsymbol{x}^d,$$

assuming that the inverse of $\boldsymbol{B}'\boldsymbol{B}$ exists. Now define a new control vector $\bar{\boldsymbol{u}}(t)$, where $\bar{\boldsymbol{u}}(t) = \boldsymbol{u}(t) - \boldsymbol{u}^d$. On this basis, Equation (1.19) becomes

$$\dot{\boldsymbol{y}}(t) = \boldsymbol{A}\boldsymbol{y}(t) + \boldsymbol{A}\boldsymbol{x}^d + \boldsymbol{B}\bar{\boldsymbol{u}}(t) + \boldsymbol{B}\boldsymbol{u}^d$$

or, using the above equation,

$$\dot{\boldsymbol{y}}(t) = \boldsymbol{A}\boldsymbol{y}(t) + \boldsymbol{B}\bar{\boldsymbol{u}}(t).$$

The form of this last equation is equivalent to that of (1.19), with the only changes being that the initial condition on $\boldsymbol{y}(t)$ is $\boldsymbol{x}(0) - \boldsymbol{x}^d$ and the desired condition is the origin $\boldsymbol{0}$. If the control vector $\boldsymbol{u}(t)$ is constrained to lie in a closed and bounded set, $\boldsymbol{u}^d$ will be required, in general, to be an interior point of the set. Then the transformed control $\bar{\boldsymbol{u}}(t)$ will also be confined to a closed and bounded set, containing $\boldsymbol{0}$ as an interior point. This implies that $\bar{u}_i$ may take on both negative and positive values for all i. Therefore, the lower bound on $\bar{u}_i$ is negative and the upper bound is positive for all i. The equivalent result holds in the discrete-time case, using Equation (1.34) for illustration,

$$\boldsymbol{x}(k+1) = \boldsymbol{\Phi}\boldsymbol{x}(k) + \boldsymbol{\Delta}\boldsymbol{u}(k) \qquad (k = 0, 1, 2, \ldots).$$

Now, we have

$$\boldsymbol{x}^d = \boldsymbol{\Phi}\boldsymbol{x}^d + \boldsymbol{\Delta}\boldsymbol{u}^d,$$

and $\boldsymbol{u}^d$ is given by $\boldsymbol{u}^d = (\boldsymbol{\Delta}'\boldsymbol{\Delta})^{-1}\boldsymbol{\Delta}'(\boldsymbol{I} - \boldsymbol{\Phi})\boldsymbol{x}^d$. All other results follow in an analogous fashion.

On the basis of these results, we may remove the requirement of considering the error of the motion and consider merely the motion itself. Although a transformation may be required to place the problem into this form, this can be done without any loss of generality.

There are a number of standard goals which the performance index may be called on to measure. As typical measures [with the initial starting condition always $\boldsymbol{x}(0)$ and $t = 0$] we may list the following.

(1)	*Terminal control* or *maximum range*	Bring state of system as close as possible to the origin at a given time t_f.
(2)	*Minimum time*	Bring state to the origin in the shortest time.
(3)	*Minimum energy*	Bring state to the origin at time t_f with minimum total expenditure of control effort.
(4)	*Regulator*	Bring state to an equilibrium point or the origin such that integral (or sum) of motion is minimized. The time required to achieve this trajectory is not specified.
(5)	*Pursuit*	Bring state to point $\boldsymbol{y}(t)$ in a minimum time.

All these measures, and others which may be specified, may be contained within a generalized formulation. Thus, without any loss of generality, we ask to extremize the scalar function $I[\boldsymbol{x}(0), t_f]$ called the performance index,

$$I[\boldsymbol{x}(0), t_f] = \sum_{i=1}^{n} c_i x_i(t_f) = \boldsymbol{c}'\boldsymbol{x}(t_f), \tag{1.52}$$

where $\boldsymbol{c}' = [c_1 c_2 \ldots c_n]$. The symbolism here is that I depends on the starting value $\boldsymbol{x}(0)$ and the final time t_f. In some circumstances it will prove advantageous to express this functionality in a different manner. Equation (1.52) expresses a weighted set of the state variables at a final time t_f, and we wish to seek its extremum. The term "extremum" will henceforth be replaced by "minimum," keeping in mind that to maximize we merely need to change the sign of this expression.

There are a number of immediate points which require discussion regarding Equation (1.52). Since we take the origin to be the desired state, it follows that we are considering the terminal control or maximum range problem. If the c_i, $i = 1, 2, \ldots, n$ are taken as 1.0, the result is an unweighted minimization of the deviation of the state at the time t_f; by calling some of the $c_i = 0$, these states are ignored in the sense that we do not care what their deviation is at time t_f. Finally, we note that only those values at the time t_f, when the goal is reached, are involved (called *final values*); how we came to this final state is unimportant in the sense that the trajectory actually followed is not involved in our performance index.

Obviously, this performance index satisfies a number of important physical considerations; however, it does have the defect that the motion from $\boldsymbol{x}(0)$, 0 to $\boldsymbol{x}(t_f)$, t_f is ignored. Thus we shall improve on Equation (1.52) to remove this defect. Consider a nonnegative scalar function f with the property that its integral (sum) is a positive number which can serve as a figure of merit for any trajectory from $x(0)$, 0 to $x(t_f)$, t_f. We may call this integral J in the form

$$J[x(0), t_f] = \int_0^{t_f} f[x(\lambda), u(\lambda), \lambda]\, d\lambda \tag{1.53}$$

or

$$J[x(0), P] = \sum_{k=1}^{P} f[x(k), u(k-1), k]. \tag{1.54}$$

The functionality within J is taken to mean that the integral of f (which is a function of the state, the control, and the time during the performance of a trajectory) is a function of the starting state and the final time. Keeping in mind that the state vector $x(t)$ has n components, we now introduce the new variable $x_0(t)$ with the properties

$$\dot{x}_0(t) = f[x(t), u(t), t], \qquad x_0(0) = 0. \tag{1.55}$$

If now we decrease the lower limit on the summation of Equation (1.52) to $i = 0$, we can incorporate Equation (1.55) directly with our system equations to yield a new set of dimension $n + 1$. Now we are in a position to see the importance of this addition. Since the value of $x_0(t)$ at time t_f is the integral (or sum) of $f[x(t), u(t), t]$, the choice of $c_i = 0$, $i = 1, 2, \ldots, n$ and $c_0 = 1.0$ leads to the minimization of the integral (sum) of f as expressed by Equations (1.53) or (1.54); this is the regulator problem. Thus, the over-all trajectory is now involved in the minimization. If the $c_i = 1.0$, $i = 0, 1, 2, \ldots, n$ are chosen, the minimization involves both the integral of motion and the finally achieved state at t_f, that is,

$$\begin{aligned} I(x(0), t_f) &= \text{a function of the final values of } x(t) \text{ and } t \text{ at time } t_f \\ &\quad + \text{an integral evaluated from start to goal at time } t_f \\ &= \sum_{i=1}^{n} c_i x_i(t_f) + c_0 \int_0^{t_f} f[x(\lambda), u(\lambda), \lambda]\, d\lambda. \end{aligned} \tag{1.56}$$

Equation (1.56) is also susceptible to a number of further and important variations. If we let $c_i = 0$, $i = 1, 2, \ldots, n$ and if f is a function of only $u(t)$, that is, $f[u(t)]$, the result is a type of minimum-energy control. Furthermore, if $c_i = 0$, $i = 1, 2, \ldots, n$ and $f = 1.0$, the result is a minimum-time control. In addition, the pursuit problem is a special case of this minimum-time problem although we shall not detail this here. In summary, we see that the final state or terminal performance index of Equation (1.52) is sufficiently general so that most other performance indices can be imbedded in Equation (1.52).

It is of importance to note that when the f-function of the system equations contains time explicitly, $f(x, u, t)$, this time inclusion can be removed by introducing a new variable $x_{n+1}(t)$ into Equation (1.52) with the form

$$\dot{x}_{n+1}(t) = 1.0, \qquad x_{n+1}(0) = 0, \tag{1.57}$$

and by the replacement of t, whenever it occurs, with x_{n+1}. Thus, the formulation of $f(\boldsymbol{x}, \boldsymbol{u}, t)$ is equivalent to the simpler form $f(\boldsymbol{x}, \boldsymbol{u})$, which may be used without loss of generality.

To place these results in a proper perspective, we note that when the system starts from a given state and time, $\boldsymbol{x}(0)$ and 0, the choice of $\boldsymbol{u}(t)$ automatically determines a trajectory of $\boldsymbol{x}(t)$ in $\boldsymbol{x}$, t space. Of those paths which conform to the use of admissible controls, we select the "best" trajectory by comparing the values of the performance index. Thus, the performance index allows us to select that trajectory among the many trajectories which intersects the goal or final values set up for the system.

We should also point out that frequently $t_f = \infty$. The proper choice of the performance index makes this problem a meaningful one. In such a case, however, the desired state $\boldsymbol{x}^d$ will be an equilibrium state $\boldsymbol{x}_e$. Thus, the transformation to the origin is carried out with $\boldsymbol{x}_e = \boldsymbol{x}^d$.

As a final point, it is worth while to relate these various performance indices to those classically defined in the literature. The optimization of the most general index, Equation (1.56), which is the sum of the final and integrated values is referred to as a *Bolza problem*. By contrast, the final state index only, Equation (1.52), is referred to as a *Mayer* problem, whereas the integrated state only, Equation (1.53), is referred to as a *Lagrange* problem. As we have pointed out all of these problems are *imbedded in one problem* which is the Mayer problem.

1.7. The quadratic performance index

As a special case of the performance index of Equation (1.56), we shall consider a quadratic form which has been used by Kalman and others [19, 21, 24, 27]. For the continuous-time system we specify the *quadratic performance index* as

$$2I(\boldsymbol{x}(0), t_f) = \boldsymbol{x}(t_f)'\boldsymbol{S}\boldsymbol{x}(t_f) + \int_0^{t_f} [\boldsymbol{x}(\lambda)'\boldsymbol{Q}\boldsymbol{x}(\lambda) + \boldsymbol{u}(\lambda)'\boldsymbol{R}\boldsymbol{u}(\lambda)]\, d\lambda$$

$$= \|\boldsymbol{x}(t_f)\|_{\boldsymbol{S}}^2 + \int_0^{t_f} [\|\boldsymbol{x}(\lambda)\|_{\boldsymbol{Q}}^2 + \|\boldsymbol{u}(\lambda)\|_{\boldsymbol{R}}^2]\, d\lambda, \tag{1.58}$$

where $\boldsymbol{S}$, $\boldsymbol{Q}$, and $\boldsymbol{R}$ are suitably chosen (see the following discussion) positive semi-definite or definite symmetric matrices. The analogous discrete-time index is given by

$$I[\boldsymbol{x}(0), P] = \boldsymbol{x}(P)'\boldsymbol{S}\boldsymbol{x}(P) + \sum_1^P [\boldsymbol{x}(k)'\boldsymbol{Q}\boldsymbol{x}(k) + \boldsymbol{u}(k-1)'\boldsymbol{R}\boldsymbol{u}(k-1)]$$

$$= \|\boldsymbol{x}(P)\|_{\boldsymbol{S}}^2 + \sum_1^P [\|\boldsymbol{x}(k)\|_{\boldsymbol{Q}}^2 + \|\boldsymbol{u}(k-1)\|_{\boldsymbol{R}}^2]. \tag{1.59}$$

Either form of the performance index is extremely versatile in the sense that we are free, within certain constraints, to choose appropriate $\boldsymbol{S}$, $\boldsymbol{Q}$, and $\boldsymbol{R}$. Thus if $\boldsymbol{S}$, $\boldsymbol{Q}$, and $\boldsymbol{R}$ are merely diagonal matrices, Equation (1.58) or (1.59) represents a suitable weighting on the sum of the squares of each appropriate term; that is, for $\boldsymbol{S}$ diagonal, the first term in (1.58) is a weighted sum-of-squares of the elements x_i of the state vector at the final or terminal time t_f. If $\boldsymbol{S}$, $\boldsymbol{Q}$, and $\boldsymbol{R}$ are taken as the suitably sized identity matrices, the result is an unweighted sum-of-squares of the terms. Furthermore, if $\boldsymbol{S}$, $\boldsymbol{Q}$, and $\boldsymbol{R}$ are not diagonal matrices, not only will squared terms on the individual elements be obtained but also weighting on the cross-products among the elements.

The elements selected for $\boldsymbol{S}$ specify the distance from the origin that $\boldsymbol{x}(t)$ is allowed to be at the end of the control sequence, that is, the criterion when the desired goal is reached; the elements of $\boldsymbol{Q}$ affect the integral of $\boldsymbol{x}(t)$ over the entire control sequence; the elements of $\boldsymbol{R}$ are used to penalize the system for too much control over the entire control sequence. Note the correspondence to the formulation of Equation (1.56), except that squared terms are used here. As we will see in Chapter 3, the actual choice of the matrices $\boldsymbol{S}$, $\boldsymbol{Q}$, and $\boldsymbol{R}$ is largely an engineering decision based on such requirements as accuracy and the amount of control to be used. However, it is apparent that when $\boldsymbol{S} = \boldsymbol{Q} = \boldsymbol{0}$, $\boldsymbol{R} \neq \boldsymbol{0}$, the result is minimum energy control; when $\boldsymbol{Q} = \boldsymbol{0}$, $\boldsymbol{R} = \boldsymbol{0}$, $\boldsymbol{S} \neq \boldsymbol{0}$, the result is a control which depends only on the final value of the trajectory; and that when $\boldsymbol{S} = \boldsymbol{0}$, $\boldsymbol{R} = \boldsymbol{0}$, $\boldsymbol{Q} \neq \boldsymbol{0}$, the result is a control which depends on the entire set of $\boldsymbol{x}(t)$ over the control interval but is independent of the amount of control actually used.

There remains one final point of interest here which deals with the fact that we have always used the state $\boldsymbol{x}(t)$ in the performance index. Rather, it may be that the output $\boldsymbol{y}(t)$ of Equation (1.11) should be used. Thus, the performance index of Equation (1.58) should be written as

$$2I[\boldsymbol{x}(0), t_f] = \|\boldsymbol{y}(t_f)\|_{\boldsymbol{S}}^2 + \int_0^{t_f} [\|\boldsymbol{y}(\lambda)\|_{\boldsymbol{Q}}^2 + \|\boldsymbol{u}(\lambda)\|_{\boldsymbol{R}}^2]\, d\lambda,$$

where the $\boldsymbol{y}(t)$ have replaced the $\boldsymbol{x}(t)$. However, from Equation (1.11), $\boldsymbol{y}(t) = \boldsymbol{H}\boldsymbol{x}(t)$, we see that

$$\boldsymbol{y}(t)'\boldsymbol{Q}\boldsymbol{y}(t) = [\boldsymbol{H}\boldsymbol{x}(t)]'\boldsymbol{Q}[\boldsymbol{H}\boldsymbol{x}(t)]$$

or, using the fact that separating the transpose of products inverts the order, this results in

$$\boldsymbol{y}(t)'\boldsymbol{Q}\boldsymbol{y}(t) = \boldsymbol{x}(t)'\boldsymbol{H}'\boldsymbol{Q}\boldsymbol{H}\boldsymbol{x}(t).$$

And, similarly,

$$\boldsymbol{y}'(t_f)\boldsymbol{S}\boldsymbol{y}(t_f) = \boldsymbol{x}'(t_f)(\boldsymbol{H}'\boldsymbol{S}\boldsymbol{H})\boldsymbol{x}(t_f).$$

Thus Equation (1.58) can be written as

$$2I[\boldsymbol{x}(0), t_f] = \|\boldsymbol{x}(t_f)\|_{\boldsymbol{H}'\boldsymbol{S}\boldsymbol{H}}^2 + \int_0^{t_f} [\|\boldsymbol{x}(\lambda)\|_{\boldsymbol{H}'\boldsymbol{Q}\boldsymbol{H}}^2 + \|\boldsymbol{u}(\lambda)\|_{\boldsymbol{R}}^2]\, d\lambda \qquad (1.60)$$

to cover the case where the performance index specifies the output variables. An analogous form can be developed for the discrete index.

1.8. The optimal control problem and the control law

We are now in a position to state the *optimal control problem.* For the continuous-time system, with the obvious extension to the discrete-time system, we want to determine the control function $\boldsymbol{u}(t)$ from among the admissible set which takes the system from the initial state $\boldsymbol{x}(0)$ at time $t = 0$ to a final condition or goal such that some suitable performance index is minimized. Now, we are going to designate the optimal control which satisfies this problem as $\boldsymbol{u}^\circ(t)$ or in the discrete-time case $\boldsymbol{u}^\circ(k)$. Note that here we must determine an entire function rather than merely one value as in normal optimization. In conceptual terms, this optimal control function may be said to yield a *control law* in which the control is some function of the initial state and time. Thus,

$$\boldsymbol{u}^\circ(t) = \boldsymbol{g}[\boldsymbol{x}(0), t] \tag{1.61}$$

or

$$\boldsymbol{u}^\circ(k) = \boldsymbol{g}[\boldsymbol{x}(0), k]. \tag{1.62}$$

When such a functionality is obtained, the system is said to be operating in an *open-loop* manner; that is, $\boldsymbol{u}^\circ(t)$ is not an explicit function of $\boldsymbol{x}(t)$. In the same sense, a *closed-loop* control law could have the form

$$\boldsymbol{u}^\circ(t) = \boldsymbol{g}[\boldsymbol{x}(t), t] \tag{1.63}$$

or

$$\boldsymbol{u}^\circ(k) = \boldsymbol{g}[\boldsymbol{x}(k), k], \tag{1.64}$$

in which the current value of the state variable is included in the functionality. If $\boldsymbol{g}$ is linear in $\boldsymbol{x}(t)$, the control law will be called a linear control law, and if $\boldsymbol{g}$ does not depend on t explicitly, the control law is called a stationary control law. As illustration, we shall encounter in Chapter 3 the control law

$$\boldsymbol{u}^\circ(t) = -\boldsymbol{K}(t)\boldsymbol{x}(t) \tag{1.65}$$

or, even simpler,

$$\boldsymbol{u}^\circ(t) = -\boldsymbol{K}\boldsymbol{x}(t), \tag{1.66}$$

where $\boldsymbol{K}$ is a constant matrix. Equation (1.66) is seen to be a stationary, linear control law. The negative sign indicates the use of a negative feedback with elements of $\boldsymbol{K}$ being related to the gain of the feedback system.

When the output variables rather than the state variables are to be used in the control law, a few modifications must be made. Thus, if the system equation is given by

$$\dot{\boldsymbol{x}}(t) = \boldsymbol{A}\boldsymbol{x}(t) + \boldsymbol{B}\boldsymbol{u}(t),$$

the control law is given by

$$\boldsymbol{u}^\circ(t) = -\boldsymbol{K}\boldsymbol{x}(t),$$

and the outputs are related to the state variables by

$$\boldsymbol{y}(t) = \boldsymbol{H}\boldsymbol{x}(t),$$

then the differential equation in terms of the output becomes

$$\dot{y}(t) = H\dot{x}(t) = HAH^{-1}y(t) + HBu(t)$$

or

$$\dot{y}(t) = \bar{A}y(t) + \bar{B}u(t), \tag{1.67}$$

where $y(t) = Hx(t)$, $\bar{A} = HAH^{-1}$, and $\bar{B} = HB$. In the same fashion, the control law can be expressed in terms of the output as

$$u^{\circ}(t) = -\bar{K}y(t), \tag{1.68}$$

where $\bar{K} = KH^{-1}$. Thus Equations (1.67) and (1.68) are the new system equation and the corresponding control law, provided that H^{-1} exists.

Perhaps a few words are in order regarding the distinction between the open-loop control laws, Equations (1.61) and (1.62), and the closed-loop laws, Equations (1.63) and (1.64). In open-loop control the development of the control law can be visualized as measuring the initial state of the system at time $t = 0$; this is fed into a computer which calculates the necessary control law, and the system controllers are then set to follow this law. No corrections or changes in the applied control are ever made on the basis of actual measurements of the realized trajectory of the process. In other words, the dynamic model is assumed to be completely correct with the process under control behaving exactly as predicted by the model equations. Since this is an unlikely situation in real practice, feedback or closed-loop operation is introduced by periodically updating the control program; this is accomplished by recomputing the control law while considering the state of the process at that time to be an "initial state."

As a final point, we should mention the *suboptimal* or *quasi-optimal* control as defined by Pearson [29], Friedland [15] and others [1, 13, 14]. In such a case, we settle for a control which is not exactly optimal but instead is close to optimal. From an engineering point of view this suboptimal control, usually obtained by making some simplification in the system definition, may be as good as the true optimal control. Many of the techniques in Chapters 4 and 5 are in the suboptimal class.

1.9. Controllability, observability, and the inverse control problem

In the last three to four years there have evolved a number of important extensions to linear optimal control theory. Paramount among these concepts are the *controllability* and *observability* which appear as necessary and sometimes as sufficient conditions for the existence of a solution to a control problem. We shall here only skim the surface of these topics, but the interested reader can delve into the pioneering papers by Kalman [23] and then by Gilbert [16], Sarachik [26, 36, 37], and Hermes [17].

In broad terms, a system is *completely controllable* if every desired change of the system state can be effected in finite time by some unconstrained control inputs. This means that any initial state can be transferred to any desired state in a finite length of time by some control action. In a dual sense, a system is *completely observable* if every change of the system state eventually affects some of the system output.

To give these statements some concreteness, we shall use the standard time-varying continuous-time system model

$$\dot{\boldsymbol{x}}(t) = \boldsymbol{A}(t)\boldsymbol{x}(t) + \boldsymbol{B}(t)\boldsymbol{u}(t) \tag{1.69}$$

and the output relationship

$$\boldsymbol{y}(t) = \boldsymbol{H}(t)\boldsymbol{x}(t), \tag{1.70}$$

where $\boldsymbol{y}(t)$ is of size $(m \times 1)$, $m \leq n$.

The solution to Equation (1.69) is

$$\boldsymbol{x}(t) = \boldsymbol{\Phi}(t, t_0)\boldsymbol{x}(t_0) + \int_{t_0}^{t} \boldsymbol{\Phi}(t, \lambda)\boldsymbol{B}(\lambda)\boldsymbol{u}(\lambda)\, d\lambda, \tag{1.71}$$

where t_0 is the initial time and $\boldsymbol{\Phi}$ is the transition matrix. Substitution of Equation (1.71) into Equation (1.70) gives immediately the output

$$\boldsymbol{y}(t) = \boldsymbol{H}(t)\boldsymbol{\Phi}(t, t_0)\boldsymbol{x}(t_0) + \int_{t_0}^{t} \boldsymbol{H}(t)\boldsymbol{\Phi}(t, \lambda)\boldsymbol{B}(\lambda)\boldsymbol{u}(\lambda)\, d\lambda. \tag{1.72}$$

Now we can define controllability more explicitly.

(1) The system is *completely state-controllable on a time interval* $[t_0, t_f]$ if for given t_0 and t_f each initial state $\boldsymbol{x}(t_0)$ can be transferred to any final state $\boldsymbol{x}(t_f)$ using some control $\boldsymbol{u}(t)$ over the closed interval $[t_0, t_f]$.

From Equation (1.71), it follows immediately that the system is completely state-controllable on $[t_0, t_f]$ if and only if the relation

$$\boldsymbol{x}(t_0) = \boldsymbol{\Phi}(t_0, t_f)\boldsymbol{x}(t_f) - \int_{t_0}^{t_f} \boldsymbol{\Phi}(t_0, \lambda)\boldsymbol{B}(\lambda)\boldsymbol{u}(\lambda)\, d\lambda \tag{1.73}$$

holds for some control $\boldsymbol{u}(\lambda)$.

(2) The system is *completely state-controllable* if for *any* t_0 each initial state $\boldsymbol{x}(t_0)$ can be transferred to any final state $\boldsymbol{x}(t_f)$ in a finite time $t_f \geq t_0$.

However, controllability as defined in terms of the state is neither necessary nor sufficient for the existence of a solution to the problem of controlling the outputs of the system. We, therefore, also define controllability in terms of the output.

(3) The system is said to be *completely output-controllable on a time interval* $[t_0, t_f]$ if for a given t_0 and t_f any final output $\boldsymbol{y}(t_f)$ can be reached starting with arbitrary initial conditions at t_0.

From Equation (1.72), it follows immediately that the system is completely output-controllable on $[t_0, t_f]$ if and only if the relation

$$\boldsymbol{x}(t_0) = \boldsymbol{\Phi}(t_0, t_f)\boldsymbol{H}^{-1}(t_f)\boldsymbol{y}(t_f) - \int_{t_0}^{t_f} \boldsymbol{\Phi}(t_0, \lambda)\boldsymbol{B}(\lambda)\boldsymbol{u}(\lambda)\, d\lambda \tag{1.74}$$

holds for some control $\boldsymbol{u}(\lambda)$. Here $\boldsymbol{H}$ must be a square matrix for the inverse to exist (that is, $m = n$).

(4) The system is said to be *completely output-controllable* if for *any* t_0 and some finite t_f, where $t_f \geq t_0$ any final output $\boldsymbol{y}(t_f)$, can be reached starting with arbitrary initial conditions at t_0.

Actually, there are a number of further definitions expressing the quality of controllability, but we shall not go into these here.

By considering the simple system shown in diagram form below, the reader can immediately see the difference between state controllability and output controllability. Here the system is completely output-controllable but not completely state-controllable.

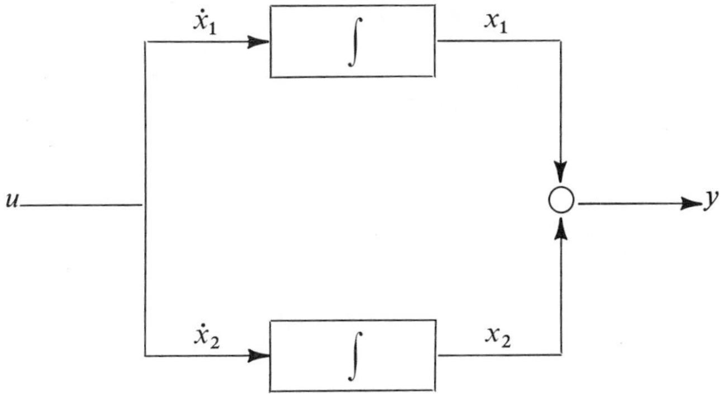

Since we are concerned more with output controllability than state controllability, let us outline two fundamental theorems concerning the former. Consider the case of constant $\boldsymbol{A}$, $\boldsymbol{B}$, and $\boldsymbol{H}$; that is,

$$\dot{\boldsymbol{x}}(t) = \boldsymbol{A}\boldsymbol{x}(t) + \boldsymbol{B}\boldsymbol{u}(t) \tag{1.75}$$

and

$$\boldsymbol{y}(t) = \boldsymbol{H}\boldsymbol{x}(t). \tag{1.76}$$

▶ THEOREM 1.1. *The system described by Equations* (1.75) *and* (1.76) *is completely output-controllable on* $[t_0, t_f]$ *if and only if the* rows *of the matrix* $\boldsymbol{H}\boldsymbol{\Phi}(t_f, \lambda)\boldsymbol{B}$ *are linearly independent on the time interval* $[t_0, t_f]$.

Proof ▪ Using Equation (1.71), we can write the solution to Equations (1.75) and (1.76) in the form

$$\boldsymbol{y}(t) = \boldsymbol{H}[\boldsymbol{\Phi}(t, t_0)\boldsymbol{x}(t_0) + \int_{t_0}^{t} \boldsymbol{\Phi}(t, \lambda)\boldsymbol{B}\boldsymbol{u}(\lambda)\, d\lambda]. \tag{1.77}$$

We shall define

$$\boldsymbol{y}^d(t_f) = \boldsymbol{y}(t_f) - \boldsymbol{H}\boldsymbol{\Phi}(t_f, t_0)\boldsymbol{x}(t_0) \tag{1.78}$$

so that the problem of moving to $\boldsymbol{y}(t_f)$ from some arbitrary initial condition is converted to that of moving to $\boldsymbol{y}^d(t_f)$ from zero initial condition and follow the proof as given by Kreindler and Sarachik [26]. Combining Equations (1.77) and (1.78) gives

$$\boldsymbol{y}^d(t_f) = \int_{t_0}^{t_f} \boldsymbol{H}\boldsymbol{\Phi}(t_f, \lambda)\boldsymbol{B}\boldsymbol{u}(\lambda)\, d\lambda. \tag{1.79}$$

For the system described by Equations (1.75) and (1.76) to be output-controllable, it is necessary and sufficient that every point $\boldsymbol{y}^d(t_f)$ be within reach of the origin. This is only true if the scalar product of $\boldsymbol{y}^d(t_f)$ with every fixed-length nonzero vector ξ can be made arbitrarily large by some choice of $\boldsymbol{u}$. We shall choose $\boldsymbol{u}$ to be

$$\boldsymbol{u}(\lambda) = k\boldsymbol{B}'\boldsymbol{\Phi}'(t_f, \lambda)\boldsymbol{H}'\xi, \tag{1.80}$$

where k is positive. Then the scalar product of $\boldsymbol{y}^d(t_f)$ with ξ gives

$$\xi \cdot \boldsymbol{y}^d(t_f) = k \int_{t_0}^{t_f} [\boldsymbol{B}'\boldsymbol{\Phi}'(t_f, \lambda)\boldsymbol{H}'\xi] \cdot [\boldsymbol{B}'\boldsymbol{\Phi}'(t_f, \lambda)\boldsymbol{H}'\xi]\, d\lambda. \tag{1.81}$$

A sufficient condition for complete output-controllability on $[t_0, t_f]$ is, therefore, that

$$\boldsymbol{B}'\boldsymbol{\Phi}'(t_f, \lambda)\boldsymbol{H}'\xi \neq \boldsymbol{0} \tag{1.82}$$

in $t_0 \leq \lambda \leq t_f$ for each $\xi \neq \boldsymbol{0}$, since the integral in Equation (1.81) is then positive and $\xi \cdot \boldsymbol{y}^d(t_f)$ can be made arbitrarily large by a proper choice of k. The condition (1.82) is also necessary, because if it is violated by some $\xi = \xi^*$, then no matter how $\boldsymbol{u}(\lambda)$ is chosen in Equation (1.80), $\xi^* \cdot \boldsymbol{y}^d(t_f) = 0$ and no point $\boldsymbol{y}^d(t_f)$ in the direction of ξ^* can be reached. Equation (1.82) expresses the linear dependence of the rows of $\boldsymbol{H}\boldsymbol{\Phi}(t_f, \lambda)\boldsymbol{B}$ on $[t_0, t_f]$.

▶ THEOREM 1.2. *The system described by Equations* (1.75) *and* (1.76) *is completely output-controllable if and only if the composite* $m \times nr$ *matrix*

$$[\boldsymbol{HB}, \boldsymbol{HAB}, \boldsymbol{HA}^2\boldsymbol{B}, \ldots, \boldsymbol{HA}^{n-1}\boldsymbol{B}] \tag{1.83}$$

is of rank m.

Proof ▪ We shall outline the proof as given by Kreindler and Sarachik [26]. By the Cayley–Hamilton theorem, the matrix A' satisfies its characteristic equation

$$\sum_{k=0}^{n} c_k \boldsymbol{A}'^k = \mathbf{0}. \tag{1.84}$$

We can premultiply Equation (1.84) by $\boldsymbol{B}'$ and postmultiply by $\exp(\boldsymbol{A}'t)\boldsymbol{H}'\boldsymbol{\xi}$ to give

$$\sum_{k=0}^{n} \boldsymbol{B}' c_k \boldsymbol{A}'^k \exp(\boldsymbol{A}'t)\boldsymbol{H}'\boldsymbol{\xi} = \mathbf{0}. \tag{1.85}$$

But

$$(d^k/dt^k)\exp(\boldsymbol{A}'t) = \boldsymbol{A}'^k \exp(\boldsymbol{A}'t)$$

and

$$\exp(\boldsymbol{A}'t) = \boldsymbol{\Phi}'(t, 0) \equiv \boldsymbol{\Phi}'(t).$$

Since for a fixed system we may arbitrarily set $t_0 = 0$, there is no loss in generality. With this substitution, Equation (1.85) becomes

$$\sum_{k=0}^{n} c_k \left[\frac{d^k}{dt^k} \boldsymbol{B}'\boldsymbol{\Phi}'(t)\boldsymbol{H}'\boldsymbol{\xi} \right] = \mathbf{0}. \tag{1.86}$$

For the condition (1.82) to hold on any interval, it is necessary and sufficient that at least one of the initial conditions for the differential Equation (1.86) be nonzero, that is,

$$\left[\frac{d^k}{dt^k} \boldsymbol{B}'\boldsymbol{\Phi}'(t)\boldsymbol{H}'\boldsymbol{\xi} \right]_{t=0} = \boldsymbol{B}'\boldsymbol{A}'^k\boldsymbol{\Phi}'\boldsymbol{\xi} \neq \mathbf{0} \tag{1.87}$$

for at least one of $k = 0, 1, 2, \ldots, n-1$. This is equivalent to the requirement that for each $\boldsymbol{\xi} \neq \mathbf{0}$ at least one of the vectors

$$\boldsymbol{B}'\boldsymbol{H}'\boldsymbol{\xi},\ \boldsymbol{B}'\boldsymbol{A}'\boldsymbol{H}'\boldsymbol{\xi}, \ldots, \boldsymbol{B}'\boldsymbol{A}^{n-1}\boldsymbol{H}'\boldsymbol{\xi}$$

be nonzero. This condition can be put into the form

$$\begin{bmatrix} \boldsymbol{B}'\boldsymbol{H}' \\ \boldsymbol{B}'\boldsymbol{A}'\boldsymbol{H}' \\ \vdots \\ \boldsymbol{B}'\boldsymbol{A}'^{n-1}\boldsymbol{H}' \end{bmatrix} \boldsymbol{\xi} \neq \mathbf{0} \qquad (\text{for each } \boldsymbol{\xi} \neq \mathbf{0}).$$

This holds if and only if the m columns of this matrix are linearly independent, that is, if and only if (1.83) has rank m. This completes the proof.

We should note at this time that the system described by Equations (1.75) and (1.76) is completely state-controllable if and only if the composite $n \times nr$ matrix

$$[\boldsymbol{B}, \boldsymbol{AB}, \ldots, \boldsymbol{A}^{n-1}\boldsymbol{B}] \tag{1.88}$$

is of rank n. This follows directly from Theorem 1.2 by putting $\boldsymbol{H} = \boldsymbol{I}$.

The basic question under investigation is whether a system can be decoupled so that control is exerted only over portions of the system. If such a decoupling can be made, then some portions of the system will not be influenced by the inputs; that is, the inputs cannot be related to all of the output (or state) variables. When this cannot be done (the system cannot be decoupled and Equation (1.77) holds), an optimal control system is assured. Note that if a system is made up of even two simultaneous equations, controllability is not assured.

Observability may be thought of as the dual of state controllability and relates to the question of whether the outputs can be related back to all of the states. We shall follow the presentation of Kreindler and Sarachik [26], where they define observability, and then show the relationship between controllability and observability.

Consider an unforced system whose state is given by

$$\dot{\boldsymbol{x}}(t) = \boldsymbol{A}(t)\boldsymbol{x}(t) \tag{1.89}$$

and whose output is

$$\boldsymbol{y}(t) = \boldsymbol{H}(t)\boldsymbol{x}(t). \tag{1.90}$$

Equation (1.89) may be integrated to give the state

$$\boldsymbol{x}(t) = \boldsymbol{\Phi}(t, t_0)\boldsymbol{x}(t_0), \tag{1.91}$$

and hence

$$\boldsymbol{y}(t) = \boldsymbol{H}(t)\boldsymbol{\Phi}(t, t_0)\boldsymbol{x}(t_0). \tag{1.92}$$

The unforced system is said to be *completely observable on* $[t_0, t_f]$ if for given t_0 and t_f every state $\boldsymbol{x}(t_0)$ can be determined from the knowledge of $\boldsymbol{y}(t)$ on $[t_0, t_f]$.

Or, the unforced system will be *completely observable* if for *every* t_0 and some finite $t_f > t_0$ every state $\boldsymbol{x}(t_0)$ can be determined from the knowledge of $\boldsymbol{y}(t)$.

▶ THEOREM 1.3. *The system described by Equations* (1.89) *and* (1.90) *is completely observable on* $[t_0, t_f]$ *if and only if the* columns *of* $\boldsymbol{H}(t)\boldsymbol{\Phi}(t, t_0)$ *are linearly independent on* $[t_0, t_f]$.

The reader should note the resemblance of this theorem on observability to Theorem 1.1 on controllability. For a system with constant matrices $\boldsymbol{A}$ and $\boldsymbol{H}$, we have a theorem corresponding to Theorem 1.2.

▶ THEOREM 1.4. *The system with constant matrices is completely observable if and only if the composite* $n \times nm$ *matrix*

$$[\boldsymbol{H}', \boldsymbol{A}'\boldsymbol{H}', \ldots, \boldsymbol{A}'^{(n-1)}\boldsymbol{H}'] \tag{1.93}$$

is of rank n.

Thus, a system is observable if it is not possible to find a coordinate system in which the original system is separated into two groups such that the second group does not affect either the first group or the outputs.

As a simple illustration of these concepts, Kalman used the system

$$\dot{x}_1 = -\frac{1}{K_1}x_1 + K_1u_1(t), \qquad \dot{x}_2 = -\frac{1}{K_2}x_2 + K_2u_1(t).$$

$$y_1(t) = \frac{1}{K_1}x_1 - \frac{1}{K_2}x_2 + u_1(t),$$

and if the change of variables

$$z_1 = \frac{1}{2}\left[\frac{1}{K_1}x_1 + \frac{1}{K_2}x_2\right], \qquad z_2 = \frac{1}{2}\left[\frac{1}{K_1}x_1 - \frac{1}{K_2}x_2\right]$$

is made, the original system becomes

$$\dot{z}_1 = -\frac{1}{2}\left[\frac{1}{K_1} + \frac{1}{K_2}\right]z_1 - \frac{1}{2}\left[\frac{1}{K_1} - \frac{1}{K_2}\right]z_2 + u_1(t),$$

$$\dot{z}_2 = -\frac{1}{2}\left(\frac{1}{K_1} - \frac{1}{K_2}\right)z_1 - \frac{1}{2}\left(\frac{1}{K_1} + \frac{1}{K_2}\right)z_2, \qquad y_1(t) = 2z_2 + u_1(t).$$

Thus z_1 is controllable but not observable; z_2 is observable but not controllable.

It is possible to show a direct connection between these results and those obtained by the classic transfer-function analysis of linear systems. Thus, the impulse-response matrix, $\boldsymbol{H}(t)\boldsymbol{\Phi}(t, \lambda)\boldsymbol{B}(\lambda)$ in our terms, characterizes all the dynamic modes of a system, over every time interval, if and only if the system is controllable and observable. In other words, cancellation of terms in a transfer function can be shown to be equivalent to a system which is either not controllable or not observable or is both, not controllable and not observable. This is clearly shown by Butman and Sivan [11], and we shall not expand on it here. That such a result has importance in terms of analysis and simulation goes without saying. The implications to linearized systems may actually be quite important but as yet have not been analyzed.

The relation between observability and state controllability is formalized by the statement: *a system is completely observable if and only if the adjoint system is completely state-controllable.*

To show the truth of this statement, we consider the adjoint system of the form

$$\dot{z}(t) = -A'z(t) + H'u(t).$$

This adjoint system is completely state-controllable if relation (1.88) holds (here we have H' instead of B and $-A'$ instead of A); that is,

$$[H', -A'H', \ldots, (-1)^{n-1}A'^{(n-1)}H']$$

has rank n. Since the minus sign does not change the rank, this relation is equivalent to the relation (1.93), which expresses the condition for complete observability of the original system.

There is no meaningful dual for the concept of output controllability; however, there is a meaningful counterpart. We shall refer the reader to the paper by Kreindler and Sarachik [26] for details on the relationship of *output predictability* to output controllability.

Of interest for later discussion are certain extensions of the concept of controllability. We illustrate these points for the special case $H = I$. An equivalent theorem to that of Theorem 1.1 but with variable A and B is the following.

▶ THEOREM 1.5. *The system* (1.69) *is completely controllable at time* t_0 *if and only if the symmetric matrix, termed the* controllability matrix,

$$W(t_0, t_f) = \int_{t_0}^{t_f} \Phi(t_0, \lambda)B(\lambda)B'(\lambda)\Phi'(t_0, \lambda)\, d\lambda \tag{1.94}$$

is positive-definite for some $t_f > t_0$.

In this form it can be seen that the concept of controllability is related *only to the system equations.*

Proceeding a step further, we wish to mention the case of *local complete controllability* of a *nonlinear system.* We may look on Equation (1.69) as the variational or linearized form of our general nonlinear equation with

$$A(t) = \left(\frac{\partial f'}{\partial x}\right)' \qquad B(t) = \left(\frac{\partial f'}{\partial u}\right)'. \tag{1.95}$$

In this case it is possible to show the following.

▶ THEOREM 1.6. *A nonlinear system is locally completely controllable at the origin at time* t_0 *if the linear system of Equation* (1.69) *with coefficients derived from* (1.95) *is completely controllable at time* t_0.

This theorem is of use when we discuss any control problem in which a linear set of system equations is taken as an approximation to a nonlinear system.

In the above discussion, we have used the continuous-time system throughout. It should be pointed out that an equivalent development can be obtained for the discrete-time system. We shall not go into detail here due to the similarity and its detailed presentation in the literature, except to mention that the transition matrix of discrete-time systems may be singular, so that complete state controllability over a certain time interval does not imply complete state controllability over every longer time interval. This difference between the discrete-time system and the continuous-time system is also present in observability on a time interval.

An interesting question arises when the discrete-time system is derived from a continuous-time system by sampling: Are the controllability and observability properties of the continuous-time system preserved in the sampled-data system? For periodic sampling of a time-invariant system, the answer is affirmative, provided that the sampling frequency does not interact with the natural frequencies of the system.

The *inverse control problem* was first proposed by Kalman [24] to answer the question "What performance indices (if any) are available for which a given control law is optimal?" In other words, instead of fixing the performance index and then calculating the control law (the direct control problem), the control law is fixed at, say, $\boldsymbol{u}^\circ(t) = -\boldsymbol{K}\boldsymbol{x}(t)$, and all performance indices that may lead to the control law are sought. The analysis detailed in this search leads to a number of significant results. A typical example deals with the complete specification of when a feedback system is optimal; another result is that conditions of optimality can be expressed most conveniently by means of frequency-domain formulas.

1.10. Stability and Liapunov's second method

One of the fundamental problems associated with the implementation of any optimal control law is to assure the *stability* of the resulting physical system. The definition of the meaning of stability is also of importance since it is possible to conceive of stability in a mathematical sense and strictly in a physical sense. Thus, a certain applied control may cause a system to increase its temperature quite materially; this temperature may ultimately be reduced by further portions of the control, and thus a mathematical analysis may say that the control is stable. If, however, the temperature achieved during the optimal control excursions is beyond the physical limit of the system, it may, in a sense, be unstable since it can never be brought back to a safe point.

From a mathematical point of view, the question of stability is associated with the behavior of a system when it is subjected to some disturbance. If the system is disturbed from its equilibrium and, as time increases indefinitely, the state variables return to their original equilibrium values, then it is said that the system is *asymptotically stable*. To express these ideas in a more concrete form, let $S(R)$ be the hyperspherical region of radius $R > 0$ about the origin. Then $S(R)$ consists of the points satisfying $\|\boldsymbol{x}\| < R$:

The origin is said to be stable if corresponding to each $S(R)$ there is an $S(r)$ such that a solution starting in $S(r)$ does not leave $S(R)$. If, in addition, there is a neighborhood $S(R_0)$ such that every solution starting in $S(R_0)$ approaches the origin as $t \to \infty$, the system is said to be asymptotically stable. Conversely, the system is called unstable if it is not stable.

For stability determination, it is not necessary to know the detailed time behavior of each individual state variable. To illustrate this point, one could consider the simple case of a marble rolling on a concave mirror. Intuitively, it is realized that due to the physical damping, the system is stable, and eventually the marble will come to rest at the lowest point on the mirror. To describe the dynamics of this system, two state variables must be specified. These could, for example, be the distance of the marble from the equilibrium point and the velocity of the marble. Even for a simple physical system like this, exact expressions for the state variables as functions of time cannot be obtained. One could, on the other hand, simply consider the total energy of the marble and show with the help of the differential equation describing its motion that the friction, noise, and air drag reduce the energy, and since there is nothing in the system which restores the energy, the system is asymptotically stable (i.e., the marble will eventually come to rest at the equilibrium point). Liapunov's second method generalizes this approach of determining stability of systems directly without solving the dynamic equation. For this reason the second method is also called "direct." If a positive-definite function $V(\mathbf{x})$ can be found for a system such that its derivative $\dot{V}(\mathbf{x})$ is negative definite, then the system is asymptotically stable. Such a function is called a Liapunov function, and for stability determination one simply has to find such a function. Chapters 5 and 6 include the development of Liapunov's second method with applications in some detail. It should be noted that the Liapunov function is not unique, and this provides, therefore, a more powerful tool than conventional energy considerations.

1.11 Physical systems and preliminary computations

In the present section, we shall define some of the common features of most of the numerical work to be described and, at the same time, detail certain physical systems which will be used in later chapters. In this manner we hope to avoid, in the control and stability chapters, dwelling in any detail on the physical systems investigated.

1.11.1 DIGITAL COMPUTER AND LIBRARY SUBROUTINES

For all the numerical work to be described in this book, the IBM 7090/94 digital computer located at Princeton University was the main computing device. This facility has associated with it a very extensive set of library subroutines which are written, in many cases, specifically for this installation. As an example, there is a highly efficient ordinary-differential-equation integrating routine, DEQ, employing a modified fourth-order Runge-Kutta-Gill algorithm which has been used extensively by the present authors. Furthermore, there is a complete vector-matrix package which was used for many of the calculations discussed in this work. Other routines such as off-line plotting of output, etc., were also used as found necessary.

1.11.2 ACCURATE COMPUTATION OF CERTAIN MATRIX SERIES

In developing the linear difference equation, (1.34), which represents the sampled-data equivalent of the continuous system, Equation (1.26), it was implicit that the matrix exponential series

$$\boldsymbol{\Phi}(T) = \exp\,[AT] = \boldsymbol{I} + AT + \frac{(AT)^2}{2!} + \frac{(AT)^3}{3!} + \cdots + \frac{(AT)^n}{n!} + \cdots \tag{1.96}$$

and the equivalent integral

$$\int_0^T \exp\,[A\lambda]\,d\lambda = T\left[\boldsymbol{I} + \frac{AT}{2!} + \frac{(AT)^2}{3!} + \cdots + \frac{(AT)^n}{(n+1)!} + \cdots\right] \tag{1.97}$$

be calculated accurately. Although both matrix series may be shown to exist for all A and any fixed value of T and for all T and any fixed value of A, the question of convergence of these series during digital computation is difficult to answer. As an illustration of the problem involved, consider the scalar analog of Equation (1.96),

$$\exp T = 1 + T + \frac{T^2}{2!} + \cdots + \frac{T^n}{n!} + \cdots, \tag{1.98}$$

and suppose that $T = -100$. Then it is known that $\exp(-100) = 3.75 \times 10^{-44}$; however, the 100th term in the series expansion has a value of -1.07×10^{42}. Since the IBM 7090/94, operating in single precision arithmetic, has only 8 decimal-digit accuracy, it is apparent that the computer program cannot merely add up the sequential terms of the series to produce a correct value of exp $[T]$ for any value of T. On this basis, and even more important when matrix series are involved, it is necessary to establish certain rules for guaranteeing the desired accuracy of such series (Lesser [28]).

Before detailing such a guide, we note that for any value of T, say $T = T_1$, the largest term of this series occurs for $n = [|T_1|]$, where the brackets imply "the greatest integer in." This follows from the fact that the next term will be

$$\frac{T_1^{n+1}}{(n+1)!} = \frac{T_1^n}{n!} \cdot \frac{T_1}{n+1},$$

which implies

$$\left|\frac{T_1^{n+1}}{(n+1)!}\right| = \left|\frac{T_1^n}{n!}\right| \cdot \left|\frac{T_1}{n+1}\right| < \left|\frac{T_1^n}{n!}\right|$$

since $n + 1 > |T_1|$. Thus, if exp $[T]$ is to have a value of, say, 10^{-6}, the largest term in the series can be tested to ascertain that its magnitude is less than 10^{-2}, thereby assuring four-place accuracy in the answer. Shown in Table 1.1 are some values of T with the corresponding largest terms of the series.

TABLE 1.1. **Largest Terms of Series**

T	$\max_n \left\|\frac{T^n}{n!}\right\|$
1	1
2	2
3	4.5
4	10.7
5	26.0
6	64.8
7	163.8
8	416.1

In addition, if $|T|$ has sufficient magnitude, say 100, so that the sum of the series will be meaningless, $|T|$ can be divided by factors of 2 until a reasonable argument for Equation (1.98) is obtained. After the series is computed, the desired series may be reconstructed by using the identity

$$\exp\,[T] = \left[\exp\left(\frac{T}{\alpha}\right)\right]^\alpha,$$

where $\alpha = 2^k$. For example, if we take $T = -100$, we could take k such that $2^k = 400$. Then we have

$$\exp\left(\frac{-100}{400}\right) = \exp\,(-0.25) = 1 - 0.25 + \frac{0.0625}{2} - \frac{0.0156}{6} + \frac{0.00340}{24} - \frac{0.000975}{120} + \cdots \simeq 0.7788.$$

Now, we know that

$$\exp\,(-100) = [0.7788]^{400} = (4.5 \times 10^{-5})^{10} = (1.81 \times 10^3)^2 \times 10^{-50} = 3.27 \times 10^{-44},$$

which is quite close (a slide rule calculation is used above) to the true value.

With this background, rules may now be developed for ensuring the accuracy of the matrix expansions. The norm of a matrix A denoted by $\|A\|$ may be given by

$$\|A\| = \min\left\{\max_j \sum_i |a_{ij}|, \max_i \sum_j |a_{ij}|\right\}. \tag{1.99}$$

▶ THEOREM 1.5. *If* $\|A\|$ *is defined as in Equation* (1.99), *then*

$$\|A^n\| \le \|A\|^n.$$

Proof ▪ The matrix A^2 is obtained by matrix multiplication:

$$A^2 = \begin{bmatrix} \sum_j a_{1j}a_{j1} & \cdots & \sum_j a_{1j}a_{jn} \\ \vdots & & \vdots \\ \sum_j a_{nj}a_{j1} & \cdots & \sum_j a_{nj}a_{jn} \end{bmatrix}.$$

Successive multiplications by the matrix A will yield

$$A^n = \begin{bmatrix} \overset{n-1 \text{ summations}}{\sum_r \cdots \sum_k \sum_v} \overset{n \text{ coefficients}}{(a_{1v}a_{vk}a_{kc}\cdots a_{gr}a_{r1})}, & \cdots, & \sum_r \cdots \sum_k \sum_v (a_{1v}a_{vk}a_{kc}\cdots a_{gr}a_{rn}) \\ \vdots & & \vdots \\ \sum_r \cdots \sum_k \sum_v (a_{nv}a_{vk}a_{kc}\cdots a_{gr}a_{r1}), & \cdots, & \sum_r \cdots \sum_k \sum_v (a_{nv}a_{vk}a_{kc}\cdots a_{gr}a_{rn}) \end{bmatrix}.$$

Assume that the pth row of A^n gives $\max_i \sum_j |(A^n)_{ij}|$. Then

$$\begin{aligned} \max_i \sum_j |(A^n)_{ij}| &= \sum_j \left| \sum_r \cdots \sum_k \sum_v a_{pv}a_{vk}a_{kc}\cdots a_{gr}a_{rj} \right| \\ &\le \sum_j \sum_r \cdots \sum_k \sum_v |a_{pv}|\cdot|a_{vk}|\cdot|a_{kc}|\cdots|a_{gr}|\cdot|a_{rj}|, \\ &\le \left\{\max_r \sum_j |a_{rj}|\right\}\left\{\sum_r \cdots \sum_k \sum_v |a_{pv}|\cdot|a_{vk}|\cdot|a_{kc}|\cdots|a_{gr}|\right\}, \\ &\ \ \vdots \\ &\le \left\{\max_i \sum_j |a_{ij}|\right\}^n. \end{aligned}$$

Similarly, it can be shown that

$$\max_j \sum_i |(A^n)_{ij}| \le \left[\max_j \sum_i |a_{ij}|\right]^n.$$

Therefore,

$$\|A^n\| \le \left[\max_i \sum_j |a_{ij}|\right]^n \quad \text{and} \quad \|A^n\| \le \left[\max_j \sum_i |a_{ij}|\right]^n.$$

But one of these bracketed quantities is $\|A\|$. Therefore,

$$\|A^n\| \le \|A\|^n.$$

In computing the sum of a matrix series, it is necessary that the magnitude of no element of any term exceed some limiting value ε. This requirement prevents the summation of the terms of the series from becoming meaningless due to the restricted accuracy of arithmetic operations on the computer. The definition of the norm of a matrix and the preceding theorem can be implemented to establish a rule for guaranteeing this requirement for series (1.96):

$$\left|\left(\frac{A^nT^n}{n!}\right)_{ij}\right| \leq \left\|\frac{A^nT^n}{n!}\right\| \leq \|A\|^n \frac{|T^n|}{n!} \leq \max_n \frac{1}{n!}(\|A\| \cdot |T|)^n \leq \varepsilon. \quad (1.100)$$

But $\|A\| \cdot |T|$ is equivalent to the scalar quantity T appearing in Table 1.1. Thus, given an ε, Table 1.1 is consulted to find the right-hand entry which is nearest to and less than ε. The left-hand entry gives the equivalent value of $\|A\| \cdot |T|$, which is the maximum value it can have if Equation (1.100) is to be satisfied. Now if either $\|A\|$ or $|T|$ is fixed, an upper limit on the other may be calculated, thereby restricting all elements of all terms of the series to be less than or equal to ε. Each element of every term of series (1.96) will also be less than ε if $\|A\| \cdot |T|$ is limited as before, and if, in addition,

$$\frac{|T|}{n+1} < 1.0,$$

where n corresponds to

$$\max_n \frac{1}{n!}(\|A\| \cdot |T|)^n.$$

In the majority of the computations in this book, $\|A\| \cdot |T|$ was restricted to be less than or equal to 6.0. This ensured that all elements of all terms would be less than 64.8. Consequently, single-precision matrix series were accurate to at least six places to the right of the decimal. Where $\|A\| \cdot |T|$ exceeded 6.0, $|T|$ was scaled down by factors of 2, as has been illustrated for the scalar series.

In addition to limiting the size of each term of a matrix series, it is necessary to include in the summation all significant terms. Thus, a rule must be adopted which will indicate when enough terms have been included. Such a rule for Equation 1.96 is the requirement

$$\left\|\frac{A^nT^n}{n!}\right\| \leq \bar{\varepsilon}\left\|\sum_{i=0}^{n} \frac{A^iT^i}{i!}\right\|, \quad (1.101)$$

where $\bar{\varepsilon}$ is a suitably chosen error limit. The magnitude of every element of the nth term of the series will be less than or equal to its norm, as defined by the left-hand side of inequality (1.101). The norm on the right-hand side will thus be less than or equal to N times the magnitude of the largest element in the summation, N being the order of A. Hence, inequality (1.101) leads to

$$\left|\left(\frac{A^nT^n}{n!}\right)_{jk}\right| \leq \bar{\varepsilon}N \left\|\max_{j,k}\left(\sum_{i=0}^{n} \frac{A^iT^i}{i!}\right)_{jk}\right\| \qquad (\text{all } j, k = 1, 2, \ldots, N).$$

In most of the single precision programs, $\bar{\varepsilon}$ was taken to be 10^{-8}. For $N = 9$

the criterion of inequality (1.101) gave the matrix series of Equation (1.96) with all elements accurate to at least $\pm 10^{-5}\%$. If the series represented by Equation (1.97) is truncated after the same number of terms as used for Equation (1.96), the accuracy will be even better. This is because the final term of the integral series will be a factor $T/(n+1)$ smaller than the corresponding term of the exponential series.

1.11.3 EXAMPLES OF LINEAR SYSTEMS

The *first linear system* was used by Lapidus and coworkers [27] and consists of a six-plate absorber controlled by the inlet feed streams (see Figure 1.3). A material balance around the mth plate of the tower yields

$$H\frac{dy_m}{dt} + h\frac{dx_m}{dt} = L(x_{m-1} - x_m) + G(y_{m+1} - y_m) \qquad (m = 1, 2, \ldots, 6), \tag{1.102}$$

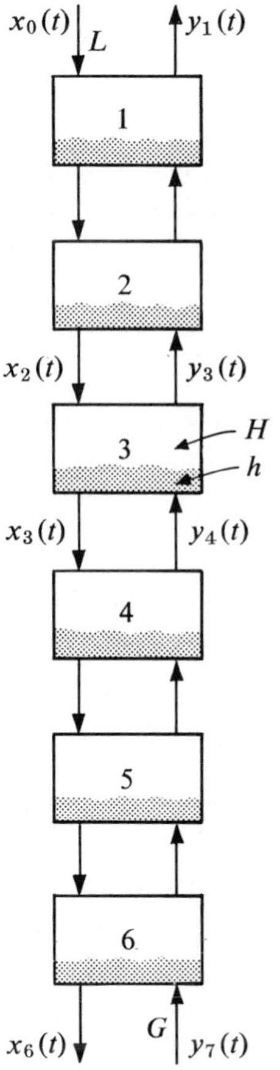

FIGURE 1.3. Gas absorber system

where

$x_m, y_m =$ compositions of liquid and vapor leaving the mth plate (lb solute/lb inert),

$h, H =$ inert liquid and vapor hold-ups on each plate (assumed constant) (lb),

$L =$ flow rate of inert liquid absorbent (lb/min),

$G =$ flow rate of inert gas stream (lb/min),

$t =$ time of operation (min).

If a linear equilibrium relationship between liquid and vapor at each plate

$$y_m = ax_m + b$$

is assumed, the material balance can be converted to

$$\frac{dx_m}{dt} = \frac{d}{e}\,x_{m-1} - \left(\frac{d+1}{e}\right) x_m + \frac{1}{e}\,x_{m+1} \qquad (m = 1, 2, \ldots, 6), \quad (1.103)$$

where $d = L/Ga$ and $e = (Ha + h)/Ga$. It is important to realize that the liquid composition at each stage is some function of time, namely, $x_m = x_m(t)$; and we shall call each $x_m(t)$, $m = 1, 2, \ldots, 6$, a state variable. Thus the dynamic system has six state variables. Assuming that the system will have an initial equilibrium point, $x_m(0) = x_{m0}$, $m = 1, 2, \ldots, 6$, we can write the system equations in the matrix-vector form

$$\dot{\boldsymbol{x}}(t) = \boldsymbol{A}\boldsymbol{x}(t) + \boldsymbol{B}\boldsymbol{u}(t), \qquad (1.104)$$

$$\boldsymbol{x}(0) = \boldsymbol{x}_0\,. \qquad (1.105)$$

The (6×6) coefficient matrix $\boldsymbol{A}$ is constant and is given by

$$\boldsymbol{A} = \begin{bmatrix} -\left(\frac{d+1}{e}\right) & \frac{1}{e} & 0 & & \cdots & 0 \\ \frac{d}{e} & -\left(\frac{d+1}{e}\right) & \frac{1}{e} & 0 & \cdots & 0 \\ 0 & \frac{d}{e} & & \cdots & & \vdots \\ \vdots & & & & & \frac{1}{e} \\ 0 & \cdots & & 0 & \frac{d}{e} & -\left(\frac{d+1}{e}\right) \end{bmatrix},$$

and the (6 × 2) control matrix $\boldsymbol{B}$, the six-dimensional state vector $\boldsymbol{x}(t)$ and the two-dimensional control vector $\boldsymbol{u}(t)$ are given by

$$\boldsymbol{B} = \begin{bmatrix} \frac{d}{e} & 0 \\ 0 & 0 \\ \vdots & \vdots \\ 0 & 0 \\ 0 & \frac{1}{e} \end{bmatrix}, \qquad \boldsymbol{x}(t) = \begin{bmatrix} x_1 \\ x_2 \\ \vdots \\ x_6 \end{bmatrix}, \qquad \boldsymbol{u}(t) = \begin{bmatrix} u_1 \\ u_2 \end{bmatrix}.$$

Note that both $\boldsymbol{A}$ and $\boldsymbol{B}$ are constant matrices and that we have a linear stationary system. In defining the control vector $\boldsymbol{u}(t)$, the elements have been taken as corresponding to the inlet liquid and vapor compositions:

$$u_1(t) = x_0(t), \qquad \bar{u}_2(t) = y_7(t)$$

or

$$u_1(t) = x_0(t), \qquad u_2(t) = \frac{\bar{u}_2(t) - b}{a}.$$

Assuming that the state of the plate tower will be controlled to approach a new steady-state equilibrium $\boldsymbol{x}_e$ different from $\boldsymbol{x}_0$, we can make the change of variables

$$\boldsymbol{z}(t) = \boldsymbol{x}(t) - \boldsymbol{x}_e, \qquad \boldsymbol{m}(t) = \boldsymbol{u}(t) - \boldsymbol{u}_e,$$

where $\boldsymbol{u}_e$ represents the inputs which yield the equilibrium $\boldsymbol{x}_e$. The dynamic system now becomes

$$\dot{\boldsymbol{z}}(t) = \boldsymbol{A}\boldsymbol{z}(t) + \boldsymbol{B}\boldsymbol{m}(t), \tag{1.106}$$

$$\boldsymbol{z}(0) = \boldsymbol{z}_0 = \boldsymbol{x}(0) - \boldsymbol{x}_e, \tag{1.107}$$

where $\boldsymbol{z}_e = \boldsymbol{0}$ and $\boldsymbol{m}_e = \boldsymbol{0}$. In this form, the dynamic balances are equivalent to the generalized Equations (1.19) with the final equilibrium condition being the origin obtained by a final control of zero. Thus, this change of variables allows us to handle any problem which starts as some prescribed initial equilibrium point and is to be controlled to any newly prescribed final equilibrium point. In application of this dynamic balance, we shall use the form of Equations (1.19), that is, we shall use the notation that $\boldsymbol{x}(t)$ is the state vector, but it should be kept in mind that the change of variables will have already been made, so that the desired state is the origin with zero control.

A convenient set of parameters for this system is

$$\begin{aligned} a &= 0.72, & G &= 66.7 \text{ lb/min}, \\ b &= 0, & H &= 1.0 \text{ lb}, \\ L &= 40.8 \text{ lb/min}, & h &= 75 \text{ lb}, \end{aligned}$$

yielding $d = 0.8496$ and $1/e = 0.6341$. An initial steady-state equilibrium can be chosen as corresponding to pure liquid feed and a gas feed of 0.2 lb solute/lb inert, $\boldsymbol{u}(0)' = [0 \quad (.2/.72)] = [0 \quad .2778]$; the final steady-state can be chosen as corresponding to pure liquid feed and a gas feed of 0.3 lb solute/lb inert, $\boldsymbol{u}_e' = [0 \quad (.3/.72)] = [0 \quad .4167]$. By solving the dynamic balances, Equations (1.104) and (1.105), with $\dot{\boldsymbol{x}}(t) = \boldsymbol{0}$, we obtain

$$\boldsymbol{x}(0)\Big|_{\boldsymbol{u}'=[0 \ .2778]} = \begin{bmatrix} .0613 \\ .1134 \\ .1577 \\ .1954 \\ .2274 \\ .2546 \end{bmatrix} \quad \text{(initial condition)}, \tag{1.108}$$

$$\boldsymbol{x}_e\Big|_{\boldsymbol{u}'=[0 \ .4167]} = \begin{bmatrix} .0919 \\ .1701 \\ .2366 \\ .2931 \\ .3411 \\ .3819 \end{bmatrix} \quad \text{(final condition)}, \tag{1.109}$$

or, if the normalization is carried out to make the final condition the origin,

$$\boldsymbol{z}(0)[\text{to be called } \boldsymbol{x}(0)]\Big|_{\boldsymbol{u}'=[0 \ -.1389]} = \begin{bmatrix} -.0306 \\ -.0568 \\ -.0788 \\ -.0977 \\ -.1138 \\ -.1273 \end{bmatrix} \quad \text{(normalized initial condition)}, \tag{1.110}$$

$$\boldsymbol{z}_e[\text{to be called } \boldsymbol{x}_e]\Big|_{\boldsymbol{u}_e'=0} = \boldsymbol{0} \qquad \text{(normalized final condition)}. \tag{1.111}$$

The dynamic balances given above are continuous-time equations, and if we desire the discrete form, the procedure outlined in Section 1.4 can be followed. Thus, Equations (1.106) and (1.107) (in normalized form) become

$$\boldsymbol{x}(k+1) = \boldsymbol{\Phi}\boldsymbol{x}(k) + \boldsymbol{\Delta}\boldsymbol{u}(k) \qquad (k = 0, 1, 2, \ldots), \tag{1.112}$$

$$\boldsymbol{x}(0) = \boldsymbol{x}_0,$$

with $\boldsymbol{x}_e = \boldsymbol{0}$ and $\boldsymbol{u}_e = \boldsymbol{0}$. The (6×6)-matrix $\boldsymbol{\Phi}(t)$ is shown below with the (6×2)-matrix $\boldsymbol{\Delta}$ as calculated from the high-order expansion discussed previously (the sampling period being $T = 1.0$ min):

$$\boldsymbol{\Phi}(T) = \boldsymbol{\Phi}(1) = \begin{bmatrix} 3.6538 & 2.1953 & .6771 & .1407 & .0221 & .0028 \\ 1.8660 & 4.2293 & 2.3149 & .6958 & .1431 & .0221 \\ .4892 & 1.9677 & 4.2452 & 2.3169 & .6958 & .1407 \\ .0864 & .5027 & 1.9693 & 4.2452 & 2.3149 & .6771 \\ .0115 & .0879 & .5027 & 1.9677 & 4.2293 & 2.1953 \\ .0012 & .0115 & .0864 & .4892 & 1.8660 & 3.6538 \end{bmatrix}, \quad (1.113)$$

$$\text{(all elements} \times 10^{-1})$$

$$\boldsymbol{\Delta}(T) = \boldsymbol{\Delta}(1) = \begin{bmatrix} 3.3080 & .0003 \\ .7253 & .0031 \\ .1165 & .0280 \\ .0146 & .1897 \\ .0015 & 1.0042 \\ .0001 & 3.8918 \end{bmatrix} \quad \text{(all elements} \times 10^{-1}). \quad (1.114)$$

On this basis, all the necessary information is available to describe either the continuous-time behavior of the plate absorber or equivalently the discrete-time behavior.

As a final point of interest, it should be noted that if the discrete-time system Equations (1.112) are forced with the inputs $\boldsymbol{u}' = [0 \quad .2778]$ or $\boldsymbol{u}' = [0 \quad .4167]$ (using the given values of $\boldsymbol{\Phi}$ and $\boldsymbol{\Delta}$), the initial conditions and final conditions of Equations (1.108) and (1.109) result. In other words, the solution of the discrete-time system equations with a constant forcing input yields the same numerical results as solving the continuous-time steady-state equations, $\dot{\boldsymbol{x}}(t) = \boldsymbol{0}$. This, of course, confirms the validity of the numerical values obtained for $\boldsymbol{\Phi}$ and $\boldsymbol{\Delta}$.

The *second linear example* has been used by Koepcke and Lapidus [25] and is a liquid–liquid countercurrent extraction train with a secondary feed to one of the middle states (Figure 1.4). For a total of six stages with the secondary feed introduced at stage 3, the material balances are

$$H\frac{dy_m}{dt} + h\frac{dx_m}{dt} = b(x_{m-1} - x_m) + w[y_{m+1} - y_m] \qquad (m = 1, 2),$$

$$H\frac{dy_m}{dt} + h\frac{dx_m}{dt} = bx_{m-1} - (b + F)x_m + Fx_F + w[y_{m+1} - y_m] \qquad (m = 3),$$

$$H\frac{dy_m}{dt} + h\frac{dx_m}{dt} = (b + F)(x_{m-1} - x_m) + w[y_{m+1} - y_m] \qquad (m = 4, 5, 6),$$

where (with any consistent set of units)

F, b = raffinate solvent flow rates,
w = extract solvent flow rate,
x_m, y_m = raffinate and extract compositions,
h, H = raffinate and extract holdups per stage (assumed constant),
t = time of operation.

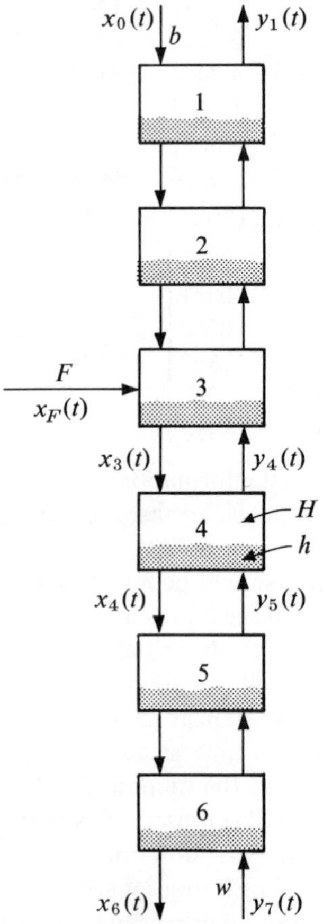

FIGURE 1.4. Liquid–liquid countercurrent extraction system

Assuming that the extract and raffinate are at equilibrium in each stage and that the equilibrium relationship is linear, we may write

$$y_m = ax_m \qquad (m = 1, 2, \ldots, 6).$$

We shall further define

$$\alpha = Ha + h, \qquad d = \frac{b}{\alpha}, \qquad f = \frac{F}{\alpha}, \qquad p = \frac{wa}{\alpha}$$

to give

$$dx_m/dt = d(x_{m-1} - x_m) + p(x_{m+1} - x_m) \qquad (m = 1, 2),$$

$$dx_m/dt = dx_{m-1} - (d+f)x_m + p(x_{m+1} - x_m) + fx_F \qquad (m = 3),$$

$$dx_m/dt = (d+f)(x_{m-1} - x_m) + p(x_{m+1} - x_m) \qquad (m = 4, 5, 6).$$

We may write this set of differential equations in vector-matrix form:

$$\begin{aligned}\dot{\boldsymbol{x}}(t) &= p\boldsymbol{A}\boldsymbol{x} + d\boldsymbol{B}\boldsymbol{x} + f\boldsymbol{C}\boldsymbol{x} + d\boldsymbol{d}_1 + f\boldsymbol{d}_2 \\ &= (p\boldsymbol{A} + d\boldsymbol{B} + f\boldsymbol{C})\boldsymbol{x} + d\boldsymbol{d}_1 + f\boldsymbol{d}_2,\end{aligned} \tag{1.115}$$

where

$$\boldsymbol{x}(t) = \begin{bmatrix} x_1 \\ x_2 \\ x_3 \\ x_4 \\ x_5 \\ x_6 \end{bmatrix} \qquad \boldsymbol{A} = \begin{bmatrix} -1 & 1 & 0 & 0 & 0 & 0 \\ 0 & -1 & 1 & 0 & 0 & 0 \\ 0 & 0 & -1 & 1 & 0 & 0 \\ 0 & 0 & 0 & -1 & 1 & 0 \\ 0 & 0 & 0 & 0 & -1 & 1 \\ 0 & 0 & 0 & 0 & 0 & -1 \end{bmatrix},$$

$$\boldsymbol{B} = \begin{bmatrix} -1 & 0 & 0 & 0 & 0 & 0 \\ 1 & -1 & 0 & 0 & 0 & 0 \\ 0 & 1 & -1 & 0 & 0 & 0 \\ 0 & 0 & 1 & -1 & 0 & 0 \\ 0 & 0 & 0 & 1 & -1 & 0 \\ 0 & 0 & 0 & 0 & 1 & -1 \end{bmatrix},$$

$$\boldsymbol{C} = \begin{bmatrix} 0 & 0 & 0 & 0 & 0 & 0 \\ 0 & 0 & 0 & 0 & 0 & 0 \\ 0 & 0 & -1 & 0 & 0 & 0 \\ 0 & 0 & 1 & -1 & 0 & 0 \\ 0 & 0 & 0 & 1 & -1 & 0 \\ 0 & 0 & 0 & 0 & 1 & -1 \end{bmatrix}, \qquad \boldsymbol{d}_1 = \begin{bmatrix} x_0 \\ 0 \\ 0 \\ 0 \\ 0 \\ 0 \end{bmatrix}, \qquad \boldsymbol{d}_2 = \begin{bmatrix} 0 \\ 0 \\ x_F \\ 0 \\ 0 \\ 0 \end{bmatrix}.$$

To control the extraction train, we could change the flow rates of raffinate solvent, of extract solvent, or of both. We shall consider the case where the raffinate-solvent flow rates are used for control, namely, b and F (or d and f). There is no loss of generality in considering p constant and using only d and f as variables.

We shall consider the case where the extraction train is operating at some particular steady state. Now suppose that the conditions of operation are changed in such a way that a new steady state will result. The problem then is to use d and f in such a way as to approach the new steady state in a desirable way.

First of all, we note that, at both steady states, $\dot{\boldsymbol{x}}(t) = \boldsymbol{0}$, so that the initial steady state is given by

$$\boldsymbol{x}_i = -[p\boldsymbol{A} + d_i\boldsymbol{B} + f_i\boldsymbol{C}]^{-1}[d_i\boldsymbol{d}_1 + f_i\boldsymbol{d}_2], \tag{1.116}$$

where the subscript i refers to initial values. Similarly, at steady state we have

$$\boldsymbol{x}_{ss} = -[p\boldsymbol{A} + d_{ss}\boldsymbol{B} + f_{ss}\boldsymbol{C}]^{-1}[d_{ss}\boldsymbol{d}_1 + f_{ss}\boldsymbol{d}_2], \tag{1.117}$$

where the subscript ss denotes steady state.

For control purposes, we may define the two control variables to be deviations from the steady-state flow rates:

$$u_1 = d - d_{ss}, \qquad u_2 = f - f_{ss}. \tag{1.118}$$

Furthermore, if we transform the state space so that $\boldsymbol{x}_{ss}$ is the origin in introducing the deviation from the desired steady state

$$\boldsymbol{z} = \boldsymbol{x} - \boldsymbol{x}_{ss}, \tag{1.119}$$

then $\boldsymbol{z} = \boldsymbol{0}$ will correspond to the desired steady state.

Substitution of Equations (1.118) and (1.119) into (1.115) and use of Equation (1.117) give

$$\dot{\boldsymbol{z}}(t) = [(p\boldsymbol{A} + d_{ss}\boldsymbol{B} + f_{ss}\boldsymbol{C}) + u_1\boldsymbol{B} + u_2\boldsymbol{C}]\boldsymbol{z} + u_1(\boldsymbol{B}\boldsymbol{x}_{ss} + \boldsymbol{d}_1) + u_2(\boldsymbol{C}\boldsymbol{x}_{ss} + \boldsymbol{d}_2).$$

For simplicity of manipulation, we shall define

$$\boldsymbol{D} = [(p\boldsymbol{A} + d_{ss}\boldsymbol{B} + f_{ss}\boldsymbol{C}) + u_1\boldsymbol{B} + u_2\boldsymbol{C}],$$

$$\boldsymbol{d}_3 = \boldsymbol{B}\boldsymbol{x}_{ss} + \boldsymbol{d}_1,$$

$$\boldsymbol{d}_4 = \boldsymbol{C}\boldsymbol{x}_{ss} + \boldsymbol{d}_2,$$

so that

$$\dot{\boldsymbol{z}}(t) = \boldsymbol{D}\boldsymbol{z} + u_1\boldsymbol{d}_3 + u_2\boldsymbol{d}_4. \tag{1.120}$$

Note that the coefficient matrix, $\boldsymbol{D}$, is a function of the controls u_1, u_2, which are variables, so that $\boldsymbol{D}$ is an implicit function of time.

Suppose that we integrate Equation (1.120) over a small interval of time $[0, T]$ for which we may keep u_1 and u_2 constant. Then also $\boldsymbol{D}$ will be constant and Equation (1.120) may be integrated to give

$$\boldsymbol{z}(T) = \exp(\boldsymbol{D}T)\boldsymbol{z}(0) + \left\{\int_0^T \exp[\boldsymbol{D}(T - \lambda)]\, d\lambda\right\}(u_1\boldsymbol{d}_3 + u_2\boldsymbol{d}_4).$$

Now let

$$\xi = T - \lambda;$$

then we see that

$$d\xi = -d\lambda$$

and

$$\boldsymbol{z}(T) = \exp(\boldsymbol{D}T)\boldsymbol{z}(0) + \left[\int_0^T \exp(\boldsymbol{D}\xi)\, d\xi\right](u_1\boldsymbol{d}_3 + u_2\boldsymbol{d}_4). \tag{1.121}$$

We can thus visualize integrating Equation (1.120) over small sampling times to give a difference equation for the dynamic balance

$$\boldsymbol{z}(k + 1) = \exp(\boldsymbol{D}T)\boldsymbol{z}(k) + \left[\int_0^T \exp(\boldsymbol{D}\xi)\, d\xi\right](u_1\boldsymbol{d}_3 + u_2\boldsymbol{d}_4)$$

or

$$\boldsymbol{z}(k + 1) = \boldsymbol{\Phi}(k)\boldsymbol{z}(k) + \boldsymbol{\Delta}(k), \tag{1.122}$$

where

$$\boldsymbol{\Phi}(k) = \exp(\boldsymbol{D}T), \qquad \boldsymbol{\Delta}(k) = \left[\int_0^T \exp(\boldsymbol{D}\xi)\,d\xi\right](u_1\boldsymbol{d}_3 + u_2\boldsymbol{d}_4)$$

and where it should be emphasized that both $\boldsymbol{\Phi}$ and $\boldsymbol{\Delta}$ are functions of k, which marks the time interval.

For computation purposes, we define

$$\boldsymbol{\theta} = \int_0^T \exp(\boldsymbol{D}\xi)\,d\xi,$$

and use infinite-series expansions to evaluate $\boldsymbol{\Phi}$ and $\boldsymbol{\theta}$:

$$\boldsymbol{\Phi} = \boldsymbol{I} + \boldsymbol{D}T + \frac{\boldsymbol{D}^2T^2}{2!} + \cdots = \sum_{i=0}^{\infty} \frac{(\boldsymbol{D}T)^i}{i!},$$

$$\boldsymbol{\theta} = \boldsymbol{I}T + \boldsymbol{D}\frac{T^2}{2!} + \frac{\boldsymbol{D}^2T^3}{3!} + \cdots = \sum_{i=0}^{\infty} \frac{(\boldsymbol{D}T)^iT}{(i+1)!},$$

$$\boldsymbol{\Delta} = \boldsymbol{\theta}(u_1\boldsymbol{d}_3 + u_2\boldsymbol{d}_4).$$

Actually it is necessary to use only one series solution to evaluate $\boldsymbol{\Phi}$ and $\boldsymbol{\theta}$. This follows from the identity

$$\boldsymbol{\Phi} = \boldsymbol{I} + \boldsymbol{D}\boldsymbol{\theta},$$

which the reader may wish to confirm.

It should be noted that Equation (1.122) is equivalent to the dynamic balance equation developed for the plate absorber. Thus the question is raised whether it is possible to control the extraction train by means of flow rates instead of feed concentrations. This is a realistic approach to a real physical situation.

To give physical meaning to the problem, we shall define a convenient set of numerical parameters:

$w = 60,$	$b_i = 50,$	$p = wa/\alpha = 1.32,$
$\alpha = 100,$	$b_{ss} = 100,$	$d_i = b_i/\alpha = .50,$
$a = 2.2,$	$F_i = 50$	$f_i = F_i/\alpha = .50,$
$y_7 = 0$ (pure solvent),	$F_{ss} = 50,$	$d_{ss} = b_{ss}/\alpha = 1.0,$
$x_0 = .0400,$		$f_{ss} = F_{ss}/\alpha = .50.$
$x_F = .0300,$		

Then from Equation (1.116), we get the initial state corresponding to $b = 50$ as

$$\boldsymbol{x}_i = \begin{bmatrix} .024552 \\ .018701 \\ .016485 \\ .010525 \\ .006011 \\ .002591 \end{bmatrix},$$

and from Equation (1.117) we get the steady state corresponding to $b = 100$ as

$$\mathbf{x}_{ss} = \begin{bmatrix} .033335 \\ .028285 \\ .024460 \\ .019463 \\ .013785 \\ .007332 \end{bmatrix}.$$

Therefore, we have

$$\mathbf{z}(0) = \begin{bmatrix} -.008782 \\ -.009584 \\ -.007975 \\ -.008937 \\ -.007774 \\ -.004741 \end{bmatrix},$$

and we wish to find the controls u_1 and u_2 as functions of time to take the system from $\mathbf{z}(0)$ to $\mathbf{z} = \mathbf{0}$ subject to minimizing some index. For convenience we shall consider $\mathbf{z}$ to be zero when $|z_m| < 0.0001$ for $m = 1, 2, \ldots, 6$.

1.11.4. EXAMPLES OF NONLINEAR SYSTEMS

The *first nonlinear system* was originally formulated by Aris and Amundson [8] and consists of a first-order irreversible chemical reaction carried out under non-isothermal conditions in a continuous stirred tank reactor (CSTR). Control of this reactor is to be achieved by manipulation of the flow of cooling fluid through a cooling coil inserted in the reactor. For the reaction $A \rightarrow B$ in such a CSTR, then, dynamic mass and heat balances are given by (Figure 1.5)

$$V dc_A/d\theta = q(c_{A0} - c_A) - VR, \tag{1.123}$$

$$Vc_p\rho(dT_R/d\theta) = qc_p\rho(T_0 - T_R) - VU^* + (-\Delta H)VR, \tag{1.124}$$

where

c_A = concentration of species A leaving reactor,
T_R = temperature of reactants leaving reactor,
c_{A0} = feed concentration of species A to reactor,
T_0 = temperature of feed stream to reactor,
θ = time,
V = volume of reactor,
q = flow rate of input and output streams to reactor,
R = generalized reaction-rate term,
$-\Delta H$ = heat of reaction,
c_p, ρ = heat capacity and density of stream leaving reactor,
U^* = heat-transfer term corresponding to cooling coil in reactor.

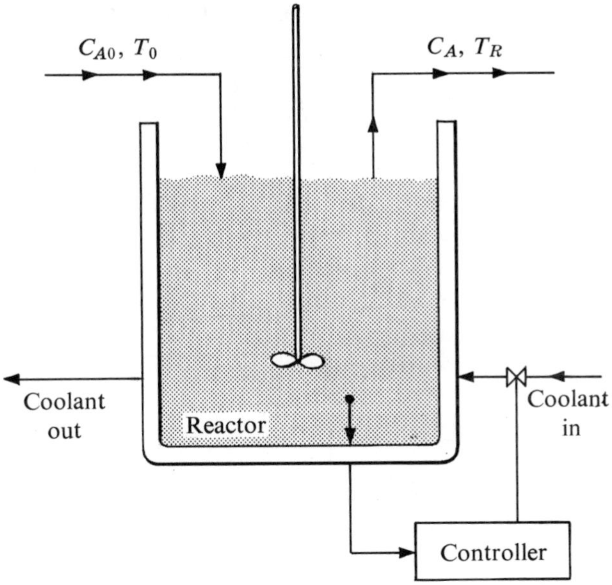

FIGURE 1.5. CSTR system with feedback controller

These equations may be reduced to dimensionless form by the following substitutions:

$$\xi = c_A/c_{A0} = \text{dimensionless concentration},$$

$$\eta = \frac{\rho c_p T_R}{(-\Delta H)c_{A0}} = \text{dimensionless temperature},$$

$$t = \frac{\theta q}{V} = \text{dimensionless time},$$

$$P = \frac{VR}{qc_{A0}} = \text{dimensionless reaction rate},$$

$$U = \frac{VU^*}{qc_{A0}(-\Delta H)} = \text{dimensionless heat-transfer term},$$

yielding

$$\dot{\xi} = 1 - \xi - P(\xi, \eta), \tag{1.125}$$

$$\dot{\eta} = (\eta_0 - \eta) - U(\eta) + P(\xi, \eta), \tag{1.126}$$

where η_0 is the dimensionless temperature of the inlet stream. If it is assumed that the heat-transfer term is regulated as a function of the opening or closing of a valve in the cooling water stream, Aris and Amundson have shown that

$$U(\eta) = \begin{cases} (U_s + k\eta_r)(\eta - \eta_c) & (\eta \geq \eta_s + \eta_r), \\ U_s(\eta - \eta_c) + k(\eta - \eta_c)(\eta - \eta_s) & (|\eta - \eta_s| \leq \eta_r), \\ 0 & (\eta \leq \eta_s - \eta_r), \end{cases} \tag{1.127}$$

where

U_s = dimensionless heat-transfer term corresponding to the steady state achieved with $k = 0$,

η_s = dimensionless reactor temperature corresponding to the steady state achieved with $k = 0$,

n_c = dimensionless cooling-water temperature,

η_r = half range of dimensionless temperature causing cooling-water valve to move,

k = a proportional control constant.

A typical set of numerical parameters are given by

$$\begin{aligned} P(\xi, \eta) &= \xi \exp [50(\tfrac{1}{2} - (1/\eta))], \\ \eta_0 &= \eta_c = 1.75, \\ U_s &= 1.0, \\ k\eta_r &= 1.0, \\ \eta_s &= 2.0. \end{aligned}$$

When these numerical parameters are used, the mass and heat-balance Equations (1.125) and (1.126) become

$$\dot{\xi} = 1 - \xi - \xi \exp [50(\tfrac{1}{2} - (1/\eta))], \tag{1.128}$$

$$\dot{\eta} = -(\eta - 1.75) + \xi \exp [50(\tfrac{1}{2} - (1/\eta)] - u_1(\eta - 1.75), \tag{1.129}$$

where

$$u_1 = \begin{cases} 2 & (\eta \geq 2 + 1/k), \\ 1 + k(\eta - 2.0) & |\eta - 2.0| \leq 1/k), \\ 0 & (\eta \leq 2 - (1/k), \end{cases} \tag{1.130}$$

and if we assume $|\eta - 2.0| \leq 1/k$, the proportional control for the reactor yields the following equations:

$$\dot{\xi} = 1 - \xi - \xi \exp [50(\tfrac{1}{2} - (1/\eta))], \tag{1.131}$$

$$\dot{\eta} = -2(\eta - 1.75) - k(\eta - 1.75)(\eta - 2.0) + \xi \exp [50(\tfrac{1}{2} - (1/\eta))]. \tag{1.132}$$

If on–off control is used, Equation (1.132) becomes

$$\dot{\eta} = -3(\eta - 1.75) + \xi \exp [50(\tfrac{1}{2} - (1/\eta))] \tag{1.133}$$

when the reactor is fully cooled (the valve is fully open) and

$$\dot{\eta} = -(\eta - 1.75) + \xi \exp [50(\tfrac{1}{2} - (1/\eta))] \tag{1.134}$$

when the reactor is adiabatic (the valve is fully closed). We shall encounter Equations (1.131) and (1.132) again in Chapter 2 when the time-optimal control for the reactor is considered. Let us now transform the coordinate system so that $\xi = \frac{1}{2}$, $\eta = 2$ is the origin. This is accomplished by defining the new variables

$$C = \xi - 0.5, \qquad T = \eta - 2.0,$$

yielding

$$\dot{C} = 0.5 - C - (C + 0.5)\exp\left[\frac{25T}{T+2}\right], \tag{1.135}$$

$$\dot{T} = -2[T + 0.25] - kT[T + 0.25] + (C + 0.5)\exp\left[\frac{25T}{T+2}\right]. \tag{1.136}$$

Of specific interest in this system is the dynamic behavior when different values of k are used. The discussion of this feature will be presented in Chapter 6.

The *second nonlinear system* has been used by Jensen [18] and consists of a photochemical reaction carried out isothermally in a CSTR. Control of the CSTR is achieved by manipulation of the flow rate of two inlet feed streams and the light intensity input. The rate of the particular reaction step is taken to be proportional to the square root of the light intensity $\bar{I}$. The molecular equations for the interactions of the species A, B, C, D, E, F, and G are given by

$$A + B \xrightarrow{k_1} 2D,$$

$$C + B \xrightarrow{k_2} CB,$$

$$CB + B \xrightarrow{k^*} 3E,$$

$$E + D \xrightarrow{k_3} 2F,$$

$$F + A \xrightarrow{k_4} 2G,$$

where the fifth reaction is photochemical and its rate is proportional to the square root of the light intensity, $\bar{I}$; CB is an intermediate which is postulated to be present in immeasurably small quantities, so it satisfies the stationary condition, namely $d(CB)/dt = 0$.

The following dimensionless material balances are obtained:

$$\dot{x}_1 = F_1 - Fx_1 - k_1x_1x_2 - k_4x_1x_6\bar{I}^{1/2},$$
$$\dot{x}_2 = F_2 - Fx_2 - k_1x_1x_2 - k_2x_2x_3 - k^*(CB)x_2,$$
$$\dot{x}_3 = F_3 - Fx_3 - k_2x_2x_3,$$
$$\dot{x}_4 = -Fx_4 + 2k_1x_1x_2 - k_3x_4x_5,$$
$$\dot{x}_5 = -Fx_5 + 3k^*(CB)x_2 - k_3x_4x_5,$$
$$\dot{x}_6 = -Fx_6 + 2k_3x_4x_5 - k_4x_1x_6\bar{I}^{1/2},$$
$$\dot{x}_7 = -Fx_7 + 2k_4x_1x_6\bar{I}^{1/2},$$

and, for the intermediate, we have

$$d(CB)/dt = -F(CB) + k_2 x_2 x_3 - k^*(CB)x_2 = 0.$$

However, (CB) is very small and k^* is very large, so that

$$k^*(CB) = k_2 x_3 .$$

Substitution of this into the above balances gives

$$\begin{aligned}
\dot{x}_1 &= F_1 - Fx_1 - k_1 x_1 x_2 - k_4 x_1 x_6 \bar{I}^{1/2}, \\
\dot{x}_2 &= F_2 - Fx_2 - k_1 x_1 x_2 - 2k_2 x_2 x_3 , \\
\dot{x}_3 &= F_3 - Fx_3 - k_2 x_2 x_3 , \\
\dot{x}_4 &= -Fx_4 + 2k_1 x_1 x_2 - k_3 x_4 x_5 , \\
\dot{x}_5 &= -Fx_5 + 3k_2 x_2 x_3 - k_3 x_4 x_5 , \\
\dot{x}_6 &= -Fx_6 + 2k_3 x_4 x_5 - k_4 x_1 x_6 \bar{I}^{1/2}, \\
\dot{x}_7 &= -Fx_7 + 2k_4 x_1 x_2 \bar{I}^{1/2},
\end{aligned} \tag{1.137}$$

where

$x_1, \ldots, x_7$ = weight fractions of species $A, \ldots, G$,
$k_1, \ldots, k_4$ = reaction velocity constants for reaction steps,
F_1, F_2, F_3 = inlet feed rate of pure components A, B, and C,
$\bar{I}$ = light intensity,
F = outlet feed rate of combined streams with $F = F_1 + F_2 + F_3$.

Because of conservation of mass, the relationship

$$\sum_{i=1}^{7} x_i = 1.0 \tag{1.138}$$

may also be specified. Note that this system has seven state variables, $x_1, \ldots, x_7$, and a considerable number of coupled nonlinearities.

Equations (1.137) may be written in matrix notation as

$$\dot{\boldsymbol{x}}(t) = \boldsymbol{f}[\boldsymbol{x}(t), \boldsymbol{u}(t), \boldsymbol{v}], \tag{1.139}$$

where

$$\boldsymbol{x}(t) = \begin{bmatrix} x_1 \\ \vdots \\ x_7 \end{bmatrix}, \quad \boldsymbol{u}(t) = \begin{bmatrix} F_2 \\ F_3 \\ \bar{I} \end{bmatrix}, \quad \boldsymbol{v} = \begin{bmatrix} k_1 \\ \vdots \\ k_4 \\ F_1 \end{bmatrix}.$$

In this formulation the control vector $\boldsymbol{u}(t)$ is taken as consisting of the two inlet flow rates F_2 and F_3 and the light intensity $\bar{I}$. The vector $\boldsymbol{v}$ contains the fixed system parameters $k_1, \ldots, k_4$ and the remaining inlet flow rate F_1 or analogously the total outlet flow rate F. The particular choice of the control variables was made with no fixed idea in mind in the sense that these variables could as well have been F_1, F_2, and F_3 or F_1, F_2, F_3, and $\bar{I}$.

A convenient set of parameters is given by

$$k_1 = 17.6, \quad k_3 = 51.3, \quad F_1 = 3.00 \text{ initially},$$
$$k_2 = 73.0, \quad k_4 = 23.0, \quad F_1 = 6.00 \text{ finally},$$

and solving Equation (1.139) with $\dot{\boldsymbol{x}}(t) = \boldsymbol{0}$, there results for two settings of the control variables and the two values of F_1,

$$\boldsymbol{x}(0)\Big|_{\substack{F_1=3.00,\\ F_2=4.75,\\ F_3=1.25,\\ \bar{I}=0.60}} = \begin{bmatrix} .1883 \\ .2507 \\ .0467 \\ .0899 \\ .1804 \\ .1394 \\ .1046 \end{bmatrix} \quad \text{(initial values)}, \tag{1.140}$$

$$\boldsymbol{x}_e\Big|_{\substack{F_1=6.00,\\ F_2=7.00,\\ F_3=1.75,\\ \bar{I}=0.90}} = \begin{bmatrix} .2847 \\ .2562 \\ .0532 \\ .1170 \\ .1380 \\ .0817 \\ .0692 \end{bmatrix} \quad \text{(final values)}. \tag{1.141}$$

Thus, the control problem will consist of selecting F_2, F_3, and $\bar{I}$ such that the state variables $\boldsymbol{x}(t)$ start with the initial steady-state condition $\boldsymbol{x}(0)$ and finish at or close to the final steady-state condition $\boldsymbol{x}_e$, so that a suitable performance index is extremized.

The performance index for this system will always be of the form

$$I[\boldsymbol{x}(0), t_f] = \int_0^{t_f} [c_1(Fx_1 - F_1) - c_2F_2 - F_3c_3 + c_4Fx_4 + c_5Fx_5 + c_6Fx_6 + c_7Fx_7 - c_8\bar{I} - c_9]\, dt, \tag{1.142}$$

where

$I[\boldsymbol{x}(0), t_f]$ = integrated rate of profit in dollars/hr,

$c_1, \ldots, c_7$ = values in dollars/weight of $x_1, \ldots, x_7$,

c_8 = cost of light,

c_9 = operation cost.

This performance index may be interpreted as follows: all unreacted x_1 is recovered, products x_4, x_5, x_6, and x_7 are fully recovered, but x_2 and x_3 are lost (unrecovered). A suitable set of parameters for the performance index is as follows.

$$\begin{aligned} c_1 &= 5.8, & c_4 &= 23.0, & c_7 &= 35.0, \\ c_2 &= 3.7, & c_5 &= 11.0, & c_8 &= 5.0, \\ c_3 &= 4.1, & c_6 &= 28.0, & c_9 &= 0.099. \end{aligned} \tag{1.143}$$

Actually, the steady-state conditions of Equations (1.137) and (1.138) were not chosen simply by selecting the controls at random but rather by a careful analysis of the behavior of the performance indices. The values used ensure that the profit rate will have a maximum point in a finite time [18].

The *third nonlinear system* which we shall use for illustration is the cross-current extraction with immiscible solvents of a single solute. This system has been used by Aris, Rudd, and Amundson [9], Converse [13], Fan and Wang [2], and a number of other authors. Our concern with this system is mainly one of having an essentially trivial case (one-state variable) which can be used to illustrate the computation procedures. The physical system is so written that the reader will have no difficulty in visualizing the behavior under a variety of circumstances.

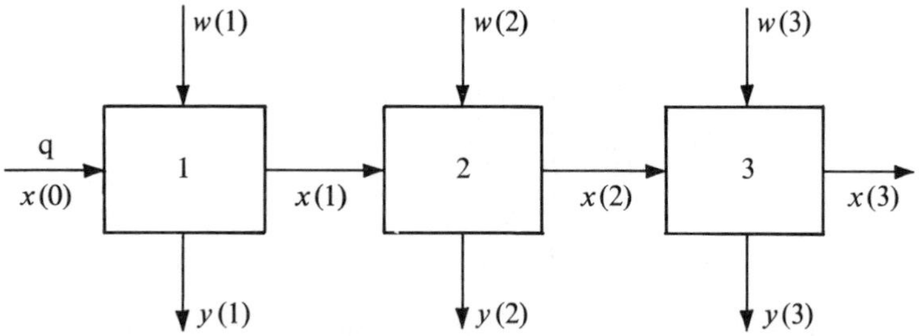

FIGURE 1.6. Liquid–liquid crosscurrent extraction system

The basic physical system is shown in Figure 1.6 with three equilibrium extraction stages. Using the symbolism that

q = solvent (raffinate) flow rate,
$w(k)$ = solvent (extract) flow rate to k-stage,
$x(k)$ = solute concentration leaving k-stage in raffinate,
$y(k)$ = solute concentration leaving k-stage in extract,
$y(k) = \phi[x(k)]$ = equilibrium relationship between raffinate and extract leaving stage k,

a material balance yields

$$q[x(k) - x(k-1)] = -w(k)y(k). \tag{1.144}$$

Since $q = \text{const}$, this equation may be rewritten as

$$x(k) = x(k-1) - v(k)y(k), \tag{1.145}$$

where $v(k) = w(k)/q$. Equation (1.145) serves as our discrete-time system model with $v(k)$ taken as the control variable. In other words, we try to select $v(1)$, $v(2)$, and $v(3)$ such that for a prescribed feed $x(0)$ we extremize the performance index

$$I[x(0), 3] = q[x(0) - x(3)] - \lambda \sum_{k=1}^{3} w(k) \tag{1.146}$$

or

$$I^*[x(0), 3] = \frac{I[x(0), 3]}{q} = x(0) - x(3) - \lambda \sum_{k=1}^{3} v(k). \tag{1.147}$$

Some care is necessary in interpreting this performance index. Thus, if we wish to extremize only $q[x(0) - x(3)]$, the obvious result is to force $x(3)$ to zero. Instead, we extremize $q[x(0) - x(3)]$ subject to a "cost of solvent" λ. As we will see in Section 2.6, this may be achieved by converting the constrained problem to an unconstrained one by attaching the constraints with a Lagrange multiplier λ. Thus, λ may be interpreted as either a cost of solvent or a Lagrange multiplier.

Equation (1.147) may be rephrased in different terms by noting that

$$\sum_{k=1}^{3} [x(k) - x(k-1)] = x(3) - x(0),$$

and from summing the system equation, we have

$$\sum_{k=1}^{3} [x(k) - x(k-1)] = \sum_{k=1}^{3} v(k)y(k) = x(3) - x(0).$$

Thus, Equation (1.147) can be written as

$$I^*[x(0), 3] = \sum_{k=1}^{3} v(k)[y(k) - \lambda]. \tag{1.148}$$

If we now define a new variable $p(k)$ such that

$$p(k) = p(k-1) + v(k)[y(k) - \lambda] \tag{1.149}$$

and

$$p(0) = 0, \tag{1.150}$$

we can see that $p(3) = I^*[x(0), 3]$. Thus, in terms of $p(k)$, our problem is to maximize the final state value $p(3)$.

In summary, we may write the new system as

$$\boldsymbol{x}(k) = \boldsymbol{x}(k-1) + \boldsymbol{g}(k), \tag{1.151}$$

where, from Equations (1.145) and (1.149),

$$\boldsymbol{x}(k) = \begin{bmatrix} x(k) \\ p(k) \end{bmatrix}, \quad \boldsymbol{x}(k-1) = \begin{bmatrix} x(k-1) \\ p(k-1) \end{bmatrix}, \quad \boldsymbol{g}(k) = \begin{bmatrix} -v(k)y(k) \\ v(k)[y(k) - \lambda] \end{bmatrix}. \tag{1.152}$$

The initial conditions are

$$\boldsymbol{x}(0) = \begin{bmatrix} x(0) \\ 0 \end{bmatrix}, \tag{1.153}$$

and we ask to select $v(1)$, $v(2)$, and $v(3)$ so as to maximize $p(3)$.

As a final point, we need to specify the equilibrium conditions $y(k) = \phi[x(k)]$. Table 1.2 shows a tabulated set of these as presented from Rosen [34].

TABLE 1.2

$y(k)$	$x(k)$
.0	.0
.0250	.0100
.0500	.0200
.0751	.0300
.1000	.0400
.1234	.0500
.1422	.0600
.1550	.0700
.1634	.0800
.1697	.0900
.1739	.1000
.1763	.1100
.1779	.1200
.1790	.1300
.1787	.1400
.1787	.1500
.1793	.1600
.1815	.1700
.1815	.1800
.1907	.1900
.1997	.2000

These equilibrium data exhibit a considerable amount of nonlinearity. As a result, the current system may be used in its linear form by specifying the equilibrium condition as

$$y(k) = \alpha x(k) \qquad (\alpha = \text{const})$$

or in the nonlinear form by using the data of Table 1.2.

References

BOOKS

1. M. AKOI, "On Optimal and Suboptimal Policies in Control Systems," *Advances in Control Systems I*, Academic Press, 1964.
2. L. FAN and C. WANG, *The Discrete Maximum Principle*, John Wiley and Sons, 1964.
3. H. FREEMAN, *Discrete-Time Systems*, John Wiley and Sons, 1965.
4. L. LAPIDUS, *Digital Computation for Chemical Engineers*, McGraw-Hill Book Co., 1962.
5. T. L. SAATY and J. BRAM, Nonlinear Mathematics, McGraw-Hill Book Co., 1964.
6. J. T. TOU, *Modern Control Theory*, McGraw-Hill Book Co., 1964.
7. L. A. ZADEH and C. A. DESOER, *Linear System Theory*, McGraw-Hill Book Co., 1963.

ARTICLES

8. R. ARIS and N. R. AMUNDSON, *Chem. Eng. Sci.*, *7*, 121, 132, 148 (1958).
9. R. ARIS, D. RUDD, and N. AMUNDSON, *Chem. Eng. Sci.*, *12*, 88 (1960).
10. R. BELLMAN and R. KALABA, *J. Math. Anal. Appl. 7*, 322 (1963).
11. S. BUTMAN and R. SIVAN, *IEEE Trans. Auto. Control, AC-9*, 317 (1964).
12. A. CHANG, *IEEE Trans. Auto. Control, AC-10*, 112 (1965).
13. O. CONVERSE, *Chem. Eng. Progress Symposium, Series 59*, 127 (1963).
14. R. C. DURBECK, *IEEE Trans. Auto. Control, AC-10*, 144 (1965).
15. B. FRIEDLAND, "A Technique of Quasi-Optimum Control," presented at *1965 Joint Auto. Control. Conf., Troy, N. Y.* (1965).
16. E. G. GILBERT, *J. SIAM Control 2*, 128 (1963).
17. H. HERMES, *J. SIAM Control*, *4*, 241 (1965).
18. T. JENSEN, "Dynamic Control of Large Dimension Nonlinear Chemical Processes," *Ph.D. Dissertation, Princeton University* (1964).
19. R. KALMAN, and R. KOEPCKE, *Trans. ASME*, *80*, 1820 (1958).
20. R. KALMAN and J. E. BERTRAM, *J. Frank. Inst.*, *267*, 405 (1959).

21. R. E. KALMAN, *Bull. Soc. Mat. Mexicana*, 102 (1960).
22. R. E. KALMAN, Y. C. HO., and K. S. NARENDRA, "Controllability of Linear Dynamical Systems," in *Contributions of Differential Equations, I*, John Wiley and Sons, 1961.
23. R. E. KALMAN, *J. SIAM Control*, *1*, 152 (1963).
24. R. E. KALMAN, *J. Basic Eng.*, *86D*, 51 (1964).
25. R. KOEPCKE and L. LAPIDUS, *Chem. Eng. Sci.*, *16*, 252 (1961).
26. E. KREINDLER and P. E. SARACHIK, *IEEE Trans. Auto. Control*, *AC-9*, 129 (1964).
27. L. LAPIDUS, E. SHAPIRO, S. SHAPIRO, and R. E. STILLMAN, *A.I.Ch.E.J.*, *7*, 290 (1961).
28. H. LESSER, "The Time Optimal Control of High Order Linear Systems with Bounded Controls," *Ph.D. Dissertation, Princeton University* (1964).
29. J. D. PEARSON, *J. Elect. Control*, *13*, 453 (1962).
30. A. E. PEARSON and P. E. SARACHIK, *J. Basic Eng.*, *87D*, 125 (1965).
31. R. PENROSE, *Proc. Cambridge Phil. Soc.*, *51*, 406 (1955).
32. E. POLAK, *IEEE Trans. Auto. Control*, *AC-8*, 49 (1964).
33. R. A. ROHRER and M. SOBRAL, *IEEE Trans. Auto. Control*, *AC-10*, 43 (1965).
34. E. M. ROSEN, *Chem. Eng. Sci.*, *19*, 999 (1964).
35. H. H. ROSENBROCK, *Chem. Eng. Progr.*, *58*, 43 (September 1962).
36. P. E. SARACHIK and G. M. KRANC, *J. Basic Eng.*, *85D*, 143 (1963).
37. P. E. SARACHIK and G. M. KRANC, *J. Franklin Inst.*, *277*, 237 (1964).
38. L. WEISS, *Proc. Natl. Acad. Sci. U.S.*, *51*, 1122 (1965).
39. L. WEISS, *J. Math. Anal. Appl.*, *10*, 442 (1965).
40. L. A. ZADEH, *IEEE Trans. Auto. Control*, *AC-8*, 59 (1963).

2

General Mathematical Procedures

In this chapter we shall develop a number of different mathematical procedures which are of interest by themselves and, in addition, can be used in subsequent chapters. In particular we shall outline the concepts of dynamic programming, the maximum principle, and Liapunov's stability criterion. At the same time, we shall have need to discuss the adjoint variables and the inclusion of constrained variables. Certain liberties will be taken with some of the derivations, but adequate references will be mentioned to allow the reader to pursue further detail.

2.1. Dynamic programming

One of the more powerful techniques we shall use to generate optimal trajectories is *dynamic programming*, developed originally by Bellman [4, 5] and used in chemical engineering work by Aris [1, 2], Roberts [15], and Lapidus [59]. The main concept of this technique lies in the *principle of optimality*, which may be stated in a form suitable for our present work:

An optimal policy has the property that whatever the initial state and the initial decision are, the remaining decisions must constitute an optimal policy with regard to the state resulting from the first decision.

Our experience has shown, however, that it is quite difficult for a person who is first exposed to dynamic programming to grasp immediately the implications and usefulness of this principle. Thus, we shall develop the basic ideas with a few simple examples and then build up to the point where the application of this principle to control is self-evident.

Let us start by posing a rather simple problem.

PROBLEM ▪ Given the system equation in the discrete scalar form

$$x(k+1) = ax(k) + bu(k), \qquad x(0) = \text{prescribed}$$
$$(k = 0, 1, 2, \ldots; a, b = \text{const}), \tag{2.1}$$

with a performance index of the form

$$I[x(0), P] = \sum_{k=1}^{P} [x^2(k) + u^2(k-1)], \tag{2.2}$$

where P = the number of time stages, find $u(0), u(1), \ldots, u(P-1)$ such that $I[x(0), P]$ is minimized.

Solution ▪ The final state $x(P)$ is taken to be the origin. We first consider $P = 1$, that is, there is only one time stage involved and we wish to go from $x(0)$ to $x(1)$ by a selection of $u(0)$ which minimizes $I[x(0), 1]$. Here

$$I[x(0), 1] = x^2(1) + u^2(0).$$

But it is noted that since the origin is to be reached in one step, $x(1) = 0$ = origin, this equation becomes

$$I[x(0), 1] = u^2(0).$$

Obviously, if the system equation, Equation (2.1), is to be satisfied, it is necessary that

$$u(0) = \frac{x(1) - ax(0)}{b} = -\frac{a}{b}x(0). \tag{2.3}$$

Note that this value of $u(0)$ is independent of the performance index (this being a special case). This follows from the fact that the final state, $x(1)$, has been specified (in this case to be the origin); we are then not free to choose the control since, if $x(0)$ is also given, there is only one unique $u(0)$ which connects $x(0)$ and $x(1)$ in one step. However, once the value of $u(0)$ is known, we can assign a value to the performance index:

$$I[x(0), 1] = \frac{a^2}{b^2}x^2(0). \tag{2.4}$$

Thus, for the process considered as consisting of only one time stage, the *a priori* specification of the final state precludes (in this case) any minimization of the performance index.

As a side point, we note that if the control is constrained by bounds of the form $|u(0)| \leq 1.0$, it may not be possible to find an admissible $u(0)$ which holds for all values of $x(0)$. In other words, it is quite possible that for certain values of $x(0)$ the control specified by Equation (2.3) is beyond the constraints allowed. In such a case, it is impossible to reach the origin in one step.

Next, we consider $P = 2$ and ask to find $u(0)$ and $u(1)$ which take the system from $x(0)$ to $x(2)$ while minimizing $I[x(0), 2]$. To keep our nomenclature consistent, $x(2) = 0 =$ origin, and

$$I[x(0), 2] = x^2(1) + u^2(0) + x^2(2) + u^2(1).$$

Figure 2.1 shows a schematic of the steps for $P = 1$ and $P = 2$. We note one item at this point; from Equation (2.1) (ignoring any constraints) we know that

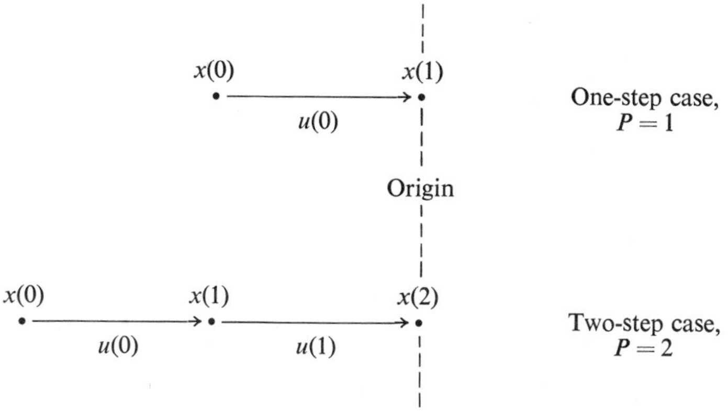

FIGURE 2.1. Two steps in the dynamic programming example

given any value of $x(1)$ in the two-stage process, we can immediately calculate the corresponding value of $u(1)$ such that $x(2)$ is the origin, that is,

$$x(2) = 0 = ax(1) + bu(1),$$

from which

$$u(1) = -a/bx(1),$$

and thus

$$I[x(0), 2] = x^2(1) + u^2(0) + u^2(1) = \left(1 + \frac{a^2}{b^2}\right)x^2(1) + u^2(0).$$

To obtain the extremum of $I[x(0), 2]$ for a choice of $u(0)$, we can differentiate $I[x(0), 2]$ with respect to $u(0)$ and set the result equal to zero; then we need to show that this results in a true minimum. Thus,

$$\frac{\partial I[x(0), 2]}{\partial u(0)} = 0 = 2u(0) + 2\left(1 + \frac{a^2}{b^2}\right)x(1)\,\frac{\partial x(1)}{\partial u(0)}.$$

From Equation (2.1), we see that

$$x(1) = ax(0) + bu(0),$$

so that

$$\frac{\partial x(1)}{\partial u(0)} = b.$$

Hence,

$$\frac{\partial I[x(0), 2]}{\partial u(0)} = 0 = 2u(0) + 2\left(1 + \frac{a^2}{b^2}\right)[ax(0) + bu(0)]b$$

or

$$u(0) = -\left\{\frac{ab + (a^3/b)}{1 + a^2 + b^2}\right\}x(0).$$

While we have these equations fresh in our mind, perhaps we should rewrite certain of them so that the material to follow is easily understood. Thus, let us rewrite Equation (2.3) as

$$u(P - 1) = -\frac{a}{b}x(P - 1) \qquad (P = 1, 2, \ldots), \tag{2.5}$$

where P is the number of stages used in the process. Thus, for $P = 1$, a one-stage process,

$$u(0) = -(a/b)x(0),$$

and for $P = 2$, a two-stage process,

$$u(1) = -(a/b)x(1).$$

In the same sense, we may generalize the last equation for $u(0)$ derived for the two-stage process as

$$u(P - 2) = -\left[\frac{ab + (a^3/b)}{1 + a^2 + b^2}\right]x(P - 2) \qquad (P = 2, 3, \ldots), \tag{2.6}$$

so that for $P = 2$ we get

$$u(0) = -\left[\frac{ab + (a^3/b)}{1 + a^2 + b^2}\right]x(0).$$

To show that this last equation really gives a minimum for $I[x(0), 2]$ we note that

$$\frac{\partial^2 I[x(0), 2]}{\partial u(0)^2} = 2 + 2\left(1 + \frac{a^2}{b^2}\right)b^2 > 0.$$

We now have solved the problem over two time stages. Given any value of $x(0)$, Equation (2.6) tells us (with $P = 2$) the value of $u(0)$ to use to minimize $I[x(0), 2]$ and reach the origin in two steps. With this knowledge, we may also find $x(1)$ and $u(1)$ since, given $x(0)$ and $u(0)$, Equation (2.1) yields $x(1)$, and with $x(1)$ given, Equation (2.5) tells us what $u(1)$ to apply to reach the origin. Ignoring any constraints, this result is perfectly general for any $x(0)$.

It is most important at this point to grasp the reasoning and implications behind the two-step procedure. The two-step solution has been obtained by imbedding the second-stage solution (obtained by considering only a single final stage) into the two stages. In other words, we have inserted Equation (2.3) into the performance index so that given any $x(1)$ as generated by the proper choice of $u(0)$, the second stage must go to the origin. Stated in another way, by considering the second of the two stages as already determined for any $x(1)$, it is possible to hunt only for that value of $u(0)$ which minimizes $I[x(0), 2]$. But every time we select a $u(0)$, we can immediately find $x(1)$, and from Equation (2.3) we then have $u(1)$. If we had not carried out this procedure, it would have been necessary to differentiate the performance index first with respect to $u(0)$, second with respect to $u(1)$, and then to set the resulting derivatives equal to zero. This would have yielded two algebraic equations to be solved *simultaneously*. *Thus the solution of two simultaneous equations is replaced by a procedure which evaluates one single equation but does it twice* (a serial computation instead of a parallel computation).

Now we add another time stage and ask to go from $x(0)$ to $x(3)$ by a proper selection of $u(0)$, $u(1)$, and $u(2)$ while we minimize $I[x(0), 3]$. In this case, $x(3) = 0$ = origin, and

$$I[x(0), 3] = x^2(1) + u^2(0) + x^2(2) + u^2(1) + u^2(2).$$

Using Figure 2.2 as illustration, we can see that the three-stage process is conceptually equivalent to a two-stage process in the sense that we must determine $u(0)$ that generates an $x(1)$; but for any value of $x(1)$ we know the rest of the control values needed to bring the system to the origin. Thus, the remaining

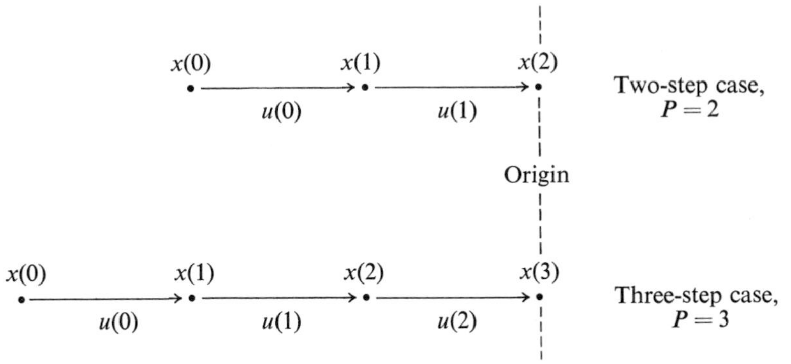

FIGURE 2.2. Three steps in the dynamic programming example

stages may be thought of as one large stage. In other words, once we select a $u(0)$ and thus generate an $x(1)$, Equation (2.6) yields $u(1)$ and this generates $x(2)$; this is then followed by Equation (2.5) to yield $u(2)$, which drives the system to the origin.

This procedure can be generalized for any integer P. So long as we proceed along these same lines, we are always searching for $u(0)$ such that $x(1)$ is generated, and then we follow this up with a control sequence which guarantees that the origin will be reached. Always the procedure continues to look like a two-stage process with the second "step" including many real steps. Note the equivalence of this procedure to the principle of optimality, which is the basis of dynamic programming.

The same approach can be used for the continuous-time system.

PROBLEM ▪ If the system model is given by

$$\dot{x}(t) = ax(t) + bu(t), \qquad x(0) = \text{initial condition}, \tag{2.7}$$

and the performance index by

$$I[x(0), t_f] = \int_0^{t_f} [(x(\lambda)^2 + u(\lambda)^2]\, d\lambda, \tag{2.8}$$

we seek the continuous function $u(t)$ which minimizes $I[x(0), t_f]$, subject to the equality of Equation (2.7) (ignoring any constraints on the control variables).

Solution ▪ First, we rewrite Equation (2.8) between limits of $t = 0$ and $t = \Delta t$ and then between $t = \Delta t$ and $t = t_f$, where Δt is considered small compared to t_f:

$$I[x(0), t_f] = \int_0^{\Delta t} (x^2 + u^2)\, d\lambda + \int_{\Delta t}^{t_f} (x^2 + u^2)\, d\lambda. \tag{2.9}$$

The right-hand side is the value of the performance index which results from starting at $x(0)$, $t = 0$ and going to $x(t_f) = 0$, $t = t_f$ by some choice of $u(t)$. But if we expect some control over the interval $[0, \Delta t]$, Equation (2.7) can be used to calculate $x(\Delta t)$, given a specific $x(0)$. Thus Equation (2.8) represents the value of $I[x(0), t_f]$ involving a starting value $x(0)$ and a total time t_f while the second term on the right-hand side of Equation (2.9) represents the same situation but with a starting initial state $x(\Delta t)$ and total time of $t_f - \Delta t$. Thus we write, in analogy to Equation (2.8),

$$I[x(\Delta t), t_f - \Delta t] = \int_{\Delta t}^{t_f} [x(\lambda)^2 + u(\lambda)^2]\, d\lambda, \tag{2.10}$$

and if we call $I^\circ[\ \ ]$ the optimal value of $I[\ \ ]$ by a proper selection of $u(t)$,

$$I^\circ[x(0), t_f] = \min_{u(t)} \left\{ \int_0^{\Delta t} (x^2 + u^2)\, d\lambda + I^\circ[x(\Delta t), t_f - \Delta t] \right\} \qquad (0 \le t \le \Delta t). \tag{2.11}$$

In this form, we see that it is necessary to seek the value of $u(t)$ only over the time interval $[0, \Delta t]$ and then follow this up with the optimal policy starting at $x(\Delta t)$. Obviously, this is conceptually equivalent to the procedure developed for the discrete system and embodies the principle of optimality.

Let us now increase the complexity of our problem by generalizing the system equation and the performance index. This will serve to illustrate further features associated with the use of dynamic programming. Consider that the scalar system model is given in discrete form as

$$x(k+1) = h[x(k), u(k)], \tag{2.12}$$

with initial state $x(0)$. Let us discretize the state variable at the kth stage into N values and the control variable into Q values. Thus

$$x(k) \Rightarrow \begin{Bmatrix} x_1(k) \\ x_2(k) \\ \vdots \\ x_N(k) \end{Bmatrix} = \begin{Bmatrix} x_1 \\ x_2 \\ \vdots \\ x_N \end{Bmatrix}; \qquad u(k) \Rightarrow \begin{Bmatrix} u_1(k) \\ u_2(k) \\ \vdots \\ u_Q(k) \end{Bmatrix} = \begin{Bmatrix} u_1 \\ u_2 \\ \vdots \\ u_Q \end{Bmatrix},$$

where $x_i(k) = x_i, i = 1, 2, \ldots, N$ and $u_j(k) = u_j, j = 1, 2, \ldots, Q$, with the dependence of k implied. Obviously, since the normal system is continuous in x, u, and t, this discretization may be valid only as the increments go to zero. If we have P stages of control and there is a final state performance index,

$$I[x(0), P] = I[x(P)],$$

then we may pose the following problem.

PROBLEM ▪ Find the set of inputs $u(0), u(1), \ldots, u(P-1)$ such that $I[x(P)]$ is minimized as the system goes from $x(0)$ to $x(P)$, subject to the use of the discretized x_i and u_j.

Solution ▪ Let us construct Figure 2.3, in which we tabulate the allowable $x_i(k)$ at the different stages of control. Working backward in this table (note that this was done in the previous example), we compute the value of $I[x_i(P)]$ corresponding to the last column and each x_i in that column. Figure 2.3 shows the addition of these values.

Now we move back one stage in the sequence and consider one of the $x_i(P-1)$, say $x_2(P-1)$. For this value of $x_2(P-1)$ we consider the use of Equation (2.12) with each of the discrete values of $u_j(P-1)$, assuming for this example that each of the $u_j(P-1)$ when substituted into Equation (2.12) will yield one of the tabulated $x_i(P)$ (this is a bold assumption which will be removed later). As illustration, $x_3(P)$ is formed from $x_2(P-1)$ by using $u_1(P-1)$; $x_5(P)$ is formed from $x_2(P-1)$ by using $u_2(P-1), \ldots$; and $x_2(P)$ is formed from

Stage 0	$\cdots$	Stage $P-1$	Stage P	
$x_1(0)$		$x_1(P-1)$	$x_1(P)$,	$I[x_1(P)]$
$x_2(0)$		$x_2(P-1)$	$x_2(P)$,	$I[x_2(P)]$
.		.	.	.
.		.	.	.
.		.	.	.
$x_N(0)$	$\cdots$	$x_N(P-1)$	$x_N(P)$,	$I[x_N(P)]$

FIGURE 2.3. Tabulation of discretized state for different stages of control

$x_2(P-1)$ by using $u_Q(P-1)$. For each of these steps we shall have a specific value for the performance index; that is, when we use $u_1(P-1)$ to generate $x_3(P)$, this results in $I[x_3(P)], \ldots,$ and when we use $u_Q(P-1)$ to generate $x_2(P)$, this results in $I[x_2(P)]$. Now we scan all the results of applying the $u_j(P-1)$ with $j = 1, 2, \ldots, Q$ to $x_2(P-1)$ and pick that $I[x_i(P)]$ which is the minimum value. Therefore, for a given $x_2(P-1)$, we know which of the discrete controls to apply to yield the minimum value of the performance index, $I^\circ[x_i(P)]$. In Figure 2.4 we show this feature by connecting $x_2(P-1)$ and $x_N(P)$ by a line carrying the notation $u_8(P-1)$; now we repeat the entire process for $x_1(P-1), x_3(P-1), \ldots,$ and $X_N(P-1)$, yielding the results shown in Figure 2.4. Obviously, the diagram is here used only for tabulation, whereas the actual results can be stored in any manner desired in the digital computer.

To summarize the results to this point, we see that given any of the discrete values $x_i(P-1)$ at stage $P-1$, we know which of the discrete $u_j(P-1)$ to use such that one of the $x_i(P)$ results, and these $u_j(P-1)$ also generate the minimum value of the performance index $I^\circ[x_i(P)]$.

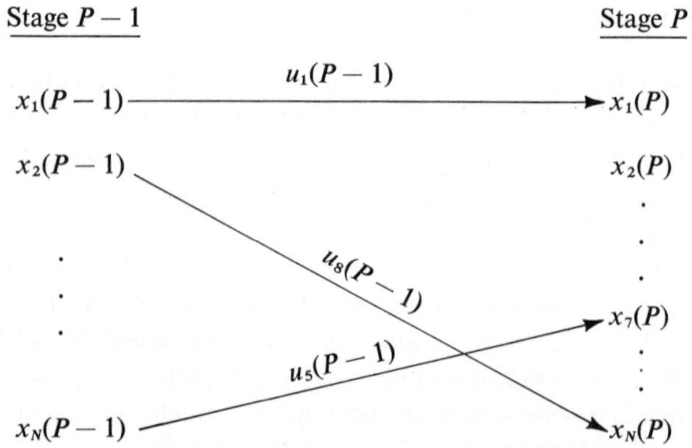

FIGURE 2.4. Optimal controls for one stage

Next, we move back to stage $P-2$ and for each $x_i(P-2)$ we scan all the possible $u_j(P-2)$ to find that particular $u_j(P-2)$ which yields the minimum value of $I[x_i(P)]$. For example, suppose that the application of $u_4(P-2)$ to $x_1(P-2)$ gives $x_2(P-1)$; then it follows that the application of $u_8(P-1)$ to $x_2(P-1)$ yields $x_N(P)$. The resulting performance index value is $I[x_N(P)]$. This is repeated for other paths from $x_1(P-2)$ using the other possible controls; the best control is then the one yielding the smallest $I[x_i(P)]$. Figure 2.5 shows such an optimum path from $x_1(P-2)$. Now we repeat this with $x_2(P-2)$, $x_3(P-2), \ldots, X_N(P-2)$ and complete Figure 2.5.

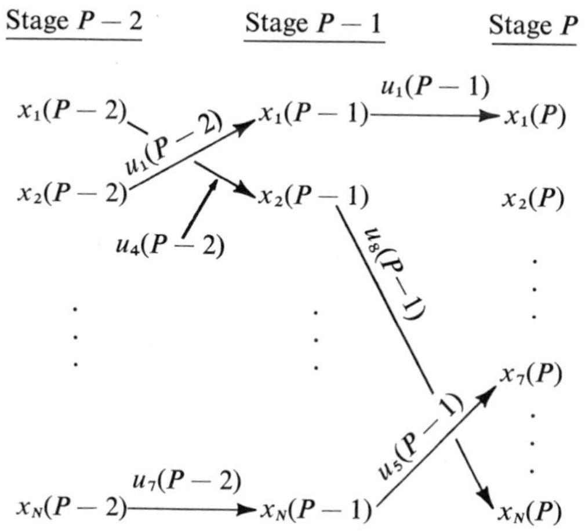

FIGURE 2.5. Optimal controls for two stages

This procedure may be continued by moving backward one stage at a time until finally the 0th stage is reached. At any stage, we consider the one new stage plus all the remaining stages viewed as a single large stage yielding some $I[x_i(P)]$. Any connected set of lines between stages 0 and P specifies $x_i(0)$, $x_i(P)$, and $I^\circ[x_i(P)]$; in other words, the minimum value of $I[x_i(P)]$ and the associated $u_j(0), u_j(1), \ldots, u_j(P-1)$ are obtained for any specific $x_i(0)$. Thus, we have solved our problem. Once again we note that in this procedure we consider the addition of one stage at a time and that all the already computed stages are lumped into an equivalent single stage.

It is important for the reader to note that we have used in this example a final-value performance index. Thus all the computations involve only that value of the performance index which is achieved at the final state. If some other index such as a cumulative one had been used, it would have been necessary to calculate the value of the index at each stage and combine this with the calculated values for the resulting stages.

There are a number of interesting points which can be realized from this example. These points are common to all dynamic programming computations. First, we note the sequential nature of the calculations in which one new stage is added to those stages already handled; such a procedure is ideally suited for digital computation in the sense that essentially the same program is repeated over and over. Second, two "passes" are required in a calculation of this type. In pass one the "tables" or information as outlined in Figure 2.5 are generated starting from the P-stage and continuing backward to the 0-stage. In pass two the specific value of $x_i(0)$ is selected, and proceeding from stage 0 to stage P in a forward direction, the $u_j(k)$ and $x_i(k+1)$ of the optimal sequence are generated. Third, we see that we have really solved more than we started out to solve. We are now in a position to calculate the optimal sequence for not only the given $x_i(0)$ but for all the other discrete values of the initial state, that is, $x_1(0)$, $x_2(0), \ldots, x_{i-1}(0), x_{i+1}(0), \ldots, x_N(0)$. In other words, the problem has been solved by imbedding it in a larger problem than originally required. Fourth, the inclusion of constraints on either the control or state variables actually helps the calculation instead of increasing its complexity. If the control variables are constrained, as illustration, it means that at worst we will need to consider all the discrete values $u_1(k), u_2(k), \ldots, u_Q(k)$, but probably we will only need to consider a part of the sequence, let us say, $u_5(k), u_6(k), \ldots, u_{Q-4}(k)$. Thus, constraints merely tend to restrict the range of discretization which has to be carried out on the variables, and the problem is simpler.

At the same time, there are a number of further points of interest. In scanning the $u_1(k), u_2(k), \ldots, u_Q(k)$ for any state, a considerable amount of computation time may be necessary. As a means of reducing this, we might adopt the following scheme: (1) scan all the controls for $x_1(P-1)$ and pick out the best one; (2) now, since for $x_2(P-1)$ the chances are that the optimal control is not too different from that with $x_1(P-1)$, merely scan the control values around the best one for $x_1(P-1)$; (3) continue this for $x_3(P-1), x_4(P-1), \ldots$ in each case using the results for $x_k(P-1)$ to constrict the controls to be scanned for $x_{k+1}(P-1)$.

While this problem is fresh in our minds, let us consider an interesting variation of it. Suppose that only a certain number of the $x_i(P)$ are to be considered as valid final values. Let us call these $x_i(P)$ admissible final states and the $x_i^*(P)$ inadmissible final states. Thus, in Figure 2.6, $x_2^*(P)$ and $x_{N-1}^*(P)$ are inadmissible states. Obviously, we need only specify the $I[x_i(P)]$ and not the $I[x_i^*(P)]$. Now we go backward one stage and carry out a search on each $x_i(P-1)$ with all $u_j(P-1)$. However, the only results which can be used are those which pass to an admissible state $x_i(P)$. Thus, if we use $x_2(P-1)$ and scan $u_1(P-1)$, $u_2(P-1), \ldots, u_Q(P-1)$, we have to consider only those inputs which yield $I[x_i(P)]$; those inputs which yield for example $I[x_2^*(P)]$ or $I[x_{N-1}^*(P)]$ are not to be considered in finding the minimum value. If no admissible state can be reached from some $x_i(P-1)$, then we label that $x_i(P-1) = x_i^*(P-1)$ since it will be

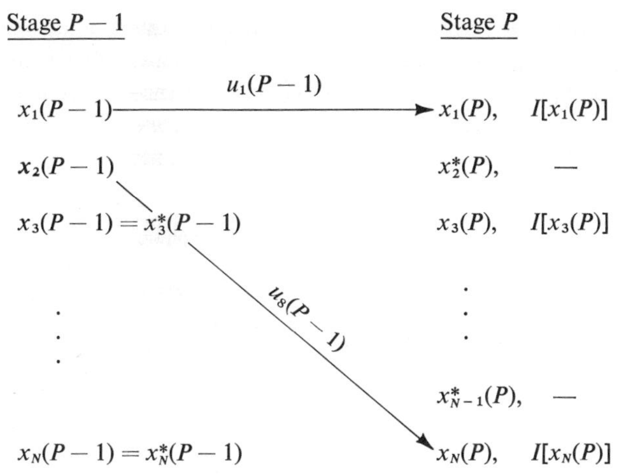

FIGURE 2.6. Consideration of inadmissible states

inadmissible for the $x_i(P-2)$-states. In Figure 2.6, $x_3(P-1)$ and $x_N(P-1)$ are inadmissible, indicating that if we apply any of $u_1(P-1), u_2(P-1), \ldots, u_Q(P-1)$, an admissible state $x_i(P)$ cannot be attained. Obviously, we can continue the entire process backward to stages $P-2, P-3, \ldots, 1, 0$. Now selecting the given $x_i(0)$, we can generate the optimal sequence in a forward pass, assuming that an admissible state can be reached from this $x_i(0)$.

We are in a position to illustrate in a more formal way the basic algorithm of dynamic programming as applied to a generalized problem of interest. For convenience we shall do this in a sequence of steps, each following along the ideas presented previously. We shall still maintain the scalar nature of x and u since we intend to finish this section with a discussion of the advantages and problems of dynamic programming, and the vector system deserves special consideration.

(1) *System and performance specification.* We consider the generalized scalar system equation

$$x(k+1) = h[x(k), u(k)] \qquad (k = 0, 1, \ldots, P), \tag{2.13}$$

with the initial condition $x(0) = \text{const}$ and the performance index

$$I[x(0), P] = \sum_{k=1}^{P} \phi[x(k), u(k-1)] \tag{2.14}$$

and request the following.

Given a set of admissible controls, find $u^\circ(k-1)$, $k = 1, 2, \ldots, P$, such that $I[x(0), P]$ is minimized for any initial state $x(0)$.

In this form we have defined a fairly general optimal control problem.

(2) *Optimal value of performance index.* When we have achieved our desired optimal performance, the left-hand side of Equation (2.14) will represent this optimal value. Thus, we define the optimal value of the performance index for a system starting at $x(0)$ and carried through P stages as

$$I^{\circ}[x(0), P] = \min_{u(k)} I[x(0), P] = \min_{u(k)} \sum_{k=1}^{P} \phi[x(k), u(k-1)] \tag{2.15}$$

or, for $R+1$ stages, as

$$I^{\circ}[x(0), R+1] = \min_{u(k)} \sum_{k=1}^{R+1} \phi[x(k), u(k-1)]. \tag{2.16}$$

Separating the first term in the summation from the others, we may also write Equation (2.16) in the form

$$I^{\circ}[x(0), R+1] = \min_{u(k)} \left\{ \phi[x(1), u(0)] + \sum_{k=2}^{R+1} \phi[x(k), u(k-1)] \right\}. \tag{2.17}$$

But recalling our previous discussion on moving backward stage by stage, we note that if we fix $u(0)$, then Equation (2.13) will determine $x(1)$. However, the second term on the right-hand side of Equation (2.17) is exactly the same as Equation (2.15) except that one less stage is in the summation. Thus, we may write

$$I^{\circ}[x(1), R] = \min_{u(k)} \sum_{k=2}^{R+1} \phi[x(k), u(k-1)], \tag{2.18}$$

and substituting into Equation (2.17), we have

$$I^{\circ}[x(0), R+1] = \min_{u(0)} \{\phi(x(1), u(0)) + I^{\circ}[x(1), R]\}. \tag{2.19}$$

Equation (2.19) expresses the fundamental recurrent or step-wise nature of dynamic programming. It is called the *recurrence relation* for the particular problem under study. Note that it specifies that if R stages of the optimal control have been determined, the $R+1$ stage may be obtained by considering a new first stage *plus* the already established policy for the remaining R stages.

(3) *Discretization of variables.* As the next step in preparing for computation, we discretize the control and state variables. Thus, the control variable is discretized to the Q-values,

$$u(k) \rightarrow \begin{Bmatrix} u_1(k) \\ u_2(k) \\ \vdots \\ u_Q(k) \end{Bmatrix} = \begin{Bmatrix} u_1 \\ u_2 \\ \vdots \\ u_Q \end{Bmatrix}, \tag{2.20}$$

where u_Q might be a positive upper bound and u_1 a negative lower bound on the control. In the same manner and with the same implications, the state variable is restricted to the N values:

$$x(k) \rightarrow \begin{Bmatrix} x_1(k) \\ x_2(k) \\ \vdots \\ x_N(k) \end{Bmatrix} = \begin{Bmatrix} x_1 \\ x_2 \\ \vdots \\ x_N \end{Bmatrix}. \tag{2.21}$$

Although we shall assume that these restricted values hold for every stage in the computation, it is a simple matter to extend this to different limits in each stage. Finally, we note that the time of operation has already been discretized into the staged sequence using k as the appropriate index.

(4) *Start of computation.* Because of the way we have assigned the functionality in the performance index, the last stage involved includes $\phi[x(P), u(P-1)]$. Thus, we are not really able to assign values of the index until we have scanned the controls applied to $x_i(P-1)$. However, we do note that if a state is inadmissible, we will arbitrarily assign a large value of the index to it. Since we are minimizing the index, such a large value will prevent us from ever reaching this inadmissible state. This is an artificial formulation which works well computationally.

Let us now move back to the $P-1$ stage. Considering $x_3(P-1)$ for illustration, we apply all the possible controls $u_1(P-1)$, $u_2(P-1), \ldots, u_Q(P-1)$ and in each case calculate the performance index associated with this one step. We shall call this $I[x_i(P-1), u_j(P-1), x_k(P)]$, where we denote the state started from, the control used and the resulting state, respectively. Figure 2.7 shows such a possible sequence with a coordinate axis laid out for reasons which will be apparent shortly. Each line radiating from $x_3(P-1)$ indicates the control used and the corresponding value of $I[x_3(P-1), u_j(P-1), x_k(P)]$. We note two items which we have not encountered before. First, some of the controls, for example $u_1(P-1)$ and $u_7(P-1)$ as shown in Figure 2.7, may yield a state which is not one of the tabulated values (in fact, this probably occurs more frequently than not). At this stage of the calculation, this does not cause us any concern. It should be recognized, however, that there are many physical situations (not necessarily control problems) where the discretization can be only on an integral basis and involves only the tabulated values (see Example 1 at the end of this chapter). Second, some of the controls, for example, $u_Q(P-1)$ as shown in Figure 2.7, may lead us to a state which is outside the prescribed range. This control obviously cannot be used in finding the optimal control to apply to $x_3(P-1)$. Now all the possible values of control which lead into the domain of $x_1(P) \leq x_k(P) \leq x_N(P)$ or do not reach inadmissible states are scanned and the control yielding the minimum value for the performance index is selected. This procedure is repeated for the remaining $x_1(P-1)$, $x_2(P-1)$, $x_4(P-1), \ldots,$ $x_N(P-1)$, yielding a corresponding set of index values. If one state is such that

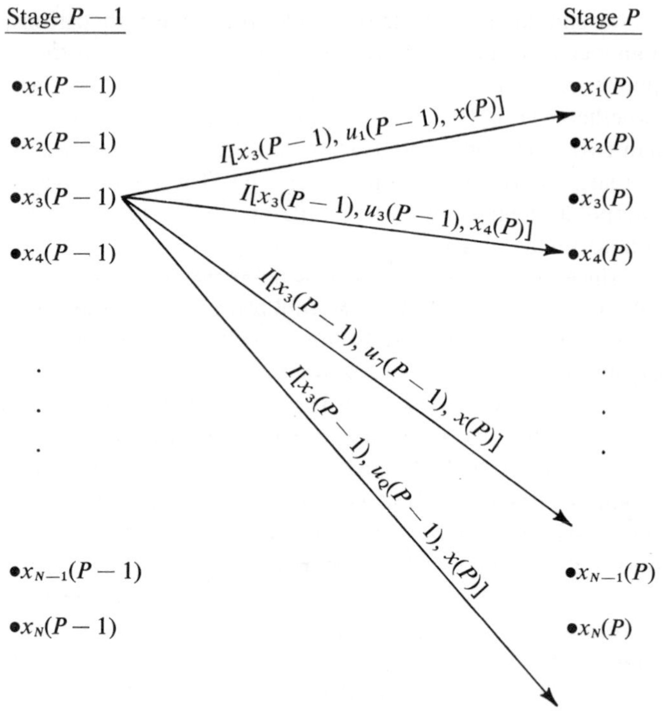

FIGURE 2.7. Consideration of nontabulated states

none of the controls leads it into the bounded $x_k(P)$ region or reaches only inadmissible states, then this $x_i(P-1)$ must be termed inadmissible, and a large value for the performance index is imparted to this state.

(5) *Moving another stage backward.* At this point, we have the discrete values $x_1(P-1), \ldots, x_N(P-1)$ and the corresponding $I^\circ[x_i(P-1), u_j(P-1), x(P)]$. Now we move back one more stage and repeat the procedure of picking an $x_i(P-2)$, scanning all the $u_j(P-2)$ such that we determine that one which yields the smallest $I[x_i(P-2), u_j(P-2), x_k(P-1)] + I[x_k(P-1), u_j(P-1), x(P)]$. This is obtained by summing the performance index for the $P-2$ stage plus that which naturally evolves from the $P-1$ state. However, we can see a problem here, namely, what to do when $u_5(P-2)$ applied to $x_7(P-2)$ yields a state which is *between* $x_5(P-1)$ and $x_6(P-1)$. We have $I[x_5(P-1), u_j(P-1), x_k(P)]$ and $I[x_6(P-1), u_j(P-1), x_k(P)]$ but not for any state in between. It is thus necessary to resort to some type of interpolation between the tabulated $x_i(P-1)$ and the associated I's. Assuming that this is carried out (note that this implies that the functions are continuous and smooth), we can then determine the optimal information at $x_7(P-2)$. This procedure can then be applied to all the $x_i(P-2)$.

Actually, we should give more than a passing word to the interpolation mentioned above. In terms of implementation, there is the question of whether only the points $x_5(P-1)$ and $x_6(P-1)$ should be used (and the associated $I_j^\circ[\ \ ]$) or whether $x_4(P-1)$, $x_5(P-1)$, $x_6(P-1)$ and $x_7(P-1)$ should be used. If more than two points are used, certain problems arise near the ends of the state space, that is, near $x_1(P-1)$ and $x_N(P-1)$. The point to be made here is that the interpolation may be quite simple or it may require some complex interpolation formula; this is especially important in terms of the over-all computation since any errors made at this point may influence the subsequent results. As a final point, it should be emphasized that the *interpolation is in the x-space*; in Chapter 4 we shall consider a variation on dynamic programming in which the interpolation is not in the x-space.

Obviously, we are now in an equivalent position to that of the previous stage; that is, for each $x_i(P-2)$ we have the corresponding $I[x_i(P-2), u_j(P-2), x_k(P-1)] + I[x_k(P-1), u_j(P-1), x(P)]$. We may now continue to move backward, stage by stage, carrying out the same type of calculations until we reach the set $x_i(0)$. When this occurs, we have precalculated all the necessary information for an optimal trajectory starting at any of the $x_i(0)$. Thus, for a particular case we may specify a certain $x_i(0)$ as the initial condition on the trajectory; from the tables we immediately pick up the corresponding I° and the $u_j^\circ(0)$. This in turn yields an $x_i(1)$, I°, $u_j^\circ(1)$ and $x_i(2)$. Continuing along, we eventually recover the sequence of optimal controls $u_j^\circ(0), u_j^\circ(1), \ldots, u_j^\circ(P-1)$ and the trajectory itself. Note, however, that in carrying out this forward pass, it will undoubtedly be necessary to interpolate between the tabulated values. This is especially true if the initial condition $x_i(0)$ is not one of the tabulated values.

To summarize the discussion, we can see that the main advantage to dynamic programming lies in its sequential stage-by-stage character of computation. Of further importance is the fact that constraints on either the control or state variables actually simplify the computation rather than make it more difficult since the discretized range on the variables is reduced. In carrying out the actual computation, two "passes" are required; in the first, the necessary single-stage tables are built up along with the associated cost functions by proceeding from the last stage back to the first stage. It is in this pass that the economy of dynamic programming lies. Rather than investigate all the trajectories, only the optimal variations of partial paths are retained. Suboptimal variations are immediately discarded. In the second pass, the direction of travel is from the given initial condition to the final condition with the appropriate controls and the states of the actual trajectory being picked up. In certain cases, the tables can be dispensed with and actual functionals used. This is illustrated in detail in Chapter 3.

There are, of course, a number of problems associated with the use of dynamic programming. The first of these can be illustrated in terms of the problem as described above and has been called by Bellman the "*menace of the expanding grid*." This phenomenon is due to the generation of inadmissible states at the ends of the state's discretization; as the calculation propagates, this may lead to many inadmissible values. This can be partly compensated for by expanding the range of the grid of state variables as one builds up successive tables. However, associated with the phenomenon is the misfortune that interpolation may become unreliable if the inadmissible values are involved.

The second problem, and the most serious one, results from the dimension of the state variables. An increase in the number of control variables, by contrast, may increase the computing time seriously but the problem can still be handled. Thus, if we have three control variables, we must search a large number of combinations of possible control associated with any state (see previous discussion on how to reduce the number) but this can be done directly. When, however, we have three or more state variables, we have a very difficult problem. This has been called by Bellman "*the curse of dimensionality*." If we have three state variables and each is discretized into 50 values, then at each stage in the dynamic programming structure we must store $(50)^3$ values. This is because of the interpolation mentioned above; we must provide 50 values of x_1, 50 values of x_2 for each value of x_1, and 50 values of x_3 for each value of x_2. This requires an exponential type of build-up of storage. Thus, it is frequently impossible to handle even a three-state variable problem with straightforward dynamic programming. Because of this *storage problem*, whose requirement is beyond present-day digital computers, one is frequently forced to use adaptations of dynamic programming.

A third serious problem may reside in the *multiple interpolations* required. The word "may" is used because there does not seem to be any work to date showing if such procedures are error-propagating, etc. In any event, it is fairly obvious that even in two or three dimensions such interpolations may be extremely time-consuming. To illustrate how complex this interpolation can become, let us consider that we have three state variables x_1^*, x_2^*, and x_3^*. These have been discretized into the equal intervals $\Delta x_1^*, \Delta x_2^*$, and Δx_3^*. Obviously, we are now talking about interpolation in a three-dimensional grid, and if we ask to find $I^\circ[x_1^*, x_2^*, x_3^*]$ from the known values in Figure 2.8 (the eight corner points) on p. 86, we might proceed as follows. First, we denote the corner points as involving y_1, y_2, and y_3, that is, those values of x_i^* at the corners,

$$y_1 \le x_1^* \le y_1 + \Delta x_1^*,$$

$$y_2 \le x_2^* \le y_2 + \Delta x_2^*,$$

$$y_3 \le x_3^* \le y_3 + \Delta x_3^*.$$

Second, we shall let $x_i^* - y_i = \delta x_i^*$. Now in the simplest possible terms we can obviously estimate $I^\circ[x_1^*, x_2^*, x_3^*]$ by linear interpolation between the points A

and B. Furthermore, A (and B) can be obtained by linear interpolation between D and C (and E and F), which in turn follows by linear interpolation between the corner points. This logic leads to the equation

$$
\begin{aligned}
I^\circ[x_1^*, x_2^*, x_3^*] &= I^\circ[y_1 + \delta x_1^*, y_2 + \delta x_2^*, y_3] \\
&\quad + \frac{\delta x_3^*}{\Delta x_3^*}\{I^\circ[y_1 + \delta x_1^*, y_2 + \delta x_2^*, y_3 + \Delta x_3^*] \\
&\quad - I^\circ[y_1 + \delta x_1^*, y_2 + \delta x_2^*, y_3]\} \\
&= \left(1 - \frac{\delta x_3^*}{\Delta x_3^*}\right)\left[\left(1 - \frac{\delta x_2^*}{\Delta x_2^*}\right)(I^\circ[y_1 + \delta x_1, y_2, y_3])\right. \\
&\quad \left. + \frac{\delta x_2^*}{\Delta x_2^*} I^\circ[y_1 + \delta x_1^*, y_2 + \Delta x_2^*, y_3]\right] \\
&\quad + \frac{\delta x_3^*}{\Delta x_3^*}\left[\left(1 - \frac{\delta x_2^*}{\Delta x_2^*}\right) I^\circ(y_1 + \delta x_1^*, y_2, y_3 + \Delta x_3^*)\right. \\
&\quad \left. + \frac{\delta x_2^*}{\Delta x_2^*} I^\circ[y_1 + \delta x_1^*, y_2 + \Delta x_2^*, y_3 + \Delta x_3^*]\right] \\
&= \left(1 - \frac{\delta x_3^*}{\Delta x_3^*}\right)\left(1 - \frac{\delta x_2^*}{\Delta x_2^*}\right)\left[\left(1 - \frac{\delta x_1^*}{\Delta x_1^*}\right) I^\circ[y_1, y_2, y_3]\right. \\
&\quad \left. + \frac{\delta x_1^*}{\Delta x_1^*} I^\circ[y_1 + \Delta x_1^*, y_2, y_3]\right] \\
&\quad + \left(1 - \frac{\delta x_3^*}{\Delta x_3^*}\right)\frac{\delta x_2^*}{\Delta x_2^*}\left[\left(1 - \frac{\delta x_1^*}{\Delta x_1^*}\right) I^\circ[y_1, y_2 + \Delta x_2^*, y_3]\right. \\
&\quad \left. + \frac{\delta x_1^*}{\Delta x_1^*} I^\circ[y_1 + \Delta x_1^*, y_2 + \Delta x_2^*, y_3]\right] \\
&\quad + \left(1 - \frac{\delta x_2^*}{\Delta x_2^*}\right)\frac{\delta x_3^*}{\Delta x_3^*}\left[\left(1 - \frac{\delta x_1^*}{\Delta x_1^*}\right) I^\circ[y_1, y_2, y_3 + \Delta x_3^*]\right. \\
&\quad \left. + \frac{\delta x_1^*}{\Delta x_1^*} I^\circ[y_1 + \Delta x_1^*, y_2, y_3 + \Delta x_3^*]\right] \\
&\quad + \frac{\delta x_2^*}{\Delta x_2^*}\frac{\delta x_3^*}{\Delta x_3^*}\left[\left(1 - \frac{\delta x_1^*}{\Delta x_1^*}\right) I^\circ[y_1, y_2 + \Delta x_2^*, y_3 + \Delta x_3^*]\right. \\
&\quad \left. + \frac{\delta x_1^*}{\Delta x_1^*} I^\circ[y_1 + \Delta x_1^*, y_2 + \Delta x_2^*, y_3 + \Delta x_3^*]\right].
\end{aligned}
$$

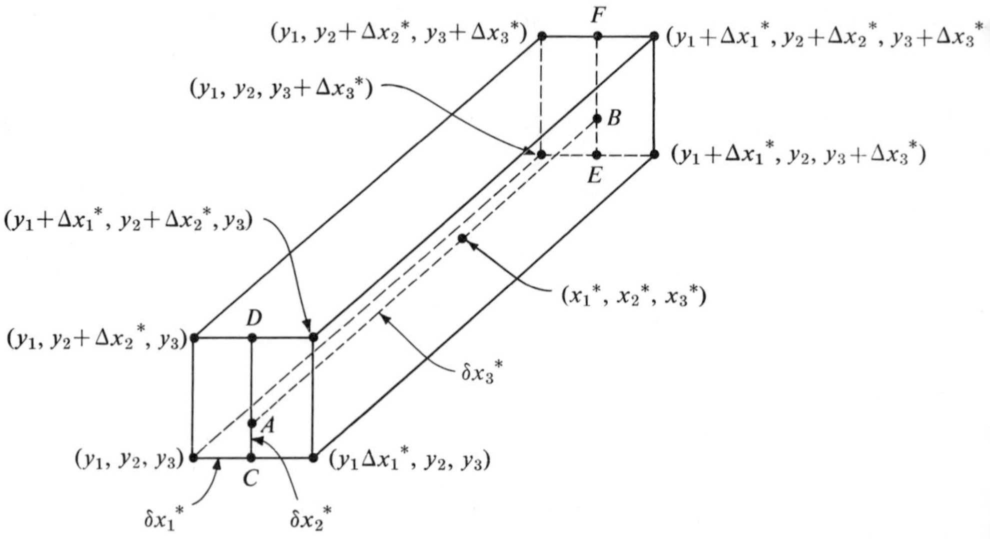

FIGURE 2.8. Three-dimensional interpolation for dynamic programming

That such a formulation requires considerable computing time and may lead to computational errors in the value of $I^\circ(x_1^*, x_2^*, x_3^*)$ goes without saying. Nevertheless, this type of calculation is a necessary part of the dynamic programming computation.

Before finishing this discussion, we wish to point out one slight variation of the recurrence relation, which we shall call on later. If we had started with a performance index

$$I[x(0), P] = \sum_{k=1}^{P} \phi[x(k), u(k-1)] + \psi[x(P)] \tag{2.22}$$

(note that we have added a final-state term), the recurrence relation would be exactly the same as Equation (2.19), namely,

$$I^\circ[x(0), R+1] = \min_{u(0)} \{\phi[x(1), u(0)] + I^\circ[x(1), R]\}. \tag{2.23}$$

This follows, of course, from the fact that $\psi[x(P)]$ is only important in the last stage of our computation and is therefore contained within $I^\circ(x(1), R)$. In the same sense, we note that if we considered only a final-state performance index, $\phi = 0$, then we would have

$$I^\circ[x(0), R+1] = \min_{u(0)} \{I^\circ[x(1), R]\} \tag{2.24}$$

or, using Equation (2.13), we would have

$$I^{\circ}[x(0), R+1] = \min_{u(0)} \{I^{\circ}(h[x(0), u(0)], R)\}.$$

This result is, of course, intuitively obvious since only the final state is included in the performance index.

In summary, we have shown that the basic concepts of dynamic programming, as stated in the principle of optimality or its implementation as an explicit recurrence relation, lead to a straightforward algorithm for optimizing a series of stages. The algorithm leads to the optimization of one stage P times, rather than P stages at one time. However, there are certain computational problems associated with the method, the most serious being the exponential increase in computer storage associated with the number of state variables. For the interested reader, we suggest the work of Dreyfus [6], Karp and Held [53], and Tchamran [74].

It is also worth pointing out that our discussion of dynamic programming has always involved a backward pass followed by a forward pass. If we are careful in defining the principle of optimality, it is possible to reverse this procedure so that a forward pass is first used. This may be termed the dual of the normal dynamic programming algorithm. The work of Dreyfus [6], Bellman [4], Hadley [9], and Aris and coworkers [18] indicates the mechanics and advantages of this dual formulation. Bhavnani [20] also points out that in the case where the stage number appears in the system equation and the final time is not fixed the dual formulation is much better to use than the standard form of dynamic programming.

2.2. The continuous-maximum principle

An alternative procedure for obtaining the optimal control action for systems of the type considered in this book is the *maximum principle* due to Pontryagin and his collaborators [14]. This principle provides an alternative path to dynamic programming for solving complex optimal control problems; the path itself is quite dissimilar in form to that of dynamic programming, but in the end both procedures yield essentially equivalent results. Each method has its own special advantages and disadvantages, especially in terms of a computational analysis, and to solve a specific problem one may prefer one method over the other.

In this section we shall develop the maximum principle as applied to the continuous-time system, and then in the next section we shall discuss the modifications for the discrete-time case. In our analysis here, we shall first state the necessary theorem for one of the most general situations to be discussed, then we shall show what this implies in terms of actually calculating optimal trajectories, and finally we shall attempt to show the geometric basis of the method. Many of the proofs, etc., will not be included, and the interested reader may turn to the main reference [14] for this material.

We consider the autonomous continuous-time system model in the form

$$\dot{\boldsymbol{x}}(t) = \boldsymbol{f}[\boldsymbol{x}(t), \boldsymbol{u}(t)], \tag{2.25}$$

where the f_i in $\boldsymbol{f}$ as well as the $\partial f_i/\partial x_j$ are assumed to be continuous. Furthermore, we assume that the performance index to be extremized is an integral form with $f_0[\boldsymbol{x}(t), \boldsymbol{u}(t)]$ as the integrand. Finally, we assume that there exists a *smooth hypersurface* S; by a hypersurface it is meant that $\boldsymbol{x}(t)$ satisfies a relationship of the form

$$g[\boldsymbol{x}(t)] = 0. \tag{2.26}$$

If Equation (2.26) has the explicit linear form

$$a_0 + a_1x_1(t) + a_2x_2(t) + \cdots + a_nx_n(t) = 0, \tag{2.27}$$

the hypersurface is called a hyperplane. Thus, when $n = 2$, the hyperplane is a straight line, and when $n = 3$, the hyperplane is a plane. Now if $\boldsymbol{x}_0(t)$ is an arbitrary point of the hypersurface S, the vector $\nabla_{\boldsymbol{x}_0} g$ is called the normal vector of S at $\boldsymbol{x}_0$. In the case of a hyperplane the normal vectors are all the same with elements $[a_1, a_2, \ldots, a_n]$. The hyperplane passing through $\boldsymbol{x}_0(t)$ with $\nabla_{\boldsymbol{x}_0} g$ as its normal is called the tangent hyperplane of the hypersurface S at the point $\boldsymbol{x}_0$. Now let us assume that there are s hypersurfaces of the form

$$g_i[\boldsymbol{x}(t)] = 0 \qquad (i = 1, 2, \ldots, s), \tag{2.28}$$

with $s < n$. If the s vectors $\nabla_{\boldsymbol{x}} g_i$ are linearly independent at all points satisfying Equation (2.28), then the resulting intersections are called a smooth manifold or surface. If $\boldsymbol{x}(t)$ is contained in this smooth surface, which we shall now call S, then the $(n - s)$-dimensional tangent plane (T of S) at $\boldsymbol{x}$ is defined as the intersection of the s hyperplanes passing through $\boldsymbol{x}$ with normals of $\nabla_{\boldsymbol{x}} g_i$.

With this preliminary information, we may now formulate a number of general optimal problems with fixed initial conditions $\boldsymbol{x}(0)$ and variable end conditions [$\boldsymbol{x}(t_f)$ and t_f are not explicitly specified].

PROBLEM ▪ Given the system equation in the autonomous form of (2.25) and the initial condition $\boldsymbol{x}(0)$, we want to find a control function $\boldsymbol{u}(t)$ from among an admissible piecewise continuous set U such that $\boldsymbol{x}(t_f)$ is in S and the performance index

$$I[\boldsymbol{x}(0), t_f] = \int_0^{t_f} f_0[\boldsymbol{x}(t), \boldsymbol{u}(t)]\, dt$$

is minimized. Usually U would be a compact (closed and bounded) set.

Solution ▪ To state Pontryagin's maximum principle, it is convenient to reformulate the problem slightly by introducing the new variable

$$\dot{x}_0(t) = f_0[\boldsymbol{x}(t), \boldsymbol{u}(t)], \qquad x_0(0) = 0, \tag{2.29}$$

so that the entire system is now of dimension $n + 1$, that is, $\boldsymbol{x}(t) = [x_0\ x_1 \ldots x_n]'$. At the same time, we note that if Equation (2.25) had included t explicitly, we would have removed it by defining the new variable

$$x_{n+1} = t, \qquad x_{n+1}(0) = 0, \qquad \dot{x}_{n+1} = 1, \tag{2.30}$$

and increased the original system to dimension $n + 2$ (see Section 1.6).

In general, the maximum principle yields necessary but not sufficient conditions for optimal control. These conditions do not guarantee the existence of any optimal controls, nor does it follow that any $\boldsymbol{u}(t)$ which satisfies the maximum-principle equations is optimal in the sense of minimizing the performance index. Thus, since the principle is not, in general, sufficient, it merely provides a vehicle for testing whether any control is a candidate for optimality. For a lucid description of the necessary and sufficient conditions, the reader is referred to [3, pp. 272–284] and, in terms of a detailed numerical example, to [48]. The principle is derived by considering small variations in the optimal control function $\boldsymbol{u}^\circ(t)$. Since U is not necessarily an open set, some care is necessary in selecting proper variations. The variations are not necessarily small, but take place over a small interval of time. In describing how the variations are transferred backward along the trajectory, we introduce the adjoint variables $z_0(t), z_1(t), \ldots, z_n(t)$ (assuming t did not occur explicitly in Equation (2.25) defined by

$$\dot{z}_i(t) = -\sum_{j=0}^{n} \frac{\partial f_j}{\partial x_i} z_j(t). \tag{2.31}$$

Alternatively, if we define

$$\boldsymbol{z} = \begin{bmatrix} z_0 \\ z_1 \\ \vdots \\ z_n \end{bmatrix}, \qquad \boldsymbol{f} = \begin{bmatrix} f_0 \\ f_1 \\ \vdots \\ f_n \end{bmatrix}, \qquad \frac{\partial \boldsymbol{f}'}{\partial \boldsymbol{x}} = \begin{bmatrix} \dfrac{\partial f_0}{\partial x_0} & \dfrac{\partial f_1}{\partial x_0} & \cdots & \dfrac{\partial f_n}{\partial x_0} \\ \vdots & & & \vdots \\ \dfrac{\partial f_0}{\partial x_n} & & \cdots & \dfrac{\partial f_n}{\partial x_n} \end{bmatrix},$$

$$\frac{\partial \boldsymbol{f}'}{\partial \boldsymbol{x}} \boldsymbol{z} = \begin{bmatrix} \dfrac{\partial f_0}{\partial x_0} z_0 + \dfrac{\partial f_1}{\partial x_0} z_1 + \cdots + \dfrac{\partial f_n}{\partial x_0} z_n \\ \vdots \\ \dfrac{\partial f_0}{\partial x_n} z_0 + \quad \cdots \quad + \dfrac{\partial f_n}{\partial x_n} z_n \end{bmatrix},$$

then Equation (2.31) can also be written as

$$\dot{\boldsymbol{z}}(t) = -(\partial \boldsymbol{f}'/\partial \boldsymbol{x})\boldsymbol{z}(t).$$

We shall defer further discussion on these adjoint variables until Section 2.4, but for the moment we merely need to note that if initial conditions $z_i(0)$ are given, there is a unique continuous solution for Equation (2.31).

For the purposes of notational simplicity, we introduce the Hamiltonian formulation of classical mechanics, in which the Hamiltonian H is defined as

$$H(\mathbf{z}, \mathbf{x}, \mathbf{u}) = \sum_{i=0}^{n} z_i f_i(\mathbf{x}, \mathbf{u}) = \mathbf{z}'\mathbf{f} = \mathbf{f}'\mathbf{z}. \tag{2.32}$$

But we note immediately that

$$\frac{\partial H}{\partial z_i} = f_i = \dot{x}_i(t), \qquad \frac{\partial H}{\partial x_i} = \sum_{j=0}^{n} z_j \frac{\partial f_j}{\partial x_i} \qquad (i = 0, 1, \ldots, n) \tag{2.33}$$

or

$$\frac{\partial H}{\partial \mathbf{z}} = \mathbf{f} = \dot{\mathbf{x}}(t), \qquad \frac{\partial H}{\partial \mathbf{x}} = \frac{\partial \mathbf{f}'}{\partial \mathbf{x}}\, \mathbf{z}.$$

Using Equation (2.31), we see that this becomes

$$\dot{z}_i(t) = -\frac{\partial H}{\partial x_i} \qquad \text{or} \qquad \dot{\mathbf{z}}(t) = -\frac{\partial H}{\partial \mathbf{x}}. \tag{2.34}$$

The vector form of Equations (2.33) and (2.34) can also be written as

$$\dot{\mathbf{x}}(t) = \nabla_{\mathbf{z}} H, \tag{2.35}$$

$$\dot{\mathbf{z}}(t) = -\nabla_{\mathbf{x}} H. \tag{2.36}$$

If $\mathbf{z}(t)$ and $\mathbf{x}(t)$ are fixed, $H(\mathbf{z}, \mathbf{x}, \mathbf{u})$ is a function of only $\mathbf{u}$, and, in fact, we shall introduce the notation

$$M(\mathbf{z}, \mathbf{x}) \equiv \sup_{\mathbf{u}} H(\mathbf{z}, \mathbf{x}, \mathbf{u}), \tag{2.37}$$

implying that M is the supremum of H with respect to $\mathbf{u}$.

On this basis we now state the maximum principle of Pontryagin as follows.

Let $\mathbf{u}(t)$ *be an admissible control such that starting with initial conditions* $\mathbf{x}(0) = [0\ x_1(0) \ldots x_n(0)]'$, *the trajectory passes through the point* $\mathbf{x}(t_f) = [x_0(t_f)x_1(t_f) \ldots x_n(t_f)]'$ *at some time* t_f *with* $[x_1(t_f) \ldots x_n(t_f)]$ *in* S. *If* $\mathbf{u}(t)$ *is optimal in the sense of minimizing* $\int_0^{t_f} f_0\, dt$ *and fulfilling the conditions stated above, then there exists a nonzero, continuous vector* $\mathbf{z}(t)$ *satisfying Equations* (2.35) *and* (2.36); *furthermore,*

(1) *for all* t *in the interval* $[0, t_f]$, $M(\mathbf{z}, \mathbf{x}) = H(\mathbf{z}, \mathbf{x}, \mathbf{u})$,

(2) *at* t_f, $z_0(t_f) \le 0$, $M(\mathbf{z}(t_f), \mathbf{x}(t_f)) = 0$,

(3) *the vector* $\mathbf{z}(t_f)$ *is orthogonal to the tangent hyperplane* (T *of* S); *this is the so-called* transversality condition.

The main point here is that at all time instants H attains its supremum with respect to $\boldsymbol{u}$. In addition, it can be shown that $M = 0$ not only at t_f but at any time t in $[0, t_f]$, thus implying a constant value of M or H over the entire optimal trajectory.

In this mathematical form resides the basic idea of the development of the maximum principle. If U is an open set, then the maximum principle is equivalent in certain cases to the Lagrange multiplier rule and the Weierstrass condition of the famous calculus of variations. In addition, however, the maximum principle applies to more general constraints on control. Before discussing the actual use of this statement of the maximum principle, we may turn to a number of subdefinitions of the above main theorem.

If the control problem is restated in the sense that the final values of $\boldsymbol{x}(t_f)$ are fixed, and S shrinks to a point (fixed initial and final points), the theorem is still correct except that condition (3), the transversality condition, does not apply. This also illustrates that the transversality condition (as we shall use it) comes in only when the final conditions on the state variables are not specified explicitly.

The minimal-time problem can also be easily encompassed in this formulation; in this case $f_0(\boldsymbol{x}, \boldsymbol{u}) = 1.0$ and the Hamiltonian is given by

$$H(\boldsymbol{z}, \boldsymbol{x}, \boldsymbol{u}) = z_0(t) + \sum_{i=1}^{n} z_i(t) f_i(\boldsymbol{x}, \boldsymbol{u}). \tag{2.38}$$

Introducing a shortened Hamiltonian $\overline{H}(\boldsymbol{z}, \boldsymbol{x}, \boldsymbol{u})$ such that

$$H(\boldsymbol{z}, \boldsymbol{x}, \boldsymbol{u}) = z_0(t) + \overline{H}(\boldsymbol{z}, \boldsymbol{x}, \boldsymbol{u}), \tag{2.39}$$

then

$$\dot{\boldsymbol{x}}(t) = \nabla_z \overline{H}, \qquad \dot{\boldsymbol{z}}(t) = -\nabla_x \overline{H}. \tag{2.40}$$

In the same sense as Equation (2.37),

$$\overline{M}(\boldsymbol{z}, \boldsymbol{x}) \equiv \sup_{\boldsymbol{u}} \overline{H}(\boldsymbol{z}, \boldsymbol{x}, \boldsymbol{u}) = M(\boldsymbol{z}, \boldsymbol{x}) - z_0 .$$

Thus, the theorem for the minimal-time problem is identical to that above except for slight changes in conditions (1) and (2); the new versions are:

(1) *for all t in the interval* $[0, t_f]$, $\overline{M}(\boldsymbol{z}, \boldsymbol{x}) = \overline{H}(\boldsymbol{z}, \boldsymbol{x}, \boldsymbol{u})$,

(2) *at time* t_f, $\overline{M}[\boldsymbol{z}(t_f), \boldsymbol{x}(t_f)] \geq 0$.

Finally, we must recognize that in all the formulation to this point the final time t_f is not explicitly fixed. If t_f is fixed, there exists one less parameter; however, the result is merely a modification of those above since Equation (2.30) may be used to correct the problem to one with a "free" terminal time.

Now we shall specify the explicit formulations of the maximum principle which define the optimal control $\boldsymbol{u}(t)$ to be calculated. We note from our discussion above that when the *final time* state variables $\boldsymbol{x}(t_f)$ are not specified, it will be necessary to append certain conditions at $t = t_f$. We start with what would seem like the most difficult problem, namely the case of a free right-hand end, with $\boldsymbol{x}(t_f)$ unspecified and with t_f fixed. Thus, the problem is to find the optimal control function $\boldsymbol{u}(t)$ subject to the system equations and fixed initial conditions

$$\dot{\boldsymbol{x}}(t) = \boldsymbol{f}[\boldsymbol{x}(t), \boldsymbol{u}(t)] \qquad \text{with } \boldsymbol{x}(0) \text{ const} \qquad \text{(free right-hand end, final time fixed)} \tag{2.41}$$

which will minimize a final-value-type performance index

$$I[\boldsymbol{x}(0), t_f] = \sum_{i=1}^{n} c_i x_i(t_f) = \boldsymbol{c}'\boldsymbol{x}(t_f). \tag{2.42}$$

The reader will recognize that this performance index is the general one, with an integral index that can be included in the general index. The c_i in Equation (2.42) are constants related to some suitable weighting of the $x_i(t_f)$, all of which leads to the following statement.

If there exists a control $\boldsymbol{u}^\circ(t)$ which minimizes $I(\boldsymbol{x}(0), t_f)$, then there also exists an optimal adjoint vector $\boldsymbol{z}^\circ(t)$ which satisfies the differential equation and boundary conditions

$$\dot{\boldsymbol{z}}(t) = -\nabla_{\boldsymbol{x}} H, \tag{2.43}$$

$$\boldsymbol{z}(t_f) = -\boldsymbol{c} \tag{2.44}$$

and is such that at each instant (along the optimal trajectory)

$$M(\boldsymbol{z}, \boldsymbol{x}) = H(\overset{\circ}{\boldsymbol{z}}, \overset{\circ}{\boldsymbol{x}}, \overset{\circ}{\boldsymbol{u}}) = \max_{\boldsymbol{u}} H(\boldsymbol{z}, \boldsymbol{x}, \boldsymbol{u}),$$

where $M(\boldsymbol{z}, \boldsymbol{x})$ is a nonnegative constant.

In this form we can ascertain many of the interesting computational features of the maximum principle. There are a total of $2n$ differential equations, n in the state variables (the system equations) and n in the adjoint variables [Equations (2.41) and (2.43)] and $2n$ boundary conditions, n in the state variables at time zero [$\boldsymbol{x}(0)$] and n in the adjoint variables at time t_f ($\boldsymbol{z}(t_f) = -\boldsymbol{c}$). The system of $2n$ differential equations are referred to as the *canonical equations* and are compactly written as

$$\dot{\boldsymbol{x}}(t) = \nabla_{\boldsymbol{z}} H \qquad (\boldsymbol{x}(0) \text{ given}),$$

$$\dot{\boldsymbol{z}}(t) = -\nabla_{\boldsymbol{x}} H \qquad (\boldsymbol{z}(t_f) \text{ given}).$$

Thus, the solution necessary to synthesize the optimal control involves a *two-point boundary value* problem. By contrast, the form of the optimal control (if it exists) and the structure are obtained immediately merely by observing the

Hamiltonian (this point will be more obvious in the examples to be detailed shortly).

We also note that the optimal control $\boldsymbol{u}^\circ(t)$ which is obtained from this solution and which minimizes $I(\boldsymbol{x}(0), t_f)$ corresponds to maximizing the Hamiltonian along the optimal trajectory. Conversely, if we maximize $I(\boldsymbol{x}(0), t_f)$, we must minimize the Hamiltonian. Actually, it is the boundary conditions of Equation (2.44) which determine this point and, if we had used $\boldsymbol{z}(t_f) = \boldsymbol{c}$ minimization (maximization) of $I[\boldsymbol{x}(0), t_f]$ would correspond to minimization (maximization) of the Hamiltonian. This point will be brought out in the geometric discussion to follow shortly. The point is of importance since the Russian literature uses the maximization of $I[\boldsymbol{x}(0), t_f]$ while minimizing the Hamiltonian; by contrast the United States literature uses the minimization of both $I[\boldsymbol{x}(0), t_f]$ and the Hamiltonian (thus leading to the minimum principle).

Regarding the maximum value of the Hamiltonian and its implied consistency along an optimal trajectory, a few words are in order for autonomous systems. Frequently, the maximum value is obtained by setting $\partial H/\partial \boldsymbol{u} = \nabla_{\boldsymbol{u}} H = \boldsymbol{0}$, that is, by actually differentiating the Hamiltonian with respect to $\boldsymbol{u}(t)$ and setting the result equal to zero. *In this differentiation* $\boldsymbol{z}(t)$ *and* $\boldsymbol{x}(t)$ *are treated as constants.* When $\boldsymbol{u}^\circ(t)$ is interior to any constraints, not on the boundary of U, then any perturbations $\delta\boldsymbol{u}(t)$ in the control are arbitrary and it is necessary and sufficient that $\nabla_{\boldsymbol{u}} H = \boldsymbol{0}$ for a maximum. Furthermore, if we differentiate the Hamiltonian, and use Equations (2.35) and (2.36) in the result, we obtain

$$\dot{H} = (\nabla_{\boldsymbol{u}} H)' \dot{\boldsymbol{u}}(t).$$

But if $\nabla_{\boldsymbol{u}} H = \boldsymbol{0}$, then $\dot{H} = 0$ and the Hamiltonian is constant along the entire trajectory (for all t). When the optimal controls are on the constraints but the constraints are constant, $\dot{\boldsymbol{u}}(t) = \boldsymbol{0}$ and the Hamiltonian is again constant. We note also that when the optimal controls are on the constraint boundary (see bang-bang control discussed later), $\nabla_{\boldsymbol{u}} H = \boldsymbol{0}$ is not true. This point can easily be seen if a plot of H vs. u is made in which the Hamiltonian has a zero slope inside the control bounds but the maximum value of H occurs on a control boundary (the H vs. u curve is convex to the u-ordinate). In other words, $\nabla_{\boldsymbol{u}} H = \boldsymbol{0}$ occurs within the boundaries and actually corresponds to a minimum value of H. Finally, if t_f is free and to be optimized, then the maximum and constant value of the Hamiltonian is zero; $H = 0$. If t_f is fixed, then $H = \text{const} \neq 0$.

It is of interest to rephrase some of these points slightly. We have the canonical equations and the maximization condition as given by

$$\dot{\boldsymbol{x}}(t) = \nabla_{\boldsymbol{z}} H, \qquad \dot{\boldsymbol{z}}(t) = -\nabla_{\boldsymbol{x}} H, \qquad H(\boldsymbol{z}, \boldsymbol{x}, \boldsymbol{u}^\circ) \geq H(\boldsymbol{z}, \boldsymbol{x}, \boldsymbol{u}). \tag{2.45}$$

The last condition merely specifies that the Hamiltonian with $\boldsymbol{u}^\circ$ is always greater than or equal to the Hamiltonian with any other control. Frequently this condition may be relaxed in favor of $\nabla_{\boldsymbol{u}} H = \mathbf{0}$. In either form, Equations (2.45) are frequently referred to as the *Euler–Lagrange* equations. The notion of an extremal curve is of interest at this point, with $\boldsymbol{u}(t)$ being an extremal control if it satisfies the necessary conditions for optimality [Equations (2.45)]. If we can solve the third condition of Equation (2.45) (or $\nabla_{\boldsymbol{u}} H = \mathbf{0}$) for $\boldsymbol{u}(t)$ and substitute back into the first two of (2.45), we obtain the *free canonical equations*

$$\dot{\boldsymbol{x}}(t) = \nabla_{\boldsymbol{z}} H^* \qquad \dot{\boldsymbol{z}}(t) = -\nabla_{\boldsymbol{x}} H^* \tag{2.46}$$

which no longer include $\boldsymbol{u}(t)$. Subject to certain conditions to be mentioned in Chapter 4, the solution of these free canonical equations yields the optimal trajectory, i.e., provides the recipe for the optimal trajectory.

It would seem helpful at this point to work out a few short examples to illustrate the mechanics involved. Thus, we start by considering a continuous-stirred-tank-reactor with an inflow and outflow. If the inflow rate equals the outflow rate and the holdup time is unity, a mass balance on the reactor yields for an unreacting tracer

$$\dot{x}(t) + x(t) = x_i(t),$$

where $x(t)$ is the outgoing concentration and $x_i(t)$ the inflowing concentration. We now consider the following problem.

PROBLEM ▪ Given that a single unreacting component in the solvent stream is involved and that the initial outflow concentration at time $t = 0$ is $x(0)$, what admissible set $x_i(t)$ will change the solute concentration from $x(0)$ to $x(t_f)$ while minimizing the integral

$$I[x(, t_f]0) = \tfrac{1}{2}\int_0^{t_f} [x^2(t) + x_i^2(t)]\, dt \tag{2.47}$$

over the fixed interval t_f?

Solution ▪ We redefine our nomenclature such that

$$x_0(t_f) = I[x(0), t_f], \qquad x_1(t) = x(t), \qquad u(t) = x_i(t),$$

and thus

$$\dot{x}_0(t) = \tfrac{1}{2}[x_1^2(t) + u^2(t)] = f_0[\mathbf{x}, u], \qquad \dot{x}_1(t) = -x_1(t) + u(t) = f_1[\mathbf{x}, u] \tag{2.48}$$

or

$$\dot{\boldsymbol{x}}(t) = \begin{bmatrix} \dot{x}_0(t) \\ \dot{x}_1(t) \end{bmatrix} = \boldsymbol{f}[\mathbf{x}(t), u(t)]. \tag{2.49}$$

The initial conditions are

$$x_0(0) = 0, \qquad x_1(0) \text{ given.} \tag{2.50}$$

If we define a final value performance index of the form

$$I = c_0 x_0(t_f) + c_1 x_1(t_f) \tag{2.51}$$

and choose $c_0 = 1, c_1 = 0$, then minimizing I corresponds to minimizing $I[x(0), t_f]$, as given by Equation (2.47). The Hamiltonian function is given by

$$H(\mathbf{z}, \mathbf{x}, u) = \mathbf{z}'\boldsymbol{f} = z_0(t) f_0 + z_1(t) f_1,$$

and from Equation (2.48)

$$H(\mathbf{z}, \mathbf{x}, u) = \frac{z_0}{2}(x_1^2 + u^2) + z_1(-x_1 + u). \tag{2.52}$$

Since

$$\dot{\mathbf{z}}(t) = -(\partial H/\partial \mathbf{x}),$$

by differentiating Equation (2.52) we can see that

$$\dot{z}_0(t) = 0, \qquad \dot{z}_1(t) = -z_0(t)x_1 + z_1(t). \tag{2.53}$$

The boundary condition on the adjoint vector is

$$\mathbf{z}(t_f) = -\mathbf{c}$$

or, using the fact that $c_0 = 1$ and $c_1 = 0$,

$$z_0(t_f) = -1, \qquad z_1(t_f) = 0. \tag{2.54}$$

Thus, we have now obtained the system equations and the initial values [Equations (2.48) and (2.50)], the adjoint equations and the final values [Equations (2.53) and (2.54)], and we have defined the Hamiltonian [Equation (2.52)].

A simplification is possible, however, because we note that $\dot{z}_0(t) = 0$. Thus $z_0(t) = \text{const}$ and since $z_0(t_f) = -1$, it follows that $z_0(t) = -1$. The Hamiltonian can now be written as

$$H(\mathbf{z}, \mathbf{x}, \boldsymbol{u}) = -z_1 x_1 - (x_1^2/2) + z_1 u - (u^2/2).$$

To maximize $H(\mathbf{z}, \mathbf{x}, \boldsymbol{u})$ for any $\mathbf{z}$ and $\mathbf{x}$, we can see that

$$u^\circ(t) = z_1.$$

Thus, from Equation (2.48), substituting the optimal control,

$$\dot{x}_1(t) = -x_1(t) + z_1(t) \qquad [x_1(0) \text{ given}], \tag{2.55}$$

and from Equations (2.53) and (2.54),

$$\dot{z}_1(t) = z_1(t) + x_1(t) \qquad [z_1(t_f) = 0]. \tag{2.56}$$

Obviously, we now have two coupled simultaneous linear ordinary differential equations with two boundary conditions. In this case, we can actually solve explicitly for the optimal control. Thus, differentiating Equation (2.56) yields

$$\ddot{z}_1 = \dot{z}_1 + \dot{x}_1 = z_1 + x_1 - x_1 + z_1 = 2z_1.$$

It follows that

$$z_1 = K_1 e^{bt} + K_2 e^{-bt},$$

where $b = \sqrt{2}$ and K_1 and K_2 are arbitrary constants. But from (2.56) again,

$$x_1 = \dot{z}_1 - z_1 = (K_1 b - K_1)e^{bt} - K_2(1 + b)e^{-bt} = K_1(b - 1)e^{bt} - K_2(b + 1)e^{-bt}.$$

Now, substituting the boundary conditions, we have

$$0 = K_1 e^{bt_f} + K_2 e^{-bt_f}, \qquad x_1(0) = K_1(b - 1) - K_2(b + 1),$$

yielding

$$K_1 = \frac{x_1(0)}{(b - 1) + (b + 1)e^{2bt_f}}, \qquad K_2 = -\frac{x_1(0)e^{2bt_f}}{(b - 1) + (b + 1)e^{2bt_f}}.$$

But this gives, after back-substitution,

$$u^{\circ}(t) = z_1 = \frac{x_1(0)}{(\sqrt{2} - 1) + (\sqrt{2} + 1)e^{2\sqrt{2}t_f}} (e^{\sqrt{2}t} - e^{2\sqrt{2}t_f - \sqrt{2}t})$$

which is the explicit form of the optimal control. Alternatively, we might have posed the problem as desiring to reach the origin in an undetermined final time, that is, $x_1(t_f) \to 0$, t_f unknown. This merely changes the boundary conditions of the problem in that $z_1(t_f)$ is not specified. In such a situation, it can be seen from

$$x_1(t) = K_1(b - 1)e^{bt} - K_2(b + 1)e^{-bt}$$

that $K_1(b - 1) = 0$. Otherwise, the solution will become unbounded. As a result, we may write

$$x_1(t) = K_3 e^{-bt},$$

and $x_1(t_f) \to 0$ only when $t = t_f = \infty$. In other words, the origin is reached in an infinite period of time. The reader can also confirm that the Hamiltonian H is given by $H = 0$ for the optimal control.

Let us now consider a slightly different and more complex problem, namely, that the system equation is given by

$$\dot{\boldsymbol{x}}(t) = \boldsymbol{A}\boldsymbol{x} + \boldsymbol{B}\boldsymbol{u} \qquad (2.57)$$

with usual connotation; alternatively for $\boldsymbol{u}$ a scalar u, $\boldsymbol{B}$ would be written as $\boldsymbol{b}$ and the system equation as

$$\dot{\boldsymbol{x}}(t) = \boldsymbol{A}\boldsymbol{x} + \boldsymbol{b}u = \boldsymbol{f}(\boldsymbol{x}, u). \qquad (2.58)$$

The matrix $\boldsymbol{A}$ and the vector $\boldsymbol{b}$ are assumed to have constant elements, and furthermore, u is taken as a member of the piecewise continuous set U satisfying

$$|u| \leq 1.0. \qquad (2.59)$$

We select the performance index to be minimized,

$$I[\mathbf{x}(0), t_f] = \int_0^{t_f} [\mathbf{x}'\Lambda\mathbf{x} + gu^2]\, dt, \tag{2.60}$$

with g a constant and

$$\Lambda = \begin{bmatrix} a_1 & \cdots & & 0 \\ & a_2 & & \\ \vdots & & \ddots & \vdots \\ 0 & \cdots & & a_n \end{bmatrix},$$

Note that in this index u is included in quadratic form. We may introduce the new function

$$\dot{x}_0(t) = f_0(\mathbf{x}, u) = \mathbf{x}'\Lambda\mathbf{x} + gu^2,$$

and if we add this variable to the system equation, (2.58), to form the augmented set, then

$$\dot{\mathbf{x}}(t)^* = \mathbf{f}^*[\mathbf{x}^*, u], \tag{2.61}$$

where $\mathbf{x}^*(t)$ is now of dimension $n + 1$. At the same time, we may write the initial condition for (2.61) as

$$\mathbf{x}(0)^* = [0 \;\; x_1(0) \;\; x_2(0) \ldots x_n(0)]'. \tag{2.62}$$

Now we form the adjoint variables and the Hamiltonian such that

$$\dot{\mathbf{z}}^* = -\frac{\partial \mathbf{f}^{*\prime}}{\partial \mathbf{x}^*}\mathbf{z}^*, \qquad \mathbf{z}^*(t_f) = [-1 \;\; 0 \ldots 0]', \tag{2.63}$$

and

$$H = \mathbf{z}^{*\prime}\mathbf{f}^* = \mathbf{f}^{*\prime}\mathbf{z}^*. \tag{2.64}$$

But we see immediately that

$$\dot{z}_0 = 0, \qquad \dot{z}_i = -2a_i z_0 x_i + \sum_{j=1}^{n} a_{ij} z_j \qquad (i = 1, 2, \ldots, n),$$

where a_i are the elements of Λ and the a_{ij} are the elements of $\mathbf{A}$. The Hamiltonian is

$$H(\mathbf{z}, \mathbf{x}, \mathbf{u}) = z_0[\mathbf{x}'\Lambda\mathbf{x} + gu^2] + \mathbf{z}'[\mathbf{A}\mathbf{x} + \mathbf{b}u], \tag{2.65}$$

where $\mathbf{z} = [z_1 \;\; z_2 \ldots z_n]'$. But if

$$M(\mathbf{z}^*, \mathbf{x}^*) \equiv \sup_u H(\mathbf{z}^*, \mathbf{x}^*, u),$$

then from the main theorem,

$$z_0(t) = \text{const} = -1, \tag{2.66}$$

$$M[\mathbf{z}(t)^*, \mathbf{x}(t)^*] = 0. \tag{2.67}$$

But differentiating the Hamiltonian with respect to u, we get

$$\frac{\partial H}{\partial u} = \frac{\partial}{\partial u}(\boldsymbol{f}^{*\prime}\boldsymbol{z}^*) = \frac{\partial}{\partial u}\{(u\boldsymbol{b}' + \boldsymbol{x}'\boldsymbol{A})\boldsymbol{z} + (\boldsymbol{x}'\boldsymbol{\Lambda}\boldsymbol{x} + gu^2)z_0\} = \boldsymbol{b}'\boldsymbol{z} + 2guz_0,$$

and setting this equal to zero yields the optimal control

$$u^\circ(t) = \frac{1}{2g}\,\boldsymbol{b}'\boldsymbol{z}$$

since z_0 is -1. Furthermore, we note that

$$\partial^2 H/\partial u^2 = -2g < 0,$$

and thus we have a maximum for the Hamiltonian which corresponds to the minimum for I. Subject to the above-mentioned constraints,

$$u^\circ(t) = \begin{cases} \dfrac{1}{2g}\,\boldsymbol{b}'\boldsymbol{z}, & \text{for } \left|\dfrac{1}{2g}\,\boldsymbol{b}'\boldsymbol{z}\right| \le 1, \\[2ex] 1, & \text{for } \dfrac{1}{2g}\,\boldsymbol{b}'\boldsymbol{z} \ge 1, \\[2ex] -1, & \text{for } \dfrac{1}{2g}\,\boldsymbol{b}'\boldsymbol{z} \le -1. \end{cases}$$

While we have these equations in hand, we may show another interesting point. We assume that the control has the two-sided constraint of Equation (2.59), $-1 \le u \le 1$, but the final time is unspecified. We desire for the moment to minimize some final-value performance index. First, we note that if we have the general system equation (u is a scalar for convenience),

$$\dot{\boldsymbol{x}}(t) = \boldsymbol{f}(\boldsymbol{x}, u)$$

and define the Hamiltonian $H(\boldsymbol{z}, \boldsymbol{x}, u)$ as

$$H(\boldsymbol{z}, \boldsymbol{x}, u) = \boldsymbol{z}'\boldsymbol{f},$$

then for autonomous systems the total derivative of H must be zero if we are to achieve a stationary condition. Thus,

$$\dot{H} = (\nabla_z H)'\dot{\boldsymbol{z}} + (\nabla_x H)'\dot{\boldsymbol{x}} + \nabla_u H\dot{u} = 0.$$

But the first two terms on the right-hand side can be made to vanish by using the canonical equations, that is,

$$\dot{\boldsymbol{x}} = \nabla_z H, \qquad \dot{\boldsymbol{z}} = -\nabla_x H.$$

This leaves merely

$$\nabla_u H\dot{u} = 0.$$

Now we note that if H is to be a maximum with respect to u, it is necessary that

$$H(\mathbf{z}, \mathbf{x}, \overset{\circ}{u}) \geq H(\mathbf{z}, \mathbf{x}, u).$$

In other words, the optimal control must always yield a Hamiltonian which is greater than or equal to that for any other control. But from Equation (2.65) we see that so long as u enters in a linear fashion in the system equations and it enters linearly in the performance index (or if not at all in the performance index as with the final value index), then

$$H(\mathbf{z}, \mathbf{x}, u) = C(\mathbf{x}, \mathbf{z}) + D(\mathbf{x}, \mathbf{z})u,$$

where C and D are independent of u. But the only way the Hamiltonian inequality above can be satisfied is for the control to be either $+1$ or -1, depending on the sign of D. In other words, the control is *bang-bang* and switches between $+1$ and -1 as the sign of D changes. Note that in this case $\dot{H} = 0$ not because of $\nabla_u H = 0$ but rather by virtue of $\dot{u} = 0$. If $D = 0$ for a finite period of time, then the Hamiltonian cannot be used since it provides no information; this case is referred to as a *singular control*. It is important to see that so long as the system equations are linear in u, the control will be bang-bang no matter what the performance index is so long as control does not appear in a form other than zero or first-degree.

We do not wish to pass off singular control in too quick a fashion. Thus, as shown by Siebanthal and Aris [72], many practical problems may involve such singular trajectories. The difficulty, however, is trying explicitly to find the optimal control if such singular forms occur. For the interested reader, the work of Johnson [50] is highly recommended.

Now we intend to extend the theorem above in two different directions. First, let us consider that some of the final state variables are specified, say in the first m with $m < n$. Under these conditions there are $(m + n)$ specified boundary conditions made up from

$$\mathbf{x}(0) \qquad (n \text{ conditions}),$$

$$x_1(t_f), \ldots, x_m(t_f) \qquad (m \text{ conditions}),$$

and we need to add only $2n - (n + m)$ conditions on the adjoint variables. Thus

$$\begin{aligned} z_{m+1}(t_f) &= -c_{m+1}, \\ &\vdots \\ z_n(t_f) &= -c_n \end{aligned} \tag{2.68}$$

are specified. Otherwise, the theorem holds exactly.

Second, we consider the case where the final state values are constrained by relations of the form

$$\psi_j[\mathbf{x}(t_f)] = 0 \qquad (j = 1, 2, \ldots, m < n). \tag{2.69}$$

Now it is necessary to modify the final values of $z(t_f)$. This is accomplished by removing the constraints with the aid of Lagrange multipliers (see Section 2.6). Without showing the details here, we merely specify that

$$z_i(t_f) = -c_i - \sum_{j=1}^{m} \lambda_j \frac{\partial \psi_j}{\partial x_i}\bigg|_{t=t_f} \qquad (i = 1, 2, \ldots, n) \tag{2.70}$$

are the new conditions on the adjoint variables. The remainder of the theorem remains unchanged.

There are a number of further important variations on the main theorem of the maximum principle. Of particular importance is the case where the state variables are constrained over the entire trajectory. The complexity of this formulation, however, precludes our presenting the details here. The interested reader may consult a number of references [14, 63, 72] for further accounts on this point.

Let us now turn to a geometric discussion of the continuous maximum principle. To visualize the trajectories in at most three-dimensional space, we take the system model

$$\dot{x}_1(t) = f_1[x_1, x_2, u_1, u_2], \qquad \dot{x}_2(t) = f_2[x_1, x_2, u_1, u_2], \tag{2.71}$$

with initial conditions $x_1(0)$ and $x_2(0)$. If we wish to solve the minimal time problem with a free right-hand end, we can introduce time as the new state variable $x_0(t)$ such that

$$\dot{x}_0(t) = 1, \qquad x_0(0) = 0. \tag{2.72}$$

Now let us look at three-dimensional space in which the coordinates are $x_0(t)$, $x_1(t)$, and $x_2(t)$ and ask to find a curve in this space for which $x_0(t_f)$ is as small as possible; a typical trajectory which may or may not be the optimal curve is shown in Figure 2.9. We note in Figure 2.9 that the curve starts in the x_1x_2-plane with $x_0 = 0$ corresponding to the initial conditions (point 1) and then proceeds through the three-dimensional space to point 2 with some finite value of x_0. The projection down on the x_1x_2-plane corresponds to $x_0(t_f) = 0$, $x_1(t_f)$, and $x_2(t_f)$ (point 3); obviously the optimal path will correspond to a minimal height along the x_0 direction between points 2 and 3.

Now let us say that the curve in Figure 2.9 results from a control $\boldsymbol{u}(t)$ and that we generate a second curve with a different control $\bar{\boldsymbol{u}}(t)$ such that

$$\delta\dot{\boldsymbol{x}}(t) = \boldsymbol{f}[\bar{\boldsymbol{x}}(t), \bar{\boldsymbol{u}}(t)] - \boldsymbol{f}[\boldsymbol{x}, \boldsymbol{u}] = \bar{\boldsymbol{f}} - \boldsymbol{f}. \tag{2.73}$$

Since the initial condition $\boldsymbol{x}(0)$ is given, the initial condition for Equation (2.73) is

$$\delta\boldsymbol{x}(0) = \boldsymbol{0}.$$

Using this, we can integrate Equation (2.73) to give $\delta\boldsymbol{x}(t)$, which is a vector in the three-dimensional space relating the two curves. Such a result is shown in Figure 2.10, where the vector $\delta\boldsymbol{x}(t)$ is shown at various t's. Obviously, the

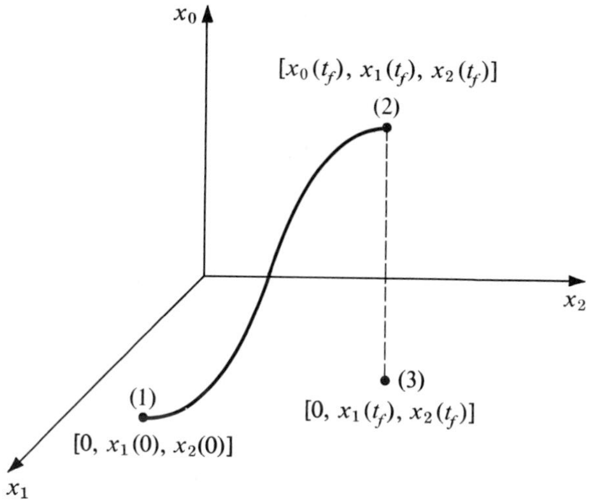

FIGURE 2.9. Two-dimensional minimum-time problem; $x_0(t)$ is time

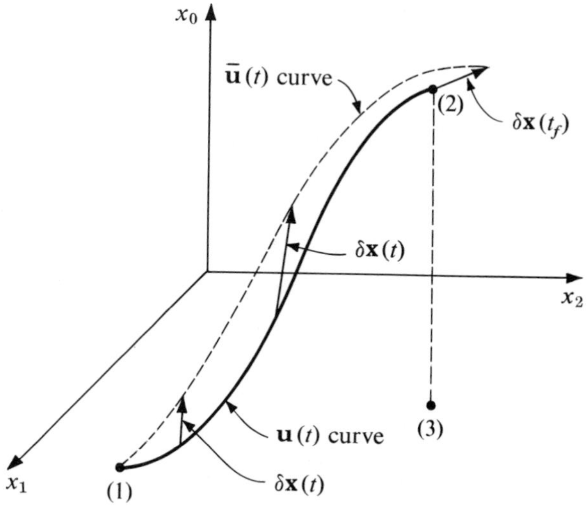

FIGURE 2.10. Perturbation trajectory due to change in control

$\delta \boldsymbol{x}(t)$ vector designates the direction of the change in the trajectory when a new control is used. In this case, the two curves must start from the same point since the initial state $\boldsymbol{x}(0)$ has been prescribed. If the original curve which uses the control $\boldsymbol{u}(t)$ is not optimal, then any vector $\delta \boldsymbol{x}(t_f)$ which points in a direction toward the x_1x_2-plane will yield an improved control; that is, if we place a plane through the point (2) parallel to the x_1x_2-plane, then any $\delta \boldsymbol{x}(t_f)$ which points below this plane indicates that the resulting trajectory is better than the original trajectory, since $x_0(t_f)$ will then be smaller. Note that in this case, because we have a free right-hand end, $x_1(t_f)$ and $x_2(t_f)$ are not fixed and the $\delta \boldsymbol{x}(t_f)$ may form a cone below the plane. If the right-hand were fixed, the only better $\delta \boldsymbol{x}(t_f)$ would be the ones which point vertically down toward the x_1x_2-plane.

Now if we define a Hamiltonian function for the original trajectory

$$H(\boldsymbol{z}, \boldsymbol{x}, \boldsymbol{u}) = \boldsymbol{z}'\boldsymbol{f} \tag{2.74}$$

and one for the new trajectory

$$\overline{H}(\boldsymbol{z}, \bar{\boldsymbol{x}}, \bar{\boldsymbol{u}}) = \boldsymbol{z}'\bar{\boldsymbol{f}}, \tag{2.75}$$

then

$$\overline{H} - H = \boldsymbol{z}(t)'[\bar{\boldsymbol{f}}(t) - \boldsymbol{f}(t)]$$

or, at $t = t_f$,

$$(\overline{H} - H)_{t=t_f} = \boldsymbol{z}'(t_f)[\bar{\boldsymbol{f}}(t_f) - \boldsymbol{f}(t_f)], \tag{2.76}$$

and using Equation (2.73),

$$(\overline{H} - H)_{t=t_f} = \boldsymbol{z}'(t_f)\delta\dot{\boldsymbol{x}}(t_f). \tag{2.77}$$

If we consider $\boldsymbol{u}(t)$ as the optimal control, then we know that $\delta \boldsymbol{x}(t_f) > \mathbf{0}$, since any other control would give a $\delta \boldsymbol{x}(t_f)$ which points away from the x_1x_2-plane. Since $\delta \boldsymbol{x}(0) = \mathbf{0}$, then it follows that in order to have $\delta \boldsymbol{x}(t_f) > \mathbf{0}$, we must have $\delta \dot{\boldsymbol{x}}(t_f) > \mathbf{0}$. Furthermore, if $\boldsymbol{z}(t_f)$ is made up of negative elements, that is, if $\boldsymbol{z}(t_f) < \mathbf{0}$, it follows from Equation (2.77) with $\delta \dot{\boldsymbol{x}}(t_f) > \mathbf{0}$ that

$$(\overline{H} - H)_{t=t_f} < 0 \tag{2.78}$$

and, therefore,

$$H > \overline{H} \qquad \text{at} \quad t = t_f. \tag{2.79}$$

Thus, it follows that the optimal trajectory will always have the maximum value of the Hamiltonian. Furthermore, we note that the choice of $\boldsymbol{z}(t_f) = -\boldsymbol{c}$ naturally leads to the minimization of the performance index and to maximization of the Hamiltonian.

Obviously, we could use this geometrical interpretation for a variety of different types of problems. We do not desire to pursue this feature too far, so we

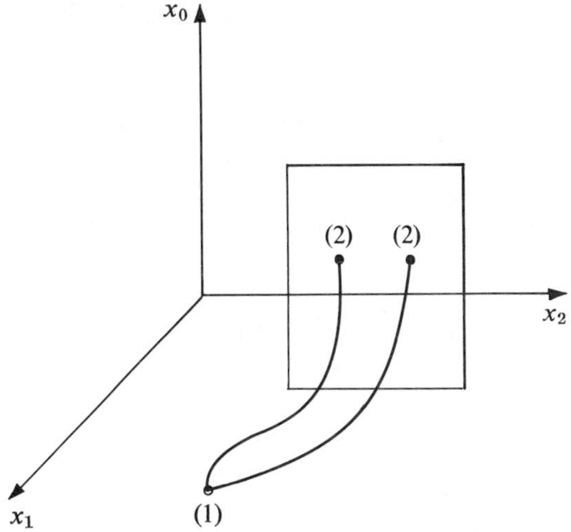

FIGURE 2.11. Trajectories for preassigned $x_1(t_f)$

shall show only two other types of curves. First, if one of the final state variables is preassigned, $x_1(t_f)$ is fixed but $x_2(t_f)$ is free, the trajectory must always end on the plane parallel to the x_0x_2-plane, as is shown in Figure 2.11. Alternatively, if $x_1(t_f)$ is fixed but $x_2(t_f)$ is free and, at the same time, $x_1(0)$ is fixed but $x_2(0)$ is free, the trajectory goes from a line to a plane (see Figure 2.12).

Actually, we have only scratched the surface of the continuous-maximum principle and its implications and applications. However, we have laid down the

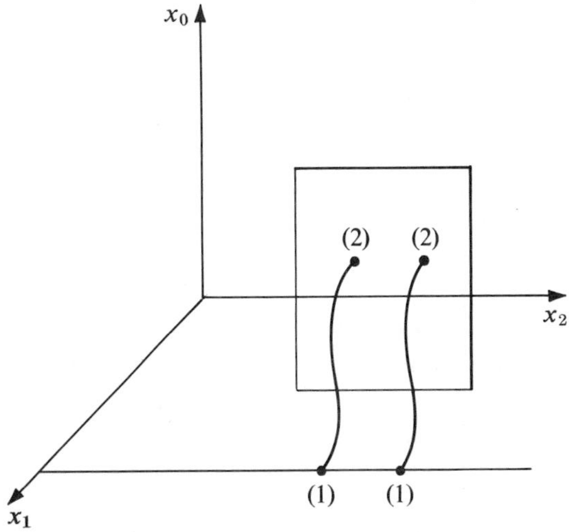

FIGURE 2.12. Trajectories for preassigned $x_1(t_f)$ and free $x_2(0)$

main guide lines and shall leave any further developments for later discussion.

We can, however, point out certain advantages and disadvantages of the maximum principle and dynamic programming. The maximum principle provides only necessary and not sufficient conditions for an optimal trajectory; by contrast, dynamic programming yields a global solution and for all initial conditions. The work of Jackson and Coward [48] reflects the difficulties in having only the necessary conditions. Further, the maximum principle introduces the adjoint variables which have no obvious physical meaning; by contrast, dynamic programming has an intuitive physical basis which the engineer can easily visualize. However, dynamic programming has the disadvantages associated with dimensionality, interpolation, and, quite frequently, excessive computer time.

We indicate, as a final comparison, that the optimal control obtained by the maximum principle is open-loop while that from dynamic programming is closed-loop (see Section 1.8). In the open-loop case, any disturbance to the system which occurs after the optimal control has started will not be detected; the closed-loop control will, however, pick up such a disturbance since the changing state of the system will be used.

2.3. The discrete-maximum principle

Having detailed the development of the continuous-maximum principle, it seems natural to extend this analysis to the case of discrete systems. We shall refer to this formulation as the discrete-maximum principle, and, as would be expected, it is in a form directly suitable for digital computation. The original work in this area was that of Rozonoer [68], Chang [26], and Katz [54]; the work of Katz was then used by Fan and co-workers [7]. However, Jordan and Pollack [51], Denn and Aris [29 through 32], Halkin [40, 41], and Horn and Jackson [45, 49] have shown that some of the implications resulting from Katz's work were erroneous. In effect, these authors have used a wide variety of approaches to show that only a weakened form of the Pontryagin continuous-maximum principle can be established for discrete systems. In this weakened form, the stagewise Hamiltonian is required to be only a local maximum or a stationary point rather than a global maximum. It is thus not generally true that the Hamiltonian must be maximized to minimize the performance index.

As pointed out by Horn and Jackson, the problems have resulted from a consideration of first-order variations. On the basis of neglecting the second-order variations, it is impossible to say that a maximum in the Hamiltonian yields a minimum in the index of performance.

Stated in another fashion, the necessary conditions for optimality via the discrete maximum principle require that certain guarantees be established for the reachable states of the system. In general, these reachable sets must be convex or, as recently developed by Halkin and Holtzmann [43, 44], directionally convex. When the assumption of convexity is fulfilled it is possible to completely specify the necessary conditions for the discrete-system maximum principle. Athans [19] summarizes these conditions in a superb manner.

Actually, much of the controversy in the literature dealing with the discrete maximum principle is concerned with physically staged steady-state systems and not discrete-time systems obtained as an approximation to continuous-time systems. Halkin [40, 41] has directed himself specifically to this distinction in terms of convexity of the reachable sets. His results indicate that, in the approximation of the continuous-time system by its discrete analog, convexity is always assured. However, when the system is discrete in nature, a series of steady-state staged units, this can no longer be assured. It is intuitively apparent that a physically staged steady-state system must imply discontinuities in the state variables, i.e., in passing through a stage, $(x_n - x_{n-1})$ cannot be arbitrarily decreased toward zero. By contrast, in the approximate continuous system, a time increment can be used which approaches zero.

Since we are concerned primarily with discrete approximations to continuous systems, i.e., systems that evolve in the time domain, our discussion of the discrete maximum principle will be essentially that of Katz. [*Note!* The defects and difficulties associated with its use should be kept in mind.]

We start the discussion with the discrete-time system

$$\boldsymbol{x}(k+1) = \boldsymbol{h}[\boldsymbol{x}(k), \boldsymbol{u}(k)] \qquad (\boldsymbol{x}(0) \quad \text{prescribed}), \tag{2.80}$$

and we shall try to find $\boldsymbol{u}(0), \boldsymbol{u}(1), \ldots, \boldsymbol{u}(P-1)$ to minimize

$$I[\boldsymbol{x}(0), P] = \boldsymbol{c}'\boldsymbol{x}(P) = \sum_{j=1}^{n} c_i x_i(P), \tag{2.81}$$

a final-state performance index. The c_i's are arbitrary constants, and we point out again that setting $c_1 = 1$, $c_i = 0$, where $i = 2, 3, \ldots, n$, for example, will lead to a minimization of $x_1(P)$.

Just as in the continuous-maximum principle, it is advantageous to introduce a discrete adjoint vector $\boldsymbol{z}(k)$ in the form

$$\boldsymbol{z}(k) = \frac{\partial \boldsymbol{h}'[\boldsymbol{x}(k), \boldsymbol{u}(k)]}{\partial \boldsymbol{x}(k)} \boldsymbol{z}(k+1). \tag{2.82}$$

In Equation (2.82), $\partial \boldsymbol{h}'/\partial \boldsymbol{x}(k)$ represents the differentiated values of Equation (2.80). Note there is no minus sign needed in this adjoint equation because of the explicit form of the difference equation. Along with the adjoint equation, we must also specify the associated boundary equations. For the case of minimizing $x_1(P)$ (a final value index), these are

$$\boldsymbol{z}(P)' = [1 \quad 0 \ldots 0] \tag{2.83}$$

or

$$z_i(P) = \begin{cases} 1, & i = 1, \\ 0, & i = 2, 3, \ldots, n. \end{cases}$$

We point out that, by convention, the boundary conditions on $\boldsymbol{z}(P)$ are taken as positive in the discrete-maximum principle. Thus, minimizing (maximizing) the performance index requires that we minimize (maximize) the Hamiltonian $H(k)$ defined as

$$H(k) = \boldsymbol{z}'(k)\boldsymbol{h}[\boldsymbol{x}(k-1), \boldsymbol{u}(k-1)]. \tag{2.84}$$

In effect, we really have a minimum principle although we continue to call it the maximum principle. Noting that

$$\boldsymbol{x}(k) = \boldsymbol{h}[\boldsymbol{x}(k-1), \boldsymbol{u}(k-1)]$$

from Equation (2.80), it follows immediately that

$$\boldsymbol{x}(k) = \frac{\partial H(k)}{\partial \boldsymbol{z}(k)} \tag{2.85}$$

and

$$\boldsymbol{z}(k) = \frac{\partial H(k)}{\partial \boldsymbol{x}(k)}. \tag{2.86}$$

We see that the discrete version of the maximum principle involves the system difference Equations (2.80) and associated initial conditions, the adjoint difference Equations (2.82) with final boundary conditions (2.83), and the Hamiltonian of Equation (2.84). We ask to find the optimal control sequence $\boldsymbol{u}(0), \boldsymbol{u}(1), \ldots, \boldsymbol{u}(P-1)$ by minimizing $H(k)$ at each stage in the sequence. Unfortunately, $H(k)$ is not necessarily constant for all k, which means that the strong form of the maximum principle cannot be satisfied, that is, only local conditions can be obtained.

The minimum value of $H(k)$ may frequently be found by calculating $\partial H/\partial \boldsymbol{u}(k-1) = \boldsymbol{0}$ to yield the optimal control $\boldsymbol{u}^{\circ}(k)$ in terms of $\boldsymbol{x}(k)$ and $\boldsymbol{z}(k)$; when this is substituted back into Equations (2.80) and (2.82), there result $2n$ equations in $2n$ unknowns. We have the $2n$ boundary conditions, $\boldsymbol{x}(0)$ and $\boldsymbol{z}(P)$, and thus we must solve, as usual, a two-point boundary value problem. Alternatively, we may find the minimum value of $H(k)$ by a numerical search in the $H(k)$ vs. $\boldsymbol{u}(k)$ space.

In the current case, however, $\partial H/\partial \boldsymbol{u}(k-1) = \boldsymbol{0}$ only assures a stationary value of $H(k)$ and not necessarily a minimum $H(k)$. In fact, as shown by Horn and Jackson [45], the stationary value may actually lead to a maximum in $H(k)$. Thus, in the discrete maximum principle it turns out that the strongest statement that we can make without considering convexity is that along an optimal trajectory the discrete Hamiltonian $H(k)$ is made stationary (rather than a minimum as would be expected by analogy to the continuous principle) with respect to interior components of $\boldsymbol{u}(k)$ and a minimum with respect to components of $\boldsymbol{u}(k)$ at constraints or boundaries of $\boldsymbol{u}(k)$. At the boundary of the constrained set, the conditions do agree with the continuous principle.

It is, of course, possible to extend the discrete-maximum principle to handle a variety of different boundary conditions and performance indices. The requirement to minimize the final value of $x_1(P)$ can be relaxed to minimize any single final $x_i(P)$ by merely changing Equation (2.83) so that the appropriate term is equal to 1 and all others are 0; or a weighted value of the final state can be used by specifying $z_i(P) = c_i$ rather than 1. Any arbitrary final or cumulative (summed) performance indices may be included by defining new state variables, as has been pointed out on numerous occasions. Finally, if some of the $\boldsymbol{x}(0)$ and some of the $\boldsymbol{x}(P)$ are specified rather than all of the $\boldsymbol{x}(0)$, this merely means that we delete some of the boundary conditions on $\boldsymbol{z}(P)$; the total of $2n$ conditions remains the same, assuming that no new state variables have been introduced. The work of Denn [23–26] is illustrative of a concise definition of these conditions. When there are terminal constraints on the state vector, as indicated by Equation (2.69), the boundary conditions on $z_i(P)$ must be relaxed in the same manner as with Equation (2.70).

Computationally, the fact that $\partial H/\partial \boldsymbol{u}(k-1) = \boldsymbol{0}$ may not lead to a unique and correct $\boldsymbol{u}(k)$ or that the result is a set of nonlinear differential equations may cause considerable difficulties. As a result, a completely numerical scheme may be required. To illustrate a possible means of handling this two-point nonlinear problem, we may guess at the optimal control sequence $\boldsymbol{u}(0), \boldsymbol{u}(1), \ldots, \boldsymbol{u}(P-1)$; with these values, Equation (2.80) can be used to generate $\boldsymbol{x}(1), \boldsymbol{x}(2), \ldots, \boldsymbol{x}(P)$. Once these two sequences are known, the adjoint equation may be used backward to generate $\boldsymbol{z}(P-1), \boldsymbol{z}(P-2), \ldots, \boldsymbol{z}(0)$, and a new and better set of $\boldsymbol{u}(k)$ can be obtained by minimizing $H(k)$ at each stage. This entire process is repeated until convergence, hopefully, occurs. Details on this iterative technique will be presented in Chapter 4.

There is, as might be expected, a close connection between the dynamic programming as presented in Section 2.1 and the discrete-maximum principle (there is an analogous connection between the continuous versions as detailed by Rozonoer [68]). It seems worthwhile to illustrate this connection as first carried out by Aris [2]. Thus we consider the discrete-time system model in the scalar form

$$x(k+1) = h[x(k), u(k)] \qquad (x(0) \text{ prescribed}) \tag{2.87}$$

and seek to minimize only the final value state $x(P)$. For this particular case the dynamic programming recurrence relation is given by Equation (2.24),

$$I^\circ[x(0), R+1] = \min_{u(0)} \{I^\circ[x(1), R]\}. \tag{2.88}$$

The discrete-maximum principle adjoint equation is

$$z(k) = \frac{\partial h(k)}{\partial x(k)}\, z(k+1), \tag{2.89}$$

$$z(P) = 1.0, \tag{2.90}$$

and the Hamiltonian is

$$H(k) = z(k)h[x(k-1), u(k-1)]. \tag{2.91}$$

Let us start with $P = 1$, or a one-stage process, as illustrated in Figure 2.13.

$P = 1$, one-stage process

•	•
$x(0)$	$x(1) = ?$
$z(0) = ?$	$z(1)$

$P = 2$, two-stage process

•	•	•
$x(0)$	$x(1) = ?$	$x(2) = ?$
$z(0) = ?$	$z(1) = ?$	$z(2)$

FIGURE 2.13. Discrete maximum principle development

Here $x(0)$ and $z(1)$ are known and $z(0)$ and $x(1)$ are unknown. Now the Hamiltonian is given by

$$H(1) = z(1)h[x(0), u(0)], \tag{2.92}$$

and since $z(1) = 1.0$,

$$H(1) = h[x(0), u(0)].$$

But from the system equation, we have

$$x(1) = h[x(0), u(0)],$$

and it follows that

$$H(1) = x(1). \tag{2.93}$$

Thus, if we minimize $H(1)$ by appropriately selecting $u(0)$, we minimize $x(1)$; the resulting value may be called

$$I^{\circ}[x(0), 1] = \min_{u(0)} [x(1)] = \min_{u(0)} [H(1)]. \tag{2.94}$$

Now we turn to two stages ($P = 2$), as illustrated in Figure 2.13, with $x(0)$ and $z(2)$ as known but $z(0)$, $z(1)$, $x(1)$, and $x(2)$ unknown.

But we already know that for the second stage (changing indices)

$$H(2) = x(2),$$

and the adjoint equation is

$$z(1) = \frac{\partial h(1)}{\partial x(1)}\, z(2) = \frac{\partial h(1)}{\partial x(1)}, \tag{2.95}$$

since $z(2) = 1.0$. Equation (2.95) corresponds to solving the adjoint equation backward one step from the final boundary. In the same sense, the system equation can be solved one step forward from the initial point to yield

$$x(1) = h[x(0), u(0)], \tag{2.96}$$

and the Hamiltonian for the first stage is

$$H(1) = z(1)h[x(0), u(0)]. \tag{2.97}$$

Using Equations (2.95) and (2.96), Equation (2.97) becomes

$$H(1) = \frac{\partial h(1)}{\partial x(1)} x(1). \tag{2.98}$$

But for the second stage $h(1) = I^\circ[x(1), 1]$, and thus Equation (2.98) becomes

$$H(1) = \frac{\partial I^\circ(x(1), 1)}{\partial x(1)} x(1),$$

and to minimize $H(1)$ with respect to $u(0)$, we differentiate this expression to give

$$\frac{\partial H(1)}{\partial u(0)} = \frac{\partial I^\circ(x(1), 1)}{\partial x(1)} \frac{\partial x(1)}{\partial u(0)} + \frac{\partial^2 I^\circ(x(1), 1)}{\partial u(0)\, \partial x(1)} x(1).$$

Let us neglect the second-order term by assuming that it is small. If we do so, there results

$$\frac{\partial H(1)}{\partial u(0)} = \frac{\partial I^\circ(x(1), 1)}{\partial u(0)}. \tag{2.99}$$

But Equation (2.99) merely says that

$$I^\circ(x(0), 2) = \min_{u(0)} \{I^\circ(x(1), 1)\}, \tag{2.100}$$

which compares favorably with Equation (2.88) using $R = 1$. There is, however, an equivalence only because we have neglected the second-order term; this is precisely the point of departure between the weak and strong principle.

Even though the end result for the two methods may be the same, the actual computational procedure is quite different, and this difference should be recognized. These are, of course, the same as previously mentioned. In the discrete maximum principle we must solve a two-point boundary value problem for a given $x(0)$; only a single optimal trajectory results. With dynamic programming, the problem is imbedded in a larger problem which ultimately leads to all the trajectories for any value of $x(0)$; thus, we do not have to explicitly solve a boundary-value problem. However, the dimensionality of the state vector is a serious deterrent to the dynamic programming procedure but not necessarily to the maximum principle. Finally, we note that constraints on the control and state variables are easily handled with dynamic programming, whereas special procedures (see Section 2.2) must be used with the maximum principle. Thus, each method has its advantages and disadvantages and it is probably not possible to state that one method is better than the other without specifying the actual system or the problem to be handled.

2.4. Linearized systems and the adjoint equations

In Sections 2.2 and 2.3 we have introduced the adjoint variables as a fundamental part of the maximum principle. In this section we shall consider the effect of linearization along the optimal trajectory; this will introduce the adjoint equation in a natural fashion. Furthermore, the material will prove useful in later chapters of this book.

We start our discussion with the nonlinear continuous-time system model

$$\dot{\boldsymbol{x}}(t) = \boldsymbol{f}[\boldsymbol{x}(t), \boldsymbol{u}(t)], \tag{2.101}$$

where, for the moment, we shall not specify a constant initial condition. In addition, we assume that a performance index is available for the measurement of the control effort, but the explicit form of this index need not concern us at this point.

Suppose that we guess at some control sequence $\boldsymbol{u}^*(t)$ over $(0, t_f)$; from Equation (2.101) and some value of $\boldsymbol{x}(0)$ we may generate the corresponding nominal trajectory $\boldsymbol{x}^*(t)$. Now we consider neighborhood trajectories to $\boldsymbol{x}^*(t)$ and proceed to linearize the nonlinear equations around the values $\boldsymbol{x}^*(t)$ and $\boldsymbol{u}^*(t)$. This may be done, as indicated in Section 1.3, by defining the new variables

$$\boldsymbol{x}(t) = \boldsymbol{x}^*(t) + \delta\boldsymbol{x}(t), \qquad \boldsymbol{u}(t) = \boldsymbol{u}^*(t) + \delta\boldsymbol{u}(t), \tag{2.102}$$

where $\delta\boldsymbol{x}(t)$ and $\delta\boldsymbol{u}(t)$ are *small variations* or *weak perturbations* in the state and control. (We shall define these more accurately in Chapter 4.) Applying these transformations to Equation (2.101), we obtain

$$\delta\dot{\boldsymbol{x}}(t) = (\partial\boldsymbol{f}'/\partial\boldsymbol{x})'\delta\boldsymbol{x} + (\partial\boldsymbol{f}'/\partial\boldsymbol{u})'\delta\boldsymbol{u} \tag{2.103}$$

or

$$\delta\dot{\boldsymbol{x}}(t) = \boldsymbol{A}(t)\delta\boldsymbol{x} + \boldsymbol{B}(t)\delta\boldsymbol{u}, \tag{2.104}$$

where

$$\boldsymbol{A}(t) = (\partial\boldsymbol{f}'/\partial\boldsymbol{x})' \qquad \text{and} \qquad \boldsymbol{B}(t) = (\partial\boldsymbol{f}'/\partial\boldsymbol{u})'.$$

Incidentally, we note at this point that if we had specified $\boldsymbol{x}(0) = \text{const}$, the linearization would yield $\delta\boldsymbol{x}(0) = \boldsymbol{0}$. The partial derivatives in Equations (2.103) or (2.104) are evaluated along $\boldsymbol{x}^*(t)$ and $\boldsymbol{u}^*(t)$, and since these are functions of time, $\boldsymbol{A}(t)$ and $\boldsymbol{B}(t)$ are functions of time. Thus, Equations (2.103) and (2.104) are linear but have time-varying coefficients.

The solution to Equation (2.104) may be written in the form (see Section 1.3)

$$\delta \boldsymbol{x}(t) = \boldsymbol{\Phi}(t, 0)\delta \boldsymbol{x}(0) + \int_0^t \boldsymbol{\Phi}(t, \lambda)\boldsymbol{B}(\lambda)\delta \boldsymbol{u}(\lambda)\, d\lambda, \qquad (2.105)$$

where the transition matrix $\boldsymbol{\Phi}(t, \lambda)$ has been previously defined as the solution of the homogeneous system

$$d\boldsymbol{\Phi}/dt = \boldsymbol{A}(t)\boldsymbol{\Phi}; \qquad \boldsymbol{\Phi}(0, 0) = \boldsymbol{I}. \qquad (2.106)$$

Green's function or the *influence function* for this system is

$$\boldsymbol{G}(t, \lambda) = \boldsymbol{\Phi}(t, \lambda)\boldsymbol{B}(\lambda). \qquad (2.107)$$

If we consider the case of $\delta \boldsymbol{x}(0) = \boldsymbol{0}$, zero initial condition of perturbed system, we can see that $\boldsymbol{G}(t, \lambda)$ is related to the *transfer* or *weighting function* of the system since it shows how an impulse at time λ affects $\delta \boldsymbol{x}(t)$.

Now we define a system which is adjoint to the linear system (2.104) by

$$\dot{\boldsymbol{z}}(t) = -\boldsymbol{A}'(t)\boldsymbol{z}, \qquad (2.108)$$

where $A'(t) = \partial \boldsymbol{f}'/\partial \boldsymbol{x}$ evaluated at $\boldsymbol{x}^*$ and $\boldsymbol{u}^*$. Using Equations (2.104) and (2.108), we note that

$$\frac{d}{dt}[\boldsymbol{z}'(t)\delta \boldsymbol{x}] = \dot{\boldsymbol{z}}'(t)\delta \boldsymbol{x} + \boldsymbol{z}'(t)\delta \dot{\boldsymbol{x}} = -(\boldsymbol{z}'\boldsymbol{A})\delta \boldsymbol{x} + \boldsymbol{z}'\boldsymbol{A}\delta \boldsymbol{x} + \boldsymbol{z}'\boldsymbol{B}\delta \boldsymbol{u}.$$

Therefore, we have

$$\frac{d}{dt}(\boldsymbol{z}'(t)\delta \boldsymbol{x}) = \boldsymbol{z}'\boldsymbol{B}\delta \boldsymbol{u}, \qquad (2.109)$$

and, if we integrate between $t = 0$ and $t = t$,

$$\boldsymbol{z}'(t)\delta \boldsymbol{x}(t) = \boldsymbol{z}'(0)\delta \boldsymbol{x}(0) + \int_0^t \boldsymbol{z}'(\lambda)\boldsymbol{B}(\lambda)\delta \boldsymbol{u}(\lambda)\, d\lambda, \qquad (2.110)$$

which is known as *Green's Identity*. But from Equation (2.105) we see that

$$\boldsymbol{z}'(t)\delta \boldsymbol{x}(t) = \boldsymbol{z}'(t)\boldsymbol{\Phi}(t, 0)\delta \boldsymbol{x}(0) + \int_0^t \boldsymbol{z}'(t)\boldsymbol{\Phi}(t, \lambda)\boldsymbol{B}(\lambda)\delta \boldsymbol{u}(\lambda)\, d\lambda. \qquad (2.111)$$

Comparing Equations (2.110) and (2.111), we see that

$$\boldsymbol{z}'(\lambda) = \boldsymbol{z}'(t)\boldsymbol{\Phi}(t, \lambda).$$

Multiplying each side by $\boldsymbol{z}(t)$ gives

$$\boldsymbol{z}(t)\boldsymbol{z}'(\lambda) = \boldsymbol{z}(t)\boldsymbol{z}'(t)\boldsymbol{\Phi}(t, \lambda)$$

and thus

$$\boldsymbol{\Phi}(t, \lambda) = [\boldsymbol{z}(t)\boldsymbol{z}'(t)]^{-1}\boldsymbol{z}(t)\boldsymbol{z}'(\lambda). \qquad (2.112)$$

In other words, the calculation of $\boldsymbol{\Phi}(t, \lambda)$ is equivalent to the calculation of the adjoint variables. These, in turn, are obtained by a relatively simple procedure in which the ordinary differential equation for $\boldsymbol{z}(t)$ is integrated backward from

$t = t$ to $t = 0$. This, then, is one of the major reasons for introducing the adjoint variable equations.

Since we have these equations available, it is worthwhile to extend the analysis one step further in the sense that we add a final value performance index $I[\boldsymbol{x}(0), t_f] = I[\boldsymbol{x}(t_f)]$. Because of the perturbation $\delta\boldsymbol{u}(t)$, there will be a change in the index as given by

$$\delta I = \left(\frac{\partial I}{\partial \boldsymbol{x}}\right)' \delta\boldsymbol{x}\bigg|_{t=t_f}, \tag{2.113}$$

where $I = I[\boldsymbol{x}(0), t_f]$. If we now let

$$\boldsymbol{z}(t_f) = \frac{\partial I}{\partial \boldsymbol{x}}\bigg|_{t=t_f} = \nabla_{\boldsymbol{x}} I\bigg|_{t=t_f}, \tag{2.114}$$

then

$$\delta I = \boldsymbol{z}'(t_f)\delta\boldsymbol{x}(t_f). \tag{2.115}$$

Equation (2.110) thus becomes for $t = t_f$

$$\delta I = \boldsymbol{z}'(0)\delta\boldsymbol{x}(0) + \int_0^{t_f} \boldsymbol{z}'(\lambda)\boldsymbol{B}(\lambda)\delta\boldsymbol{u}(\lambda)\, d\lambda, \tag{2.116}$$

showing how changes in $\boldsymbol{u}(t)$ affect the final value performance index.

At the same time, we note the following points about the boundary conditions on the adjoint variables. If t_f is fixed and the $\boldsymbol{x}(t_f)$ are unconstrained, then the *natural boundary conditions* on the adjoint variables are given by Equation (2.114), namely,

$$\boldsymbol{z}(t_f) = \nabla_{\boldsymbol{x}} I\,|_{t=t_f}.$$

Of course, it follows that, depending on the explicit form of I, the elements of $\boldsymbol{z}(t_f)$ may be 1, 0, or constants. If some of the elements of $\boldsymbol{x}(t_f)$ are fixed and variations are not allowed, then these cannot affect the performance index, and the corresponding elements of $\boldsymbol{z}(t_f)$ are undefined. In the case where the final states are constrained by relationships of the type $\psi_j[\boldsymbol{x}(t_f)] = 0$, as given in Section 2.2, the boundary conditions on the adjoint variables must be modified. This was briefly pointed out in Section 2.2, and we shall shortly derive an explicit version for the discrete case.

We may, of course, develop the same type of material for the discrete-time system, as was just done for the continuous-time case (however, see reference 69). We may start with the difference equation form

$$\boldsymbol{x}(k+1) = \boldsymbol{h}[\boldsymbol{x}(k), \boldsymbol{u}(k)], \tag{2.117}$$

linearize by perturbing around $\boldsymbol{x}^*(k)$ and $\boldsymbol{u}^*(k)$, and solve the resulting difference equations. We can also start directly from the continuous-case solution, Equation (2.105),

$$\delta\boldsymbol{x}(t) = \boldsymbol{\Phi}(t, 0)\delta\boldsymbol{x}(0) + \int_0^t \boldsymbol{\Phi}(t, \lambda)\boldsymbol{B}(\lambda)\delta\boldsymbol{u}(\lambda)\, d\lambda, \tag{2.118}$$

and consider equal intervals in time: $(0, t_1), (t_1, t_2), (t_2, t_3), \ldots$, with k used to indicate the interval number. In either case, the results obtained are substantially equivalent to those for the continuous-time case and we shall not pursue it further.

There is one interesting result which develops from this material, namely, to take the *backward* difference of the expression $\boldsymbol{z}'(k)\,\boldsymbol{x}(k)$ in analogy to the derivation of Equation (2.109). Thus

$$\nabla[\boldsymbol{z}'(k)\delta\boldsymbol{x}(k)] = \boldsymbol{z}'(k)\delta\boldsymbol{x}(k) - \boldsymbol{z}'(k-1)\delta\boldsymbol{x}(k-1). \tag{2.119}$$

Now we introduce the adjoint equation

$$\boldsymbol{z}(k) = \frac{\partial \boldsymbol{h}'(k)}{\partial \boldsymbol{x}(k)}\,\boldsymbol{z}(k+1) \tag{2.120}$$

and define

$$\boldsymbol{A}(k) = \left[\frac{\partial \boldsymbol{h}'(k)}{\partial \boldsymbol{x}(k)}\right]' \tag{2.121}$$

so that Equation (2.120) may be written in a more compact form,

$$\boldsymbol{z}(k) = \boldsymbol{A}'(k)\boldsymbol{z}(k+1). \tag{2.122}$$

Now we note that the discrete-time analog to Equation (2.104) is

$$\delta\boldsymbol{x}(k+1) = \boldsymbol{A}(k)\delta\boldsymbol{x}(k) + \boldsymbol{B}(k)\delta\boldsymbol{u}(k), \tag{2.123}$$

which we may write for our purpose as

$$\delta\boldsymbol{x}(k) = \boldsymbol{A}(k-1)\delta\boldsymbol{x}(k-1) + \boldsymbol{B}(k-1)\delta\boldsymbol{u}(k-1). \tag{2.124}$$

Substitution of Equation (2.124) into the first term of the right-hand side of Equation (2.119) and of Equation (2.122) into the second term of the right-hand side of Equation (2.119) gives

$$\boldsymbol{z}'(k)\delta\boldsymbol{x}(k) - \boldsymbol{z}'(k-1)\delta\boldsymbol{x}(k-1) = \boldsymbol{z}'(k)\boldsymbol{B}(k-1)\delta\boldsymbol{u}(k-1). \tag{2.125}$$

Summing Equation (2.125) from $k = 1$ to $k = P$ (note the cancellation of terms), we have

$$\boldsymbol{z}'(P)\delta\boldsymbol{x}(P) = \boldsymbol{z}'(0)\delta\boldsymbol{x}(0) + \sum_{k=1}^{P} \boldsymbol{z}'(k)\boldsymbol{B}(k-1)\delta\boldsymbol{u}(k-1). \tag{2.126}$$

If the Hamiltonian function is now defined as

$$H(k) = \boldsymbol{z}'(k)\boldsymbol{h}[\boldsymbol{x}(k-1), \boldsymbol{u}(k-1)] = \boldsymbol{z}'(k)\boldsymbol{h}(k-1), \tag{2.127}$$

with

$$\boldsymbol{B}(k-1) = \left[\frac{\partial \boldsymbol{h}'(k-1)}{\partial \boldsymbol{u}(k-1)}\right]',$$

Equation (2.126) may be written as

$$\mathbf{z}'(P)\delta\mathbf{x}(P) = \mathbf{z}'(0)\delta\mathbf{x}(0) + \sum_{k=1}^{P}\left[\frac{\partial H(k)}{\partial\mathbf{u}(k-1)}\right]'\delta\mathbf{u}(k-1), \tag{2.128}$$

which implies

$$\delta I = \mathbf{z}'(0)\delta\mathbf{x}(0) + \sum_{k=1}^{P}\left[\frac{\partial H(k)}{\partial\mathbf{u}(k-1)}\right]'\delta\mathbf{u}(k-1). \tag{2.129}$$

Now we turn to an entirely different-appearing approach for discrete-time systems as developed by Dreyfus [5, 35]. As we will see, the derivation is basically a simple application of the chain rule of calculus. Since the results are shown to be equivalent to those obtained previously, it points out how the discrete maximum principle can be formulated. In this analysis we start with a forward difference form of our standard nonlinear continuous-time system model,

$$\mathbf{x}(t+\Delta t) = \mathbf{x}(t) + \mathbf{h}[\mathbf{x}(t), \mathbf{u}(t)]\,\Delta t, \tag{2.130}$$

and with the performance index in the form

$$I[\mathbf{x}(0), t] = I[\mathbf{x}(t), t]. \tag{2.131}$$

The problem to be analyzed consisted of finding those $\mathbf{u}(k\Delta t) = \mathbf{u}(k)$ such that at some time $t = t_f$ which is unspecified, a specific "stopping condition" or constraint

$$\boldsymbol{\psi}(\mathbf{x}, t) = \mathbf{0} \tag{2.132}$$

is achieved. This stopping condition is equivalent to the previous $\psi_j(\mathbf{x}, t) = 0$, $j = 1, 2, \ldots, m < n$. Let us define the *nonoptimal index*

$$S(\mathbf{x}) = \text{the value of } I \text{ at } \boldsymbol{\psi} = \mathbf{0} \text{ obtained by means of any assumed set of } \mathbf{u}(k). \tag{2.133}$$

It follows immediately from Equation (2.131) that

$$S(\mathbf{x}) = S(\mathbf{x} + \mathbf{h}\Delta t), \tag{2.134}$$

which merely says that once the $\mathbf{u}(k)$ are assumed and $\mathbf{x}(t+\Delta t)$ is thus uniquely determined, the value of I is the same no matter where on the realized trajectory we start.

Now we derive a number of important relations. First we note from Equation (2.134) that

$$\frac{\partial S}{\partial\mathbf{u}(k)} = \frac{\partial\mathbf{h}'(k)}{\partial\mathbf{u}(k)}\frac{\partial S}{\partial\mathbf{x}(k+1)}\Delta t. \tag{2.135}$$

We obtain this equation from

$$S[\boldsymbol{x}(t)] = S[\boldsymbol{x}(t + \Delta t)] = S\{\boldsymbol{x}(t) + \boldsymbol{h}[\boldsymbol{x}(t), \boldsymbol{u}(t), t]\,\Delta t\},$$

and thus

$$dS = \left[\frac{\partial S}{\partial \boldsymbol{x}(t + \Delta t)}\right]' [d\boldsymbol{x}(t + \Delta t)]$$

or

$$\frac{\partial S}{\partial \boldsymbol{u}(t)} = \frac{\partial \boldsymbol{x}'(t + \Delta t)}{\partial \boldsymbol{u}(t)} \frac{\partial S}{\partial \boldsymbol{x}(t + \Delta t)}.$$

But

$$\frac{\partial \boldsymbol{x}'(t + \Delta t)}{\partial \boldsymbol{u}(t)} = \frac{\partial \boldsymbol{x}'(t)}{\partial \boldsymbol{u}(t)} + \frac{\partial \boldsymbol{h}'[\boldsymbol{x}(t), \boldsymbol{u}(t), t]}{\partial \boldsymbol{u}(t)}\,\Delta t,$$

and since $\boldsymbol{u}(t)$ cannot affect $\boldsymbol{x}(t)$,

$$\frac{\partial \boldsymbol{x}'(t + \Delta t)}{\partial \boldsymbol{u}(t)} = \frac{\partial \boldsymbol{h}'(t)}{\partial \boldsymbol{u}(t)}\,\Delta t.$$

Thus, it follows that

$$\frac{\partial S}{\partial \boldsymbol{u}(t)} = \frac{\partial \boldsymbol{h}'(t)}{\partial \boldsymbol{u}(t)} \frac{\partial S}{\partial \boldsymbol{x}(t + \Delta t)}\,\Delta t,$$

and using the terminology $k = t$ and $k + 1 = t + \Delta t$, we obtain Equation (2.135). A second relationship which can be obtained from Equation (2.134) is

$$\frac{\partial S}{\partial \boldsymbol{x}(k)} = \frac{\partial \boldsymbol{h}'(k)}{\partial \boldsymbol{x}(k)} \frac{\partial S}{\partial \boldsymbol{x}(k + 1)}\,\Delta t + \frac{\partial S}{\partial \boldsymbol{x}(k + 1)}. \tag{2.136}$$

This equation results from

$$\frac{\partial S}{\partial \boldsymbol{x}(t)} = \frac{\partial \boldsymbol{x}'(t + \Delta t)}{\partial \boldsymbol{x}(t)} \frac{\partial S}{\partial \boldsymbol{x}(t + \Delta t)} = \frac{\partial}{\partial \boldsymbol{x}(t)} \{\boldsymbol{x}'(t) + \boldsymbol{h}'[\boldsymbol{x}(t), \boldsymbol{u}(t), t]\,\Delta t\} \frac{\partial S}{\partial \boldsymbol{x}(t + \Delta t)}$$

$$= \left\{\boldsymbol{I} + \frac{\partial}{\partial \boldsymbol{x}(t)} \boldsymbol{h}'[\boldsymbol{x}(t), \boldsymbol{u}(t), t]\,\Delta t\right\} \frac{\partial S}{\partial \boldsymbol{x}(t + \Delta t)},$$

and changing to the k nomenclature, Equation (2.136) results.

Now let us differentiate the expression for the stopping condition as given by Equation (2.132) in the scalar form

$$\psi = \psi(\boldsymbol{x}, t) = 0, \qquad d\psi = \left.\frac{\partial \psi}{\partial \boldsymbol{x}}\right|_t' d\boldsymbol{x} + \left.\frac{\partial \psi}{\partial t}\right|_{\boldsymbol{x}} dt = 0,$$

and therefore

$$\frac{dt}{d\boldsymbol{x}} = -\frac{1}{\dot{\psi}} \left.\frac{\partial \psi}{\partial \boldsymbol{x}}\right|_t, \tag{2.137}$$

where $\dot{\psi} = \partial\psi/\partial t$. Also, we note from the definition of the performance index

$$I = I[\mathbf{x}, t], \qquad dI = \left(\frac{\partial I}{\partial \mathbf{x}}\bigg|_t\right)' d\mathbf{x} + \frac{\partial I}{\partial t}\bigg|_{\mathbf{x}} dt,$$

so that

$$\frac{dI}{d\mathbf{x}} = \frac{\partial I}{\partial \mathbf{x}}\bigg|_t + \frac{\partial I}{\partial t}\bigg|_{\mathbf{x}} \frac{dt}{d\mathbf{x}}.$$

At $t = t_f$, the performance index $I = S$, so that

$$\frac{dS}{d\mathbf{x}}\bigg|_{t=t_f} = \frac{\partial I}{\partial \mathbf{x}}\bigg|_{t=t_f} + \frac{\partial I}{\partial t}\bigg|_{\mathbf{x}}\left[-\frac{1}{\dot{\psi}}\frac{\partial \psi}{\partial \mathbf{x}}\bigg|_{t=t_f}\right]. \tag{2.138}$$

Equations (2.135), (2.136), and (2.138) represent the results of this analysis, with (2.138) being the transversality boundary condition for $t = t_f$. In Chapter 4 we shall show how this analysis may be extended to cover a more general type of problem.

These equations are equivalent to the unconstrained values defined previously. Thus, if we let

$$\mathbf{z}^I(t) = dS/d\mathbf{x},$$

then we note that with no stopping condition or constraint, $\partial\psi/\partial\mathbf{x} = \mathbf{0}$, and Equation (2.138) becomes

$$\mathbf{z}^I(t_f) = \frac{\partial I}{\partial \mathbf{x}}\bigg|_{t=t_f}$$

This is equivalent to Equation (2.114). In the same sense, Equation (2.136) may be written as

$$\mathbf{z}^I(t) = \frac{\partial \mathbf{h}'}{\partial \mathbf{x}(k)}\, \mathbf{z}^I(t + \Delta t)\, \Delta t + \mathbf{z}^I(t + \Delta t).$$

But this is equivalent to the adjoint Equation (2.120), taking into account the slight change in nomenclature of the system model between formulations. Thus Equation (2.136) is really the adjoint equation and (2.138) is the boundary condition at $t = t_f$.

Actually, the connection between the adjoint variable and the derivative of the performance index with respect to $\mathbf{x}$ has more profound roots. In fact, it forms the basis for an entirely different approach to the derivation of the optimal trajectory, namely through the *Hamilton-Jacobi equation* (H–J) [3, 6]. To illustrate this point in a simple manner, we write the performance index in the special (only for the present manipulations) form

$$I[x, t] = \int_0^{t_f} J(x, u)\, dt, \qquad x, u = \text{scalars},$$

with $I^\circ[x, t]$ as the optimal value of $I[x, t]$. If we expand I° in a Taylor series through first-order terms, there results

$$I^\circ[x + \Delta x, t + \Delta t] = I^\circ[x, t] + \Delta t \frac{\partial I^\circ}{\partial t} + \Delta x \frac{\partial I^\circ}{\partial x}.$$

But from the principle of optimality in its continuous form, we see that

$$I^\circ[x, t] = \min_u \{J\Delta t + I^\circ[x + \Delta x, t + \Delta t]\}$$

or, using the Taylor series,

$$I^\circ[x, t] = \min_u \left\{J\Delta t + I^\circ[x, t] + \Delta t \frac{\partial I^\circ}{\partial t} + \Delta x \frac{\partial I^\circ}{\partial x}\right\}.$$

Now if we divide by Δt, take the limit as $\Delta t \to 0$, there results

$$-\frac{\partial I^\circ}{\partial t} = \min_u \left\{J + \dot{x}\frac{\partial I^\circ}{\partial x}\right\}.$$

Assuming that the control is not constrained, we see that a necessary condition for the minimization of the term in brackets is that its derivative with respect to u is equal to zero. The result of this differentiation yields u°, which when substituted back yields

$$-\frac{\partial I^\circ}{\partial t} = J(x, u^\circ, t) + \frac{\partial I^\circ}{\partial x}\dot{x}.$$

Calling $H^\circ[x, (\partial I^\circ/\partial x), t] = J(x, u^\circ, t) + (\partial I^\circ/\partial x)\dot{x}$, we may finally write the Hamilton-Jacobi equation

$$\frac{\partial I^\circ}{\partial t} + H^\circ\left(x, \frac{\partial I^\circ}{\partial x}, t\right) = 0. \tag{2.139}$$

Now we note that if we differentiate Equation (2.139) with respect to x and compare to the canonical equations of the maximum principle, the identity

$$z^\circ = \partial I^\circ/\partial x$$

results. This equation is the connecting link between the H–J and the maximum principle theory. The extension to the vector case follows directly.

If I° is twice-differentiable, the solution of the H–J equation is both necessary and sufficient for the optimal control. Unfortunately, the solution of this equation can only be obtained in certain special cases.

2.5. Stability analysis via Liapunov's second method

In Chapter 1 we mentioned that stability information can be obtained directly by Liapunov's second method without integration of the differential (or difference) equations. Before outlining the theoretical development of this method, let us restate the definitions of stability according to Liapunov.

An equilibrium state $\boldsymbol{x}_e$ of a free dynamic system is *stable* if for each $\varepsilon > 0$ there exists a $\delta(\varepsilon, t_0) > 0$ such that for all initial states $\boldsymbol{x}_0$,

$$\|\boldsymbol{x}_0 - \boldsymbol{x}_e\| < \delta$$

implies that

$$\|\boldsymbol{x}(t; \boldsymbol{x}_0, t_0) - \boldsymbol{x}_e\| < \varepsilon$$

for all $t \geq t_0$.

An equilibrium state $\boldsymbol{x}_e$ of a free dynamic system is *asymptotically stable* if

(1) it is stable, and
(2) for every motion starting sufficiently near $\boldsymbol{x}_e$

$$\lim_{t \to \infty} \|\boldsymbol{x}(t; \boldsymbol{x}_0, t_0) - \boldsymbol{x}_e\| = 0.$$

An equilibrium state $\boldsymbol{x}_e$ of a free dynamic system is *asymptotically stable in the large* if

(1) it is stable, and
(2) for every motion

$$\lim_{t \to \infty} \|\boldsymbol{x}(t; \boldsymbol{x}_0, t_0) - \boldsymbol{x}_e\| = 0.$$

Uniform stability is stability such that δ does not depend on t_0.

These definitions hold for both continuous-time and discrete-time systems; in the latter only the notation is changed so that t is replaced by k. There are various other definitions of more precise nature such as *monotonic stability, total stability, exponential stability*, etc., but for the present treatment the above definitions suffice. For the design of chemical reactors one wants to be reassured that they are uniformly asymptotically stable in a sufficiently large region and that as the equilibrium state is approached no physical damage results to the reactor. Quite frequently in this book the term "stability" implies "uniform asymptotic stability in the region of interest." The exact meaning should be clear from the context, and no confusion is expected.

Liapunov's second method has been outlined and expanded in many excellent texts [10, 13] and in various papers [38, 52]. We shall here briefly outline the method based on the following theorem.

▶ THEOREM 2.1. *Consider the continuous-time autonomous system for which the dynamic equation can be written*

$$\dot{\boldsymbol{x}} = \boldsymbol{f}(\boldsymbol{x}) \qquad (\text{with} \quad \boldsymbol{f}(\boldsymbol{0}) = \boldsymbol{0}).$$

Suppose that there exists a scalar function $V(\boldsymbol{x})$ such that $V(\boldsymbol{0}) = 0$ and

(1) $V(\boldsymbol{x}) > 0 \qquad (\text{when} \quad \boldsymbol{x} \neq \boldsymbol{0})$,
(2) $\dot{V}(\boldsymbol{x}) = (\nabla V)' \boldsymbol{f}(\boldsymbol{x}) \leq 0$,

then the trivial solution $\boldsymbol{x}(t) = \boldsymbol{0}$ is stable.

Proof ▪ We shall outline the proof as given by Geiss [38], which is based on geometrical intuition. Since $V(\boldsymbol{x})$ is continuous and positive definite, on every ray through the origin $V(\boldsymbol{x})$ must take on all values between zero and its first local maximum value. Thus, the equation

$$V(\boldsymbol{x}) = C,$$

where C is a constant smaller than the first local maximum value of $V(\boldsymbol{x})$, will describe a closed hypersurface which surrounds the origin. Therefore, there exist constants $C_1, C_2, \ldots, C_n$ such that $C_1 < C_2 < \cdots < C_n$ which define hypersurfaces enclosing each other.

Due to the continuity of $V(\boldsymbol{x})$, these hypersurfaces can be bounded by hyperspheres. Consider the hypersphere given by

$$\boldsymbol{x}'\boldsymbol{x} = \varepsilon^2,$$

and let

$$C_i = \min_{\boldsymbol{x}'\boldsymbol{x}=\varepsilon^2} V(\boldsymbol{x}) \qquad (\text{where} \quad C_i < C),$$

and now define δ by

$$\delta^2 = \min_{V(\boldsymbol{x})=C_i} \boldsymbol{x}'\boldsymbol{x}.$$

Therefore, in the region $\|\boldsymbol{x}\| < \delta$, $V(\boldsymbol{x}) < C_i$ and since $\dot{V} \leq 0$, for every trajectory beginning in $\|\boldsymbol{x}\| < \delta$, $V(\boldsymbol{x})$ will remain less than C_i, and hence $\|\boldsymbol{x}\| < \varepsilon$. Therefore, the trivial solution $\boldsymbol{x}(t) = \boldsymbol{0}$ is stable.

▶ COROLLARY 2.1. *If $\dot{V}$ and V are both positive-definite, the trivial solution is unstable.*

▶ COROLLARY 2.2. *If $\dot{V}(\boldsymbol{x}) < 0$ and the other conditions are the same, the trivial solution $\boldsymbol{x}(t) = \boldsymbol{0}$ is* asymptotically *stable.*

The above theorem gives sufficient conditions for stability but not necessary ones. To ensure that a system is asymptotically stable, all that one has to do is to find a scalar function which satisfies the sufficient conditions, namely to find a positive-definite scalar function whose time derivative is negative-definite. However, for nonlinear systems there is no straightforward method of achieving this objective, and one must rely on ingenuity and experience to choose an appropriate trial function which could be tested for suitability.

To illustrate the approach that one may use to construct a Liapunov function, let us consider a simple linear system in the form of a damped harmonic oscillator whose dynamic behavior is described by

$$m\ddot{x} + F\dot{x} + kx = 0,$$

where m is the mass of the particle, k is the restoring force constant, and F is the damping factor. We shall assume that m, F, and k are constant. To apply Liapunov's second method to study the stability of this system, we shall write the second-order ordinary differential equation as two first-order differential equations:

$$\dot{x}_1 = x_2, \qquad \dot{x}_2 = -\frac{F}{m}x_2 - \frac{k}{m}x_1. \tag{2.140}$$

Now the problem is to construct a sign-definite scalar function such that its time derivative is also sign-definite. Suppose we would choose the following trial function:

$$V = x_1^2 + x_2^2; \tag{2.141}$$

at once it is found that

$$\dot{V} = 2(x_1\dot{x}_1 + x_2\dot{x}_2) = 2\left(x_1x_2 - \frac{F}{m}x_2^2 - \frac{k}{m}x_2x_1\right), \tag{2.142}$$

and only if $k/m = 1$ does (2.141) become a Liapunov function. If $k/m \neq 1$, $\dot{V}$ could be either positive or negative, and no information concerning the stability is gained. From physical reasoning we realize that $k/m = 1$ is a very special case, and in general this condition is not satisfied. Therefore, we try a more general type of a function in the form

$$V = a_{11}x_1^2 + 2a_{12}x_1x_2 + a_{22}x_2^2, \tag{2.143}$$

where a_{11}, a_{12}, and a_{22} will be chosen to make V positive-definite, that is

$$a_{11} > 0, \qquad a_{22} > 0, \qquad a_{11}a_{22} - a_{12}^2 > 0. \tag{2.144}$$

With these restrictions, we shall try to evaluate a_{11}, a_{12}, and a_{22} to make $\dot{V}$ negative definite. By taking the derivative of Equation (2.143) and applying Equations (2.140), we see immediately that the derivative of V is

$$\dot{V} = \left(2a_{11} - 2a_{12}\frac{F}{m} - 2a_{22}\frac{k}{m}\right)x_1x_2 + \left(2a_{12} - 2a_{22}\frac{F}{m}\right)x_2^2 - 2a_{12}\frac{k}{m}x_1^2. \tag{2.145}$$

We shall let

$$\dot{V} = -x_1^2 - x_2^2 \tag{2.146}$$

and choose a_{11}, a_{12}, and a_{22} accordingly; namely,

$$2a_{11} - 2a_{12}\frac{F}{m} - 2a_{22}\frac{k}{m} = 0, \qquad 2a_{12} - 2a_{22}\frac{F}{m} = -1, \qquad -2a_{12}\frac{k}{m} = -1. \tag{2.147}$$

Solving for the three unknowns, we get

$$a_{12} = \frac{m}{2k}, \qquad a_{22} = \frac{m^2 + km}{2Fk} \qquad \text{and} \qquad a_{11} = \frac{1}{2}\left[\frac{F^2 + k^2 + km}{Fk}\right].$$

Now, substituting these values for a_{11}, a_{12}, and a_{22} into the inequalities (2.144), we obtain

$$\frac{1}{2}\left[\frac{F^2 + k^2 + km}{Fk}\right] > 0, \qquad \frac{m^2 + km}{2Fk} > 0, \qquad \frac{m}{4F^2k}[F^2 + (m + k)^2] > 0.$$

It is immediately obvious that these three inequalities are satisfied if F, m, k all have the same sign, and then the system is asymptotically stable. Therefore, to have F, m, and k all of the same sign is a sufficient condition of stability.

This example illustrates the liberty that exists in the construction of a Liapunov function. We could have chosen some completely different negative-definite function for $\dot{V}$ instead of Equation (2.146). Also, it should be noted that one usually tries to use the simplest form of the function to keep the algebraic work to a minimum, and the search for a Liapunov function is not entirely a trial-and-error procedure.

Since we shall deal with discrete-time systems later, it will be instructive to state the analogous theorem for such systems.

▶ THEOREM 2.2. *Consider the discrete-time, autonomous system for which the dynamic equation can be written as*

$$\mathbf{x}(k + 1) = \mathbf{h}[\mathbf{x}(k)]. \tag{2.148}$$

Suppose there exists a scalar function $V[\mathbf{x}(k)]$ *such that* $V(\mathbf{0}) = 0$ *and*

(1) $V[\mathbf{x}(k)] > 0$ (when $\mathbf{x} \neq \mathbf{0}$),
(2) $\Delta V[\mathbf{x}(k)] = V[\mathbf{x}(k + 1)] - V[\mathbf{x}(k)] < 0$ (when $\mathbf{x} \neq \mathbf{0}$),
(3) $V[\mathbf{x}(k)]$ is continuous in $\mathbf{x}$,
(4) $V[\mathbf{x}(k)] \to \infty$ as $\|\mathbf{x}(k)\| \to \infty$.

Then the system (2.148) *is* uniformly asymptotically stable in-the-large.

This theorem is very similar to Theorem 2.1 except that here condition (4) has been added to guarantee global (that is, in-the-large) stability. This could have also been added to Theorem 2.1. For rigorous proof of Theorem 2.2 the reader is referred to the paper by Kalman and Bertram [52].

For discrete-time systems, as for continuous-time systems, the Liapunov function is usually sought in the form of a quadratic norm. For example, if we consider a linear system such as

$$\mathbf{x}(k + 1) = \mathbf{\Phi}\mathbf{x}(k), \tag{2.149}$$

where $\mathbf{\Phi}$ is a constant matrix, we choose as a trial function

$$V[\mathbf{x}(k)] = \mathbf{x}'(k)\mathbf{Q}\mathbf{x}(k), \tag{2.150}$$

where $\mathbf{Q}$ is a positive-definite symmetric matrix. Then conditions 1, 3, and 4 of Theorem 2.2 are immediately satisfied. To satisfy condition 2, we note that

$$\Delta V[\mathbf{x}(k)] = \mathbf{x}'(k + 1)\mathbf{Q}\mathbf{x}(k + 1) - \mathbf{x}'(k)\mathbf{Q}\mathbf{x}(k) = \mathbf{x}'(k)[\mathbf{\Phi}'\mathbf{Q}\mathbf{\Phi} - \mathbf{Q}]\mathbf{x}(k), \tag{2.151}$$

and in order for the system to be uniformly asympotically stable in-the-large, the matrix $\boldsymbol{C}$, where

$$\boldsymbol{C} = -[\boldsymbol{\Phi}'\boldsymbol{Q}\boldsymbol{\Phi} - \boldsymbol{Q}], \tag{2.152}$$

must be positive-definite.

We should mention that Liapunov's second method also extends to nonautonomous systems. For such systems the scalar function V will be a function of both $\boldsymbol{x}$ and t. It will be necessary to place certain restrictions on such a function in order that $V(\boldsymbol{x}, t)$ would characterize the actual behavior of the trajectories. This is done by requiring

(1) $V(\boldsymbol{x}, t)$ to be positive-definite,
(2) an upper bound on the time variation of $V(\boldsymbol{x}, t)$,
(3) $\dot{V}(\boldsymbol{x}, t) = \partial V/\partial t + (\nabla V)'\boldsymbol{f}(\boldsymbol{x}, t)$ to be negative-definite,
(4) $V(\boldsymbol{x}, t) \to \infty$ as $\|\boldsymbol{x}\| \to \infty$ for all $t \geq t_0$.

These conditions result in the following theorem.

▶ THEOREM 2.3. *Consider the system*

$$\dot{\boldsymbol{x}} = \boldsymbol{f}(\boldsymbol{x}, t),$$

with

$$\boldsymbol{f}(\boldsymbol{0}, t) \equiv \boldsymbol{0} \qquad \text{for} \qquad t \geq t_0,$$

for which we construct a scalar function

$$V = V(\boldsymbol{x}, t)$$

such that $V(\boldsymbol{0}, t) = 0$ *and*

(1) $0 < \alpha(\|\boldsymbol{x}\|) \leq V(\boldsymbol{x}, t)$,
(2) $\dot{V}(\boldsymbol{x}, t) \leq \gamma(\|\boldsymbol{x}\|) < 0$,
(3) $V(\boldsymbol{x}, t) \leq \beta(\|\boldsymbol{x}\|)$,
(4) $\alpha(\|\boldsymbol{x}\|) \to \infty$ as $\|\boldsymbol{x}\| \to \infty$,

where α, β, *and* γ *are some functions of the norm* $\|\boldsymbol{x}\|$. *Then the equilibrium solution* $\boldsymbol{x} = \boldsymbol{0}$ *is uniformly asymptotically stable in the large.*

We shall not detail the proof of this theorem, which is given by Kalman and Bertram [52].

The above theorems and discussions provide a sufficient background for Chapters 5 and 6, where Liapunov's second method is used in greater detail to investigate stability of systems and to synthesize appropriate control.

2.6. Gradient methods and constrained optima

Because of the chemical engineers' involvement in nonlinear system equations of large dimensions, it shall frequently turn out that the dynamic programming or maximum principle algorithms must be modified to obtain an optimal trajectory. As we shall see in Chapter 4, the revised algorithms will frequently involve some form of the steps below:

(1) Assume a sequence of the control variables.

(2) With these assumed control variables, calculate the sequence of state variables using the system equation and the initial conditions on the state.

(3) These two sequences will yield some value of the performance index which is not optimal, except for special cases.

(4) Use some procedure to define a new and improved set of control variables in the sense that steps (2) and (3) lead to an improved value of the performance index.

(5) Continue this iteration until, assuming convergence occurs, no further improvement in the performance index occurs.

In its simplest conceptual form, the problem may be stated as relating the performance index in some way to the control variables such that

$$I^\circ(\boldsymbol{u}) = \min I[\boldsymbol{u}(0), \boldsymbol{u}(1), \ldots, \boldsymbol{u}(P-1)], \tag{2.153}$$

or, alternatively, for a single stage at a time

$$I^\circ[\boldsymbol{u}(k)] = \min I[\boldsymbol{u}(k)]. \tag{2.154}$$

The terminology in Equations (2.153) and (2.154) merely indicates that some function of the control variables is to be minimized. In this sense we have all the ingredients for what might be called a steady-state optimization. Since the literature in this area is most extensive [9, 73, 77], we shall only give a brief presentation here. It should, however, be pointed out at this time that we have chosen the use of the control variables in Equations (2.153) and (2.154) for convenience. Some other set of variables may actually be better for iteration. As illustration, in the discussion of the maximum principle it was indicated that a mapping of $\boldsymbol{x}(0)$ into $\boldsymbol{z}(0)$ would generate the desired optimal control; once the $\boldsymbol{z}(0)$ are known the problem is solved. In this case it might be better to make the $\boldsymbol{z}(0)$ the variables in the iteration rather than the $\boldsymbol{u}(k)$. Chapters 3 and 4 will illustrate this point further.

The fundamental idea implicit in the optimization procedure is the use of the gradient vector which we have previously defined as

$$\nabla_{\boldsymbol{u}} I = \frac{\partial}{\partial \boldsymbol{u}} I = \begin{bmatrix} \partial I/\partial u_1 \\ \vdots \\ \partial I/\partial u_r \end{bmatrix} \tag{2.155}$$

or as

$$\nabla_{\boldsymbol{u}(k)} I = \frac{\partial}{\partial \boldsymbol{u}(k)} I = \begin{bmatrix} \partial I/\partial \boldsymbol{u}(0) \\ \vdots \\ \partial I/\partial \boldsymbol{u}(P-1) \end{bmatrix}, \tag{2.156}$$

depending on the situation involved. Let us now look into the use of this gradient vector for the unconstrained and then the constrained case, that is, for the case where $\boldsymbol{u}(t)$ may take on any values and then for the case where $\boldsymbol{u}(t)$ must meet a condition such as an amplitude constraint.

Consider that we have a function $f(x)$ which is a function of a scalar quantity x in some interval x_1 to x_2 and possesses a continuous first derivative with respect to x. If $f(x)$ has an extremum in this interval, then it follows that the extremum point must satisfy $\partial f/\partial x = 0$. However, this point could be a maximum or a minimum; when there are a multiplicity of maxima or minima, we refer to the largest or smallest, depending on whether maximum or minimum is involved, as the *global*, the *absolute*, or the *true* extremum, and all others as *relative* extrema. Furthermore, it is possible that either a global or relative extremum may occur on the boundary of our interval; in this case $\partial f/\partial x$ does not necessarily equal zero.

Consider now that we have a function, $f(x_1, x_2, \ldots, x_n) = f(\boldsymbol{x})$, of n variables. In the same manner, the necessary and sufficient conditions for a relative extremum at the point $\boldsymbol{x} = \boldsymbol{x}^*$, that is, $x_1 = x_1^*$, $x_2 = x_2^*, \ldots, x_n = x_n^*$, are that

$$\frac{\partial f}{\partial \boldsymbol{x}} = \boldsymbol{0} \qquad \text{at} \qquad \boldsymbol{x} = \boldsymbol{x}^*$$

or

$$\left.\frac{\partial f}{\partial x_i}\right|_{x_i = x_i^*} = 0 \qquad (i = 1, 2, \ldots, n). \tag{2.157}$$

Furthermore, if the positive-definite form Q has the property

$$Q = \sum_{i=1}^{n} \sum_{j=1}^{n} \frac{\partial^2 f}{\partial x_i\, \partial x_j} x_i x_j > 0 \tag{2.158}$$

for all x_i, $x_j \neq 0$ evaluated at $\boldsymbol{x} = \boldsymbol{x}^*$, then f is a relative maximum. If $Q < 0$, then f is a relative minimum.

Now suppose that we have the function $f(\boldsymbol{x})$ which we wish to extremize subject to the equality constraints

$$g(\boldsymbol{x}) = 0, \qquad h(\boldsymbol{x}) = 0.$$

The classical procedure for handling this case is to use Lagrange multipliers to form a new function which is to be extremized without any constraints. Thus, we form the new function $I[\boldsymbol{x}, \lambda]$ such that

$$I[\boldsymbol{x}, \boldsymbol{\lambda}] = f(\boldsymbol{x}) + \boldsymbol{\lambda}'\boldsymbol{\psi}, \tag{2.159}$$

where

$$\boldsymbol{\lambda}' = [\lambda_1 \quad \lambda_2], \qquad \boldsymbol{\psi} = \begin{bmatrix} g(\boldsymbol{x}) \\ h(\boldsymbol{x}) \end{bmatrix}$$

and λ_1, λ_2 are as yet undetermined Lagrange multipliers. If we specify that

$$\left.\frac{\partial I}{\partial x_i}\right|_{x_i = x_i^*} = 0 \qquad (i = 1, 2, \ldots, n),$$

then we have n equations, and with the two additional equations for g and h, we have enough equations to solve for $\boldsymbol{x}$ and $\boldsymbol{\lambda}$.

As an illustration, consider the problem of determining the maximum and the minimum distance from the origin to the intersections of the ellipsoid

$$x_1^2 + \frac{x_2^2}{2} + \frac{x_3^2}{3} = 1$$

with the plane

$$x_1 + x_2 + x_3 = 0.$$

The problem is, then, to find the extremal values of f as defined by

$$f(\boldsymbol{x}) = x_1^2 + x_2^2 + x_3^2$$

subject to the two constraints

$$g(\boldsymbol{x}) = x_1^2 + \frac{x_2^2}{2} + \frac{x_3^2}{3} - 1 = 0, \qquad h(\boldsymbol{x}) = x_1 + x_2 + x_3 = 0.$$

We define the new function $I(\boldsymbol{x}, \boldsymbol{\lambda})$ to be

$$\begin{aligned} I(\boldsymbol{x}, \boldsymbol{\lambda}) &= f(\boldsymbol{x}) + \boldsymbol{\lambda}'\boldsymbol{\psi} \\ &= x_1^2 + x_2^2 + x_3^2 + \lambda_1\left(x_1^2 + \frac{x_2^2}{2} + \frac{x_3^2}{3} - 1\right) + \lambda_2(x_1 + x_2 + x_3). \end{aligned}$$

For an extremum of I,

$$\frac{\partial I}{\partial x_1} = 2x_1 + 2\lambda_1 x_1 + \lambda_2 = 0, \qquad \frac{\partial I}{\partial x_2} = 2x_2 + \lambda_1 x_2 + \lambda_2 = 0,$$

$$\frac{\partial I}{\partial x_3} = 2x_3 + \tfrac{2}{3}\lambda_1 x_3 + \lambda_2 = 0.$$

Immediately, one finds that $\lambda_1 = -f$ and

$$x_1 = -\frac{\lambda_2}{2 - 2f}, \qquad x_2 = -\frac{\lambda_2}{2 - f}, \qquad x_3 = -\frac{\lambda_2}{2 - \frac{2}{3}f}.$$

Now, again making use of the fact that

$$x_1 + x_2 + x_3 = 0,$$

we find that

$$\frac{1}{2 - 2f} + \frac{1}{2 - f} + \frac{3}{6 - 2f} = 0,$$

which can be solved to give

$$f = \tfrac{1}{6}(11 \pm \sqrt{13}).$$

Therefore, the maximum distance is $\sqrt{(11 + \sqrt{13})/6}$ and the minimum distance is $\sqrt{(11 - \sqrt{31})/6}$.

Let us pursue this problem further in a number of different ways. Consider first that we have a function $f(\boldsymbol{x} + \lambda \boldsymbol{y})$, where $\boldsymbol{x}$ and $\boldsymbol{y}$ are n-dimensional vectors and λ is a parameter. If we are at a point $\boldsymbol{x}^*$ and we wish to move parallel to the vector $\boldsymbol{y}$ for a distance λ such that $f(\boldsymbol{x})$ is minimized, we must decide in which direction $\boldsymbol{y}$ points and what size λ to use. We expand $f(\boldsymbol{x}^* + \lambda \boldsymbol{y})$ in the neighborhood of $\boldsymbol{x}^*$ in a Taylor series, retaining second-order terms

$$f(\boldsymbol{x}^* + \lambda \boldsymbol{y}) = f(\boldsymbol{x}^*(+ \lambda \sum_{i=1}^{n} \frac{\partial f_i}{\partial x_i} y_i \bigg|_{\boldsymbol{x}=\boldsymbol{x}^*} + \frac{\lambda^2}{2} \sum_{i,j=1}^{n} \frac{\partial^2 f}{\partial x_i\, \partial x_j} y_i y_j \bigg|_{\boldsymbol{x}=\boldsymbol{x}^*}. \tag{2.160}$$

But it is obvious that after we take the step, we require that

$$f(\boldsymbol{x}^* + \lambda \boldsymbol{y}) - f(\boldsymbol{x}^*) \leq 0$$

if we are to approach a smaller value of $f(\boldsymbol{x})$. It thus follows that we desire the last two terms of Equation (2.160) to be as large negative numbers as possible. By using the Schwarz inequality [9] we see that

$$\left| \sum_{i=1}^{n} \frac{\partial f}{\partial x_i} y_i \right| \leq \left[\sum_{i=1}^{n} \left(\frac{\partial f}{\partial x_i} \right)^2 \right]^{1/2} \left(\sum_{i=1}^{n} y_i^2 \right)^{1/2} \tag{2.161}$$

and if we choose $y_i = \partial f / \partial x_i$, we get the equality in Equation (2.161). But this ensures the largest absolute value for the left-hand side. Thus the selection

$$y = -\frac{\partial f}{\partial \boldsymbol{x}} \bigg|_{\boldsymbol{x}=\boldsymbol{x}^*} = -\nabla_{\boldsymbol{x}^*} f$$

will yield the largest negative absolute value for the term in Equation (2.160) which multiplies λ (the first-order term).

To determine the value of λ which minimizes $f(\boldsymbol{x}^* + \lambda \boldsymbol{y})$, we differentiate the right-hand side of Equation (2.160) (a quadratic in λ) and set the result equal to zero. This yields

$$\lambda = \sum_{i=1}^{n} \left(\frac{\partial f}{\partial x_i} \right)^2 \Bigg/ \sum_{i,j=1}^{n} \left[\left(\frac{\partial^2 f}{\partial x_i x_j} \right) \left(\frac{\partial f}{\partial x_i} \right) \left(\frac{\partial f}{\partial x_j} \right) \right]. \tag{2.162}$$

In this way the parallel vector, $\boldsymbol{y} = -\nabla_{\boldsymbol{x}^*} f$, is known and also we have an estimate, λ, on how far along this vector we should step.

A second and slightly different problem evolves by assuming that we have an open region in the variable $\boldsymbol{x}$ of $f(\boldsymbol{x})$. Starting at $\boldsymbol{x}^*$ and $f(\boldsymbol{x}^*)$, we ask how to take a step $\delta \boldsymbol{x} = \boldsymbol{x} - \boldsymbol{x}^*$ such that the resulting $\delta f = f(\boldsymbol{x}) - f(\boldsymbol{x}^*)$ is extremized.

Let us put a hypersphere of radius r around $\boldsymbol{x}^*$ and assume that the extreme value of $f(\boldsymbol{x})$ lies on the surface of this hypersphere. In multidimensional space

$$\sum_{i=1}^{n} \delta x_i^2 = r^2, \tag{2.163}$$

and a Taylor-series expansion to first-order terms yields for r small but positive

$$\delta f = f(\boldsymbol{x}) - f(\boldsymbol{x}^*) = \sum_{i=1}^{n} \frac{\partial f}{\partial x_i} \delta x_i . \tag{2.164}$$

Now we desire to extremize δf in Equation (2.164) subject to the constraint that we end up on the hypersphere. We define the new unconstrained function δQ such that

$$\delta Q = \sum_{i=1}^{n} \frac{\partial f}{\partial x_i} \delta x_i + \lambda\left(r^2 - \sum_{i=1}^{n} \delta x_i^2\right) \tag{2.165}$$

and

$$\frac{\partial(\delta Q)}{\partial \delta x_i} = 0 = \frac{\partial f}{\partial x_i} - 2\lambda \delta x_i$$

or

$$\delta x_i = \frac{1}{2\lambda}\frac{\partial f}{\partial x_i}, \qquad \delta x_i^2 = \left(\frac{1}{2\lambda}\frac{\partial f}{\partial x_i}\right)^2. \tag{2.166}$$

Substitution of this equation into (2.163) yields

$$\sum_{i=1}^{n} \left(\frac{1}{2\lambda}\frac{\partial f}{\partial x_i}\right)^2 = r^2. \tag{2.167}$$

But this determines the Lagrange multiplier λ as

$$\lambda = \pm \frac{1}{2r}\left[\sum_{1}^{n}\left(\frac{\partial f}{\partial x_i}\right)^2\right]^{1/2},$$

and substituting into Equation (2.166) while keeping the plus sign, we obtain

$$\delta x_i = r\left[\sum_{i=1}^{n}\left(\frac{\partial f}{\partial x_i}\right)^2\right]^{-1/2} \frac{\partial f}{\partial x_i} = r\left[\sum_{i=1}^{n}\left(\frac{\partial f}{\partial x_i}\right)^2\right]^{-1/2} (\nabla_{\boldsymbol{x}} f)_i . \tag{2.168}$$

But Equation (2.168) defines the change in direction in x_i to make in order to extremize $f(\boldsymbol{x})$; the important item is that the equation has the form

$$\delta \boldsymbol{x} = r[\quad] \nabla_{\boldsymbol{x}} f. \tag{2.169}$$

In other words, we use the gradient vector of f with respect to $\boldsymbol{x}$ to determine the direction in which to change $\boldsymbol{x}$. If we put a minus sign in front of the right-hand side of Equation (2.169), the result is called steepest descent in the sense that f decreases; if the sign is left-positive, the result is termed steepest ascent.

In both of the problems above, the end result leads to a computer algorithm of stepping from one point to the next point until the extremum is reached. In our first problem, it follows that

$$\mathbf{x}^{(P+1)} = \mathbf{x}^{(P)} - \lambda^{(P)}\mathbf{y}^{(P)}, \tag{2.170}$$

where

$$\mathbf{y}^{(P)} = \nabla_{\mathbf{x}} f \big|_{\mathbf{x}=\mathbf{x}^{(P)}}.$$

This is frequently referred to as Cauchy's method of steepest descent. Equation (2.169) can, of course, be converted directly into the form of Equation (2.170).

2.7. Linear and nonlinear programming

One of the techniques which we shall call on in a later chapter to help us solve a special class of control problems is *linear programming*. We merely intend to point out here the fundamental notions and concepts associated with this method and then briefly indicate the direction for solving a problem based on these concepts. In other words, we merely wish to outline the specifications of a problem which makes it suitable for solution by linear programming. We shall leave untouched the actual solution mechanics since there exist a wide variety of computer algorithms [8, 9, 16, 78] for this purpose. Once this is accomplished, we shall extend the concepts to the *nonlinear programming* problem.

The basic features of a linear programming problem can be ascertained quite simply by the following trivial problem:

(1) Two foods x_1 and x_2 are to be used in a daily diet which requires a minimum of b_1 cal and b_2 gm of protein.

(2) Food x_1 costs c_1 cents per pound and contains a_{11} cal and a_{21} gm of protein per pound. Food x_2 costs c_2 cents per pound and contains a_{12} cal and a_{22} gm protein.

(3) What is the optimal choice of the amounts of x_1 and x_2 which meets the minimum diet requirements and minimizes the cost?

Mathematically, we may state this problem as follows. (See Figure 2.14.)

Given

$$C = \sum_{i=1}^{2} c_i x_i, \tag{2.171}$$

subject to

$$a_{11}x_1 + a_{12}x_2 \geq b_1, \qquad a_{21}x_1 + a_{22}x_2 \geq b_2, \tag{2.172}$$

and

$$x_1 \geq 0, \qquad x_2 \geq 0, \tag{2.173}$$

find

$$C^\circ = \min C, \tag{2.174}$$

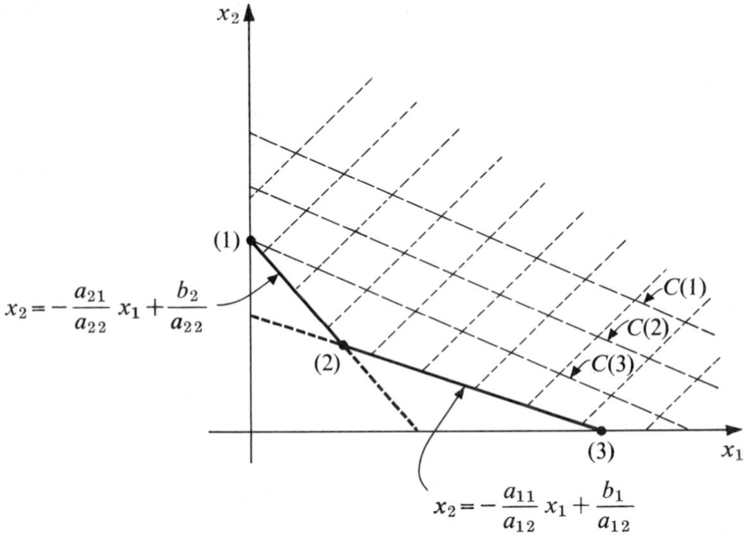

FIGURE 2.14. Two-dimensional linear programming problem in terms of cost

where C is the total cost of the diet; the parameters c_1, c_2, $a_{11}, \ldots, a_{22}$, b_1, and b_2 are known, and x_1 and x_2 are to be determined such that Equation (2.174) holds. Alternatively, we may write (2.171) through (2.174) as follows:

Given

$$C = \mathbf{c}'\mathbf{x}, \tag{2.175}$$

subject to

$$\mathbf{Ax} \geq \mathbf{b} \tag{2.176}$$

and

$$\mathbf{x} \geq \mathbf{0}, \tag{2.177}$$

find

$$C^\circ = \min C, \tag{2.178}$$

with the obvious notation.

The basic essentials of the solution of this problem can be ascertained from Figure 2.14, where we plot Equation (2.172) in the form of equalities rather than inequalities. Note that from Equation (2.173), we only need to consider the first quadrant of an x_2 versus x_1 plot since x_2 and x_1 must both be positive. It is obvious that since we have used equalities in Equation (2.172) for our plot rather than the inequalities, the only solutions must lie on or above the solid portions of the two intersecting lines (the shaded area). Now we proceed to lay down on this diagram a series of straight lines corresponding to different sets of x_2 and x_1 in Equation (2.171); each line forms a total cost $C(1)$, $C(2)$, ... It is apparent that the solution of the problem occurs with that smallest $C(j)$ (from among the parallel cost lines) which intersects the solid lines and remains within the shaded area. This will occur at one of the vertices marked (1), (2), or (3). Alternatively, we see that the solution lies at one of the vertices of a convex polygon formed by the inequality constraint Equations (2.172) and (2.173).

This problem can also be cast into a different form more suitable for illustrating certain features of the solution (this is called the *dual problem*). In this new form we have the following:

Given

$$P = \sum_{i=1}^{2} p_i y_i, \tag{2.179}$$

subject to

$$d_{11}y_1 + d_{12}y_2 \le f_1, \qquad d_{21}y_1 + d_{22}y_2 \le f_2 \tag{2.180}$$

and

$$y_1 \ge 0, \qquad y_2 \ge 0, \tag{2.181}$$

find

$$P^\circ = \max P; \tag{2.182}$$

or given

$$P = \mathbf{p}'\mathbf{y}, \tag{2.183}$$

subject to

$$\mathbf{D}\mathbf{y} \le \mathbf{f} \tag{2.184}$$

and

$$\mathbf{y} \ge \mathbf{0}, \tag{2.185}$$

find

$$P^\circ = \max P. \tag{2.186}$$

Proceeding as before, we construct Figure 2.15. This shows that the resulting optimal values of y_1 and y_2 must lie at one of the vertices marked (1), (2), or (3) associated with the closed, convex shaded area.

Three points of the solution are apparent from these two examples.

(1) The optimum values of x_1 and x_2 (or of y_1 and y_2) are positive.

(2) There is a unique solution to the problem.

(3) The optimal cost or profit is situated at one of the corners of the closed convex polygon formed by the inequality constraints.

Subject to certain minor restrictions, these three conditions are true for all linear programming solutions.

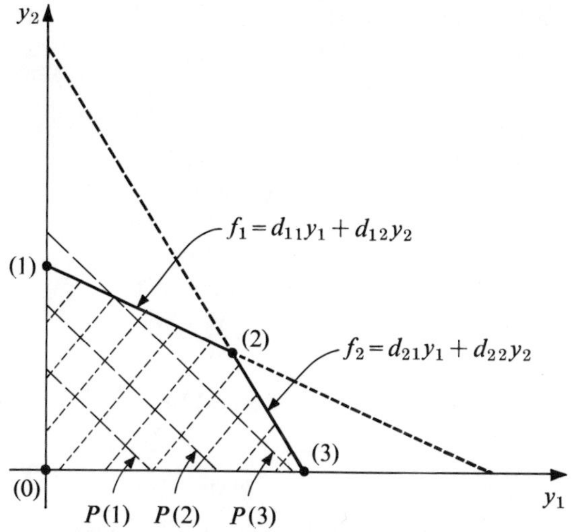

FIGURE 2.15. Two-dimensional linear programming problem in terms of profit

It is now possible to define the general linear programming problem involving n variables $y_1, y_2, \ldots, y_n$ and then to show certain features of this general problem. Thus we have the following:

Given

$$P = \boldsymbol{p}'\boldsymbol{y}, \tag{2.187}$$

subject to

$$\boldsymbol{D}\boldsymbol{y} \leq \boldsymbol{f} \tag{2.188}$$

and

$$\boldsymbol{y} \geq \boldsymbol{0}, \tag{2.189}$$

find

$$P^\circ = \max P, \tag{2.190}$$

where

$$\boldsymbol{p} = \begin{bmatrix} p_1 \\ p_2 \\ \vdots \\ p_n \end{bmatrix}, \quad \boldsymbol{y} = \begin{bmatrix} y_1 \\ y_2 \\ \vdots \\ y_n \end{bmatrix}, \quad \boldsymbol{D} = \begin{bmatrix} d_{11} & \cdots & d_{1n} \\ \vdots & & \vdots \\ d_{m1} & \cdots & d_{mn} \end{bmatrix}, \quad \boldsymbol{f} = \begin{bmatrix} f_1 \\ f_2 \\ \vdots \\ f_m \end{bmatrix}.$$

Note that we have m linear constraints, Equations (2.188). Since simultaneous

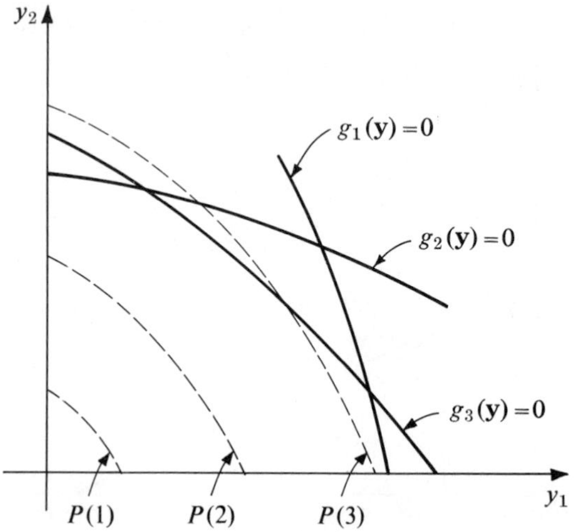

FIGURE 2.16. Two-dimensional nonlinear programming problem

equations with equalities rather than inequalities seem more natural to handle, we introduce the *slack variables* such that Equation (2.188) becomes

$$\boldsymbol{D}\boldsymbol{y} + \boldsymbol{q} = \boldsymbol{f}, \tag{2.191}$$

where

$$\boldsymbol{q} = [q_1 \ldots q_m]' \qquad \text{and} \qquad q_i \geq 0 \qquad (\text{for } i = 1, 2, \ldots, m), \tag{2.192}$$

such that we have the following.

Given

$$P = \mathbf{p}'\boldsymbol{y}, \tag{2.193}$$

subject to

$$\boldsymbol{D}\boldsymbol{y} + \boldsymbol{q} = \boldsymbol{f} \tag{2.194}$$

and

$$\boldsymbol{y} \geq \mathbf{0}, \qquad \boldsymbol{q} \geq \mathbf{0}, \tag{2.195}$$

find

$$P^{\circ} = \max P. \tag{2.196}$$

Those values of $\boldsymbol{y}$ which satisfy Equations (2.194) and (2.195) are called feasible solutions and if, in addition, they also satisfy Equations (2.193) and (2.196) these values are called optimum feasible solutions.

In this form we are able to turn to the *simplex method*, which is the basis for most of the linear programming computer algorithms. The algorithm starts with an initial guess which is a feasible solution and then proceeds to move from vertex to vertex of the constrained convex set until that vertex which corresponds to the optimum feasible solution is found. As an initial guess one may frequently start with all the slack variables chosen equal to $f_1, \ldots, f_m$; this corresponds in Figure 2.15 to an initial feasible solution at the origin with $P = 0$. Once the initial point is known and it is seen from Equation (2.193) that $\nabla_y P = \text{const}$, we merely need to follow along this constant-gradient vector to the vertex corresponding to the optimal feasible solution. The simplex algorithm is designed to do just this and, except for a special degenerate case, is guaranteed to find the unique solution in a finite number of iteration steps.

It is, of course, readily apparent that the basis of the procedure resides heavily on the linear form of all the equations. If the profit equation (the performance index) and/or the constraint equations are nonlinear, a completely revised procedure must be used. Figure 2.16 shows a possible two-dimensional nonlinear problem with the convex feasible region now bounded by the intersections and boundaries of the curves

$$g_1(y) \le 0, \qquad g_2(y) \le 0, \qquad g_3(y) \le 0,$$

and the profit equation is curved. We immediately realize that $\nabla_y P$ need not be constant, and intuitively we might guess that the optimal solution need not occur at a vertex. Thus, it is now necessary to turn to different procedures to solve this nonlinear programming problem. In fact, there does not exist any particular best procedure, but instead there are a number of procedures which are used in the literature. These may involve a linearization followed by the use of the simplex method (Graves and Wolfe [8]), a gradient-projection method (Rosen [67]) or the method of feasible directions (Zoutendijk [16]) as typical examples from among the many available. The main idea here is that in the nonlinear case there is no one best method for all problems which guarantees reaching the optimal solution. For details of some of these approaches, the interested reader is referred to the work of Wolfe [78] and Hadley [9].

2.8. Numerical examples

In this section, we shall analyze three different problems to serve as illustrations for some of the material developed in this chapter. The main emphasis will be on setting up the problems rather than on developing detailed numerical solutions.

In discussing the use of dynamic programming, we have constantly referred to the discretization of the state variables as a major feature of solving for the optimal trajectory. There do exist, however, many problems in which it is not necessary to talk about such a break-up in the "states." Instead, there are only single values of the states. As an illustration, we here consider a type of problem called the *scheduling problem*, detailed by Held and Karp [42].

EXAMPLE 2.1 ▪ We consider a set of P jobs, called $J_1, J_2, \ldots, J_P$, to be executed on a single facility; for example, the construction of an automobile is made up of a set of integral individual jobs. Associated with each job J_n is a time of execution τ_n and a cost function $c_n(t)$ giving the cost associated with completing the job at time t. For simplicity, we assume that only one job is executed at a time, that there is no interruption in a job once it is started, and that the facility is constantly in use.

Given a certain ordering of the execution of the jobs (a *schedule*), the time t_n at which each J_n is completed is automatically fixed. Associated with any schedule S is the total cost function (or performance index)

$$I(S) = \sum_{k=1}^{P} c_k(t_k), \tag{2.197}$$

and we ask to find the order of execution of jobs such that we minimize $I(S)$. It is important to point out that while each job requires a certain fixed period of time, τ_n, to finish, the cost function $c_n(t)$ is a function of the over-all time. Furthermore, there are no restrictions on the form of $c_n(t)$.

An obvious approach to trying to solve this problem is to try all possible schedules and find that one which yields the minimum cost and thus a maximum profit. However, if $P = 10$ jobs, then this means that 10! different arrangements or schedules must be considered, and even in terms of digital computation this is a fantastic number of schedules to consider. Thus, we must turn to a different approach, and in particular we shall here look into the use of dynamic programming to solve the problem.

First, we note that any schedule may be represented by an ordering of integers from 1 to P, $i_1, i_2, \ldots, i_p$ indicating that the jobs are to be executed in the order $J_{i_1}, J_{i_2}, \ldots, J_{i_P}$. The termination time t_{i_k} of J_{i_k} is $\sum_{i=1}^{k} \tau_{i_j}$ and the total cost is

$$\sum_{k=1}^{P} c_{i_k}(t_{i_k}). \tag{2.198}$$

Let $S = \{k_1, k_2, \ldots, k_{P(k)}\}$ be a subset of the ordering $\{1, 2, \ldots, P\}$, where $k_{P(S)}$ indicates that this refers to the subset S. Now denote

$$t_S = \sum_{j \varepsilon S} \tau_j$$

and the minimum cost $I^\circ(S)$ associated with executing the jobs $J_{k_1}, J_{k_2}, \ldots, J_{k_{P(S)}}$ in any order whatever in $[0, t_S]$. For n as one of the jobs in S we further let $S - n$ denote the set obtained by deleting n from S. On this basis, we may write the following recurrence relations:

$$I(\{n\}) = c_n(\tau_n) \qquad \text{for any } n,\ P(S) = 1\ , \tag{2.199}$$

$$I(S) = \min\,\{I(S - n) + c_n(t_S)\} \qquad [P(S) > 1]. \tag{2.200}$$

Equations (2.199) and (2.200) represent respectively the starting equation in which any job is executed last and then the build-up recurrence relation in dynamic programming as successive jobs are included in the set of jobs.

To illustrate how this recurrence relationship may be used in a simple fashion, let us consider that we have four total jobs J_1, J_2, J_3, and J_4 with associated τ_n and $c_n(t)$. Now we form Table 2.1, in which the set S consists of only one job.

TABLE 2.1

Job	Cost
J_1	$c_1(\tau_1)$
J_2	$c_2(\tau_2)$
J_3	$c_3(\tau_3)$
J_4	$c_4(\tau_4)$

$S = 1$

TABLE 2.2

Jobs	Cost
J_2J_1	$c_2(\tau_2) + c_1(\tau_1 + \tau_2)$
J_1J_3	.
J_1J_4	.
J_3J_2	.
J_2J_4	
J_4J_3	$c_4(\tau_4) + c_3(\tau_4 + \tau_3)$

$S = 2$

This corresponds to the use of Equation (2.199). Next, we consider that S consists of two jobs. The possible sets are $\{J_1J_2, J_1J_3, J_1J_4, J_2J_3, J_2J_4,$ and $J_3J_4\}$. At this point, the question to be answered is, "Should the order of the set $\{J_1J_2\}$ be J_1 and then J_2, or should it be J_2 and then J_1?" The minimum cost for these two job permutations can be ascertained by first calculating the cost for the ordering J_1J_2 and then J_2J_1; in each case we may use Table 2.1 to tell us the cost of, say, J_1 in the ordering J_1J_2 and of J_2 in the ordering J_2J_1. All that is needed beyond the information in Table 2.1 is the cost of adding job J_2 to J_1 and then J_1 to J_2. In other words, we may find the best ordering of the set $\{J_1J_2\}$ by using Table 2.1 and adding the cost of the second job. On this basis, we may proceed for all the possible sets and form Table 2.2.

Table 2.2 now contains all the information for the best ordering of any two of the four jobs.

Now we proceed on to $S = 3$ for the ordering of any three jobs. The possible sets are $\{J_1J_2J_3, J_1J_2J_4, J_1J_3J_4,$ and $J_2J_3J_4\}$. The question now to be answered is whether the order $J_1J_2J_3$ is better than $J_1J_3J_2$ or $J_2J_1J_3$ or any other possible arrangement of these three jobs. But using Table 2.2 we see that we can find which ordering is best by the following strategy.

(1) If J_3 is the last job, then in Table 2.2 we see that the best ordering of J_1 and J_2 is J_2 and then J_1. To calculate the cost of the three jobs, we merely need to calculate the cost of J_3 last plus $c_2(\tau_2) + c_1(\tau_1 + \tau_2)$.

(2) If J_2 is the last job, then in Table 2.2 we see that the best ordering of J_1 and J_3 is J_1 and then J_3. To calculate the cost of the three jobs, we merely need to calculate the cost of J_2 last plus $c_1(\tau_1) + c_3(\tau_1 + \tau_3)$.

(3) If J_1 is the last job, then in Table 2.2 we see that the best ordering of J_2 and J_3 is J_3 and then J_2. To calculate the cost of the three jobs, we merely need to calculate the cost of J_1 last plus $c_3(\tau_3) + c_2(\tau_2 + \tau_3)$.

(4) We now compare the costs in (1), (2), and (3) and find the ordering which is the best. In the same manner, we find the best ordering for any set of three jobs and construct Table 2.3.

Now we proceed to $S = 4$ or the ordering of any four jobs. There exists only one set of four jobs, and we may use Table 2.3 to tell us whether J_1, J_2, J_3, or J_4 should be the last job. In this way we find the last order of the four jobs and the cost associated with this best order.

TABLE 2.3

Jobs	Costs	
$J_3J_2J_1$	$c_3(\tau_3)+c_2(\tau_3+\tau_2)+c_1(\tau_3+\tau_2+\tau_1)$	
$J_2J_1J_4$	$\cdot$	
$J_1J_3J_4$	$\cdot$	$S=3$
	$\cdot$	
$J_3J_2J_4$	$c_3(\tau_3)+c_2(\tau_3+\tau_2)+c_4(\tau_3+\tau_2+\tau_4)$	

We can see in this example how the idea of dynamic programming is used to add one job at each stage in the calculation to those jobs already optimally calculated. The only computational problem is the usual one of storage corresponding to holding Tables 2.1, 2.2, 2.3, . . . in main computer memory. In the case of four jobs this is not a problem, but for 15 jobs at least 2^{15} storage spaces must be used. This follows from the fact that at least $2^S - 1$ storage spaces are involved; for $S = 4$, this is 15 (note that if we add up the jobs of Tables 2.1, 2.2, and 2.3 and add 1 more, we get 15) whereas for $S = 15$ this is 32,767. Thus, for $S > 15$ we run into the "curse of dimensionality," but in a different guise from that previously mentioned. Some approximation technique must now be resorted to but we shall not discuss this point here.

EXAMPLE 2.2 ▪ In this example we shall analyze the optimal behavior of the three-stage extraction unit detailed in Chapter 1. Instead of the nonlinear equilibrium relationship shown in Chapter 1, we shall here use a linear equilibrium of $y(k) = \alpha x(k)$ since we merely wish to show how the problem may be analyzed using dynamic programming and the maximum principle, and we are not here concerned with any detailed numerical computations. To recapitulate, we have the system equation (1.145) and the profit equation (1.149) in the form

$$x(k+1) = x(k) - v(k+1)y(k+1) \qquad (k = 0, 1, 2), \tag{2.201}$$

$$p(k+1) = p(k) + v(k+1)[y(k+1) - \lambda], \tag{2.202}$$

with the initial conditions

$$x(0) \text{ prescribed}, \qquad p(0) = 0, \tag{2.203}$$

where we wish to select $v(1)$, $v(2)$, and $v(3)$ so as to maximize $p(3)$. In these equations, $x(k)$ and $y(k)$ are the raffinate and extract concentrations, respectively; $v(k)$ is a normalized feed rate; and $p(k)$ is the profit variable. We note at this point that Equations (2.201) and (2.202) are in a form equivalent to that used in this chapter but with the index changed from that used in Chapter 1. The equilibrium between $x(k)$ and $y(k)$ is given by

$$y(k) = \alpha x(k) \qquad (\alpha = \text{const}). \tag{2.204}$$

To solve this problem by using dynamic programming, we first define

$$I^\circ[x(0), R] = \text{maximum profit or recovery from } R \text{ stages with a feed } x(0)$$
$$= \max_{v(1), \ldots, v(R)} \{p(R-1) + v(R)[y(R) - \lambda]\} \tag{2.205}$$

and note immediately that for $R = 0$ and $R = 1$ respectively,

$$I^\circ[x(0), 0] = 0$$

and

$$I^\circ[x(0), 1] = \max_{v(1)} \{v(1)[y(1) - \lambda]\}, \tag{2.206}$$

since $p(0) = 0$.

Equation (2.206) may be cast into a simpler form by using Equations (2.201) and (2.204). Thus,

$$x(1) = x(0) - v(1)\alpha x(1)$$

or

$$x(1) = \frac{x(0)}{1 + \alpha v(1)}$$

and

$$y(1) = \frac{\alpha x(0)}{1 + \alpha v(1)},$$

which when substituted into Equation (2.206) gives

$$I^\circ[x(0), 1] = \max_{v(1)} \left\{ v(1) \left[\frac{\alpha x(0)}{1 + \alpha v(1)} - \lambda \right] \right\}. \tag{2.207}$$

The basic dynamic programming recurrence relationship for this problem follows immediately in the form

$$I^\circ[x(0), R+1] = \max_{v(1)} \left\{ v(1) \left[\frac{\alpha x(0)}{1 + \alpha v(1)} - \lambda \right] + I^\circ[x(1), R] \right\}. \tag{2.208}$$

This corresponds to making a choice of $v(1)$ in stage one and following this with the optimal policy for the remaining R stages with a feed to the R stages of

$x(1)$. As a result, the optimal choice of $v(1)$, $v(2)$, and $v(3)$ can be obtained by the initial use of Equation (2.206) or (2.207) plus the recurrent application of (2.208).

In the present case, because of the linear equilibrium relationship, the steps indicated above can be carried out explicitly. Thus, using Equation (2.207), we find $v(1)$ by differentiation with respect to $v(1)$ and set the result equal to zero:

$$\frac{\partial}{\partial v(1)}\left\{v(1)\left[\frac{\alpha x(0)}{1+\alpha v(1)} - \lambda\right]\right\} = \frac{\alpha x(0) - \lambda(1+\alpha v(1))^2}{[1+\alpha v(1)]^2} = 0.$$

Thus

$$\alpha x(0) - \lambda[1+\alpha v(1)]^2 = 0.$$

Solving for $v(1)$, the optimal allocation for a one-stage process,

$$v^\circ(1) = \left(\frac{x(0)}{\alpha\lambda}\right)^{1/2} - \frac{1}{\alpha}, \tag{2.209}$$

and then using (2.201) with $k = 0$, we see that this yields an output from the one-stage process of

$$x(1) = \frac{x(0)}{1+\alpha v^\circ(1)} = \left[\frac{\lambda}{\alpha}x(0)\right]^{1/2}. \tag{2.210}$$

Finally, using Equations (2.207) and (2.209), we see that the maximum profit from the one-stage process is

$$I^\circ[x(0), 1] = v^\circ(1)\left[\frac{\alpha x(0)}{1+\alpha v^\circ(1)} - \lambda\right] = x(0) - 2\left[\frac{\lambda}{\alpha}x(0)\right]^{1/2} + \frac{\lambda}{\alpha}. \tag{2.211}$$

We now have all the information necessary to describe the optimal behavior of a one-stage process with a feed, $x(0)$, to the one stage.

Next, we turn to the use of two stages, Equation (2.208) with $R = 1$,

$$I^\circ[x(0), 2] = \max_{v(1)}\left\{v(1)\left[\frac{\alpha x(0)}{1+\alpha v(1)} - \lambda\right] + I^\circ[x(1), 1]\right\}. \tag{2.212}$$

But since $I^\circ[x(1), 1]$ represents the optimal behavior of a one-stage process with feed, $x(1)$, to the one stage, we may use Equation (2.211) and then the definition for $x(1)$ to yield

$$I^\circ[x(1), 1] = x(1) - 2\left[\frac{\lambda}{\alpha}x(1)\right]^{1/2} + \frac{\lambda}{\alpha} = \frac{x(0)}{1+\alpha v(1)} - 2\left[\frac{\lambda}{\alpha}\frac{x(0)}{1+\alpha v(1)}\right]^{1/2} + \frac{\lambda}{\alpha}.$$

It thus follows that

$$I^\circ[x(0), 2] = \max_{v(1)}\left\{v(1)\left[\frac{\alpha x(0)}{1+\alpha v(1)} - \lambda\right] + \frac{x(0)}{1+\alpha v(1)} - 2\left[\frac{\lambda}{\alpha}\frac{x(0)}{1+\alpha v(1)}\right]^{1/2} + \frac{\lambda}{\alpha}\right\}.$$

Differentiating the terms in the large brackets with respect to $v(1)$ and setting the result equal to zero yields after some algebraic manipulation,

$$v^\circ(1) = \left(\frac{x(0)}{\alpha^2\lambda}\right)^{1/3} - \frac{1}{\alpha}. \tag{2.213}$$

This yields an output from stage one of

$$x(1) = \left(\frac{\lambda x(0)^2}{\alpha}\right)^{1/3} \tag{2.214}$$

and an over-all profit for the two stages of

$$I^\circ[x(0), 2] = x(0) - 3\left(\frac{\lambda^2 x(0)}{\alpha^2}\right)^{1/3} + \frac{2\lambda}{\alpha}. \tag{2.215}$$

To summarize to this point, given the feed to stage one of $x(0)$, Equation (2.213) yields the optimal allocation $v^\circ(1)$, and Equation (2.214) yields the corresponding output or feed to stage two; Equation (2.209) then yields the optimal allocation in stage two (all index numbers up by one), and Equations (2.210) and (2.215) yield the final output and profit from the two stages. At the same time,

$$v^\circ(1) = \left(\frac{x(0)}{\alpha^2\lambda}\right)^{1/3} - \frac{1}{\alpha},$$

and using

$$x(1) = \left[\frac{\lambda x^2(0)}{\alpha}\right]^{1/3} \quad \text{in} \quad v^\circ(2) = \left[\frac{x(1)}{\alpha\lambda}\right]^{1/2} - \frac{1}{\alpha},$$

it follows that

$$v^\circ(2) = \left[\left(\frac{x^2(0)}{\alpha}\right)^{1/3}\frac{1}{\alpha\lambda}\right]^{1/2} - \frac{1}{\alpha} = \left[\frac{x(0)}{\alpha^2\lambda}\right]^{1/3} - \frac{1}{\alpha} = v^\circ(1).$$

In other words, the optimal allocation for two stages is $v^\circ(1) = v^\circ(2)$. Now,

$$I^\circ[x(0), 3] = \max_{v(1)}\left\{v(1)\left[\frac{\alpha x(0)}{1 + \alpha v(1)} - \lambda\right] + I^\circ[x(1), 2]\right\},$$

substituting the known relations for $I^\circ[x(1), 2]$, differentiating with respect to $v(1)$ and solving for $v^\circ(1)$. Without showing the details, this yields

$$v^\circ(1) = \left[\frac{x(0)}{\alpha^3\lambda}\right]^{1/4} - \frac{1}{\alpha}, \tag{2.216}$$

$$x(1) = \left[\frac{\lambda x^3(0)}{\alpha}\right]^{1/4}, \tag{2.217}$$

and

$$I^\circ[x(0), 3] = x(0) - 4\left[\frac{\lambda^3 x(0)}{\alpha^3}\right]^{1/4} + \frac{3\lambda}{\alpha}, \tag{2.218}$$

with the result that

$$v^\circ(1) = v^\circ(2) = v^\circ(3). \tag{2.219}$$

Thus, we see that the optimal policy is to distribute the solvent in equal quantities in each stage. On this basis, we see that the value of λ is given by

$$\lambda = \frac{x(0)}{\alpha^3}\left(\frac{W_T}{3q} + \frac{1}{\alpha}\right)^{-1/4},$$

where W_T = the total quantity of solvent to be distributed, and q = solvent flowrate.

Let us now turn to the use of the maximum principle, and since we are discussing a discrete-staged system, it seems appropriate to use the discrete version of the maximum principle. The discussion and the subsequent manipulations may take many forms, as shown by Fan [7] and Archer [17], but we shall attempt to use the simplest. Thus we write Equations (2.201) and (2.202) in the form

$$x(k+1) = x(k) - v(k+1)y(k+1) = f_1[x(k), v(k+1), y(k+1)], \tag{2.220}$$

$$p(k+1) = p(k) + v(k+1)[y(k+1) - \lambda] = f_2[p(k), v(k+1), y(k+1)], \tag{2.221}$$

with conditions $x(0)$ given and $p(0) = 0$. Now we set up the Hamiltonian $H(k)$ as

$$H(k) = z_1(k)f_1[x(k-1), v(k), y(k)] + z_2(k)f_2[p(k-1), v(k), y(k)], \tag{2.222}$$

where $z_1(k)$ and $z_2(k)$ are the adjoint variables defined by

$$z_1(k) = \frac{\partial f_1[x(k), v(k+1), y(k+1)]}{\partial x(k)} z_1(k+1) + \frac{\partial f_2[p(k), v(k+1), y(k+1)]}{\partial x(k)} z_2(k+1), \tag{2.223}$$

$$z_2(k) = \frac{\partial f_1[x(k), v(k+1), y(k+1)]}{\partial p(k)} z_1(k+1) + \frac{\partial f_2[p(k), v(k+1), y(k+1)]}{\partial p(k)} z_2(k+1). \tag{2.224}$$

Since we desire to maximize $p(3)$, it follows that the boundary conditions on the adjoint variables are

$$z_1(3) = 0, \qquad z_2(3) = 1. \tag{2.225}$$

We immediately see a simplification of these equations, since

$$\frac{\partial f_1[x(k), v(k+1), y(k+1)]}{\partial p(k)} = 0, \qquad \frac{\partial f_2[p(k), v(k+1), y(k+1)]}{\partial p(k)} = 1,$$

and thus $z_2(k) = z_2(k+1)$.

But using $z_2(3) = 1$ from Equation (2.225), we see that

$$z_2(k) = z_2(k+1) = 1, \tag{2.226}$$

and from here on we shall always call $z_2(k) = 1$.

Inserting the explicit forms for f_1 and f_2 in the Hamiltonian equation and rearranging yield

$$H(k) = z_1(k)x(k-1) + p(k-1) + v(k)[y(k) - \lambda - y(k)z_1(k)].$$

Thus the Hamiltonian is linear in the control variable $v(k)$, and in the case of $v(k)$ constrained between limits, the optimal allocation would be bang-bang depending on the sign of $[y(k) - \lambda - y(k)z_1(k)]$. In the present case, we neglect any bounds on $v(k)$, or, if we have bounds, we assume the singular solution corresponding to

$$y(k) - \lambda - y(k)z_1(k) = 0$$

holds. This means that

$$y(k) = \frac{\lambda}{1 - z_1(k)} \tag{2.227}$$

represents a condition which the optimal allocation must satisfy.

The results obtained to this point are perfectly general in the sense that we have not used the linear equilibrium condition. Thus, at this point we let $y(k) = \alpha x(k)$ and convert Equations (2.220) and (2.221) to

$$x(k+1) = \frac{x(k)}{1 + \alpha v(k+1)}, \tag{2.228}$$

$$\begin{aligned} p(k+1) &= p(k) + \alpha v(k+1)x(k+1) - \lambda v(k+1) \\ &= p(k) + x(k) - x(k+1) - \lambda v(k+1), \end{aligned} \tag{2.229}$$

with conditions $x(0)$ given and $p(0) = 0$. Now we set up the Hamiltonian as

$$H(k) = z_1(k)x(k) + z_2(k)p(k),$$

$$H(k) = z_1(k)\left[\frac{x(k-1)}{1 + \alpha v(k)}\right] + [p(k-1) + x(k-1) - x(k) - \lambda v(k)], \tag{2.230}$$

where we have let the adjoint variable $z_2(k)$ be 1 and where

$$z_1(k) = \frac{\partial x(k+1)}{\partial x(k)} z_1(k+1) + \frac{\partial p(k+1)}{\partial x(k)}. \tag{2.231}$$

But we note that

$$\frac{\partial x(k+1)}{\partial x(k)} = \frac{1}{1 + \alpha v(k+1)}, \qquad \frac{\partial p(k+1)}{\partial x(k)} = \frac{\alpha v(k+1)}{1 + \alpha v(k+1)}, \tag{2.232}$$

and thus Equation (2.231) becomes

$$z_1(k) = \frac{z_1(k+1)}{1 + \alpha v(k+1)} + \frac{\alpha v(k+1)}{1 + \alpha v(k+1)}. \tag{2.233}$$

This is the recurrence relationship for $z_1(k)$ equivalent to Equation (2.228) for $x(k+1)$. The boundary conditions on these two expressions are $x(0)$ prescribed and $z_1(3) = 0$, respectively.

To determine the optimal unbounded allocation of solvent, we now form $[\partial H(k)]/[\partial v(k)] = 0$. This requires the following derivatives:

$$\frac{\partial[x(k-1)/1 + \alpha v(k)]}{\partial v(k)} = -\frac{\alpha x(k)}{1 + \alpha v(k)},$$

$$\frac{\partial[p(k-1) + x(k-1) - x(k) - \lambda v(k)]}{\partial v(k)} = \frac{\alpha x(k)}{1 + \alpha v(k)} - \lambda,$$

so that

$$\frac{\partial H(k)}{\partial v(k)} = -\frac{z_1(k)\alpha x(k)}{1 + \alpha v(k)} + \frac{\alpha x(k)}{1 + \alpha v(k)} - \lambda = 0 \quad \text{or} \quad z_1(k) = 1 - \frac{\lambda[1 + \alpha v^\circ(k)]}{\alpha x(k)}, \tag{2.234}$$

where $v^\circ(k)$ is now the optimal allocation. Alternatively, Equation (2.234) may be solved for $v^\circ(k)$ to yield

$$v^\circ(k) = \frac{x(k)}{\lambda}[1 - z_1(k)] - \frac{1}{\alpha}. \tag{2.235}$$

At this point, we have the difference equation for the state, Equation (2.228), the difference equation for the adjoint variable, Equation (2.233), and the optimal allocation in terms of the state and adjoint, Equation (2.235). If we substitute the optimal allocation into Equation (2.228) and (2.233), we are then left with two equations which can be solved simultaneously. To illustrate this, we substitute Equation (2.234) into the adjoint Equation (2.233) to give

$$1 - \frac{\lambda[1 + \alpha v^\circ(k)]}{\alpha x(k)} = \frac{1}{1 + \alpha v^\circ(k+1)} - \frac{\lambda[1 + \alpha v^\circ(k+1)]}{1 + \alpha v^\circ(k+1)]\alpha x(k+1)} + \frac{\alpha v^\circ(k+1)}{1 + \alpha v^\circ(k+1)},$$

which can be immediately simplified to $-\lambda[1 + \alpha v^\circ(k)] = -\lambda[1 + \alpha v^\circ(k+1)]$ or to

$$v^\circ(k) = v^\circ(k+1). \tag{2.236}$$

But from Equation (2.228) we note again that

$$1 + \alpha v^\circ(k + 1) = \frac{x(k)}{x(k + 1)},$$

and therefore from Equation (2.236) it follows that

$$\frac{x(k - 1)}{x(k)} = \frac{x(k)}{x(k + 1)}$$

or

$$x^2(k) = x(k - 1)x(k + 1). \tag{2.237}$$

Equation (2.237) thus represents the combined solution of the state equation and the adjoint equation after the optimal control sequence is inserted. It is a second-order difference equation whose solution will involve two arbitrary constants; we have, however, two boundary conditions. The first is

$$x(0), \tag{2.238}$$

and the second is

$$z_1(N) = 0. \tag{2.239}$$

To use the second one, we must convert it into terms of $x(N)$ rather than $z_1(N)$. This can be done easily by using Equation (2.234) along with (2.239) for $k = N$ to solve for $[1 + \alpha v^\circ(N)]$. This latter expression is inserted into Equation (2.228) for $k = N - 1$, and this yields, with Equations (2.235) and (2.239),

$$x(N - 1) = \frac{\alpha}{\lambda}[x(N)]^2, \tag{2.240}$$

and the boundary conditions for the solution of Equation (2.237) are (2.238) and (2.240).

The general solution of Equation (2.237) is

$$x(k) = B(A)^k, \tag{2.241}$$

and using (2.238), we have

$$B = x(0).$$

Using (2.240) to start the backward iteration and (2.237) to continue, it follows that

$$A = \left[\frac{\lambda}{\alpha x(0)}\right]^{1/(N+1)}, \tag{2.242}$$

so that finally

$$x(k) = x(0)\left[\frac{\lambda}{\alpha x(0)}\right]^{k/(N+1)}. \tag{2.243}$$

At the same time we note from Equation (2.236) that $v°(k)$ is independent of k, and thus the optimal allocation is for equal values. Since

$$v°(k+1) = \frac{x(k)}{\alpha x(k+1)} - \frac{1}{\alpha},$$

we see that for $N = 3$

$$v°(3) = \left[\left(\frac{x(0)}{\alpha^3 \lambda}\right)^{1/4} - \frac{1}{\alpha}\right], \tag{2.244}$$

which is identical to Equation (2.216) resulting from the dynamic programming. Also, for the same value of N,

$$x(1) = x(0)\left[\frac{\lambda}{\alpha x(0)}\right]^{1/4} = \left[\frac{\lambda x^3(0)}{\alpha}\right]^{1/4}, \tag{2.245}$$

which is identical to Equation (2.217).

Thus both methods, dynamic programming and the discrete maximum principle, lead to identical results. We shall leave it to the reader to judge which method seems easier to use.

EXAMPLE 2.3 ▪ We shall illustrate the application of Pontryagin's maximum principle by establishing the time optimal control for the nonlinear CSTR detailed in Chapter 1. We shall use the same numerical values for the coolant water temperature, inlet reactant temperature, the heat of reaction, and the range of the valve, so that the heat and mass balance equations are equivalent to those before, namely,

$$dT/dt = -(T + 0.25) + (C + 0.5) \exp[25T/(T + 2)] - u_1(T + 0.25), \tag{2.246}$$

$$dC/dt = 0.5 - C - (C + 0.5) \exp[25T/(T + 2)], \tag{2.247}$$

where u_1 is the control action which has the value 2 when the valve is completely open, and hence the reactor is fully cooled, and the value 0 when the valve is completely closed; T is the deviation from the steady-state dimensionless temperature; and C is the deviation from steady-state dimensionless concentration. Note that when proportional control is used, $u_1 = 1 + kT$ with a maximum value of 2 and a minimum value of 0, and Equations (2.246) and (2.247) will be identical to Equations (1.136) and (1.135).

Since we are interested in time optimal control, we introduce an additional state variable x_0 (note that we use the subscript 0 rather than the $n + 1$) such that

$$\dot{x}_0 = 1, \tag{2.248}$$

so that

$$x_0 = t. \tag{2.249}$$

We shall leave the other state variables T and C as they are.

Now let us introduce three adjoint variables, z_0, z_1, and z_2, and construct the Hamiltonian

$$H = z_0\dot{x}_0 + z_1\dot{T} + z_2\dot{C}.$$

Therefore,

$$H = z_0 + (z_1 - z_2)(C + 0.5)\exp\left(\frac{25T}{T+2}\right) - z_1(T + 0.25) - z_1u_1(T + 0.25) + z_2(0.5 - C). \quad (2.250)$$

The adjoint differential equations are

$$dz_i/dt = -(\partial H/\partial x_i) \qquad (i = 0, 1, 2), \quad (2.251)$$

where $x_1 = T$ and $x_2 = C$; and from Equation (2.250) we get

$$dz_0/dt = 0,$$

$$dz_1/dt = z_1 - (z_1 - z_2)50\frac{(C + 0.5)}{(T + 2)^2}\exp[25T/(T + 2)] + u_1z_1, \quad (2.252)$$

$$dz_2/dt = (z_2 - z_1)\exp[25T/(T + 2)] + z_2.$$

At the final time $t = t_f$, the values of C and T are specified to be zero and z_0 is -1 (and therefore z_0 is -1 everywhere). The values of z_1 and z_2 are unspecified at t_f.

For time optimal control, u_1 must be chosen in such a way that the Hamiltonian as defined by Equation (2.250) will be as large as possible so that t will be minimized. At once we see that to maximize the Hamiltonian, we choose

$$\begin{aligned} u_1 &= 0 \quad \text{when} \quad z_1(T + 0.25) > 0, \\ u_1 &= 2 \quad \text{when} \quad z_1(T + 0.25) < 0, \end{aligned} \quad (2.253)$$

since u_1 appears only in the term $z_1u_1(T + 0.25)$, which must be minimized to maximize the Hamiltonian. There is a possibility of singular control if $z_1(T + 0.25) = 0$. For the discussion of singular control, we refer the reader to the work by Siebenthal and Aris [72], since in this example $z_1(T + 0.25)$ is zero only at the time of switching, and to expand on the singular control here would only confuse the reader.

Now let us state the problem more explicitly.

PROBLEM ▪ We wish to find the control action so that when the reactor is started at $T = 0.05$, $C = 0$, the steady-state point $T = 0$, $C = 0$ will be reached in minimum time.

Solution ▪ Since the time is not fixed, the maximum value of the Hamiltonian, H, as defined by Equation (2.250) is zero. Therefore, at the time when the origin is reached, Equation (2.250) gives

$$-1 - z_1(0.25) + (z_1 - z_2)(0.5) - u_1 z_1(0.25) + 0.5z_2 = 0,$$

that is,

$$z_1(t_f) = \frac{4}{1 - u_1}, \tag{2.254}$$

and we shall have the values for z_1 at the final time, that is,

$$z_1 = 4 \quad \text{when} \quad u_1 = 0, \qquad z_1 = -4 \quad \text{when} \quad u_1 = 2. \tag{2.255}$$

But we must assume some value for z_2 at the final time to proceed. Therefore, to calculate the optimal trajectory we take the following steps.

(1) Assume some value for $z_2(t_f)$.

(2) Choose either $z_1(t_f) = 4$ or -4 (let us say 4), and integrate the equations for T, C, z_1, z_2 *backward*, keeping $u_1 = 0$ until z_1 becomes zero.

(3) After eliminating the possibility of singular control, the other value for u_1 is taken (that is, $u_1 = 2$), so that $u_1 z_1$ is as large on the negative side as possible.

(4) When the integration has proceeded to the point where $T = 0.05$, check the value of C to see if it is the given initial value, that is, $C = 0$.

(5) If $C \neq 0$ when $T = 0.05$, repeat with a different value for $z_2(t_f)$, and continue until the boundary conditions are met.

A better way of approaching the problem is not to actually integrate the state and adjoint equations but to use Pontryagin's maximum principle only to find that off-on control is necessary for time optimal control and then to use phase-plane diagrams to obtain the actual solutions. We shall outline this in some detail now.

Note that Equation (2.247) does not contain the control variable. Hence, at steady state, $dC/dt = 0$, and the locus of steady-state points is given by

$$0.5 - C - (C + 0.5)\exp\left(\frac{25T}{T + 2}\right) = 0;$$

that is,

$$C = \frac{1}{1 + \exp(25T/(T + 2))} - 0.5 \tag{2.256}$$

Now to calculate the phase plane trajectories for the two extreme cases of fully cooled and adiabatic reactor, we first plot Equation (2.256) on the phase plane and then choose some points along this curve (including the point (0, 0)) as initial conditions to integrate the state equations (2.246) and (2.247) *forward* and *backward*. This will give a good picture of how the phase plane looks without using too many unnecessary integrations. Other initial conditions may then be used to show the phase plane in greater detail. By this procedure we obtain Figures 2.17 (below) and 2.18 (p. 148) which are the phase planes for fully cooled and adiabatic reactor, respectively. The dotted curve is the steady-state curve as given by Equation (2.256).

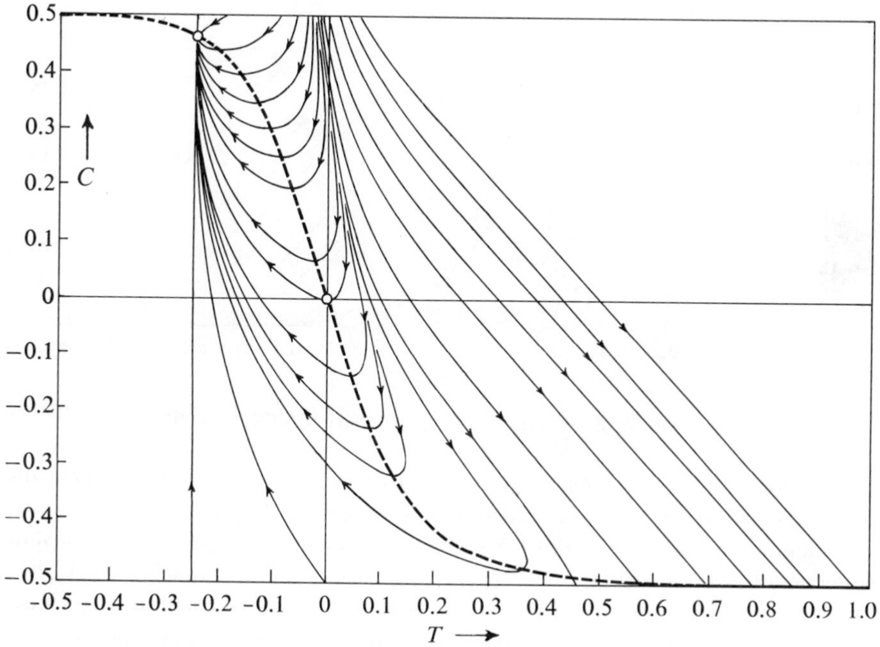

FIGURE 2.17. Phase plane for fully cooled CSTR; $u_1 = 2$

From Figures 2.17 and 2.18 it is noted that in each one there is one trajectory only that passes through the point (0, 0). Since bang-bang control gives the shortest time to reach the origin, these curves give the method of approaching the origin, once we are on the curve. We therefore plot these curves going into the origin as in Figure 2.19 (p. 149). These form a continuous curve *ABD*. Other trajectories reaching this curve are also plotted.

If an initial point is to the right of the curve *ABD*, full cooling is used ($u_1 = 2$) until the trajectory meets this curve between *B* and *D*. Then the control is switched to $u_1 = 0$ to enter the origin in minimal time.

If an initial point is to the left of the curve *ABD*, no cooling is used ($u_1 = 0$) until the trajectory meets this curve between *A* and *B*. Then the control is switched to $u_1 = 2$ (full cooling) to enter the origin in minimal time.

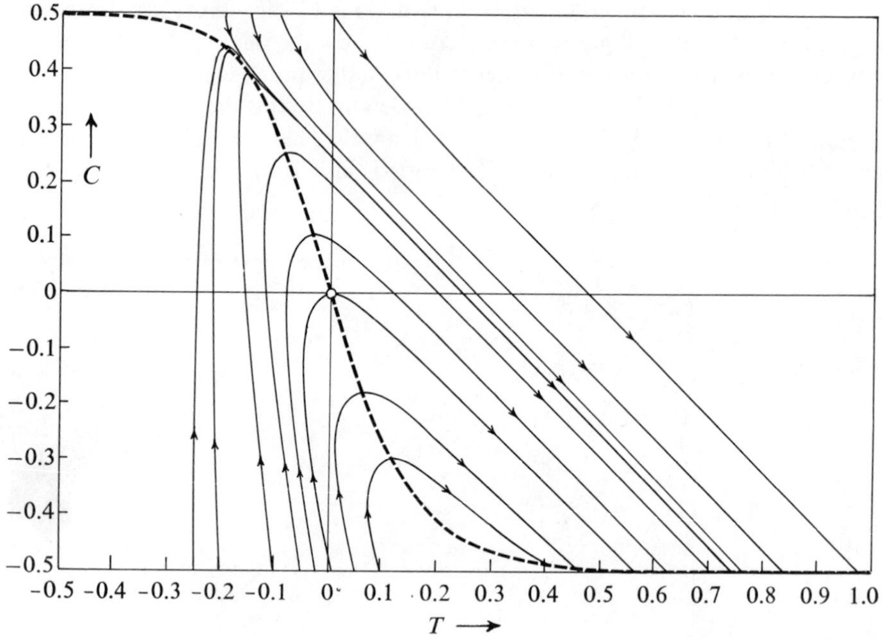

FIGURE 2.18. Phase plane for adiabatic CSTR, $u_1 = 0$

Now looking at our problem, we see that (0.05, 0) is to the right of the curve *ABD*. Hence, full cooling is used until the trajectory meets the curve *DBA* at *E*. Then no cooling is used until the origin is reached. The results are shown in some detail in Figures 2.20 and 2.21 (p. 150), where the time optimal control is compared to the proportional control. We shall deal with the proportional control for this problem in greater detail in Chapter 6, where stability is discussed.

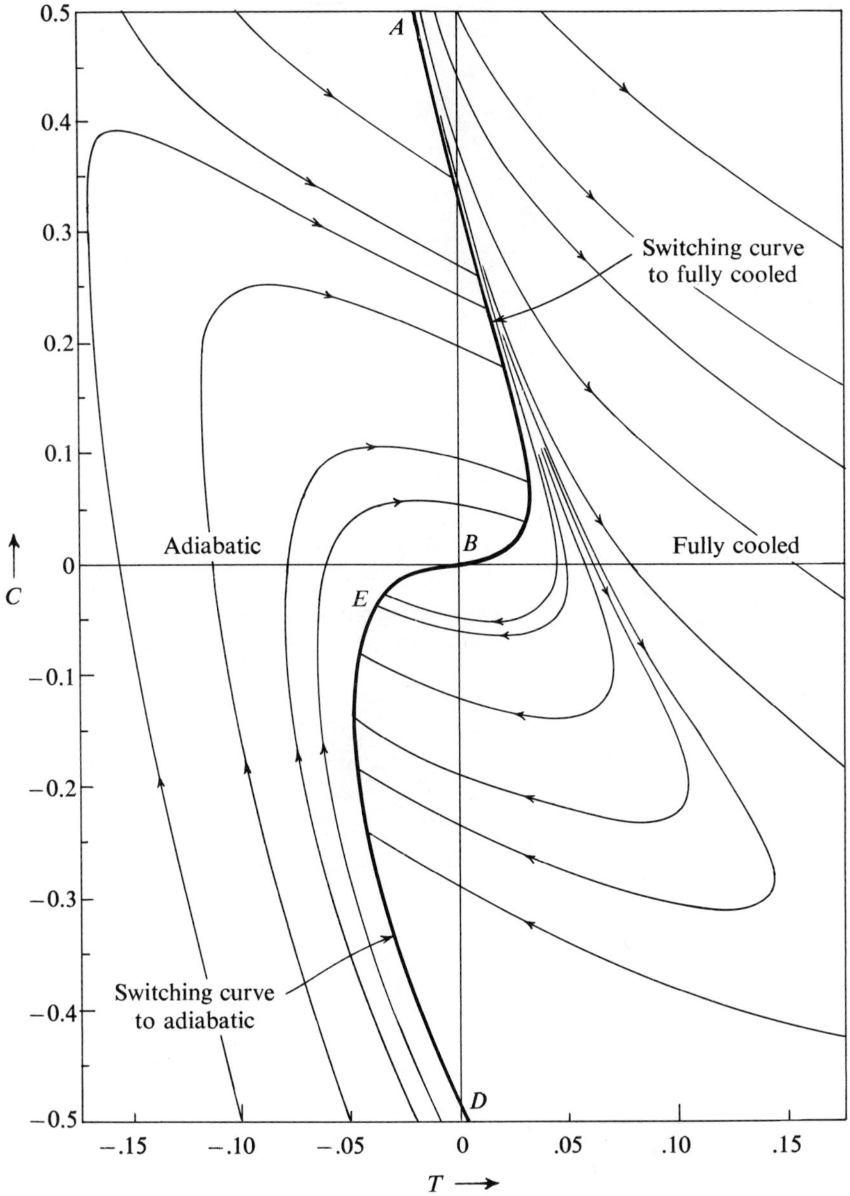

FIGURE 2.19. Time optimal control for CSTR

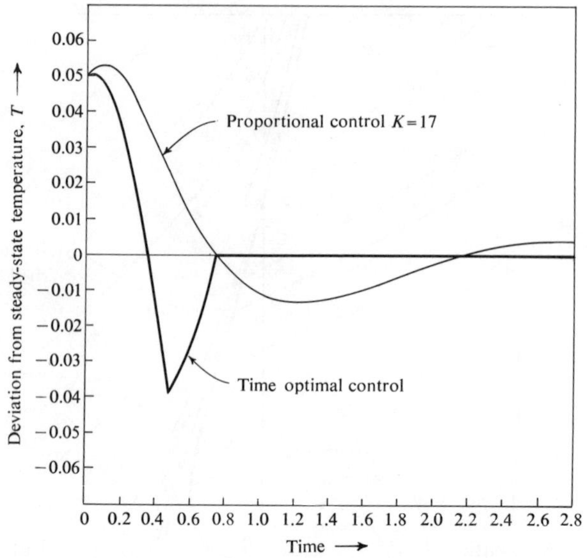

FIGURE 2.20. Comparison of time-optimal control with proportional control, T vs. time

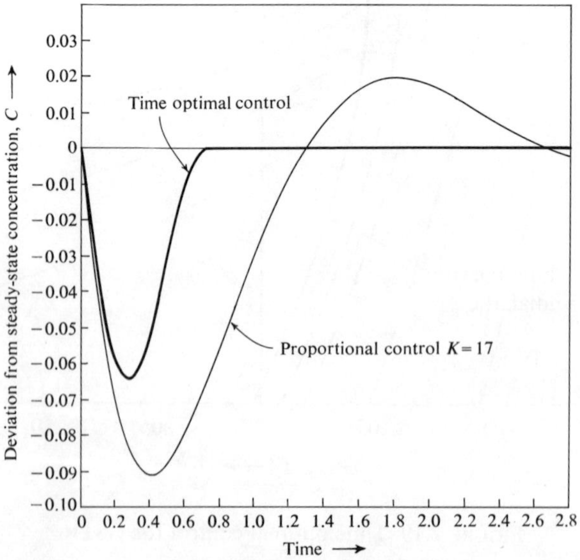

FIGURE 2.21. Comparison of time-optimal control with proportional control, C vs. time.

References

BOOKS

1. R. Aris, *The Optimal Design of Chemical Reactors*, Academic Press, 1961.
2. R. Aris, *Discrete Dynamic Programming*, Blaisdell Publishing Co., 1964.
3. M. Athans, and P. L. Falb, *Optimal Control*, McGraw-Hill Book Co., 1966.
4. R. Bellman, *Adaptive Control Processes*, Princeton University Press, 1961.
5. R. Bellman, *Applied Dynamic Programming*, Princeton University Press, 1962.
6. S. E. Dreyfus, *Dynamic Programming and the Calculus of Variations*, Academic Press, 1965.
7. L. Fan and C. Wang, *The Discrete Maximum Principle*, John Wiley and Sons, 1964.
8. R. L. Graves and P. Wolfe (Editors), *Recent Advances in Mathematical Programming*, McGraw-Hill Book Co., 1963.
9. G. Hadley, *Nonlinear and Dynamic Programming*, Addison-Wesley Publishing Co., 1964.
10. J. LaSalle and S. Lefschetz, *Stability by Liapunov's Direct Method with Applications*, Academic Press, 1961.
11. C. T. Leondes, Editor, *Advances in Control Systems I*, Academic Press, 1964.
12. W. Kipiniak, *Dynamic Optimization and Control*, M.I.T. Press, 1961.
13. J. Peschon, Editor, *Disciplines and Techniques of Systems Control*, Blaisdell Publishing Co., 1965.
14. L. S. Pontryagin, V. G. Boltyanskii, R. V. Gamkrelidze, and E. F. Mishchenko, *The Mathematical Theory of Optimal Processes*, Interscience Publishing, 1962.
15. S. M. Roberts, *Dynamic Programming in Chemical Engineering and Process Control*, Academic Press, 1964.
16. G. Zoutendijk, *Methods of Feasible Directions*, Elsevier, 1960.

ARTICLES

17. D. H. Archer and R. L. Zahradnik, *IEC Fund.*, *3*, 38 (1964).
18. R. Aris, G. L. Nemhauser, and D. J. Wilde, *A. I. Ch. E. J.*, *10*, 913 (1964).
19. M. Athans, *IEEE Trans. Auto. Control*, *AC-11*, 580 (1966).
20. K. H. Bhavnani and K. Chen, "Optimization of Time-Dependent Systems by Dynamic Programming," *JACC Proceedings* (1966).
21. R. Bellman, R. Kalaba, and B. Kotkin, *Math. of Comp.*, *17*, 155 (1963).
22. L. Berkovitz, *J. Math. Anal. Appl.* *3*, 145 (1961).
23. G. S. G. Beveridge and R. S. Schechter, *IEC Fund.*, *4*, 257 (1965).
24. P. J. Brennan and A. P. Roberts, *J. Elect. Control*, *12*, 345 (1962).
25. T. F. Bridgland, *J. SIAM Control*, *2*, 137 (1965).

ARTICLES (*continued*)

26. S. S. L. Chang, *IRE Convention Record*, *9*, 48 (1961).
27. T. C. Chen and N. H. Ceaglske, *IEC Fund.*, *5*, 422 (1966).
28. H. H. Chien, *IEC Fund.*, *5*, 66 (1966).
29. M. Denn, *IEC Fund.*, *4*, 231, 240 (1965).
30. M. Denn and R. Aris, *IEC Fund.*, *4*, 7, 213, 248 (1965).
31. M. Denn and R. Aris, *Chem. Eng. Sci.*, *20*, 373 (1965).
32. M. Denn and R. Aris, *A. I. Ch. E. J.*, *11*, 367 (1965).
33. C. Desoer, *J. Franklin Inst.*, *271*, 361 (1962).
34. S. E. Dreyfus, *J. Math. Anal. Appl. 1*, 228 (1960).
35. S. E. Dreyfus, *J. SIAM Control*, *2*, 120 (1965).
36. B. Friedland, *J. Basic Eng.*, *84D*, 1 (March 1962).
37. A. T. Fuller, *J. Electric Control*, *15*, 63 (1963); *17*, 283, 301 (1964).
38. G. R. Geiss. "The Analysis and Design of Nonlinear Control Systems via Liapunov's Direct Method," *Technical Documentary Report No. RTD-TDR-63-47076*, Grumman Aircraft Engineering Corporation, Bethpage, N. Y. (1964).
39. E. G. Gilbert, "Hybrid Computer Solution of Time-Optimal Control Problems," *Proc. Spring Joint Computer Conf.* (1963).
40. H. Halkin, Chapter 4 of *Advances in Control Systems*, Academic Press, 1964, pp. 173–196.
41. H. Halkin, "A Geometric Approach to the Theory of Optimal Control for Discrete Systems," *presented at First Eastern Conf. on Prog. and Control*, US Air Force Academy (1965).
42. M. Held and R. M. Karp, *J. SIAM*, *10*, 196 (1962).
43. J. M. Holtzman, *IEEE Trans. Auto. Control*, *AC-11*, 30 (1966).
44. J. M. Holtzman and H. Halkin, *J. SIAM Control*, *4*, 263 (1966).
45. F. Horn and R. Jackson, *IEC Fund.*, *4*, 110 (1965).
46. H. C. Hsieh, *J. Franklin Inst.*, *272*, 154 (1963).
47. R. Jackson, *Chem. Eng. Sci.*, *19*, 19 (1964); *20*, 405 (1965).
48. R. Jackson and I. Coward, *Chem. Eng. Sci. 20*, 911 (1965).
49. R. Jackson and F. Horn, *Inter. Jrn. of Control*, *1*, 389 (1965).
50. C. D. Johnson, "Singular Solutions in Problems of Optimal Control," *Advances in Control Systems 2*, Academic Press (1965).
51. B. W. Jordon and E. Pollack, *J. Electric Control*, *17*, 697 (1964).
52. R. Kalman and J. Bertram, *J. Basic Eng.*, *82D*, 371, 394 (1960).
53. R. M. Karp and M. Held, *IBM Systems Journal 4*, No. 2, 136 (1965).
54. S. Katz, *IEC Fund.*, *1*, 226 (1962).
55. S. Katz, *J. Electric Control*, *18*, 189 (1965).
56. R. P. King, Chem. Eng. Sci., *20*, 537 (1965).
57. R. P. King, *IEC Fund.*, *5*, 484 (1966).

58. R. E. Kopp, Chapter 7 in *Optimization Techniques*, Academic Press, 1963, pp. 255–279.
59. L. Lapidus, E. Shapiro, S. Shapiro, and R. Stillman. *A. I. Ch. E. J.*, *7*, 288 (1961).
60. R. S. Lehman, *J. Math. Anal. Appl.*, *5*, 499 (1962).
61. G. Leitmann, *J. SIAM Control*, *3*, 53 (1965).
62. O. L. Mangasarian, *J. SIAM Control*, *3*, 281 (1965).
63. S. Markus and E. B. Lee, *Arch. Rat. Mech. Analysis*, *8*, 36 (1961).
64. L. G. Mitten and G. L. Nemhauser, *Canad. J. Chem. Eng.*, *41*, 187 (1963).
65. G. L. Nemhauser, *Chem. Eng. Prog.*, *59*, 52 (1963).
66. L. M. Pis'men and I. I. Ioffe, *Inter. Chem. Eng.*, *2*, 567 (1962).
67. J. Rosen, *J. SIAM*, *8*, 181 (1960); *9*, 514 (1961).
68. L. I. Rozonoer, *Auto. and Remote Control*, *20*, 1288, 1405, 1517 (1959).
69. P. E. Sarachik and E. Kreindler, *IEEE Trans. Auto. Control*, *10*, 350 (1965).
70. O. T. Schultz, *AIAA Jrn.*, *1*, 2673 (1963).
71. S. Shapiro, *Automatica*, *3*, 219 (1966).
72. C. D. Siebenthal and R. Aris, *Chem. Eng. Sci.*, *19*, 729, 747 (1964).
73. H. L. Steinmetz, *Ind. Eng. Chem.*, *58*, 33 (Jan. 1966).
74. A. Tchamran, *J. Franklin Inst.*, *280*, 493 (1965).
75. M. L. Trombotta, *Chem. Eng. Prog. Symp. Series*, *61*, 42 (1965).
76. J. Weisman, C. F. Wood, and L. Rivlin, *Chem. Eng. Prog. 61*, 50 (1965).
77. D. J. Wilde, *Ind. Eng. Chem.*, *57*, No. 8, 19 (1965).
78. P. Wolfe, "Recent Developments in Nonlinear Programming," *Advances in Computers*, *III*, Academic Press, 1962, p. 155.

3

Control of Linear Systems

In this chapter, we shall examine the control of linear systems subject to certain special performance indices. As might be anticipated, considerable progress can be made here in developing the control algorithms, even in the face of a large number of state variables. The discussion will start with consideration of a quadratic performance index; because of ease of presentation, the discrete-time system model will be the first to be used with this performance index. The discrete-time system model will then be followed by the continuous-time system model. The remaining portion of the chapter will deal with the minimum-time performance index, first formulated along continuous-time lines and then along discrete-time lines. For the latter we will see that the optimal control algorithm can be obtained by solving a linear programming problem.

3.1. Discrete-time systems with a quadratic performance index

For the major portion of this section, we shall consider the discrete-time system model as given by

$$\boldsymbol{x}(k+1) = \boldsymbol{\Phi}\boldsymbol{x}(k) + \boldsymbol{\Delta}\boldsymbol{u}(k) \qquad (k = 0, 1, 2, \ldots), \tag{3.1}$$

where $\boldsymbol{\Phi}$ and $\boldsymbol{\Delta}$ are constant matrices. The initial condition $\boldsymbol{x}(0)$ will be assumed to be given. The output variable equation may be added in the form

$$y(k) = \boldsymbol{H}\boldsymbol{x}(k),$$

but for purposes of simplicity and ease of understanding, we shall not in general include this equation (see example at end of chapter, however.) The performance index is assumed to have the *quadratic form*

$$I(\boldsymbol{x}(0), P) = \sum_{k=1}^{P} [\boldsymbol{x}'(k)\boldsymbol{Q}\boldsymbol{x}(k) + \boldsymbol{u}'(k-1)\boldsymbol{R}\boldsymbol{u}(k-1)], \tag{3.2}$$

which is a slightly simplified version of Equation (1.59). The more complicated version of the performance index will be considered later. In Equation (3.2), $\boldsymbol{Q}$ and $\boldsymbol{R}$ are considered as positive-semidefinite symmetric matrices. Our control problem is now stated as finding the *unconstrained* control sequence, $\boldsymbol{u}(0), \boldsymbol{u}(1), \ldots, \boldsymbol{u}(P-1)$, such that starting with the state $\boldsymbol{x}(0)$ we minimize $I[\boldsymbol{x}(0), P]$ over P time stages subject to the linear system dynamics of Equation (3.1). It is important to emphasize that we consider here only the case of $\boldsymbol{u}(k)$ unconstrained by control bounds.

There are a number of different ways to obtain the solution to this linear system control problem. We shall investigate two such methods here and reserve a third, involving the Liapunov function, for a subsequent chapter. In our first approach we shall use the technique of dynamic programming as detailed by Deley and Franklin [14] and due originally to the brilliant work of Kalman [38–40]. Alternative derivations have been recently presented by Reynolds and Cadzow [65], Tou [3], and Luenberger [54]. Let us define

$$I^0[\boldsymbol{x}(0), P] = \min I[\boldsymbol{x}(0), P] \tag{3.3}$$

such that $I^0[\boldsymbol{x}(0), P]$ is the optimal value of the performance index for a system starting with $\boldsymbol{x}(0)$ and carried over P stages of control. It follows from this definition that

$$I^0[\boldsymbol{x}(0), P] = \min_{\boldsymbol{u}(0)} \min_{\boldsymbol{u}(1)} \ldots \min_{\boldsymbol{u}(P-1)} \sum_{k=1}^{P} [\boldsymbol{x}'(k)\boldsymbol{Q}\boldsymbol{x}(k) + \boldsymbol{u}'(k-1)\boldsymbol{R}\boldsymbol{u}(k-1)] \tag{3.4}$$

or, when we realize that only $\boldsymbol{u}(0)$, and not $\boldsymbol{u}(1), \ldots, \boldsymbol{u}(P-1)$, affects the value of $\boldsymbol{x}(1)$, that

$$I^0[\boldsymbol{x}(0), P] = \min_{\boldsymbol{u}(0)} \Big\{ \boldsymbol{x}'(1)\boldsymbol{Q}\boldsymbol{x}(1) + \boldsymbol{u}'(0)\boldsymbol{R}\boldsymbol{u}(0) + \min_{\boldsymbol{u}(1)} \ldots \min_{\boldsymbol{u}(P-1)} \sum_{k=2}^{P} [\boldsymbol{x}'(k)\boldsymbol{Q}\boldsymbol{x}(k) + \boldsymbol{u}'(k-1)\boldsymbol{R}\boldsymbol{u}(k-1)] \Big\}. \tag{3.5}$$

Equation (3.5) is obtained from Equation (3.4) by merely removing the first term in the series and noting the influence of $\boldsymbol{u}(0)$ on $\boldsymbol{x}(1)$. But the last term in

Equation (3.5) is almost identical to the right-hand side of Equation (3.4); in Equation (3.5), however, the "initial condition" is $\boldsymbol{x}(1)$, resulting from the application of $\boldsymbol{u}(0)$, and only $P-1$ stages are involved. Thus, following the principle of optimality of dynamic programming or just Equation (3.5), we write

$$I^0[\boldsymbol{x}(0), P] = \min_{\boldsymbol{u}(0)} \{\boldsymbol{x}'(1)\boldsymbol{Q}\boldsymbol{x}(1) + \boldsymbol{u}'(0)\boldsymbol{R}\boldsymbol{u}(0) + I^0[\boldsymbol{x}(1), P-1]\}. \tag{3.6}$$

Equation (3.6) is the recurrence relationship of dynamic programming for the current problem.

To see how we may make use of this equation, let us assume that

$$I^0[\boldsymbol{x}(0), P] = \boldsymbol{x}(0)'\boldsymbol{J}_P\boldsymbol{x}(0) \tag{3.7}$$

specifies the correct form of $I^0[\boldsymbol{x}(0), P]$ with $\boldsymbol{J}_P$ a positive-semidefinite symmetric matrix. Substituting Equation (3.7) in the form

$$I^0[\boldsymbol{x}(1), P-1] = \boldsymbol{x}(1)'\boldsymbol{J}_{P-1}\boldsymbol{x}(1)$$

into (3.6) along with (3.1) yields

$$I^0[\boldsymbol{x}(0), P] = \min_{\boldsymbol{u}(0)} \{[\boldsymbol{\Phi}\boldsymbol{x}(0) + \boldsymbol{\Delta}\boldsymbol{u}(0)]'(\boldsymbol{Q} + \boldsymbol{J}_{P-1})[\boldsymbol{\Phi}\boldsymbol{x}(0) + \boldsymbol{\Delta}\boldsymbol{u}(0)] + \boldsymbol{u}'(0)\boldsymbol{R}\boldsymbol{u}(0)\}. \tag{3.8}$$

Equation (3.8) may be expanded as

$$\begin{aligned} I^0[\boldsymbol{x}(0), P] = \min_{\boldsymbol{u}(0)} \{&\boldsymbol{x}'(0)\boldsymbol{\Phi}'(\boldsymbol{Q} + \boldsymbol{J}_{P-1})\boldsymbol{\Phi}\boldsymbol{x}(0) + \boldsymbol{u}(0)'[\boldsymbol{\Delta}'(\boldsymbol{Q} + \boldsymbol{J}_{P-1})\boldsymbol{\Delta} + \boldsymbol{R}]\boldsymbol{u}(0) \\ &+ \boldsymbol{x}(0)'\boldsymbol{\Phi}'(\boldsymbol{Q} + \boldsymbol{J}_{P-1})\boldsymbol{\Delta}\boldsymbol{u}(0) + \boldsymbol{u}(0)'\boldsymbol{\Delta}'(\boldsymbol{Q} + \boldsymbol{J}_{P-1})\boldsymbol{\Phi}\boldsymbol{x}(0)\}. \end{aligned} \tag{3.9}$$

Let us now define $\boldsymbol{K}_{P-k}$ by the equation

$$[\boldsymbol{\Delta}'(\boldsymbol{Q} + \boldsymbol{J}_{P-k-1})\boldsymbol{\Delta} + \boldsymbol{R}]\boldsymbol{K}_{P-k} = \boldsymbol{\Delta}'(\boldsymbol{Q} + \boldsymbol{J}_{P-k-1})\boldsymbol{\Phi} \tag{3.10}$$

or, for $k = 0$,

$$[\boldsymbol{\Delta}'(\boldsymbol{Q} + \boldsymbol{J}_{P-1})\boldsymbol{\Delta} + \boldsymbol{R}]\boldsymbol{K}_P = \boldsymbol{\Delta}'(\boldsymbol{Q} + \boldsymbol{J}_{P-1})\boldsymbol{\Phi}.$$

Furthermore, we shall define some control $\boldsymbol{u}^*(k)$ by

$$\boldsymbol{u}^*(k) = -\boldsymbol{K}_{P-k}\boldsymbol{x}(k) \tag{3.11}$$

or, for $k = 0$,

$$\boldsymbol{u}^*(0) = -\boldsymbol{K}_P\boldsymbol{x}(0),$$

and we shall show that $\boldsymbol{u}^*(k)$ thus defined is the optimal control. Manipulation of Equation (3.9) yields

$$\begin{aligned} I^0[\boldsymbol{x}(0), P] = \min_{\boldsymbol{u}(0)} [&\boldsymbol{x}(0)'\boldsymbol{\Phi}'(\boldsymbol{Q} + \boldsymbol{J}_{P-1})\boldsymbol{\Phi}\boldsymbol{x}(0) + [\boldsymbol{u}(0) - \boldsymbol{u}^*(0)]'[\boldsymbol{\Delta}'(\boldsymbol{Q} + \boldsymbol{J}_{P-1})\boldsymbol{\Delta} \\ &+ \boldsymbol{R}][\boldsymbol{u}(0) - \boldsymbol{u}^*(0)] - \boldsymbol{u}^*(0)'[\boldsymbol{\Delta}'(\boldsymbol{Q} + \boldsymbol{J}_{P-1})\boldsymbol{\Delta} + \boldsymbol{R}]\boldsymbol{u}^*(0)]. \end{aligned} \tag{3.12}$$

But the only term which now contains the control $\boldsymbol{u}(0)$ is the second one, and so long as $[\Delta'(\boldsymbol{Q} + \boldsymbol{J}_{P-1})\Delta + \boldsymbol{R}]$ remains positive-definite, the terms in brackets are minimized by the choice of $\boldsymbol{u}(0)$ given by

$$\boldsymbol{u}(0) = \boldsymbol{u}^*(0) = -\boldsymbol{K}_P\boldsymbol{x}(0).$$

Since this $\boldsymbol{u}(0)$ minimizes $I[\boldsymbol{x}(0), P]$ we see that this represents the optimal control law and we shall denote this by the superscript ^{0}; thus

$$\boldsymbol{u}^0(0) = \boldsymbol{u}^*(0) = -\boldsymbol{K}_P\boldsymbol{x}(0).$$

When this optimal sequence is used, the second term of Equation (3.12) is zero and it follows that

$$I^0[\boldsymbol{x}(0), P] = \boldsymbol{x}(0)'\boldsymbol{\Phi}'(\boldsymbol{Q} + \boldsymbol{J}_{P-1})\boldsymbol{\Phi}\boldsymbol{x}(0) - \boldsymbol{x}(0)'\boldsymbol{K}_P'[\Delta'(\boldsymbol{Q} + \boldsymbol{J}_{P-1})\Delta + \boldsymbol{R}]\boldsymbol{K}_P\boldsymbol{x}(0).$$

Equating this to Equation (3.7), we have

$$\boldsymbol{x}(0)'\{\boldsymbol{\Phi}'(\boldsymbol{Q} + \boldsymbol{J}_{P-1})\boldsymbol{\Phi} - \boldsymbol{K}_P'[\Delta'(\boldsymbol{Q} + \boldsymbol{J}_{P-1})\Delta + \boldsymbol{R}]\boldsymbol{K}_P\}\boldsymbol{x}(0) = \boldsymbol{x}(0)'\boldsymbol{J}_P\boldsymbol{x}(0). \quad (3.13)$$

But using Equation (3.10) with $k = 0$ and observing that $\boldsymbol{x}(0)$ is not zero in general, Equation (3.13) yields

$$\boldsymbol{J}_P = \boldsymbol{\Phi}'(\boldsymbol{Q} + \boldsymbol{J}_{P-1})(\boldsymbol{\Phi} - \Delta\boldsymbol{K}_P). \quad (3.14)$$

Having gone through all these manipulations, it is worthwhile for us to present a short summary of the results. By using the recurrence relationship of dynamic programming, we have shown that the optimal control is given by

$$\boldsymbol{u}^0(k) = -\boldsymbol{K}_{P-k}\boldsymbol{x}(k), \quad (3.15)$$

where the matrices $\boldsymbol{J}_P$ and $\boldsymbol{K}_P$ necessary to satisfy this result are given by

$$\boldsymbol{J}_{P-k} = \boldsymbol{\Phi}'(\boldsymbol{Q} + \boldsymbol{J}_{P-k-1})(\boldsymbol{\Phi} - \Delta\boldsymbol{K}_{P-k}) \quad (3.16)$$

and

$$\boldsymbol{K}_{P-k} = [\Delta'(\boldsymbol{Q} + \boldsymbol{J}_{P-k-1})\Delta + \boldsymbol{R}]^{-1}\Delta'(\boldsymbol{Q} + \boldsymbol{J}_{P-k-1})\boldsymbol{\Phi}. \quad (3.17)$$

We must still determine the starting conditions on the relationships (3.16) and (3.17) and show that the assumed form for Equation (3.7) of the optimal performance index is indeed correct. First, we note that

$$I^0[\boldsymbol{x}(P), 0] = \boldsymbol{x}(P)'\boldsymbol{J}_0\boldsymbol{x}(P) = 0,$$

corresponding to zero stages, and that

$$I^0[\boldsymbol{x}(P-1), 1] = \boldsymbol{x}'(P-1)\boldsymbol{J}_1\boldsymbol{x}(P-1),$$

corresponding to one stage. But if $I^0[\boldsymbol{x}(0), 0] = 0$, then it follows immediately that $\boldsymbol{J}_0 = \boldsymbol{0}$, and this is the starting condition for Equations (3.16) and (3.17). Then Equations (3.16) and (3.17) with $P = 1$ yield

$$\boldsymbol{J}_1 = \boldsymbol{\Phi}'[\boldsymbol{I} - \boldsymbol{Q}\Delta(\Delta'\boldsymbol{Q}\Delta + \boldsymbol{R})^{-1}\Delta']\boldsymbol{Q}\boldsymbol{\Phi},$$

which is a quadratic form. Thus, the assumed form for $I^0[x(0), P]$ of Equation (3.7) holds up and the form is correct.

We have now completed all the derivations necessary for this discrete unconstrained control. If we start with $\boldsymbol{J}_0 = \mathbf{0}$, Equation (3.17) can be used to calculate $\boldsymbol{K}_1$, and then Equation (3.16) can be used for $\boldsymbol{J}_1$. This requires, of course, that $\boldsymbol{Q}$ and $\boldsymbol{R}$ be specified. Once $\boldsymbol{J}_1$ is known, the sequence can be repeated for $\boldsymbol{K}_2$ and $\boldsymbol{J}_2$ and then continuing $\boldsymbol{K}_3, \boldsymbol{J}_3, \ldots, \boldsymbol{K}_P, \boldsymbol{J}_P$. But once $\boldsymbol{K}_P$ is known, Equation (3.15), along with the starting value $\boldsymbol{x}(0)$, can generate $\boldsymbol{u}^0(0)$; in turn, the discrete-time system equation yields, for $k = 0$ and $\boldsymbol{x}(0)$ and $\boldsymbol{u}^0(0)$ known, the state $\boldsymbol{x}(1)$. But when $\boldsymbol{x}(1)$ is known, we may use Equation (3.15) in the form

$$\boldsymbol{u}^0(1) = -\boldsymbol{K}_{P-1}\boldsymbol{x}(1)$$

to calculate $\boldsymbol{u}^0(1)$; Equation (3.1) with $\boldsymbol{x}(1)$ and $\boldsymbol{u}^0(1)$ yields $\boldsymbol{x}(2)$. Obviously, this can be repeated for all P stages to yield $\boldsymbol{u}^0(2), \boldsymbol{x}(3), \boldsymbol{u}^0(3), \boldsymbol{x}(4), \ldots, \boldsymbol{u}^0(P-1), \boldsymbol{x}(P)$.

Figure 3.1 illustrates the over-all serial procedure in which Equations (3.16) and (3.17) are used recursively to generate the backward (in time staging) sequence feedback coefficients $\boldsymbol{K}_1, \boldsymbol{K}_2, \ldots, \boldsymbol{K}_P$, and then the optimal-control-law equation plus the system equation are used to generate the actual optimal control and the state resulting from same. This is, of course, exactly what we would have expected from dynamic programming with a backward pass to generate the tables or functions in this case and a forward pass to generate the actual control corresponding to a particular $\boldsymbol{x}(0)$.

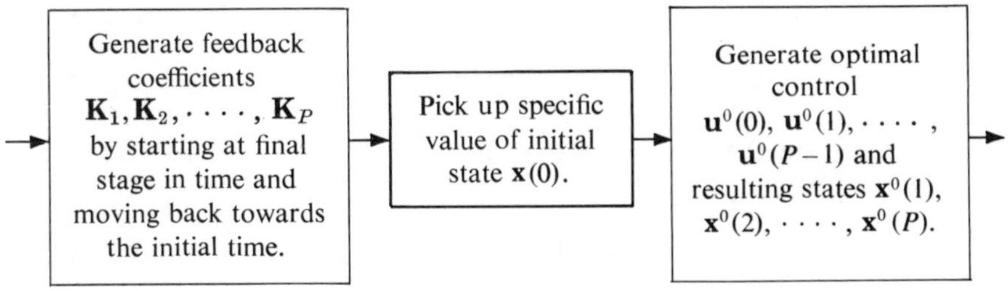

FIGURE 3.1. Block diagram for determination of closed-loop control algorithm

There are a number of interesting extensions and variations on this procedure which we mention now in a preliminary way and which we shall discuss more fully later. First, we note that the sequence of $\boldsymbol{K}_i$'s which are generated vary in numerical values as $\boldsymbol{K}_1, \boldsymbol{K}_2, \ldots, \boldsymbol{K}_P$ are formed. Thus, even though the system itself is *stationary*, the control law is *nonstationary;* the state variables are fed back through variable multipliers to generate the control sequence.

However, Kalman [39–43] has shown that if the system is completely controllable, the sequence of $\boldsymbol{K}_i$'s will tend to a finite and constant unique limit, $\boldsymbol{K}_P \to \boldsymbol{K}$, as $P \to \infty$. When this occurs, the infinite-stage feedback matrix is the constant $\boldsymbol{K}$ and the control law becomes stationary; the state variables are fed back through constant multipliers. Second, we note that we have established a closed-loop control algorithm, with the optimal control determined as a function of the current state.

Let us now solve this discrete-time linear control problem by a seemingly different procedure which uses a more obvious analysis. Consider again the performance index as given by Equation (3.2) in the form

$$I[\boldsymbol{x}(0), P] = \sum_{k=1}^{P} [\boldsymbol{x}'(k)\boldsymbol{Q}\boldsymbol{x}(k) + \boldsymbol{u}'(k-1)\boldsymbol{R}\boldsymbol{u}(k-1)] \tag{3.18}$$

and now try to minimize $I[x(0), P]$ by the obvious technique of differentiating with respect to $\boldsymbol{u}(k)$ and setting the result equal to zero. Thus, starting at the $P-1$ stage and observing that $\boldsymbol{u}(P-1)$ can only affect $\boldsymbol{x}(P)$ and not $\boldsymbol{x}(P-1), \boldsymbol{x}(P-2), \ldots$, we have

$$\frac{\partial I[\boldsymbol{x}(0), P]}{\partial \boldsymbol{u}(P-1)} = 2\frac{\partial \boldsymbol{x}'(P)}{\partial \boldsymbol{u}(P-1)}\boldsymbol{Q}\boldsymbol{x}(P) + 2\boldsymbol{R}\boldsymbol{u}^0(P-1) = \boldsymbol{0}. \tag{3.19}$$

But from Equation (3.1), with $k+1 = P$, the system balance can be written in the form

$$\boldsymbol{x}(P) = \boldsymbol{\Phi}\boldsymbol{x}(P-1) + \boldsymbol{\Delta}\boldsymbol{u}(P-1). \tag{3.20}$$

Thus, it follows that

$$\frac{\partial \boldsymbol{x}'(P)}{\partial \boldsymbol{u}(P-1)} = \boldsymbol{\Delta}', \tag{3.21}$$

where once again the fact that $\boldsymbol{u}(P-1)$ can only affect $\boldsymbol{x}(P)$ has been used. Equation (3.19) becomes, on substitution of (3.21),

$$\boldsymbol{\Delta}'\boldsymbol{Q}\boldsymbol{x}(P) + \boldsymbol{R}\boldsymbol{u}^0(P-1) = \boldsymbol{0}. \tag{3.22}$$

Substituting Equation (3.20) into (3.22) and solving for $\boldsymbol{u}^0(P-1)$ yields

$$\begin{aligned} \boldsymbol{\Delta}'\boldsymbol{Q}[\boldsymbol{\Phi}\boldsymbol{x}(P-1) + \boldsymbol{\Delta}\boldsymbol{u}^0(P-1)] + \boldsymbol{R}\boldsymbol{u}^0(P-1) &= \boldsymbol{0}, \\ \boldsymbol{u}^0(P-1) &= -(\boldsymbol{\Delta}'\boldsymbol{Q}\boldsymbol{\Delta} + \boldsymbol{R})^{-1}\boldsymbol{\Delta}'\boldsymbol{Q}\boldsymbol{\Phi}\boldsymbol{x}(P-1), \end{aligned} \tag{3.23}$$

which may be written in short form as

$$\boldsymbol{u}^0(P-1) = -\boldsymbol{K}_1\boldsymbol{x}(P-1), \tag{3.24}$$

where $\boldsymbol{K}_1 = (\boldsymbol{\Delta}'\boldsymbol{Q}\boldsymbol{\Delta} + \boldsymbol{R})^{-1}\boldsymbol{\Delta}'\boldsymbol{Q}\boldsymbol{\Phi}$. Note that this agrees with Equation (3.17) if we put $\boldsymbol{J}_0 = \boldsymbol{0}$.

The process can now be repeated for the last two stages in the control sequence by differentiating the performance index with respect to $\boldsymbol{u}(P-2)$:

$$\frac{\partial I[\boldsymbol{x}(0), P]}{\partial \boldsymbol{u}(P-2)} = 2\,\frac{\partial \boldsymbol{x}'(P)}{\partial \boldsymbol{u}(P-2)}\,\boldsymbol{Q}\boldsymbol{x}(P) + 2\,\frac{\partial \boldsymbol{x}'(P-1)}{\partial \boldsymbol{u}(P-2)}\,\boldsymbol{Q}\boldsymbol{x}(P-1)$$

$$+ 2\,\frac{\partial \boldsymbol{u}'(P-1)}{\partial \boldsymbol{u}(P-2)}\,\boldsymbol{R}\boldsymbol{u}^0(P-1) + 2\boldsymbol{R}\boldsymbol{u}^0(P-2) = \boldsymbol{0}. \quad (3.25)$$

To simplify this equation, we note that from Equations (3.20) and (3.24)

$$\boldsymbol{x}(P) = \boldsymbol{\Phi}\boldsymbol{x}(P-1) - \boldsymbol{\Delta}\boldsymbol{K}_1\boldsymbol{x}(P-1) = (\boldsymbol{\Phi} - \boldsymbol{\Delta}\boldsymbol{K}_1)\boldsymbol{x}(P-1),$$

and thus we may say that

$$\frac{\partial \boldsymbol{x}'(P)}{\partial \boldsymbol{u}(P-2)} = \frac{\partial \boldsymbol{x}'(P-1)}{\partial \boldsymbol{u}(P-2)}\,[\boldsymbol{\Phi} - \boldsymbol{\Delta}\boldsymbol{K}_1]', \qquad \frac{\partial \boldsymbol{u}'(P-1)}{\partial \boldsymbol{u}(P-2)} = -\,\frac{\partial \boldsymbol{x}'(P-1)}{\partial \boldsymbol{u}(P-2)}\,\boldsymbol{K}_1'.$$

In turn, it follows that Equation (3.25) may be written as

$$\frac{\partial \boldsymbol{x}'(P-1)}{\partial \boldsymbol{u}(P-2)}\,[(\boldsymbol{\Phi} - \boldsymbol{\Delta}\boldsymbol{K}_1)'\boldsymbol{Q}\boldsymbol{x}(P) + \boldsymbol{Q}\boldsymbol{x}(P-1) - \boldsymbol{K}_1'\boldsymbol{R}\boldsymbol{u}^0(P-1)] + \boldsymbol{R}\boldsymbol{u}^0(P-2) = \boldsymbol{0} \quad (3.26)$$

or as

$$\boldsymbol{\Delta}'\{[(\boldsymbol{\Phi} - \boldsymbol{\Delta}\boldsymbol{K}_1)'\boldsymbol{Q}][\boldsymbol{\Phi}\boldsymbol{x}(P-1) + \boldsymbol{\Delta}\boldsymbol{u}^0(P-1)]$$
$$+ \boldsymbol{Q}\boldsymbol{x}(P-1) - \boldsymbol{K}_1'\boldsymbol{R}\boldsymbol{u}^0(P-1)\} + \boldsymbol{R}\boldsymbol{u}^0(P-2) = \boldsymbol{0}.$$

Now, removing $\boldsymbol{u}^0(P-1)$ by using Equation (3.24) and $\boldsymbol{x}(P-1)$ by using the system equation, we may solve for $\boldsymbol{u}^0(P-2)$ as

$$\boldsymbol{u}^0(P-2) = -[\boldsymbol{\Delta}'(\boldsymbol{Q} + \boldsymbol{J}_1)\boldsymbol{\Delta} + \boldsymbol{R}]^{-1}\boldsymbol{\Delta}'(\boldsymbol{Q} + \boldsymbol{J}_1)\boldsymbol{\Phi}\boldsymbol{x}(P-2), \quad (3.27)$$

where $\boldsymbol{J}_1 = (\boldsymbol{\Phi} - \boldsymbol{\Delta}\boldsymbol{K}_1)'\boldsymbol{Q}(\boldsymbol{\Phi} - \boldsymbol{\Delta}\boldsymbol{K}_1) + \boldsymbol{K}_1'\boldsymbol{R}\boldsymbol{K}_1$. Alternatively, we may write

$$\boldsymbol{u}^0(P-2) = -\boldsymbol{K}_2\boldsymbol{x}(P-2), \quad (3.28)$$

where $\boldsymbol{K}_2 = [\boldsymbol{\Delta}'(\boldsymbol{Q} + \boldsymbol{J}_1)\boldsymbol{\Delta} + \boldsymbol{R}]^{-1}\boldsymbol{\Delta}'(\boldsymbol{Q} + \boldsymbol{J}_1)\boldsymbol{\Phi}$. Comparing these results to Equations (3.16) and (3.17), we see the equivalence in the formulas, and thus an explicit correspondence.

We may conclude that if we use the functional equations of dynamic programming or an explicit differentiation, the result is equivalent; namely, an iteration sequence is developed for generating a sequence of feedback coefficients $\boldsymbol{K}_1, \boldsymbol{K}_2, \ldots, \boldsymbol{K}_P$. These results are due to the special quadratic form of the performance index and to the fact that no constraints are placed on the control variables.

Equation (3.2), it was previously mentioned, is a slightly simplified version of the more general performance index

$$I[\boldsymbol{x}(0), P] = \boldsymbol{x}(P)'\boldsymbol{S}\boldsymbol{x}(P) + \sum_{k=1}^{P}[\boldsymbol{x}(k)'\boldsymbol{Q}\boldsymbol{x}(k) + \boldsymbol{u}(k-1)'\boldsymbol{R}\boldsymbol{u}(k-1)], \quad (3.29)$$

in which the final state has been included explicitly. If we had used this index instead of Equation (3.2), we would have obtained a slight change in the above results. First, we note that if the infinite stage case, $P \to \infty$, is involved, then, subject to the restrictions mentioned below, $\boldsymbol{x}(P)'\boldsymbol{S}\boldsymbol{x}(P) \to 0$. This follows because $\boldsymbol{x}(P)$, as $P \to \infty$, is the origin. On this basis, the inclusion or exclusion of $\boldsymbol{x}(P)'\boldsymbol{S}\boldsymbol{x}(P)$ in the performance index is immaterial. However, when P is finite, the inclusion of the term causes a change ; in developing the start of the iteration sequence of Equations (3.16) and (3.17), use was made of

$$I[\boldsymbol{x}(P), 0] = 0.$$

But this means that after P stages of control the value of $\boldsymbol{x}(P)$ has reached the origin, $\boldsymbol{x}(P) = \boldsymbol{0}$. If an error is allowed in the final stage, $\boldsymbol{x}(P)'\boldsymbol{S}\boldsymbol{x}(P) \neq 0$, then it follows that

$$I[\boldsymbol{x}(P), 0] = \boldsymbol{x}(P)'\boldsymbol{S}\boldsymbol{x}(P)$$

or $\boldsymbol{J}_0 = \boldsymbol{S}$. Thus Equations (3.16) and (3.17) still hold, but now we specify

$$\begin{aligned} \boldsymbol{J}_0 &= \boldsymbol{0} \qquad \text{(infinite-stage case)}, \\ \boldsymbol{J}_0 &= \boldsymbol{S} \qquad \text{(finite-stage case)}. \end{aligned} \tag{3.30}$$

While we are on this point of an infinite number of stages, it is worth pointing out that $P \to \infty$ means that P approaches a large number in computational sense. Our experience has led us to estimate that $P \approx 3n$ to $4n$, where n equals number of state variables, is sufficient to generate a constant matrix for $\boldsymbol{K}_P$ in the backward iteration.

There are a few interesting subtleties involved in the equations developed and in their use. Thus it is worth summarizing the above procedures and their extensions by the following.

(1) Using the recurrence relations of Equations (3.16) and (3.17) and either $\boldsymbol{J}_0 = \boldsymbol{0}$ or $\boldsymbol{J}_0 = \boldsymbol{S}$ as a starting value, we generate $\boldsymbol{K}_1, \boldsymbol{K}_2, \ldots, \boldsymbol{K}_P$. If P is finite, we retain these values ; if P is infinite, we continue to generate $\boldsymbol{K}_P = \boldsymbol{K}$ for $P \to \infty$.

(2) For the finite-stage case, we use Equation (3.15) in the form

$$\begin{aligned} \boldsymbol{u}^0(0) &= -\boldsymbol{K}_P\boldsymbol{x}(0), \\ \boldsymbol{u}^0(1) &= -\boldsymbol{K}_{P-1}\boldsymbol{x}(1), \\ \boldsymbol{u}^0(2) &= -\boldsymbol{K}_{P-2}\boldsymbol{x}(2), \\ &\vdots \\ \boldsymbol{u}^0(P-1) &= -\boldsymbol{K}_1\boldsymbol{x}(P-1) \end{aligned}$$

to generate the control vectors.

(3) At the same time the discrete-time system model, Equation (3.1), is used to generate the appropriate $\boldsymbol{x}(k+1)$ from the known $\boldsymbol{x}(k)$ and $\boldsymbol{u}^0(k)$.

(4) For the infinite-stage case step (2) above is simplified to

$$\boldsymbol{u}^0(k) = -\boldsymbol{K}\boldsymbol{x}(k),$$

and only the single value of the feedback matrix is required.

Now in specifying these sequences, it has been implied, although not actually specified, that for the infinite-stage case the system has been normalized so that the desired final state $\boldsymbol{x}^d$ is an equilibrium point $\boldsymbol{x}_e$ and that both are the origin; furthermore, the control has been normalized so that $\boldsymbol{x}^d = \boldsymbol{x}_e = \boldsymbol{0}$ corresponds to $\boldsymbol{u}^d = \boldsymbol{u}_e = \boldsymbol{0}$. If this is not done, the optimal control sequence can still be obtained but some care must be used. Suppose we had attempted to minimize the sum

$$\|\boldsymbol{x} - \boldsymbol{x}^d\|_{\boldsymbol{Q}}^2 + \|\boldsymbol{u}\|_{\boldsymbol{R}}^2,$$

where $\boldsymbol{x} \neq \boldsymbol{x}^d$ if $\boldsymbol{u} = \boldsymbol{0}$. This is analogous to minimizing

$$a^2 + b^2$$

subject to

$$a + b = c \neq 0.$$

In such a case, the optimal policy makes neither a nor b equal to zero. Thus, asymptotic approach to $\boldsymbol{x}^d$ cannot be optimal if $\boldsymbol{R} \neq \boldsymbol{0}$. The observed behavior, on the other hand, is optimal because it expresses a balance of control cost against error cost.

If asymptotic approach to $\boldsymbol{x}^d$ is desired, then there are a number of ways to proceed (the correct normalization mentioned above, will, of course, remove all the problems) among which are the following.

(1) Let $\boldsymbol{R} = \boldsymbol{0}$. Now the problem above is not involved so long as $\boldsymbol{x}^d$ is the range of $(\boldsymbol{I} - \boldsymbol{\Phi})^{-1}\boldsymbol{\Delta}$ corresponding to solving the system equation at steady state.

(2) Let $\boldsymbol{R} \neq \boldsymbol{0}$, but define the performance index in the form

$$\|\boldsymbol{x} - \boldsymbol{x}^d\|_{\boldsymbol{Q}}^2 + \|\boldsymbol{u} - \boldsymbol{u}^d\|_{\boldsymbol{R}}^2.$$

On this basis we may go through the dynamic programming procedure and define a completely new set of recurrence relations [42, 43]. These, of course, simplify to Equations (3.16) and (3.17) by the proper normalization.

Tyler [73] has also presented another variation on the performance index in which an ideal model system equation for a plant or process is included. The performance index is defined in terms of the difference between the state $\boldsymbol{x}$ and another model $\boldsymbol{L}\boldsymbol{\eta}$ coming from the equation $\dot{\boldsymbol{\eta}} = \boldsymbol{L}\boldsymbol{\eta}$. This is equivalent to replacing $\boldsymbol{x}^d$ above with $\boldsymbol{L}\boldsymbol{\eta}$. He has then shown how the coefficients in the normal system may be modified as the control proceeds so that these approach those of the ideal model. This concept has interesting connotations in an adaptive control system.

Finally, we should point out that the weighting matrices in the performance index are not required to be constant; that is, $\boldsymbol{R}$ could vary in some prescribed manner yielding a nonstationary optimal control law. In fact, $\boldsymbol{R}$ could be a function of stage number going to, say, the null matrix as time proceeds forward. This allows a considerable amount of flexibility in specifying that in one region of control, certain weightings are put on the amount of control and a different weighting in a different region of control. More will be said about this point later.

The situation becomes more interesting when one considers the possibility that $\boldsymbol{x}^d \neq \boldsymbol{x}_e$ and that certain nonlinear systems may have a multiplicity of $\boldsymbol{x}_e$ or even yield limit-cycle behavior. In such cases, there is no work available regarding the linearized behavior of a nonlinear system with such peculiar but not unusual behavior.

3.2. Discrete-time system with a quadratic performance index and a delay in the control variables

It is of interest to consider the effect of an input delay on the previous control algorithms. Thus, we start with the discrete-time model of Section 1.4.

$$\boldsymbol{x}(k+1) = \boldsymbol{\Phi}\boldsymbol{x}(k) + \boldsymbol{\Delta}\boldsymbol{u}(k-\alpha), \tag{3.31}$$

where it is assumed that the sampling period T is small enough such that α is a multiple of T and therefore an integer. Let us define a new variable

$$\boldsymbol{v}(k) = \boldsymbol{u}(k-\alpha) \tag{3.32}$$

such that Equation (3.31) becomes

$$\boldsymbol{x}(k+1) = \boldsymbol{\Phi}\boldsymbol{x}(k) + \boldsymbol{\Delta}\boldsymbol{v}(k). \tag{3.33}$$

But equation (3.33) is identical in form to the normal discrete-time model, and thus the algorithm defined in Section 3.1 can be used to specify the finite-stage control

$$\boldsymbol{v}^0(0) = -\boldsymbol{K}_P\boldsymbol{x}(0) \tag{3.34}$$

or the infinite-stage control

$$\boldsymbol{v}^0(k) = -\boldsymbol{K}\boldsymbol{x}(k). \tag{3.35}$$

To return to our original variables, we first note that for the infinite-stage control

$$\boldsymbol{u}^0(k) = \boldsymbol{v}^0(k+\alpha) = -\boldsymbol{K}\boldsymbol{x}(k+\alpha), \tag{3.36}$$

and then recall that Equation (1.44) was obtained in the form

$$\boldsymbol{x}(k+P) = \boldsymbol{\Phi}^P\boldsymbol{x}(k) + \sum_{i=0}^{P-1} \boldsymbol{\Phi}^{P-1-i}\boldsymbol{\Delta}\boldsymbol{u}(k+i-P).$$

In this equation P is an integer just as α is an integer in Equation (3.36). Thus, we may write

$$\boldsymbol{u}^0(k) = -\boldsymbol{K}\left[\boldsymbol{\Phi}^\alpha \boldsymbol{x}(k) + \sum_{i=0}^{\alpha-1} \boldsymbol{\Phi}^{\alpha-1-i} \boldsymbol{\Delta u}(k+i-\alpha)\right] \tag{3.37}$$

for the infinite-stage process. An analogous, but more complicated form, can be written for a finite stage process. Equation (3.37) allows the calculation of the optimal control sequence with only a modest amount of extra computation beyond that for the nondelay case. In effect, the system is allowed to move with no control for α stages of time, at which point the control corresponding to $\boldsymbol{u}^0(0)$ for the nondelay case is imposed. The problem thus becomes one of using a "different" initial condition, depending upon the value of α. For further details, the reader should consult the work of Kramer [46] and, for the state-delay case, the work of Koepcke [45].

3.3. Continuous-time systems with a quadratic performance index

In this section, we shall consider the system model as given by

$$\dot{\boldsymbol{x}}(t) = \boldsymbol{A}\boldsymbol{x}(t) + \boldsymbol{B}\boldsymbol{u}(t) \tag{3.38}$$

and a performance index

$$\begin{aligned} I[\boldsymbol{x}(0), t_f] &= \tfrac{1}{2}\left\{\boldsymbol{x}'(t_f)\boldsymbol{S}\boldsymbol{x}(t_f) + \int_0^{t_f}[\boldsymbol{x}'(\lambda)\boldsymbol{Q}\boldsymbol{x}(\lambda) + \boldsymbol{u}(\lambda)'\boldsymbol{R}\boldsymbol{u}(\lambda)]\,d\lambda\right\} \\ &= \tfrac{1}{2}\left\{\|\boldsymbol{x}(t_f)\|_{\boldsymbol{S}}^2 + \int_0^{t_f}[\|\boldsymbol{x}(\lambda)\|_{\boldsymbol{Q}}^2 + \|\boldsymbol{u}(\lambda)\|_{\boldsymbol{R}}^2]\,d\lambda\right\}, \end{aligned} \tag{3.39}$$

where $\boldsymbol{Q}$ and $\boldsymbol{S}$ are positive-semidefinite symmetric matrices and $\boldsymbol{R}$ is positive-definite and symmetric. The control problem to be analyzed is to determine that *unconstrained* $\boldsymbol{u}^0(t)$ which minimizes $I[\boldsymbol{x}(0), t_f]$; to carry this out we shall turn to the minimum principle, although dynamic programming would work equally well. We shall take a few mathematical liberties along the way, but none of these influence the final result. As a side point, if we wish to include output variables, all our equations will involve $\boldsymbol{H}'\boldsymbol{Q}\boldsymbol{H}$ instead of $\boldsymbol{Q}$.

To use the minimum principle, we first must cast our problem into the standard form of Chapter 2. To do this, we define a new scalar variable $x_0(t)$ such that

$$\dot{x}_0(t) = \tfrac{1}{2}\|\boldsymbol{x}(t)\|_{\boldsymbol{Q}}^2 + \tfrac{1}{2}\|\boldsymbol{u}(t)\|_{\boldsymbol{R}}^2, \tag{3.40}$$

$$x_0(0) = 0, \tag{3.41}$$

and define a new performance index

$$I^*[\boldsymbol{x}(0), t_f] = \boldsymbol{c}'\boldsymbol{x}(t_f) + c_0 x_0(t_f), \tag{3.42}$$

where $\boldsymbol{c}$ is a vector with constant elements $c_1, c_2, \ldots, c_n$. The expression $I^*[\boldsymbol{x}(0), t_f]$ has the form desired for the minimum principle, and we see that if we take $\boldsymbol{c}' = \boldsymbol{x}'(t_f)\boldsymbol{S}$ and $c_0 = +1.0$, we will be able to connect this with our original problem. Finally, we define the Hamiltonian

$$H = \boldsymbol{z}'\dot{\boldsymbol{x}} + z_0\dot{x}_0, \tag{3.43}$$

where $\boldsymbol{z}$ is the adjoint vector of dimension n, and then substitute Equations (3.38) and (3.40) into (3.43). This yields

$$H = \boldsymbol{z}'[\boldsymbol{A}\boldsymbol{x} + \boldsymbol{B}\boldsymbol{u}] + z_0[\tfrac{1}{2}(\boldsymbol{x}'\boldsymbol{Q}\boldsymbol{x}) + \tfrac{1}{2}(\boldsymbol{u}'\boldsymbol{R}\boldsymbol{u})]. \tag{3.44}$$

The boundary conditions on the adjoint variables are

$$\boldsymbol{z}(t_f) = \boldsymbol{S}\boldsymbol{x}(t_f) \qquad z_0(t_f) = 1. \tag{3.45}$$

In addition, we know that

$$\dot{z}_0 = -(\partial H/\partial x_0),$$

and from Equation (3.44) we see that

$$\dot{z}_0 = 0.$$

This means that $z_0(t) = \text{const}$, and since the boundary condition, Equation (3.45), states that $z_0(t_f) = 1$, it follows that $z_0(t) = 1$, and Equation (3.44) can be written as

$$H = \boldsymbol{z}'[\boldsymbol{A}\boldsymbol{x} + \boldsymbol{B}\boldsymbol{u}] + \tfrac{1}{2}\boldsymbol{x}'\boldsymbol{Q}\boldsymbol{x} + \tfrac{1}{2}\boldsymbol{u}'\boldsymbol{R}\boldsymbol{u}. \tag{3.46}$$

Our original problem has now been reduced to minimizing the Hamiltonian H of Equation (3.46) with respect to $\boldsymbol{u}(t)$. This will lead to $\boldsymbol{u}^0(t)$ which minimizes the performance index as defined by Equation (3.39) subject to Equation (3.38).

To minimize H with respect to $\boldsymbol{u}(t)$ we note from the right-hand side of Equation (3.46) that only two terms in H actually involve $\boldsymbol{u}(t)$; differentiation of H yields

$$\partial H/\partial \boldsymbol{u} = \boldsymbol{B}'\boldsymbol{z} + \boldsymbol{R}\boldsymbol{u} = \boldsymbol{0}$$

and

$$\partial^2 H/\partial \boldsymbol{u}^2 = \boldsymbol{R}$$

to show that we really obtain a minimum of H. But from the first equation

$$\boldsymbol{u}^0(t) = -\boldsymbol{R}^{-1}\boldsymbol{B}'\boldsymbol{z}, \tag{3.47}$$

and if we define the matrix $\boldsymbol{J}(t)$ by (a *Riccati transformation*),

$$\boldsymbol{z}(t) = \boldsymbol{J}(t)\boldsymbol{x}(t), \tag{3.48}$$

Equation (3.47) becomes

$$\boldsymbol{u}^0(t) = -\boldsymbol{R}^{-1}\boldsymbol{B}'\boldsymbol{J}(t)\boldsymbol{x}(t). \tag{3.49}$$

Alternatively, we may write (3.49) as

$$\boldsymbol{u}^0(t) = -\boldsymbol{K}(t)\boldsymbol{x}(t), \tag{3.50}$$

where

$$\boldsymbol{K}(t) = \boldsymbol{R}^{-1}\boldsymbol{B}'\boldsymbol{J}(t). \tag{3.51}$$

This is the form of the optimal control law; only an explicit definition for $\boldsymbol{J}(t)$ is required to obtain the final continuous-time law.

Before developing the optimal control law, we should say a few words regarding the need for $\boldsymbol{R}$ in the continuous-time performance index. It has already been shown above that $\boldsymbol{R}$, a positive-definite matrix, ensures a unique maximum; this is merely another way of saying that the possibility of singular control cannot exist. If $\boldsymbol{R} = \boldsymbol{0}$, the system equations and the performance index are linear in the control and a singular arc may exist (see Womack and Dashiell [78] for a discussion of this explicit point). Furthermore, we note that if we interpret $\boldsymbol{u}'\boldsymbol{R}\boldsymbol{u}$ as a "cost of control," then the case $\boldsymbol{R} = \boldsymbol{0}$ implies that there is no penalty or cost associated with the amount of control used. In such a case, $\boldsymbol{u}^0(t)$ may well turn out to be an impulse function which is obviously undesirable from an implementation point of view. In the discrete system case this cannot occur, and thus $\boldsymbol{R} = \boldsymbol{0}$ is perfectly feasible.

To develop the necessary form for $\boldsymbol{J}(t)$ [and thus $\boldsymbol{K}(t)$], we first observe from Equation (3.45) that $\boldsymbol{z}(t_f) = \boldsymbol{S}\boldsymbol{x}(t_f)$ and thus from (3.48) that

$$\boldsymbol{J}(t_f) = \boldsymbol{S}. \tag{3.52}$$

Furthermore, since by definition we have

$$\dot{\boldsymbol{z}}(t) = -\partial H/\partial \boldsymbol{x},$$

then it follows that

$$\dot{\boldsymbol{z}}(t) = -\boldsymbol{Q}\boldsymbol{x} - \boldsymbol{A}'\boldsymbol{z}. \tag{3.53}$$

But we know that

$$\dot{\boldsymbol{x}} = \boldsymbol{A}\boldsymbol{x} + \boldsymbol{B}\boldsymbol{u}.$$

Using the optimal control, Equation (3.49), we obtain

$$\dot{\boldsymbol{x}} = \boldsymbol{A}\boldsymbol{x} - \boldsymbol{B}\boldsymbol{R}^{-1}\boldsymbol{B}'\boldsymbol{J}(t)\boldsymbol{x}.$$

If we differentiate Equation (3.48), we get

$$\dot{\boldsymbol{z}}(t) = \dot{\boldsymbol{J}}\boldsymbol{x} + \boldsymbol{J}\dot{\boldsymbol{x}} = \dot{\boldsymbol{J}}\boldsymbol{x} + \boldsymbol{J}[\boldsymbol{A} - \boldsymbol{B}\boldsymbol{R}^{-1}\boldsymbol{B}'\boldsymbol{J}]\boldsymbol{x}. \tag{3.54}$$

Equating Equations (3.53) and (3.54) and using (3.49) yield

$$\dot{\boldsymbol{J}}(t) + \boldsymbol{J}\boldsymbol{A} + \boldsymbol{A}'\boldsymbol{J} - \boldsymbol{J}\boldsymbol{B}\boldsymbol{R}^{-1}\boldsymbol{B}'\boldsymbol{J} + \boldsymbol{Q} = \boldsymbol{0}. \tag{3.55}$$

Equation (3.55) is a *first-order Riccati nonlinear differential equation* which has from Equation (3.52) a final condition $\boldsymbol{J}(t_f) = \boldsymbol{S}$. Although we shall discuss further properties of this Riccati equation shortly, it suffices for the moment to note that by integrating Equation (3.55) the explicit form of the optimal control law can be obtained.

In summary, for the linear stationary continuous-time system with a quadratic performance index and unconstrained control, the optimal control law is given by

$$\boldsymbol{u}^0(t) = -\boldsymbol{K}(t)\boldsymbol{x}(t), \tag{3.56}$$

where

$$\boldsymbol{K}(t) = \boldsymbol{R}^{-1}\boldsymbol{B}'\boldsymbol{J}(t). \tag{3.57}$$

We obtain $\boldsymbol{J}(t)$ by integrating the Riccati equation (3.55) with a final condition $\boldsymbol{J}(t_f) = \boldsymbol{S}$ or in a backward-time direction with an initial condition $\boldsymbol{J}(t_f) = \boldsymbol{S}$. Alternatively, this may be done in a forward-time direction with an initial condition $\boldsymbol{J}(t - t_f) = \boldsymbol{S}$.

We also note that the canonical equations for the present case are given by

$$\dot{\boldsymbol{x}}(t) = \boldsymbol{A}\boldsymbol{x}(t) + \boldsymbol{B}\boldsymbol{u}(t),$$

$$\dot{\boldsymbol{z}}(t) = -\boldsymbol{Q}\boldsymbol{x}(t) - \boldsymbol{A}'\boldsymbol{z}(t).$$

The free canonical equations (the Euler–Lagrange equations) are given by

$$\begin{bmatrix} \dot{\boldsymbol{x}}(t) \\ \dot{\boldsymbol{z}}(t) \end{bmatrix} = \begin{bmatrix} \boldsymbol{A} & -\boldsymbol{B}\boldsymbol{R}^{-1}\boldsymbol{B}' \\ -\boldsymbol{Q} & -\boldsymbol{A}' \end{bmatrix} \begin{bmatrix} \boldsymbol{x}(t) \\ \boldsymbol{z}(t) \end{bmatrix}. \tag{3.58}$$

In Chapter 4 we shall explore some implications of the solution to the current problem. We shall see how it may be used in an iterative fashion to solve the fully nonlinear control problem.

Just as in the discrete case, the optimal control law has certain interesting features as $t_f \to \infty$. As shown by Kalman [39–43], the limit of $\boldsymbol{J}(t)$ as $t \to \infty$ exists and is finite if the system is completely controllable. When $\boldsymbol{S} = \boldsymbol{0}$, the limit which results is an equilibrium state of the Riccati equation, that is,

$$\lim_{t \to \infty} \boldsymbol{J}(t) = \boldsymbol{J}_e \qquad \text{for} \quad \boldsymbol{S} = \boldsymbol{0}.$$

When $\boldsymbol{S} \neq \boldsymbol{0}$, it is possible that different limits exist (see later discussion). Thus, when $\boldsymbol{S} = \boldsymbol{0}$, Equation (3.56) may be written in the form

$$\boldsymbol{u}^0(t) = -\boldsymbol{K}_e\boldsymbol{x}(t), \tag{3.59}$$

corresponding to

$$\boldsymbol{K}_e = \boldsymbol{R}^{-1}\boldsymbol{B}'\boldsymbol{J}_e. \tag{3.60}$$

We note with considerable interest that in the infinite-time case the original two-point boundary-value problem in which the system equation has an initial condition $\boldsymbol{x}(0)$ and the Riccati equation has a final condition $\boldsymbol{J}(0) = \boldsymbol{0}$ is transformed into an equivalent problem of two uncoupled initial-value equations. That this is a simplification is apparent.

While we are at it, we should observe that there is one important difference between the continuous-time and discrete-time control laws. Because of the form of Equations (3.57) and (3.60), the case $\boldsymbol{R} = \boldsymbol{0}$ cannot be treated in the continuous-time formulation. It can, however, be included as a special case of discrete control. In the continuous case, $\boldsymbol{R} = \boldsymbol{0}$ implies that any control can be used; this in turn may lead to an impulse control. The inclusion of $\boldsymbol{R}$ positive-definite prevents such possibilities.

When the infinite-time control is used, the system equation may be written as

$$\dot{\boldsymbol{x}}(t) = \boldsymbol{A}\boldsymbol{x}(t) + \boldsymbol{B}\boldsymbol{u}^0(t),$$

and substituting Equation (3.59) into this, we have

$$\dot{\boldsymbol{x}}(t) = \boldsymbol{A}\boldsymbol{x}(t) + \boldsymbol{B}[-\boldsymbol{K}_e\boldsymbol{x}(t)]$$

or

$$\dot{\boldsymbol{x}}(t) = [\boldsymbol{A} - \boldsymbol{B}\boldsymbol{K}_e]\boldsymbol{x}(t).$$

But since $\boldsymbol{A}$, $\boldsymbol{B}$ and $\boldsymbol{K}_e$ are constant matrices, the solution to this equation can be written as

$$\boldsymbol{x}(t) = \exp\,[(\boldsymbol{A} - \boldsymbol{B}\boldsymbol{K}_e)t]\boldsymbol{x}(0), \tag{3.61}$$

where the initial condition $\boldsymbol{x}(0)$ has been used in the integration. This is an explicit use of the decoupling of the original two-point boundary-value problem mentioned above. Only an exponential routine and a matrix-vector multiplication is required to generate the optimal state trajectory.

As to the means of evaluating $\boldsymbol{J}(t)$ or $\boldsymbol{J}_e$, first we mention the rather obvious procedure of integrating backward the original nonlinear Riccati equation using $\boldsymbol{J}(t_f) = \boldsymbol{S}$ as a starting condition. It turns out that convergence to the steady state is exponential, and thus $\boldsymbol{J}_e$ can be determined in this matter. As we see from the steady-state form of Equation (3.55),

$$\boldsymbol{J}_e\boldsymbol{A} + \boldsymbol{A}'\boldsymbol{J}_e - \boldsymbol{J}_e\boldsymbol{B}\boldsymbol{R}^{-1}\boldsymbol{B}'\boldsymbol{J}_e + \boldsymbol{Q} = \boldsymbol{0},$$

a quadratic algebraic equation in $\boldsymbol{J}_e$ is involved. Thus, there may be two possible roots of the steady-state equation. If $\boldsymbol{S} = \boldsymbol{0}$, we can guarantee that there is at least one stable equilibrium point or root. This is obtained by integrating the Riccati equation with $t_f \to \infty$, that is, integrating backward in time. However, if the integration is done with $t_f \to -\infty$, then we may obtain, depending on the system, an unstable point or perhaps a stable but different limit. If $\boldsymbol{S} \neq \boldsymbol{0}$ but is merely nonnegative, then there is no guarantee that a stable solution exists. It is true that a stable limit may exist for $\boldsymbol{S}$ nonnegative, but it should be kept in mind that this is not always the case. We could just as well have a system where no stable solutions exist or where several stable but different limits exist.

An alternative method for evaluating $\boldsymbol{J}(t)$ may be obtained by a transformation of variable which converts the Riccati equation into a linear equation [39]. Thus, we introduce the new variable $\boldsymbol{\theta}$ such that

$$\dot{\boldsymbol{\theta}} = \boldsymbol{E\theta}, \tag{3.62}$$

where

$$\boldsymbol{E} = \begin{bmatrix} \boldsymbol{A} & -\boldsymbol{BR}^{-1}\boldsymbol{B}' \\ -\boldsymbol{Q} & -\boldsymbol{A}' \end{bmatrix}.$$

For convenience in manipulation, we shall write

$$\boldsymbol{E} = \begin{bmatrix} \boldsymbol{F} & \boldsymbol{G} \\ \boldsymbol{L} & \boldsymbol{M} \end{bmatrix}$$

with $\boldsymbol{F} = \boldsymbol{A}$, $\boldsymbol{G} = -\boldsymbol{BR}^{-1}\boldsymbol{B}'$, $\boldsymbol{L} = -\boldsymbol{Q}$ and $\boldsymbol{M} = -\boldsymbol{A}'$. But we may also write $\boldsymbol{\theta}$ in partitioned form as

$$\boldsymbol{\theta} = \left[\begin{array}{c|c} \boldsymbol{\theta}_{11} & \boldsymbol{\theta}_{12} \\ \hline \boldsymbol{\theta}_{21} & \boldsymbol{\theta}_{22} \end{array}\right]$$

and thus

$$\left[\begin{array}{c|c} \dot{\boldsymbol{\theta}}_{11} & \dot{\boldsymbol{\theta}}_{12} \\ \hline \dot{\boldsymbol{\theta}}_{21} & \dot{\boldsymbol{\theta}}_{22} \end{array}\right] = \left[\begin{array}{c|c} \boldsymbol{F\theta}_{11} + \boldsymbol{G\theta}_{21} & \boldsymbol{F\theta}_{12} + \boldsymbol{G\theta}_{22} \\ \hline \boldsymbol{L\theta}_{11} + \boldsymbol{M\theta}_{21} & \boldsymbol{L\theta}_{12} + \boldsymbol{M\theta}_{22} \end{array}\right].$$

Alternatively,

$$\begin{aligned} \dot{\boldsymbol{\theta}}_{11} &= \boldsymbol{F\theta}_{11} + \boldsymbol{G\theta}_{21}, \\ &\vdots \qquad\qquad \vdots \\ \dot{\boldsymbol{\theta}}_{22} &= \boldsymbol{L\theta}_{12} + \boldsymbol{M\theta}_{22}. \end{aligned} \tag{3.63}$$

Now if we let $\boldsymbol{J}(t)$ be related to $\boldsymbol{\theta}(t)$ by the equation

$$\boldsymbol{J}[\boldsymbol{\theta}_{11} + \boldsymbol{\theta}_{12}\boldsymbol{J}(0)] = [\boldsymbol{\theta}_{21} + \boldsymbol{\theta}_{22}\boldsymbol{J}(0)], \tag{3.64}$$

then differentiating both sides yields

$$\dot{\boldsymbol{J}}[\boldsymbol{\theta}_{11} + \boldsymbol{\theta}_{12}\boldsymbol{J}(0)] + \boldsymbol{J}[\dot{\boldsymbol{\theta}}_{11} + \dot{\boldsymbol{\theta}}_{12}\boldsymbol{J}(0)] = [\dot{\boldsymbol{\theta}}_{21} + \dot{\boldsymbol{\theta}}_{22}\boldsymbol{J}(0)].$$

But if we now substitute into this equation the definitions above for $\dot{\boldsymbol{\theta}}_{11}, \ldots, \dot{\boldsymbol{\theta}}_{22}$ and the equation relating $\boldsymbol{J}$ and $\boldsymbol{\theta}$, Equations (3.63) and (3.64), some manipulations show that the Riccati equation results. Thus, the new variable $\boldsymbol{\theta}$ transforms the Riccati equation into the linear form (3.62). If $\boldsymbol{E} = \text{const}$ in (3.62) ($\boldsymbol{A}$, $\boldsymbol{B}$, $\boldsymbol{R}$ and $\boldsymbol{Q}$ are constant); the solution of (3.62) is merely

$$\boldsymbol{\theta}(t) = \exp[\boldsymbol{E}t]\boldsymbol{\theta}(0) \qquad (\boldsymbol{\theta}(0) = \boldsymbol{I}). \tag{3.65}$$

But since Equation (3.64) relates $\boldsymbol{J}(t)$ to the submatrices of $\boldsymbol{\theta}(t)$, from Equation (3.65) we may use the submatrices at any t to calculate the corresponding $\boldsymbol{J}(t)$.

In this form only an exponential and an inversion routine are required to evaluate $J(t)$.

One of the features which makes the Riccati equation converge rapidly to its steady-state value is that the performance index is a Liapunov function (the equivalent statement can also be made for the discrete system). Although we shall detail this point in Chapter 5, we note in passing that

$$I^0[\mathbf{x}(0), t_f] = \tfrac{1}{2}\left\{\|\mathbf{x}(t_f)\|_{\mathbf{S}}^2 + \int_0^{t_f} (\|\mathbf{x}\|_{\mathbf{Q}}^2 + \|\mathbf{u}^0\|_{\mathbf{R}}^2)\, dt\right\}$$

and that

$$\dot{I}^0[\mathbf{x}(0), t_f] = -[\mathbf{x}'\mathbf{Q}\mathbf{x} + \mathbf{x}'\mathbf{K}'\mathbf{R}^{-1}\mathbf{K}\mathbf{x}].$$

Since the matrices $\mathbf{Q}$ and $\mathbf{R}$ are by definition positive semi-definite, the matrix $\mathbf{K}'\mathbf{R}\mathbf{K}$ is at least nonnegative-definite. Thus, if the system is completely controllable and completely observable, all the state variables contribute to the expression for $\dot{I}^0$, and I^0 is a decreasing function.

At this point, it seems worthwhile to detail some of the points above by means of a trivial example. Thus, we consider the scalar system equation

$$\dot{x} = ax + bu \tag{3.66}$$

so that $A = [a]$, $B = [b]$ with $a,\ b \neq 0$. The performance index has scalar positive weighting terms $\mathbf{Q} = [q]$, $\mathbf{R} = [r]$, and $\mathbf{S} = [s]$. On this basis the Riccati equation takes the form

$$\dot{j} + 2aj - \frac{b^2 j^2}{r} + q = 0. \tag{3.67}$$

Obviously, this equation will have two roots in the case of infinite time, since $\dot{j}$ then becomes zero, leaving an algebraic quadratic equation in terms of j. The two roots are merely

$$j_1 = \{a + \sqrt{a^2 + (b^2 q/r)}\}r/b^2, \qquad j_2 = \{a - \sqrt{a^2 + (b^2 q/r)}\}r/b^2,$$

with $j_1 > 0$ and $j_2 < 0$. Thus, j_1 is a root on the positive side of a $\dot{j}$ vs. j plot, whereas j_2 is on the negative side. We can now rewrite Equation (3.67) as

$$\dot{j} = \frac{b^2}{r}(j - j_1)(j - j_2)$$

and immediately see that

$$\begin{aligned} &\dot{j} > 0 \quad \text{if} \quad j > j_1 \quad \text{or} \quad j < j_2, \\ &\dot{j} < 0 \quad \text{if} \quad j_2 < j < j_1. \end{aligned}$$

Remembering that the Riccati equation is integrated backward, we see that these inequalities show that if $j > j_1$, j will decrease, and if $j < j_1$, j will increase;

and if $j < j_2$, j will decrease, and if $j > j_2$, j will increase. As a result, j_1 is a stable equilibrium point of the Riccati equation; j_2 is an unstable point.

We thus note that if we choose $j(0) = s = 0$, then j will always approach j_1. In fact, if we pick $j(0) = s \geq 0$, then j will still always approach the stable equilibrium point.

Proceeding further, we can ascertain from Equation (3.57) that

$$k(t) = (1/r)bj(t)$$

or, at the equilibrium point obtained with $j(0) = s \geq 0$,

$$k = (1/r)bj_1.$$

But this means that

$$\dot{x} = [a - bk]x,$$

and since it is relatively simple to show that $(a - bk) < 0$, the resulting control is always stable.

We have already mentioned in Chapter 1 the significance and versatility of the quadratic performance index and the matrices $\boldsymbol{Q}$, $\boldsymbol{R}$, and $\boldsymbol{S}$, but some further details are appropriate at this point. We shall concentrate on the continuous-time system, but the discussion will apply equally well to the discrete-time version. First, we note from Equations (3.52), (3.56), and (3.57) that

$$\boldsymbol{u}^0(t_f) = -\boldsymbol{R}^{-1}\boldsymbol{B}'\boldsymbol{S}\boldsymbol{x}(t_f) = -\boldsymbol{K}(t_f)\boldsymbol{x}(t_f).$$

Thus, increasing the magnitude of the elements in $\boldsymbol{S}$ has two effects so long as a finite-stage system is involved. First, it minimizes the final error by weighting $\boldsymbol{x}(t_f)^2$ more heavily (note the connection to the penalty function concept of Chapter 4); second, it increases the magnitude of the final feedback matrix, which also tends to minimize the final error. Error is here taken to mean the deviation from the origin.

By contrast, $\boldsymbol{Q}$ and $\boldsymbol{R}$ affect the entire trajectory, and each acts in opposing direction in terms of the error. Thus, increasing $\boldsymbol{Q}$ will reduce the error in the state vector along the trajectory whereas increasing $\boldsymbol{R}$ will reduce the amount of control used and thereby will increase the error in the state vector. If $\boldsymbol{S}$ and $\boldsymbol{Q}$ are both $\boldsymbol{0}$ but $\boldsymbol{R}$ is not, the result will be to minimize the amount of control used, irrespective of the resulting states. But this simply leads to $\boldsymbol{u}^0(t) = \boldsymbol{0}$.

We see that the optimal trajectory can be varied considerably by only "adjusting" the magnitudes of the elements of $\boldsymbol{Q}$, $\boldsymbol{R}$, and $\boldsymbol{S}$. In fact, although the theory is based entirely on unconstrained control and, of course, on unconstrained state variations, our experience has shown that if this manipulation of $\boldsymbol{Q}$, $\boldsymbol{R}$, and $\boldsymbol{S}$ is carried out, the response obtained can actually be bounded in terms of the control and state, even though the theory is not explicitly predicting the same. One of the numerical examples at the end of this chapter details this point more fully.

Finally, and to conclude this section, we might dwell briefly on a point mentioned previously, namely, the nonstationary case. Nonstationary here might mean in terms of the system equations that $\boldsymbol{A} = \boldsymbol{A}(t)$ and $\boldsymbol{B} = \boldsymbol{B}(t)$ or, in terms of the performance index, that $\boldsymbol{Q} = \boldsymbol{Q}(t)$, $\boldsymbol{R} = \boldsymbol{R}(t)$, and $\boldsymbol{S} = \boldsymbol{S}(t)$. In the former case the system equations are time-varying; this does not really bother us so long as we know the explicit time variation. In the latter case we might write, following Tyler [73],

$$\boldsymbol{Q} = \boldsymbol{Q}_0 e^{2\alpha t}, \qquad \boldsymbol{R} = \boldsymbol{R}_0 e^{2\alpha t}, \qquad \boldsymbol{S} = \boldsymbol{S}_0 e^{2\alpha t}, \tag{3.68}$$

where $\boldsymbol{Q}_0$, $\boldsymbol{R}_0$ and $\boldsymbol{S}_0$ are constant matrices such that at the final time $\boldsymbol{Q} = \boldsymbol{Q}_0 e^{2\alpha t_f}$, $\boldsymbol{R} = \boldsymbol{R}_0 e^{2\alpha t_f}$, and $\boldsymbol{S} = \boldsymbol{S}_0 e^{2\alpha t_f}$. Now as we move backward in time while integrating the Riccati equation, the actual $\boldsymbol{Q}$, $\boldsymbol{R}$, and $\boldsymbol{S}$ matrices decrease as we approach $t = 0$. In this case, the Riccati equation has the form

$$\dot{\boldsymbol{J}}(t) + \boldsymbol{J}\boldsymbol{A} + \boldsymbol{A}'\boldsymbol{J} - \boldsymbol{J}\boldsymbol{B}\boldsymbol{R}_0^{-1} e^{-2\alpha t}\boldsymbol{B}'\boldsymbol{J} + \boldsymbol{Q}_0 e^{2\alpha t} = \boldsymbol{0}$$

rather than Equation (3.56). The feedback matrix resulting is

$$\overline{\boldsymbol{K}}(t) = \boldsymbol{R}_0^{-1}\boldsymbol{B}'\boldsymbol{J}(t) e^{-2\alpha t}, \tag{3.69}$$

which is seen to be time-varying. In this way, we are able to penalize the system by different amounts in different regions of the control cycle.

Although our derivations here have used dynamic programming and the minimum principle to obtain the optimal control law, it is also possible to use the Hamilton-Jacobi partial differential equation of Chapter 2. In this way the necessary and sufficient condition for optimal control can be specified immediately. For details of this approach to the problems under consideration in this chapter see Falb and Kleinman [20], Kalman [38–43], and Tchamran [68–70].

Finally, it is important to observe that the synthesis methods developed here and in other chapters of this book are based on the assumption of a complete knowledge of the system parameters. In other words, the coefficients in the system equations are known completely. In many practical engineering situations such an assumption is not valid. As a result, the recent literature [11, 15, 32, 60, 62, 77] has been concerned with the sensitivity of parameter variations, i.e., how much are the optimal trajectory and performance index changed for various perturbations in the parameters. If the change in the trajectory and index is small for moderate variations in the parameters, a form of suboptimal control may actually be quite adequate. In addition, this matter is of importance in comparing open- and closed-loop controls.

Obviously, the question of the sensitivity of the optimal control to parameter variations is an important one. It is mentioned in the present chapter because much of the work carried out concerns the behavior of the linear system–quadratic index problem. The interested reader can pursue the references given above.

3.4. The Kalman ASP program

As probably is apparent to the reader, Kalman has been the basic motivating force behind much of the work in Sections 3.1 through 3.3 as well as providing much of the theoretical development. However, he has gone even further and with Engler has written the Automatic Synthesis Program [42, 43], ASP, which provides a means of implementing all these concepts.

The program is available for the IBM 7090/94 series of digital computers and is made up of a series of internal subroutines or is, in other words, a special-purpose executive program. The internal subroutines involve an exponential and integral matrix routine, routines for all matrix manipulations, a Riccati-equation-solving routine, a system-integrating routine, plus others needed to use the above concepts. Of particular importance are the error checks used in developing each of the routines so as to minimize any computational errors.

To perform any set of control calculations, it is only necessary to connect these subroutines with a series of macro-instructions. Thus to run the continuous-time optimal program we need only to punch up the elements of $\boldsymbol{A}$, $\boldsymbol{B}$, $\boldsymbol{Q}$, $\boldsymbol{R}$, and $\boldsymbol{S}$, in an appropriate computer card format and then use a single input card which calls the Riccati routine. This routine then performs all the calculations of solving the Riccati nonlinear differential equations and prints out the corresponding values of $\boldsymbol{K}(t)$ and $\boldsymbol{J}(t)$. Another input card then calls the system or transient routine to generate the sequence of $\boldsymbol{u}^0(t)$ and $\boldsymbol{x}(t)$. In this way, all optimal control calculations of this type may be carried out by merely punching up the series of input cards.

Such a computer program is of absolute importance to everyone interested in control calculations. It makes available, for the first time and in a manner conceptually equivalent to the use of a subroutine from a library tape, a comprehensive and detailed tool for control analysis. It is work such as this which will ultimately make control calculations a most feasible tool.

3.5. Linear systems with a quadratic performance index and control constraints

It has been emphasized that all the material discussed in Sections 3.1 through 3.3 deals with unconstrained control systems. A brief mention was made at the end of Section 3.3 that by a proper selection of the $\boldsymbol{Q}$, $\boldsymbol{R}$, and $\boldsymbol{S}$ matrices, a control and state trajectory can probably be obtained which does not violate any physical constraints. However, this necessitates a performance index which may be outside of that physically desired. Nevertheless, this is one approach to handling the constrained control problem.

Actually, the problem arises because of the simple form of the feedback system. Because the backward (time) relations are in essentially closed form, one must take the control which arises as it comes. But since the equations can be derived by dynamic programming, it would be assumed that in some way it is possible to handle control constraints.

In particular, the problem has been analyzed by Johnson and Wonham [36] and by Deley and Franklin [14]. We shall point out some of the features of the latter work since it fits in rather easily with the analysis of Section 3.1. We shall not attempt to present the derivation since it follows that already given, but instead shall present only the essential results.

We start with our normal discrete-time system equation,

$$\boldsymbol{x}(k+1) = \boldsymbol{\Phi x}(k) + \boldsymbol{\Delta u}(k), \tag{3.70}$$

except that only one control variable is involved and it is bounded in the form

$$-\gamma \leq u \leq \gamma. \tag{3.71}$$

For example, we might choose $\gamma = 1.0$. Now analogous to Equation (3.7), we assume the optimal performance index has the form

$$I_0[\boldsymbol{x}(0), P] = \boldsymbol{x}'(0)\boldsymbol{J}_P\boldsymbol{x}(0) + \boldsymbol{x}(0)'\,\boldsymbol{d}_P + \boldsymbol{d}'_P\boldsymbol{x}(0) + c_P, \tag{3.72}$$

where $\boldsymbol{d}_P$, an $(n \times 1)$ vector, and c_P, a scalar, have been introduced. Corresponding to the optimal control law, Equation (3.11), we now define

$$u^0(0) = -\boldsymbol{K}_P\boldsymbol{x}(0) - g_P, \tag{3.73}$$

where $\boldsymbol{K}_P$ is defined as before (since u is now a scalar, $\boldsymbol{K}_P$ is a $(1 \times n)$ vector),

$$\boldsymbol{K}_P = [\boldsymbol{\Delta}'(\boldsymbol{Q} + \boldsymbol{J}_{P-1})\boldsymbol{\Delta} + \boldsymbol{R}]^{-1}\boldsymbol{\Delta}'(\boldsymbol{Q} + \boldsymbol{J}_{P-1})\boldsymbol{\Phi}, \tag{3.74}$$

and g_P is a scalar defined as

$$g_P = [\boldsymbol{\Delta}'(\boldsymbol{Q} + \boldsymbol{J}_{P-1})\boldsymbol{\Delta} + \boldsymbol{R}]^{-1}\boldsymbol{\Delta}'\boldsymbol{d}_P \tag{3.75}$$

Using these definitions and the same procedure as in Section 3.1, Deley and Franklin show that the following sequences hold :

Unconstrained

$$\begin{aligned} \boldsymbol{J}_P &= \boldsymbol{\Phi}'(\boldsymbol{Q} + \boldsymbol{J}_{P-1})(\boldsymbol{\Phi} - \boldsymbol{\Delta K}_P), \\ \boldsymbol{d}_P &= [\boldsymbol{\Phi} - \boldsymbol{\Delta K}_P]'\,\boldsymbol{d}_{P-1}, \\ c_P &= c_{P-1} - \boldsymbol{d}'_{P-1}\boldsymbol{\Delta} g_P, \end{aligned} \tag{3.76}$$

Constrained

$$\begin{aligned} \boldsymbol{J}_P &= \boldsymbol{\Phi}'(\boldsymbol{Q} + \boldsymbol{J}_{P-1})\boldsymbol{\Phi}, \\ \boldsymbol{d}_P &= \boldsymbol{\Phi}'[\boldsymbol{d}_{P-1} + (\boldsymbol{Q} + \boldsymbol{J}_{P-1})\boldsymbol{\Delta}\gamma], \\ c_P &= c_{P-1} + \gamma^2[\boldsymbol{\Delta}'(\boldsymbol{Q} + \boldsymbol{J}_{P-1})\boldsymbol{\Delta} + R] + 2\gamma\boldsymbol{\Delta}'\,\boldsymbol{d}_{P-1}. \end{aligned} \tag{3.77}$$

The initial conditions for these sequences are

$$\boldsymbol{J}_0 = \boldsymbol{0}, \qquad \boldsymbol{d}_0 = \boldsymbol{0}, \qquad c_0 = 0. \tag{3.78}$$

We immediately observe that in the unconstrained case, $\boldsymbol{d}_P = \boldsymbol{0}$, $g_P = 0$, and

$c_P = 0$ from the starting conditions in Equation (3.78) ; since $\boldsymbol{K}_P$ and $\boldsymbol{J}_P$ are not changed, the results are the same as in the previous unconstrained case.

The computational problem here is that one does not know which, if any, controls $u(0)$, $u(1)$, . . . will be on the constraint bounds. If we proceed backward in time, we would expect that near P the state is close to the origin and thus the control would not be large for that part of the trajectory. However, at some point one of the controls may reach a constraint and, if so, one would expect all the rest back to $u(0)$ to be beyond the constraint bounds. Thus, one must either iterate the entire procedure of the unconstrained recurrence relationships backward, finding which $u(k)$ is the first to overstep the bounds, and then continue the iteration using the alternative constrained recurrence relationships at the appropriate point, or devise an alternative scheme. This may be looked on as a requirement to solve the coupled boundary-value system. We shall, however, not pursue this point here but again refer the interested reader to the paper by Deley and Franklin [14].

3.6. Minimum-time control of linear systems

There exists at present a considerable amount of theoretical material dealing with the minimum-time control of linear systems, that is, control of systems in which the performance index is the time of control itself. In particular, we shall restrict ourselves to the case where the control is constrained in amplitude (see Section 1.5) and develop the necessary algorithms for both the continuous-time and discrete-time systems. In both cases a definitive algorithm can be written, although the computation time required may vary considerably, depending on the particular dynamic model, continuous or discrete, used. The work of Lesser [52, 53] is illustrative of the approach we shall use.

A few words regarding the importance and implications of constraining the control amplitude are in order. Starting with an initial condition $\boldsymbol{x}(0)$ and seeking the unconstrained control $\boldsymbol{u}^0(t)$ which forces the system into the origin, $\boldsymbol{x}(t_f) = \boldsymbol{0}$, in a minimum time $t_f = t_f^{\min}$, an intuitive proposal would be to use as much control as possible at the beginning. If the control is constrained to a value less than the predicted unconstrained value, it will obviously take a longer time to reach the origin. Thus, the minimum time in the constrained case is probably related to the maximum allowable control value. As we will show, the optimal control is the type called *bang-bang* or *on-off*, in which the control alternates or *switches* in some manner between upper and lower constraints, assuming the control is constrained on its upper and lower value. The *switching times*, the times at which the control is switched from its upper to lower bound or vice versa, will be the major quantities which we shall seek to predict for optimal control.

To illustrate this question of the switching times, let us consider an idealized system with two state variables and a single control variable which is bounded between 0 and 1, $0 \le u \le 1$. If we start with $x(0)$ and wish to reach the origin in, say, one switch, then we might have the situation shown in Figure 3.2. The state starts at $x(0)$ at time $t = 0$, and when $u = 1$ is applied the states follow the trajectory of the solid line. At some time t_1 (or t_2) the control is switched to $u = 0$ and the trajectory reaches the origin at time t_3 (or t_4). The problem is, of course, to find that t_1 (or t_2, or some time) which causes the origin to be reached in the shortest time. When one thinks of multidimensional x and a large number of switches, it becomes evident that finding the switching times is not trivial.

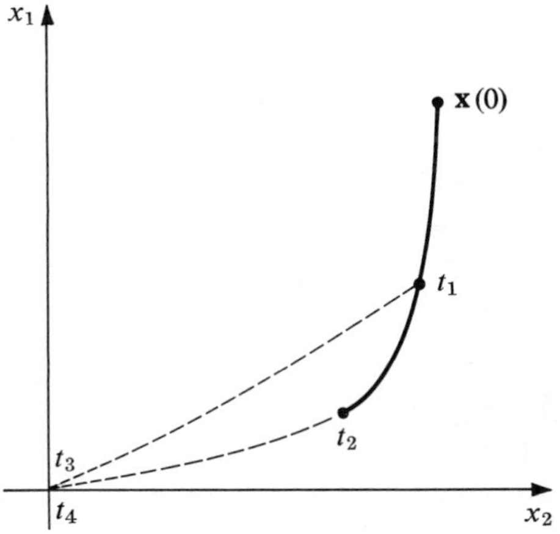

FIGURE 3.2. Possible switches in minimum-time control

Before we start our detailed discussion, it will be instructive if we point out an alternative method for solving the minimum-time problem suggested by Ho [29, 30]. This method is based on the previous analysis in this chapter. Suppose that we ask to minimize the error at a terminal or final state using a fixed control time, that is, min $\|x(t_f)\|_S^2$. If this minimum error is finite at the t_f selected, the optimal control cannot reach the origin in time t_f. If, however, the error is zero, then the control can reach the origin in time t_f. In the latter case, we then repeat the problem but with a smaller value of t_f; this is continued until a point is reached at which the error cannot be forced to zero. The time immediately preceding this is then the minimum time. In other words, Ho suggests a successive approximation method in which the optimal control is approached from a series of sub- (or non-) optimal controls.

Now we turn to the analysis of the minimum-time control of linear continuous-time systems. The specific algorithm to be discussed is due to Neustadt [57], and the reader should consult this article for certain mathematical proofs which we shall not include. Actually, the historical development in this area is of interest and dates back to the work of Bushaw in 1952 [10]. Bellman, Glicksberg, and Gross in 1956 [7] considered the case of $r = n$, that is, the number of control variables is equal to the number of state variables. Using a continuous-time system equation of the form

$$\dot{\boldsymbol{x}}(t) = \boldsymbol{A}(t)\boldsymbol{x}(t) + \boldsymbol{B}(t)\boldsymbol{u}(t), \tag{3.79}$$

with $\boldsymbol{B} = \boldsymbol{I}$ and $A(t) = \boldsymbol{A} =$ const with real distinct negative eigenvalues, they proved that bang-bang control is time-optimal. Furthermore, each control variable changes sign, at most, $(n - 1)$ times. These results were extended to obtain sufficient conditions for the existence of an optimal solution, and in 1958 Gamkredlidze [24] considered the full equation with $\boldsymbol{B}$ allowed to be general. He showed that for so-called "*normal*" (this is equivalent to controllable) systems, a control exists which will drive $\boldsymbol{x}(t)$ to the origin in minimum time; furthermore, the control is unique. In 1960 LaSalle [50] proved that this control is unique. A system is said to be normal if no component of the transposed vector $[\boldsymbol{\eta}' \exp(-\boldsymbol{A}t)\boldsymbol{B}]$ vanishes over any finite time interval for any nonzero vector $\boldsymbol{\eta}$. As we will see shortly, it is in the finding of this nonzero vector $\boldsymbol{\eta}$ that the problem of solving the minimum-time control resides. It was Neustadt who outlined an iterative procedure for finding the true value. Other procedures for accomplishing this determination of $\boldsymbol{\eta}$ have since been proposed by Eaton [17] and by Fadden and Gilbert [19]. The papers of Wing and Desoer [75, 76], Harvey [27, 28], Oldenburger and Thompson [59], and Snow [67] are also indicative of the techniques available for solving the minimum-time problem. Isaacs and Leondes [33] have extended the work of Neustadt to include performance indices with quadratic terms in the state and control.

Our system model will be as given in Equation (3.79), and the control will be constrained in the form

$$-\gamma_i \leq u_i \leq \gamma_i \qquad (i = 1, 2, \ldots, r \quad \text{and} \quad r < n), \tag{3.80}$$

where γ_i could be 1 for simplicity. On this basis, the admissible control is restricted to a closed, bounded, and convex polygon containing the origin as an interior point. The control problem may be stated as finding $\boldsymbol{u}(t)$, which is assumed continuous at $t = 0$ and $t = t_f$ and piecewise continuous for $0 < t < t_f$, such that $t_f^{\min}$ is the smallest value of t_f for which $\boldsymbol{x}(t_f) = \boldsymbol{0}$.

To illustrate the form of the control sequence, we may turn to the maximum principle and define the Hamiltonian as (note that we do not augment the n equations)

$$H(\boldsymbol{z}, \boldsymbol{x}, \boldsymbol{u}) = \boldsymbol{z}'\boldsymbol{f}[\boldsymbol{x}, \boldsymbol{u}] = \boldsymbol{z}'(\boldsymbol{A}(t)\boldsymbol{x} + \boldsymbol{B}(t)\boldsymbol{u}). \tag{3.81}$$

The adjoint vector $\boldsymbol{z}(t)$ is defined by

$$\dot{\boldsymbol{z}}(t) = -(\partial H/\partial \boldsymbol{x}) \tag{3.82}$$

or

$$\dot{\boldsymbol{z}}(t) = -\boldsymbol{A}(t)'\boldsymbol{z}(t). \tag{3.83}$$

For $\boldsymbol{u}(t)$ to be time-optimal, $H(\boldsymbol{z}, \boldsymbol{x}, \boldsymbol{u})$ must be maximized with respect to $\boldsymbol{u}$ for all time t, $0 \leq t \leq t_f$ (equivalent to minimizing t_f in a performance index), $\boldsymbol{z}(t)$ must be a nonzero continuous vector function and $H(\boldsymbol{z}, \boldsymbol{x}, \boldsymbol{u})$ must be positive at time t_f.

For simplicity, we consider $\boldsymbol{A}(t) = \boldsymbol{A}$ and $\boldsymbol{B}(t) = \boldsymbol{B}$ in Equation (3.79), and thus the solution of Equation (3.83) is given by

$$\boldsymbol{z}(t) = \exp(-\boldsymbol{A}'t)\boldsymbol{\eta}, \tag{3.84}$$

where $\boldsymbol{\eta} = \boldsymbol{z}(0)$. *Note* that $\boldsymbol{\eta}$ is defined to be the value of the adjoint vector at the time $t = 0$. The Hamiltonian can now be written as

$$H(\boldsymbol{z}, \boldsymbol{x}, \boldsymbol{u}) = \boldsymbol{\eta}' \exp(-\boldsymbol{A}t)[\boldsymbol{A}\boldsymbol{x} + \boldsymbol{B}\boldsymbol{u}], \tag{3.85}$$

where we have used $\boldsymbol{z}'(t) = \boldsymbol{\eta}' \exp(-\boldsymbol{A}t)$. To maximize H by varying $\boldsymbol{u}(t)$ in Equation (3.85), we choose $\boldsymbol{u}(t)$ to be the maximum value when $\boldsymbol{\eta}' \exp(-\boldsymbol{A}t)\boldsymbol{B}$ is positive, and the minimum value when this is negative, that is,

$$u_i^0(t) = \begin{cases} \gamma_i & \text{when} \quad [\boldsymbol{\eta}' \exp(-\boldsymbol{A}t)\boldsymbol{B}]_i > 0, \\ -\gamma_i & \text{when} \quad [\boldsymbol{\eta}' \exp(-\boldsymbol{A}t)\boldsymbol{B}]_i < 0, \end{cases} \tag{3.86}$$

provided that no element of $[\boldsymbol{\eta}' \exp(-\boldsymbol{A}t)\boldsymbol{B}] = 0$ for a finite period of time. This confirms that the bang-bang control is optimal for normal systems. In the special case where the direct maximization of the Hamiltonian cannot be used to obtain the optimal control, that is, an element of $[\boldsymbol{\eta}' \exp(-\boldsymbol{A}t)\boldsymbol{B}]$ is zero for a finite period of time, an alternative procedure must be used. This case is called a *singular* control and has been treated in detail by Johnson and Gibson [34, 35]. We shall not pursue this nonnormal case here. Thus the minimum-time control problem resolves itself into the problem of finding that initial adjoint vector $\boldsymbol{\eta}$ such that $\boldsymbol{x}(t)$ is driven to the origin and into yielding a final H greater than zero. Once $\boldsymbol{\eta}$ is known, $\boldsymbol{u}^0(t)$ follows directly from Equation (3.86). This discussion points out how the maximum principle allows one to say what the control should be but does not yield a simple procedure for obtaining its explicit form.

It is Neustadt's method which determines the correct value of $\boldsymbol{\eta}$. Thus, Paiewonsky and Woodrow [61] have successfully carried out the necessary calculations and Gilbert [25] has illustrated the potentialities of a hybrid type of computation [23] in which analog and digital computers are combined.

The solution of Equation (3.79), with $\boldsymbol{A}(t) = \boldsymbol{A}$ and $\boldsymbol{B}(t) = \boldsymbol{B}$, is given by

$$\boldsymbol{x}(t) = \exp(\boldsymbol{A}t)\boldsymbol{x}(0) + \int_0^t \exp[\boldsymbol{A}(t - \lambda)]\boldsymbol{B}\boldsymbol{u}(\lambda)\, d\lambda$$

or

$$\boldsymbol{x}(t) = \exp(\boldsymbol{A}t)\left\{\boldsymbol{x}(0) + \int_0^t \exp(-\boldsymbol{A}\lambda)\boldsymbol{B}\boldsymbol{u}(\lambda)\, d\lambda\right\}\cdot$$

If we select $\boldsymbol{x}(t_f) = \boldsymbol{0}$ as our final requirement, then

$$\boldsymbol{x}(0) = -\int_0^{t_f} \exp(-\boldsymbol{A}\lambda)\boldsymbol{B}\boldsymbol{u}(\lambda)\, d\lambda. \tag{3.87}$$

This equation has some interesting features in the sense that it defines all the *reachable sets*. In other words, it consists of all points in state space from which the origin can be reached by some $\boldsymbol{u}(t)$ in time t_f ; alternatively, it defines all the initial points which can be reached from the origin by a reverse time integration. In particular, when the optimal control, $\boldsymbol{u}^0(t)$, is used,

$$\boldsymbol{x}(0) = -\int_0^{t_{f\min}} \exp(-\boldsymbol{A}\lambda)\boldsymbol{B}\boldsymbol{u}^0(\lambda)\, d\lambda \tag{3.88}$$

results. Thus, we need to find that $\boldsymbol{\eta}$ which satisfies this equation.

Before detailing such a procedure, however, let us at this point work out a very simple example to illustrate the mechanics of the problem involved. Consider the simple second-order scalar system equation

$$\ddot{x}_1(t) + a\dot{x}_1(t) + bx_1(t) = u(t),$$

and if we select $a = b = 0$, the result is to remove all damping and oscillatory terms [3]. But if we define

$$\dot{x}_1 = x_2, \qquad \dot{x}_2 = u, \qquad (a = b = 0),$$

we can write the system equation in the standard matrix form

$$\dot{\boldsymbol{x}}(t) = \boldsymbol{A}\boldsymbol{x}(t) + \boldsymbol{B}\boldsymbol{u}(t),$$

where

$$\boldsymbol{x} = \begin{bmatrix} x_1 \\ x_2 \end{bmatrix}, \qquad \boldsymbol{A} = \begin{bmatrix} 0 & 1 \\ 0 & 0 \end{bmatrix}, \qquad \boldsymbol{B} = \begin{bmatrix} 0 \\ 1 \end{bmatrix}, \qquad \boldsymbol{u}(t) = [u].$$

Now if our control $\boldsymbol{u}(t)$ is bounded by -1 and $+1$ and $\boldsymbol{x}(t_f) = \boldsymbol{0}$ is taken as corresponding to $\boldsymbol{u}(t) = \boldsymbol{0}$, we ask to find the minimum time to take the system from $\boldsymbol{x}(0)$ to the origin.

If we are to use Equation (3.87), we can see that $\exp(-\boldsymbol{A}t)$ must be evaluated. Since $\exp(-\boldsymbol{A}t) = \boldsymbol{\Phi}(t)^{-1}$, where $\boldsymbol{\Phi}(t) = \exp(\boldsymbol{A}t)$, we first will find $\boldsymbol{\Phi}(t)$. This transition matrix $\boldsymbol{\Phi}$ is defined as the solution of

$$\dot{\boldsymbol{\Phi}}(t) = \boldsymbol{A}\boldsymbol{\Phi}(t)$$

with an initial condition of $\boldsymbol{\Phi}(0) = \boldsymbol{I}$. Thus, if we denote the elements of $\boldsymbol{\Phi}(t)$ by p_{ij}, it follows that

$$\begin{bmatrix} \dot{p}_{11} & \dot{p}_{12} \\ \dot{p}_{21} & \dot{p}_{22} \end{bmatrix} = \begin{bmatrix} 0 & 1 \\ 0 & 0 \end{bmatrix} \begin{bmatrix} p_{11} & p_{12} \\ p_{21} & p_{22} \end{bmatrix},$$

and therefore

$$\dot{p}_{11} = p_{21}, \qquad \dot{p}_{12} = p_{22}, \qquad \dot{p}_{21} = \dot{p}_{22} = 0.$$

Carrying out the indicated integrations and then evaluating the arbitrary constants which result by means of $\boldsymbol{\Phi}(t = 0) = \boldsymbol{I}$, we obtain

$$\boldsymbol{\Phi} = \begin{bmatrix} 1.0 & t \\ 0 & 1.0 \end{bmatrix}.$$

Fortunately, this matrix is simple enough that we may evaluate its inverse easily. Using any standard method yields

$$\boldsymbol{\Phi}(t)^{-1} = \exp(-\boldsymbol{A}t) = \begin{bmatrix} 1.0 & -t \\ 0 & 1.0 \end{bmatrix}.$$

Inserting this matrix and the other known vector into Equation (3.87) and carrying out the indicated integration (in this case this can be done easily), one finds

$$\boldsymbol{x}(0) = -\int_0^{t_f} \begin{bmatrix} 1.0 & -\lambda \\ 0 & 1.0 \end{bmatrix} \begin{bmatrix} 0 \\ 1 \end{bmatrix} [u]\, d\lambda = \begin{bmatrix} \dfrac{ut_f^2}{2} \\ -ut_f \end{bmatrix},$$

where u has been taken as a constant in the integration. This equation, then, defines the reachable sets for our particular problem ; to make it more general we may solve for $\boldsymbol{x}(t)$,

$$\boldsymbol{x}(t) = \begin{bmatrix} \dfrac{u}{2}t_f^2 + \dfrac{u}{2}t^2 - ut\,t_f \\ u(t - t_f) \end{bmatrix},$$

and note that if we eliminate t from the two simultaneous equations,

$$x_1 - (x_2^2/2u) = 0.$$

When $u = +1$ or -1, this equation then becomes

$$x_1 = \tfrac{1}{2}x_2^2 \qquad (u = +1),$$
$$x_1 = -\tfrac{1}{2}x_2^2 \qquad (u = -1).$$

But this merely means that the optimal trajectory is made up of the intersection of two parabolas in x_2x_1-space with the change in control occurring at the intersection of the parabolas or when $x_1 - (x_2^2/2u) = 0$ is satisfied.

To illustrate this feature more fully, we plot in Figure 3.3 (p. 182) the family of curves resulting from using $u = +1$ and $u = -1$. These curves result from adding an arbitrary constant to each equation above,

$$x_1 = \tfrac{1}{2}x_2^2 + a \qquad (u = +1) \qquad \text{(Curve I)},$$
$$x_1 = -\tfrac{1}{2}x_2^2 + b \qquad (u = -1) \qquad \text{(Curve II)}.$$

Also shown on these curves is the direction of travel of a point along any parabola (only the first and fourth quadrants are shown for purposes of simplification). Starting with an initial point P, the optimal curve follows the trajectory until it intersects the upward-traveling parabola which passes through the origin. When this intersection is reached, the control is switched from $u = -1$ to $u = +1$. Finally, when the origin is reached, the control is switched to $u = 0$ and the system remains at the origin.

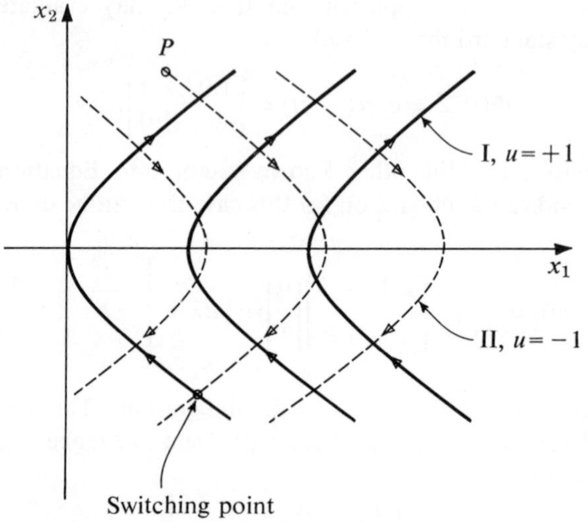

FIGURE 3.3. Switching curves for minimum-time example

Returning now to the means of finding $\boldsymbol{\eta}$ which satisfies Equation (3.88), first we note that

$$\boldsymbol{\eta}' \int_0^{t_f} \exp(-\boldsymbol{A}\lambda)\boldsymbol{B}\boldsymbol{u}^0(\lambda)\, d\lambda > 0$$

and that this function increases with t_f. If we now define

$$d[t_f, \boldsymbol{\eta}, \boldsymbol{x}(0)] = \boldsymbol{\eta}'\left\{\boldsymbol{x}(0) + \int_0^{t_f} \exp(-\boldsymbol{A}\lambda)\boldsymbol{B}\boldsymbol{u}^0(\lambda)\, d\lambda\right\}$$

and choose an initial guess on $\boldsymbol{\eta}$ to satisfy

$$\boldsymbol{\eta}'\boldsymbol{x}(0) < 0,$$

then $d[t_f, \boldsymbol{\eta}, \boldsymbol{x}(0)]$ will be an increasing function of time but will at some time t_f become equal to zero. When it becomes equal to zero and if Equation (3.88) is satisfied, the minimum-time optimal control problem is solved. If Equation (3.88) is not satisfied, another value of $\boldsymbol{\eta}$ must be chosen and the process repeated until the solution is achieved.

The problem thus is to develop a suitable algorithm which starts with an initial guess on $\boldsymbol{\eta}$ not satisfying Equation (3.88) and then changes $\boldsymbol{\eta}$ in such a way as to finally achieve the correct values. To show how this iterative technique can be carried out, we define $t^*[\boldsymbol{\eta}, \boldsymbol{x}(0)]$ as the time at which $d[t_f, \boldsymbol{\eta}, \boldsymbol{x}(0)] = 0$. Thus,

$$d\{t^*[\boldsymbol{\eta}, \boldsymbol{x}(0)], \boldsymbol{\eta}, \boldsymbol{x}(0)\} = 0 \tag{3.89}$$

or

$$\boldsymbol{\eta}'\left[\boldsymbol{x}(0) + \int_0^{t^*} \exp(-\boldsymbol{A}\lambda)\boldsymbol{B}\boldsymbol{u}^0(\lambda)\, d\lambda\right] = 0. \tag{3.90}$$

But Neustadt has shown that the maximum $t^*[\boldsymbol{\eta}, \boldsymbol{x}(0)]$ which satisfies Equation (3.89) is the minimum time and the corresponding $\boldsymbol{u}(t)$ is the optimal control $\boldsymbol{u}^0(t)$. Thus we need to maximize t^* as a function of our guess or successive iterations of $\boldsymbol{\eta}$. This may be accomplished by means of a gradient procedure for climbing the $t^*\boldsymbol{\eta}$ "hill." Differentiating Equation (3.90) with respect to $\boldsymbol{\eta}$ yields

$$\boldsymbol{x}(0) + \int_0^{t^*} \exp[-\boldsymbol{A}\lambda]\boldsymbol{B}\boldsymbol{u}^0(\lambda)\, d\lambda + [\boldsymbol{\eta}' \exp(-\boldsymbol{A}t^*)\boldsymbol{B}\boldsymbol{u}^0(t^*)]\nabla_{\boldsymbol{\eta}} t^* = \boldsymbol{0}$$

or

$$\nabla_{\boldsymbol{\eta}} t^* = -[\boldsymbol{\eta}' \exp[-\boldsymbol{A}t^*]\boldsymbol{B}\boldsymbol{u}^0(t^*)]^{-1}\left[\boldsymbol{x}(0) + \int_0^{t^*} \exp(-\boldsymbol{A}\lambda)\boldsymbol{B}\boldsymbol{u}^0(\lambda)\, d\lambda\right]. \tag{3.91}$$

Note that when $\nabla_{\boldsymbol{\eta}} t^* = (\partial/\partial\boldsymbol{\eta})t^* = \boldsymbol{0}$, Equation (3.88) is satisfied and the optimal problem is completed. Actually, Equation (3.91) represents an unusual situation in the sense that the gradient vector is known in closed form and numerical differentiation is not necessary. However, although this simplifies certain procedures, the usual form of the $t^*\boldsymbol{\eta}$-hill is a very flat function, and even though we may be near the top of the hill with a specific value of $t^*[\boldsymbol{\eta}, \boldsymbol{x}(0)]$, the small change in t^* required to get to the true top produces large changes in $\boldsymbol{\eta}$. Since we are not really interested in t^* but rather in the $\boldsymbol{\eta}$ which makes t^* maximum, the actual specification of $\boldsymbol{\eta}$ at the top becomes a very difficult determination.

A possible steepest-ascent recursion formula.is given by the form

$$\boldsymbol{\eta}^{(j+1)} = \boldsymbol{\eta}^{(j)} + k[\nabla_{\boldsymbol{\eta}} t^*]^{(j)}, \tag{3.92}$$

where j indicates the iteration step. But we note that

$$\boldsymbol{\eta}^{(j+1)'}\boldsymbol{x}(0) = \boldsymbol{\eta}^{(j)'}\boldsymbol{x}(0) + k[\nabla_{\boldsymbol{\eta}} t^*]^{(j)'}\boldsymbol{x}(0),$$

and if $\boldsymbol{\eta}^{(j)'}\boldsymbol{x}(0) < 0$ then for k sufficiently small, $\boldsymbol{\eta}^{(j+1)'}\boldsymbol{x}(0) < 0$. Thus, if we make an initial choice such that $\boldsymbol{\eta}'\boldsymbol{x}(0) < 0$, all succeeding iterations will have this property also. From Equation (3.90) we see that if $\boldsymbol{\eta}'\boldsymbol{x}(0)$ is zero, then $t^* = 0$; however, when $t^* > 0$, $\boldsymbol{\eta}'\boldsymbol{x}(0) < 0$. Finally, Equation (3.91) indicates that the gradient of t^* is $\boldsymbol{0}$ if, and only if, the optimal condition (3.88) is met. This fact rules out the occurrence of saddle points and local maxima and guarantees arrival at the true maximum.

Thus the Neustadt procedure for determining the minimum-time control consists of guessing an initial value for the adjoint vector $\boldsymbol{\eta}$ such that $\boldsymbol{\eta}'\boldsymbol{x}(0) < 0$ and then iterating in the $t^*\boldsymbol{\eta}$-space to reach an absolute maximum. When this maximum has been reached, and convergence is guaranteed, the corresponding $\boldsymbol{\eta}$ can be used to specify the optimal bang-bang control. Computationally, there exists the important question of the speed of convergence of the hill-climbing steepest-ascent technique. In fact, it may be better to use an alternative ascent procedure with faster convergence than Equation (3.92). Details of an alternative procedure will be left, however, for an appropriate numerical example at the end of this chapter.

3.7. Minimum-time control of linear discrete systems

In this section we consider the minimum-time control of a discrete system; minimum time here means the smallest number of sampling periods, P, each of constant duration T time units. The pioneer work in this area is due to Zadeh and Whalen [80] and then Lesser [52]. Our system model is given as

$$\boldsymbol{x}(k+1) = \boldsymbol{\Phi}\boldsymbol{x}(k) + \boldsymbol{\Delta}\boldsymbol{u}(k) \qquad (k = 0, 1, 2, \ldots) \tag{3.93}$$

with the usual meaning for $\boldsymbol{\Phi}$ and $\boldsymbol{\Delta}$. The recurrent solution of this equation yields, from Equation (1.37),

$$\boldsymbol{x}(P) = \boldsymbol{\Phi}^P\boldsymbol{x}(0) + \sum_{k=0}^{P-1} \boldsymbol{\Phi}^{P-1-k}\boldsymbol{\Delta}\boldsymbol{u}(k)$$

or calling $\boldsymbol{\Phi}^{P-1-k}\boldsymbol{\Delta} = \boldsymbol{L}(P-1-k)$,

$$\boldsymbol{x}(P) = \boldsymbol{\Phi}^P\boldsymbol{x}(0) + \sum_{k=0}^{P-1} \boldsymbol{L}(P-1-k)\boldsymbol{u}(k). \tag{3.94}$$

On this basis, we may state a possible sampled-data (discrete), time-optimal control problem *with no constraints* as follows.

PROBLEM ▪ Given an n-dimensional state vector $\boldsymbol{x}$ with an initial condition $\boldsymbol{x}(0)$ and whose final position in phase space is given by Equation (3.94), find that sequence of sample-and-hold controls $\boldsymbol{u}(k)$, $k = 0, 1, \ldots, P-1$ which makes $\boldsymbol{x}(P) = \boldsymbol{x}^d$ and minimizes the number of sampling periods P.

Solution ▪ The solution to this problem can be developed by noting that the final condition is

$$\boldsymbol{L}\boldsymbol{u}^* = \boldsymbol{x}^d - \boldsymbol{\Phi}^P\boldsymbol{x}(0), \tag{3.95}$$

where

$$\boldsymbol{u}^* = \begin{bmatrix} \boldsymbol{u}(0) \\ \boldsymbol{u}(1) \\ \vdots \\ \boldsymbol{u}(P-1) \end{bmatrix}, \qquad \boldsymbol{L} = [\boldsymbol{L}(P-1)\, \boldsymbol{L}(P-2) \ldots \boldsymbol{L}(1)\, \boldsymbol{\Delta}],$$

and where $\boldsymbol{u}^*$ has dimension $(Pr \times 1)$ and $\boldsymbol{L}$ has dimension $(n \times Pr)$. The minimum number of sampling periods follows by requiring that Equation (3.95) be a set of n-scalar equations in n unknowns. This implies that $Pr = n$

or that $P = n/r$ be the minimum number of sampling periods. Thus, the solution to the unconstrained problem is given by

$$\boldsymbol{u}^* = (\boldsymbol{L}'\boldsymbol{L})^{-1}\boldsymbol{L}'[\boldsymbol{x}^d - \boldsymbol{\Phi}^P\boldsymbol{x}(0)], \tag{3.96}$$

with $P = n/r$ and provided det $(\boldsymbol{L}'\,\boldsymbol{L}) \neq 0$.

Obviously, the solution given by Equation (3.96) may or may not violate such items as constraints on the control vectors; that is, it may or may not lead to negative input concentrations, unattainable flow rates, etc. When the control specified by Equation (3.96) is not outside any preselected bounds, then this becomes the optimal solution. When any one of the controls is outside the bounds, a new procedure must be adopted to conform to the physical requirements. Let us say, as before, that the control bounds are given by

$$-\boldsymbol{\alpha} \leq \boldsymbol{u} \leq \boldsymbol{\beta}, \tag{3.97}$$

and, to simplify the discussion, that $\boldsymbol{x}^d = \boldsymbol{0}$. Thus the equation to be satisfied is

$$\boldsymbol{L}\boldsymbol{u}^* = -\boldsymbol{\Phi}^P\boldsymbol{x}(0), \tag{3.98}$$

and the minimum-time constrained control problem can be stated as follows.

PROBLEM ▪ Given an n-dimensional state vector $\boldsymbol{x}$ and initial condition $\boldsymbol{x}(0)$ and whose final position in state space is given by Equation (3.94), find that $\boldsymbol{u}^*$ which satisfies Equation (3.98) and minimizes the number of sampling periods P, subject to the control constraints of Equation (3.97).

Solution ▪ To solve this problem when the constraints are invoked, we shall turn to a linear programming formulation (see Section 2.7). It will be shown that such a formulation is ideal for handling the problem.

First, we introduce an error vector $\boldsymbol{e}$, where

$$\boldsymbol{e} = \boldsymbol{L}\boldsymbol{u}^* + \boldsymbol{\Phi}^P\boldsymbol{x}(0). \tag{3.99}$$

The problem is solved when that $\boldsymbol{u}^*$ is found which makes $\boldsymbol{e} = \boldsymbol{0}$ and minimizes P. The vector $\boldsymbol{e}$ may be forced to $\boldsymbol{0}$ by seeking to minimize $\max_i|e_i|$ over the control vector $\boldsymbol{u}^*$, subject to the control constraints. This is equivalent to minimizing g (a positive quantity) subject to the $2n$ constraints

$$\begin{aligned} g + e_i &\geq 0, \\ g - e_i &\geq 0, \end{aligned} \qquad i = 1, 2, \ldots, n. \tag{3.100}$$

Minimizing g will force $\boldsymbol{e}$ to be $\boldsymbol{0}$ for the minimum number or any larger number of sampling periods. The procedure consists then of fixing P and minimizing g. If $g = 0$, then all $e_i = 0$; the procedure is repeated after decreasing P until the smallest P is found such that $g = 0$. This P and the corresponding $\boldsymbol{u}^*$ are the desired results. If the initial P yields a nonzero g, then a larger P must obviously be tried. Note the similarity to the previous discussion on minimizing $\|\boldsymbol{x}(t_f)\|_S^2$.

Because linear programming requires the unknown variables to be nonnegative, a new control vector $\boldsymbol{u}^{**}$, whose components are all nonnegative, is introduced by subtracting the lower bound from each of the control variables:

$$\boldsymbol{u}^{**} = \boldsymbol{u}^* + \begin{bmatrix} \alpha \\ \vdots \\ \alpha \end{bmatrix} = \boldsymbol{u}^* + \boldsymbol{\alpha}^*, \tag{3.101}$$

where $\boldsymbol{\alpha}$ is defined by Equation (3.97). In addition, $2n$ slack variables, s_i and q_i, $i = 1, 2, \ldots, n$ and Pr control slack variables c_i are introduced. The purpose of the state slack variables, which, like the control variables, must be nonnegative, is to remove the inequality signs in Equations (3.100). Thus, if we define the vectors (certain of which will be used shortly)

$$\mathbf{1} = \begin{bmatrix} 1 \\ \vdots \\ 1 \end{bmatrix}, \quad \boldsymbol{s} = \begin{bmatrix} s_1 \\ \vdots \\ s_n \end{bmatrix}, \quad \boldsymbol{q} = \begin{bmatrix} q_1 \\ \vdots \\ q_n \end{bmatrix}, \quad \boldsymbol{c}^* = \begin{bmatrix} c_1 \\ \vdots \\ c_{Pr} \end{bmatrix},$$

it follows that

$$\begin{aligned} g + e_i - s_i &= 0, \\ g - e_i - q_i &= 0, \end{aligned} \qquad (i = 1, 2, \ldots, n) \tag{3.102}$$

are equivalent to Equations (3.100) if s_i and q_i are nonnegative for all i. Similarly, the control slack variables are also nonnegative and ensure that the control variables will not exceed their upper limits. Typically,

$$(\boldsymbol{u}_k^{**})_i - (\boldsymbol{\alpha} + \boldsymbol{\beta})_i + c_i^* = 0$$

ensures that $(\boldsymbol{u}_k^{**})_i$ will not exceed $(\boldsymbol{\alpha} + \boldsymbol{\beta})_i$.

Equations (3.97), (3.99), (3.100), and (3.101) may be combined with the slack variables to give

$$\begin{aligned} g\mathbf{1} + \boldsymbol{L}\boldsymbol{u}^{**} - \boldsymbol{L}\boldsymbol{\alpha}^* + \boldsymbol{\Phi}^P\boldsymbol{x}(0) - \boldsymbol{s} &= \mathbf{0}, \\ g\mathbf{1} - \boldsymbol{L}\boldsymbol{u}^{**} + \boldsymbol{L}\boldsymbol{\alpha}^* - \boldsymbol{\Phi}^P\boldsymbol{x}(0) - \boldsymbol{q} &= \mathbf{0}, \\ \boldsymbol{u}^{**} - (\boldsymbol{\alpha}^* + \boldsymbol{\beta}^*) + \boldsymbol{c}^* &= \mathbf{0}, \end{aligned}$$

where $\boldsymbol{\beta}^*$ is a Pr-dimensional vector defined similarly to $\boldsymbol{\alpha}^*$. The three vector equations are rewritten as

$$g\mathbf{1} + \boldsymbol{L}\boldsymbol{u}^{**} - \boldsymbol{s} = \boldsymbol{L}\boldsymbol{\alpha}^* - \boldsymbol{\Phi}^P\boldsymbol{x}(0), \tag{3.103}$$

$$g\mathbf{1} - \boldsymbol{L}\boldsymbol{u}^{**} - \boldsymbol{q} = -\boldsymbol{L}\boldsymbol{\alpha}^* + \boldsymbol{\Phi}^P\boldsymbol{x}(0), \tag{3.104}$$

$$\boldsymbol{u}^{**} + \boldsymbol{c}^* = \boldsymbol{\alpha}^* + \boldsymbol{\beta}^*. \tag{3.105}$$

Equations (3.103), (3.104), and (3.105) represent a set of $n + n + Pr$ or $(2n + Pr)$ scalar equations. The unknowns to be determined are $\boldsymbol{u}^{**}$, $\boldsymbol{s}$, $\boldsymbol{q}$, g

and $\boldsymbol{c}^*$, which represent $Pr + n + n + 1 + Pr$ or $(2n + 2Pr + 1)$ unknowns. Hence, there are $(1 + Pr)$ more unknowns than equations. There are several linear programming alogrithms for solving such a system. The basic technique is to, first, find a set of $(1 + Pr)$ unknowns which, when set equal to zero, will leave a solvable set of $(2n + Pr)$ equations in the same number of unknowns. The solution of these equations must, in addition, be a feasible solution; that is, the solution must yield all nonnegative quantities. The set of equations is solvable if the determinant of the coefficients of the $(2n + Pr)$ variables does not vanish. The value of the quantity being minimized, a linear sum of the unknown variables, is recorded. In this case, the quantity being minimized is g. A decrease in g is sought by setting one of the $(2n + Pr)$ variables equal to zero and replacing it with one of the $(1 + Pr)$ variables which were originally set equal to zero. The new set of $(2n + Pr)$ equations produces a new feasible solution, the new value of g is recorded, and the procedure is continued until no further improvement in g can be obtained. Systematic schemes have been developed for picking successive sets of $(2n + Pr)$ equations which will produce successive feasible solutions and monotonic convergence of g to a minimum.

If P is sufficiently large, so that g can be reduced to zero, all the s_i, q_i will be zero. This follows from Equations (3.100) and (3.102). Then Equation (3.103) will be identical to Equation (3.104) and we are now left with $(n + Pr)$ scalar equations in Pr control variables, $\boldsymbol{u}^{**}$, and Pr control slack variables, $\boldsymbol{c}^*$. Of those $2Pr$ variables, $(Pr - n)$ of them must be set equal to zero. If a variable set equal to zero is a control variable, $(\boldsymbol{u}^{**})_i$, then that control variable, $(\boldsymbol{u}^*)_i$, is on its lower bound. If a control slack variable, $(\boldsymbol{c}^*)_i$, is set equal to zero, its corresponding control variable, $(\boldsymbol{u}^*)_i$, is forced to be on its upper bound. Therefore, of the Pr scalar control variables, at least $(Pr - n)$ of them will be at their bounds, and the remaining control variables are free to be within their bounds. These results can now be summarized in a theorem.

▶ THEOREM 3.1. *If an n-dimensional state vector whose transient behavior is given by Equation* (3.93) *can be brought from an initial state* $\boldsymbol{x}(0)$ *to the origin in a finite number of sampling periods P and if the r-dimensional control vectors* $\boldsymbol{u}(k)$, $k = 0, 1, \ldots, (P - 1)$ *are bounded according to Equation* (3.97), *then*

(1) *the desired control sequence* $\{\boldsymbol{u}(k)\}$ *arises as a solution to the linear programming problem associated with Equations* (3.103), (3.104), *and* (3.105), *where the quantity being minimized is g,*

(2) *of the Pr control variables contained in the P control vectors* $\boldsymbol{u}(k)$, *at least* $(Pr - n)$ *of them will be on their bounds if* $\min(g) = 0$, *and the remaining ones may appear anywhere within their respective bounds, and*

(3) *the minimum P, for which* $g = 0$ *is the solution of the linear program, is the minimum number of sampling periods sought in the second problem detailed before, and the* $\boldsymbol{u}(k)$ *associated with this P is the corresponding* $\boldsymbol{u}(k)$ *sought in the problem.*

Two further problems similar to the second problem detailed before should also be mentioned here. These are the problems where $\boldsymbol{u}^*$ is bounded above or below, but not both. If $\boldsymbol{u}^*$ is bounded only below, then the control-vector constraint Equation (3.105) is dropped from Equation set (3.103) through (3.105). We shall then have Equations (3.103) and (3.104) ($2n$ scalar equations), and there will be $(1 + Pr + 2n)$ unknowns. The solution proceeds as before, except that the final equation set has n equations [when Equations (3.103) and (3.104) become identical)] in Pr unknown control variables (the components of $\boldsymbol{u}^{**}$). This leads to at least $(Pr - n)$ controls, $(\boldsymbol{u}^{**})_i$ being zero, which is equivalent to the corresponding $(\boldsymbol{u}^*)_i$ being on their lower bounds and the remaining controls being free to be anywhere above.

In addition, it is possible to bound $\boldsymbol{u}^*$ from above only. This can be made equivalent to the lower-bound problem:

$$\boldsymbol{u}^* \leq \boldsymbol{\beta}^*$$

implies

$$0 \leq \boldsymbol{\beta}^* - \boldsymbol{u}^* = \boldsymbol{v}^*. \tag{3.106}$$

Combine this with Equation (3.99) instead of Equation (3.101). The solution to the linear programming problem will be the same as for the lower-bound (only) problem except that $\boldsymbol{v}^*$ will be obtained instead of $\boldsymbol{u}^*$. There will be at least $(Pr - n)$ components of $\boldsymbol{v}^*$ set equal to zero, which is equivalent to the corresponding components of $\boldsymbol{u}^*$ being on their upper bounds.

Of further interest and decided importance is the fact that in addition to this linear programming algorithm solving the minimum-time discrete control problem with constraints on the control, it can also be used when constraints are placed on the state variables. To illustrate this feature, let us write Equation (3.94) for j sampling periods,

$$\boldsymbol{x}(j) = \boldsymbol{\Phi}^j \boldsymbol{x}(0) + \sum_{k=0}^{j-1} \boldsymbol{L}(j-1-k)\boldsymbol{u}(k) \qquad (j = 1, 2, \ldots, P-1). \tag{3.107}$$

The $2n(P-1)$ slack variables ψ_i are introduced, along with the constraint vectors $-\boldsymbol{\lambda}$ and $\boldsymbol{\theta}$, that is, $-\boldsymbol{\lambda} \leq \boldsymbol{x} \leq \boldsymbol{\theta}$. The elements of $-\boldsymbol{\lambda}$ and $\boldsymbol{\theta}$ are all positive and correspond to the lower and upper limits, respectively, of the elements of $\boldsymbol{x}$. Then the condition that $\boldsymbol{x}(j)$ be within its constraints (for j between 1 and $P-1$) is equivalent to

$$\boldsymbol{\Phi}^j \boldsymbol{x}(0) + \sum_{k=0}^{j-1} \boldsymbol{L}(j-1-k)\boldsymbol{u}(k) - \boldsymbol{\theta} + \begin{bmatrix} \psi_{2nj-2n+1} \\ \vdots \\ \psi_{2nj-n} \end{bmatrix} = \boldsymbol{0},$$

$$-\boldsymbol{\Phi}^j \boldsymbol{x}(0) - \sum_{k=0}^{j-1} \boldsymbol{L}(j-1-k)\boldsymbol{u}(k) - \boldsymbol{\lambda} + \begin{bmatrix} \psi_{2nj-n+1} \\ \vdots \\ \psi_{2nj} \end{bmatrix} = \boldsymbol{0}.$$

Once the vectors $\boldsymbol{\lambda}$ and $\boldsymbol{\theta}$ are transferred to the other side and the $\boldsymbol{u}(k)$'s are converted to $\boldsymbol{u}^*(k)$'s, the equations may be combined with those of Equation (3.102). This will, of course, change the make-up of Equations (3.103) through (3.105), but the procedure should be clear.

If it is desired that $\boldsymbol{x}(P) = \mathbf{0}$, this may also be accomplished by adding more equations to those already present. Equations (3.93) and (3.94) are combined with $\boldsymbol{u}(P) = \mathbf{0}$ to give

$$\dot{\boldsymbol{x}}(P) = \boldsymbol{A}\boldsymbol{x}(P) = \boldsymbol{A}\boldsymbol{\Phi}^P\boldsymbol{x}(0) + \boldsymbol{A}\sum_{k=0}^{P-1}\boldsymbol{L}[P-1-k]\boldsymbol{u}(k) = \mathbf{0}.$$

The $2n$ slack variables v_i and w_i are introduced, and the equations which reduce $\dot{\boldsymbol{x}}(P)$ to $\mathbf{0}$ at the same time $\boldsymbol{x}(P)$ is reduced to $\mathbf{0}$ are

$$g\mathbf{1} + \boldsymbol{A}\boldsymbol{L}\boldsymbol{u}^* - \boldsymbol{A}\boldsymbol{L}\boldsymbol{\alpha}^* + \boldsymbol{A}\boldsymbol{\Phi}^P\boldsymbol{x}(0) - \boldsymbol{v} = \mathbf{0},$$

$$g\mathbf{1} - \boldsymbol{A}\boldsymbol{L}\boldsymbol{u}^* + \boldsymbol{A}\boldsymbol{L}\boldsymbol{\alpha}^* - \boldsymbol{A}\boldsymbol{\Phi}^P\boldsymbol{x}(0) - \boldsymbol{w} = \mathbf{0},$$

where

$$\boldsymbol{v} = \begin{bmatrix} v_1 \\ \vdots \\ v_n \end{bmatrix}, \qquad \boldsymbol{w} = \begin{bmatrix} w_1 \\ \vdots \\ w_n \end{bmatrix},$$

and $\boldsymbol{L}$, $\boldsymbol{u}^*$, and $\boldsymbol{\alpha}^*$ are defined as before by Equations (3.96) and (3.101). Now the minimization of g will simultaneously force $\boldsymbol{x}(P)$ and $\dot{\boldsymbol{x}}(P)$ to $\mathbf{0}$.

In summary, it can be seen that although the formulation in linear programming format is quite complicated, once it has been carried out, the linear programming algorithm, which is readily available for all digital computers, can be used to solve the minimum-time problem with constraints on the control variables. This may also be extended to constraints on the state variables. Needless to say, computer-storage limitations may place stringent limits on the values of P, r, and n that can be handled. However, current programs which do not require the problem to be core-contained will accept problems with as many as 1024 equations and about 200,000 unknowns.

The only really serious problem associated with this linear programming formulation rests in the nonuniqueness of the resulting solution. Given that P is the minimum number of sampling periods and that a solution $\boldsymbol{u}^*$ exists such that exactly $(Pr - n)$ controls are on their bounds, it can be shown that other solutions for $\boldsymbol{u}^*$ exist with $(Pr - n)$ controls on their bounds. In some cases, an infinite number of solutions exist with less than $(Pr - n)$ controls on their bounds. The linear program will not generate any of these.

The occurrence of multiple solutions is governed by the composition of the matrix $\boldsymbol{L}$ and the vector $\boldsymbol{\Phi}^P\boldsymbol{x}(0)$ of Equation (3.98), as well as the constraints of Equation (3.97). A detailed proof of the multiplicity of solutions will not be given here. It will suffice to point out that the linear program finds one solution

u^* which makes $g = 0$ and does not seek out additional solutions. For the interested reader the papers by Torng [71] and Fegley and Hsu [21] illustrate the nonuniqueness and a possible way of choosing between alternative solutions.

3.8. Numerical examples

In this section, we shall develop in depth three examples illustrating the features of the control of linear systems. In the first case, we shall use the optimal control theory developed for the case of a quadratic performance index, and in the second and third examples we shall analyze the minimum-time situation.

EXAMPLE 3.1 ▪ In this first example, we shall investigate the behavior of the discrete-time and continuous-time gas absorber defined in Section 1.11. The equations of interest have been detailed in that section, and we merely need to recapitulate here. Once the system equations are transformed such that the final equilibrium condition is the origin, the discrete-time system equations are [Equations (1.110) and (1.112)],

$$\boldsymbol{x}(k+1) = \boldsymbol{\Phi x}(k) + \boldsymbol{\Delta u}(k), \tag{3.108}$$

$$\boldsymbol{x}(0) \qquad \text{(prescribed)}, \tag{3.109}$$

with $\boldsymbol{\Phi}$ and $\boldsymbol{\Delta}$ given numerically in Equations (1.113) and (1.114) for a sampling period of 1 min. The continuous-time system equations are given by [Equations (1.106) and (1.107)]

$$\dot{\boldsymbol{x}}(t) = \boldsymbol{A x}(t) + \boldsymbol{B u}(t), \tag{3.110}$$

$$\boldsymbol{x}(0) \qquad \text{(prescribed)}, \tag{3.111}$$

with $\boldsymbol{A}$ and $\boldsymbol{B}$ containing constant elements defined by the listed parameters.

Because of the voluminous amount of results to be discussed here, it seems appropriate in the presentation to break up the discussion into subsections, each of which will be directed toward a single major objective. In addition, we shall adopt the convention that, as an illustration, the matrix $\boldsymbol{Q}(1\ 1\ 1\ 2\ 2\ 2)$ is taken to mean

$$\boldsymbol{Q}(1\ 1\ 1\ 2\ 2\ 2) = \begin{bmatrix} 10^1 & & & \cdots & & 0 \\ & 10^1 & & & & \\ \vdots & & 10^1 & & & \vdots \\ & & & 10^2 & & \\ & & & & 10^2 & \\ 0 & & & \cdots & & 10^2 \end{bmatrix}.$$

In other words, we merely show the powers of 10 used on the main diagonal of the matrix, with all other elements assumed zero. In certain other cases, namely when the identity matrix is involved, we shall dispense with this nomenclature and use $\boldsymbol{Q} = \boldsymbol{I}$ instead. In all cases described the output matrix $\boldsymbol{H} = \boldsymbol{I}$ unless comments to the contrary are made.

(1) As a first step in the calculation we raise a question: Given a specific set of elements in the weighting matrices $\boldsymbol{Q}$, $\boldsymbol{R}$, and $\boldsymbol{S}$ in the quadratic performance index and a given sampling period, how many backward steps in the iteration sequence of either Equations (3.16) and (3.17) or (3.55) are required to approximate the infinite-stage case?

This implies that once we select $\boldsymbol{Q} = \boldsymbol{I}$, $\boldsymbol{R} = \boldsymbol{I}$, $\boldsymbol{S} = \boldsymbol{0}$ and $T = 1$ min for example, how many stages of the backward iteration do we require such that in the feedback control law

$$\boldsymbol{u}(k) = -\boldsymbol{K}\boldsymbol{x}(k),$$

where $\boldsymbol{K} =$ const not dependent on the iteration stage number. To illustrate this point, Table 3.1 shows some of the results obtained in the discrete-time case with $\boldsymbol{Q} = \boldsymbol{I}$, $\boldsymbol{R} = \boldsymbol{I}$, $\boldsymbol{S} = \boldsymbol{0}$ and $T = 1$ min. Certain selected elements (the corner elements) for $\boldsymbol{K}_P$ are shown with the iteration initial condition being $\boldsymbol{J}_0 = \boldsymbol{0}$. As we can see, 22 stages are required to achieve the infinite case ($\boldsymbol{K} =$ const) using four-digit accuracy in the calculations. By contrast, the case $\boldsymbol{Q} = \boldsymbol{I}$, $\boldsymbol{R} = \boldsymbol{0}$, $\boldsymbol{S} = \boldsymbol{0}$ requires only 15 stages, the lower number resulting from the simpler definition of the problem. The results for the continuous-time system are quite comparable and will not be detailed here.

(2) It is relatively obvious that the numerical magnitude of the sampling period used in the discrete-time system may strongly influence the feedback matrix and the resulting optimal trajectory. This follows because the sampling period determines the time interval over which the control is held constant. Furthermore, it would seem logical that as the sampling period is decreased, the control trajectory should approach that for the continuous-time system. To illustrate this point, Table 3.2 shows certain selected values obtained for the initial control ($k = 0$) in the discrete-time case for a set of different sampling periods. Also shown is the final control for the continuous-time case. These results are for the case $\boldsymbol{Q} = \boldsymbol{I}$, $\boldsymbol{R} = \boldsymbol{I}$, $\boldsymbol{S} = \boldsymbol{0}$ and $\boldsymbol{K}$ obtained by the infinite-stage calculation.

As we can see from Table 3.2, decreasing T in the discrete-time case yields an initial control which approaches that for the continuous-time case. Although not shown in Table 3.2, the trajectories for all the states, $x_i, \ldots, x_6$, and the controls approach those for the continuous-time case. On the basis of these results a discrete-time sampling period of $T < 0.5$ for the absorber is sufficient to assure accurate answers in all calculations. Actually, we shall use $T = 1.0$ in most of the remaining calculations so as to minimize computer time; this seems

TABLE 3.1

$Q = I$, $R = I$, $S = 0$, Discrete-time system

Stage number	First and sixth row of K_P (All $\times 10^{-1}$)	
0	1.2108	.0045
	.0048	1.4249
2	1.6595	.0982
	.0942	2.0137
4	1.7708	.1964
	.1839	2.1864
6	1.8122	.2489
	.2309	2.2586
8	1.8291	.2729
	.2523	2.2905
10	1.8362	.2835
	.2616	2.3044
12	1.8392	.2880
	.2656	2.3105
14	1.8405	.2900
	.2673	2.3131
16	1.8411	.2908
	.2680	2.3142
18	1.8413	.2912
	.2684	2.3147
20	1.8414	.2913
	.2685	2.3149
22	1.8414	.2913
	.2685	2.3150

No change in further stages

$$\text{final } \boldsymbol{K} = \begin{bmatrix} 1.8414 & .2913 \\ 2.0045 & .6931 \\ 1.5087 & 1.2028 \\ 1.0108 & 1.8149 \\ .6015 & 2.4288 \\ .2685 & 2.3150 \end{bmatrix} \text{(all elements} \times 10^{-1}\text{)}$$

feasible since we are merely attempting to illustrate how the optimal control varies with the system parameters.

(3) As the next step in our calculation, we shall investigate the effect of the selection of the matrices $\boldsymbol{Q}$ and $\boldsymbol{R}$ on the resulting optimal sequence. In all the calculations we take $\boldsymbol{S} = \boldsymbol{0}$ for simplicity. Before discussing these results,

TABLE 3.2

$Q = I,\ R = I,\ S = 0$

Discrete-system, $k = 0$			Continuous-system			
Sampling period	$u_1(0)$	$u_2(0)$	t	x_6	$u_1(t)$	$u_2(t)$
5.0	.0342	.0422	0	−.1273	.0552	.1166
3.0	.0408	.0584	1	−.0386	.0447	.0741
2.0	.0444	.0708	2	−.0126	.0376	.0524
1.0	.0490	.0891	3	−.0037	.0317	.0392
0.8	.0501	.0938	4	−.0003	.0266	.0301
0.5	.0516	.1013	5	.0010	.0222	.0236
			6	.0014	.0183	.0186
			7	.0015	.0151	.0148
			8	.0014	.0123	.0119
			9	.0012	.0100	.0095
			10	.0010	.0082	.0077

however, we should inquire into the state controllability of the system. As pointed out in Section 1.9, if we have the system equation

$$\dot{\boldsymbol{x}}(t) = \boldsymbol{A}\boldsymbol{x}(t) + \boldsymbol{B}\boldsymbol{u}(t) \tag{3.112}$$

and the output relation

$$\boldsymbol{y}(t) = \boldsymbol{H}\boldsymbol{x}(t), \tag{3.113}$$

the system is state-controllable if and only if the controllability matrix $\boldsymbol{W}$,

$$\boldsymbol{W} = [\boldsymbol{B}\ \ \boldsymbol{AB} \ldots \boldsymbol{A}^{n-1}\boldsymbol{B}], \tag{3.114}$$

has rank n. In other words, among the nr columns of $\boldsymbol{W}$ there is a set of n linearly independent vectors.

Although this definition seems straightforward enough, the implementation of it may be quite difficult. Thus we shall spend a little effort looking into an efficient manner for determining the necessary rank of $\boldsymbol{W}$. One excellent way to determine the rank of a matrix with the use of a digital computer is to attempt to orthogonalize the vectors which constitute the columns. To illustrate the method, let us consider a set of $N = nr$ vectors which we shall denote by $\boldsymbol{v}_1, \boldsymbol{v}_2, \ldots, \boldsymbol{v}_N$. First of all, determine the dot products of each vector with itself, that is, form

$$\boldsymbol{v}_i \cdot \boldsymbol{v}_i = \boldsymbol{v}_i'\boldsymbol{v}_i \qquad (i = 1, 2, \ldots, N). \tag{3.115}$$

Then choose one nonzero dot product (preferably the largest) and call that vector, which forms this, $\boldsymbol{v}_M$, where $1 \le M \le N$. Using the other vectors, construct a new set of vectors orthogonal to $\boldsymbol{v}_M$, that is,

$$\boldsymbol{w}_i = \boldsymbol{v}_i - \left(\frac{\boldsymbol{v}_i \cdot \boldsymbol{v}_M}{\boldsymbol{v}_M \cdot \boldsymbol{v}_M}\right)\boldsymbol{v}_M, \tag{3.116}$$

where $i = 1, 2, \ldots, N$. It should be noted, of course, that

$$\boldsymbol{w}_M = \boldsymbol{0}. \tag{3.117}$$

With this new set of vectors, the dot products are again calculated and another orthogonalization is carried out with respect to a vector which gives a nonzero dot product with itself. This procedure is continued until all the dot products become zero. The number of linearly independent vectors (and hence the rank of the matrix which has the vectors as columns) is the number of such orthogonalizations that can be carried out.

For the sake of illustration, let us consider the following matrix :

$$W = \begin{bmatrix} 1 & 2 & 1 \\ 1 & 2 & 2 \end{bmatrix}.$$

In this case

$$\boldsymbol{v}_1 = \begin{bmatrix} 1 \\ 1 \end{bmatrix}, \qquad \boldsymbol{v}_2 = \begin{bmatrix} 2 \\ 2 \end{bmatrix}, \qquad \text{and} \qquad \boldsymbol{v}_3 = \begin{bmatrix} 1 \\ 2 \end{bmatrix};$$

$$\boldsymbol{v}_1 \,.\, \boldsymbol{v}_1 = 1 + 1 = 2, \qquad \boldsymbol{v}_2 \,.\, \boldsymbol{v}_2 = 4 + 4 = 8, \qquad \boldsymbol{v}_3 \,.\, \boldsymbol{v}_3 = 1 + 4 = 5.$$

Here we shall choose the largest of these to be $\boldsymbol{v}_M \cdot \boldsymbol{v}_M$ and form the set $(M = 2)$

$$\boldsymbol{w}_1 = \begin{bmatrix} 1 \\ 1 \end{bmatrix} - \left([1 \quad 1]\begin{bmatrix} 2 \\ 2 \end{bmatrix}\Big/8\right)\begin{bmatrix} 2 \\ 2 \end{bmatrix} = \begin{bmatrix} 1 \\ 1 \end{bmatrix} - \begin{bmatrix} 1 \\ 1 \end{bmatrix} = \begin{bmatrix} 0 \\ 0 \end{bmatrix}, \qquad \boldsymbol{w}_2 = \boldsymbol{0},$$

$$\boldsymbol{w}_3 = \begin{bmatrix} 1 \\ 2 \end{bmatrix} - \left([1 \quad 2]\begin{bmatrix} 2 \\ 2 \end{bmatrix}\Big/8\right)\begin{bmatrix} 2 \\ 2 \end{bmatrix} = \begin{bmatrix} -\frac{1}{2} \\ \frac{1}{2} \end{bmatrix}.$$

With this new set,

$$\boldsymbol{w}_1 \,.\, \boldsymbol{w}_1 = 0, \qquad \boldsymbol{w}_2 \,.\, \boldsymbol{w}_2 = 0, \qquad \boldsymbol{w}_3 \,.\, \boldsymbol{w}_3 = \tfrac{1}{4} + \tfrac{1}{4} = \tfrac{1}{2}.$$

And we can carry out one further orthogonalization, namely,

$$\boldsymbol{w}_1^* = \boldsymbol{w}_1 - \left(\frac{\boldsymbol{w}_1 \cdot \boldsymbol{w}_3}{\boldsymbol{w}_3 \cdot \boldsymbol{w}_3}\right)\boldsymbol{w}_3 = \boldsymbol{0}, \qquad \boldsymbol{w}_2^* = \boldsymbol{w}_2 - \left(\frac{\boldsymbol{w}_2 \cdot \boldsymbol{w}_3}{\boldsymbol{w}_3 \cdot \boldsymbol{w}_3}\right)\boldsymbol{w}_3 = \boldsymbol{0},$$

$$\boldsymbol{w}_3^* = \boldsymbol{w}_3 - \boldsymbol{w}_3 = \boldsymbol{0}.$$

With this new set, all the dot products are zero and we cannot proceed any further. Looking back at our steps, we conclude that the matrix

$$W = \begin{bmatrix} 1 & 2 & 1 \\ 1 & 2 & 2 \end{bmatrix}$$

has rank 2.

Now let us look at our gas-absorber problem, where

$$
\boldsymbol{A} = \begin{bmatrix} -1.173 & 0.6341 & \cdots & 0 \\ 0.5390 & -1.173 & & \vdots \\ \vdots & & & \\ & & & 0.6341 \\ 0 & \cdots & 0.5390 & -1.173 \end{bmatrix}; \quad \boldsymbol{B} = \begin{bmatrix} 0.5390 & 0 \\ 0 & 0 \\ \vdots & \vdots \\ 0 & 0.6341 \end{bmatrix}
$$

$$(6 \times 6) \qquad\qquad (6 \times 2)$$

and the transposed value $\boldsymbol{W}'$ of the controllability matrix is given by

$$
\boldsymbol{W}' = \begin{bmatrix}
0.5390 & 0 & 0 & 0 & 0 & 0 \\
0 & 0 & 0 & 0 & 0 & .6341 \\
-.6323 & .2905 & 0 & 0 & 0 & 0 \\
0 & 0 & 0 & 0 & .4021 & -.7439 \\
.9260 & -.6816 & .1566 & 0 & 0 & 0 \\
0 & 0 & 0 & .2550 & -.9434 & 1.0894 \\
-1.5185 & 1.3980 & -.5511 & .0844 & 0 & 0 \\
0 & 0 & .1617 & -.8974 & 1.9350 & -1.7865 \\
2.6679 & -2.8080 & 1.4535 & -.3960 & .0455 & 0 \\
0 & .1025 & -.7587 & 2.3668 & -3.8865 & 3.1387 \\
-4.9103 & 5.6538 & -3.4698 & 1.2769 & -.2668 & .0245 \\
.0650 & -.6014 & 2.4462 & -5.6500 & 7.8253 & -5.7768
\end{bmatrix}.
$$

The transpose of $\boldsymbol{W}$ is used here merely for ease in writing. With these values of the elements, the dot products of the 12 vectors constituting the columns of $\boldsymbol{W}$ (that is, rows of $\boldsymbol{W}'$) are calculated. These are as follows.

.2905
.4021
.4842
.7151
1.3466
2.1418
4.5712
7.7671
17.2741
31.1441
69.8182
132.8788

Now a new set of vectors is calculated. All the dot products are nonzero, so that any vector could be the basis, but we shall choose $\boldsymbol{v}_{12}$ which gives the largest dot product. The new system becomes

$$\boldsymbol{w}_1 = \boldsymbol{v}_1 - \left(\frac{\boldsymbol{v}_1 \cdot \boldsymbol{v}_{12}}{132.8788}\right)(\boldsymbol{v}_{12}),$$

$$\boldsymbol{w}_2 = \boldsymbol{v}_2 - \left(\frac{\boldsymbol{v}_2 \cdot \boldsymbol{v}_{12}}{132.8788}\right)(\boldsymbol{v}_{12}),$$

$$\vdots$$

$$\boldsymbol{w}_{11} = \boldsymbol{v}_{11} - \left(\frac{\boldsymbol{v}_{11} \cdot \boldsymbol{v}_{12}}{132.8788}\right)(\boldsymbol{v}_{12}),$$

$$\boldsymbol{w}_{12} = \boldsymbol{0}.$$

The new controllability matrix becomes

$$W^* = [\boldsymbol{w}_1 \ldots \boldsymbol{w}_{12}]$$

$$= \begin{bmatrix} .5390 & .0002 & -.0006 & .0015 & -.0021 & .0015 \\ .0018 & -.0166 & .0674 & -.1558 & .2157 & .4749 \\ -.6322 & .2895 & .0040 & -.0092 & .0127 & -.0094 \\ -.0036 & .0337 & -.1370 & .3165 & -.0363 & -.4203 \\ .9256 & -.6778 & .1409 & .0363 & -.0502 & .0371 \\ .0074 & -.0684 & .2783 & -.3879 & -.0532 & .4322 \\ -1.5172 & 1.3855 & -.5002 & -.3031 & .1628 & -.1202 \\ -.0151 & 1.400 & -.4077 & .4177 & .1136 & -.4419 \\ 2.6640 & -2.7717 & 1.3061 & -.0554 & -.4263 & .3483 \\ .0312 & -.1864 & .4164 & -.3474 & -.1272 & .3635 \\ -4.8997 & 5.5558 & -3.0712 & .3563 & 1.0082 & -.9168 \\ 0 & -0 & 0 & -0 & 0 & -0 \end{bmatrix}',$$

and the dot products are as follows.

$$\begin{matrix} .2905 \\ .3011 \\ .4838 \\ .2980 \\ 1.3411 \\ .4221 \\ 4.5136 \\ .5686 \\ 16.7910 \\ .4781 \\ 66.2903 \\ 0 \end{matrix}$$

Now using the 11th nonzero vector, a new controllability matrix is calculated from

$$w_1^* = w_1 - \left(\frac{w_1 \cdot w_{11}}{66.2903}\right)(w_{11}),$$

$$\vdots$$

$$w_{10}^* = w_{10} - \left(\frac{w_{10} \cdot w_{11}}{66.2903}\right)(w_{11}),$$

$$w_{11}^* = \mathbf{0},$$

$$w_{12}^* = \mathbf{0}.$$

When this procedure is continued, it is found that the 7th controllability matrix is made up of only zero elements, and all the dot products of the vectors are zero. Since we were able to carry out 6 orthogonalizations, the rank of the original $\boldsymbol{W}$ matrix is 6. Furthermore, since $n = 6$ for our system, this means that the system is state-controllable. As a consequence, we should expect excellent results in all optimal control and trajectory calculations.

Now that we have determined that the system is controllable, we may proceed with confidence to investigate the effect of the matrices $\boldsymbol{Q}$ and $\boldsymbol{R}$ in the performance index on the optimal control and optimal trajectories. Certain selected tabulated results are shown in Table 3.3 and Figures 3.4 through 3.6 for the

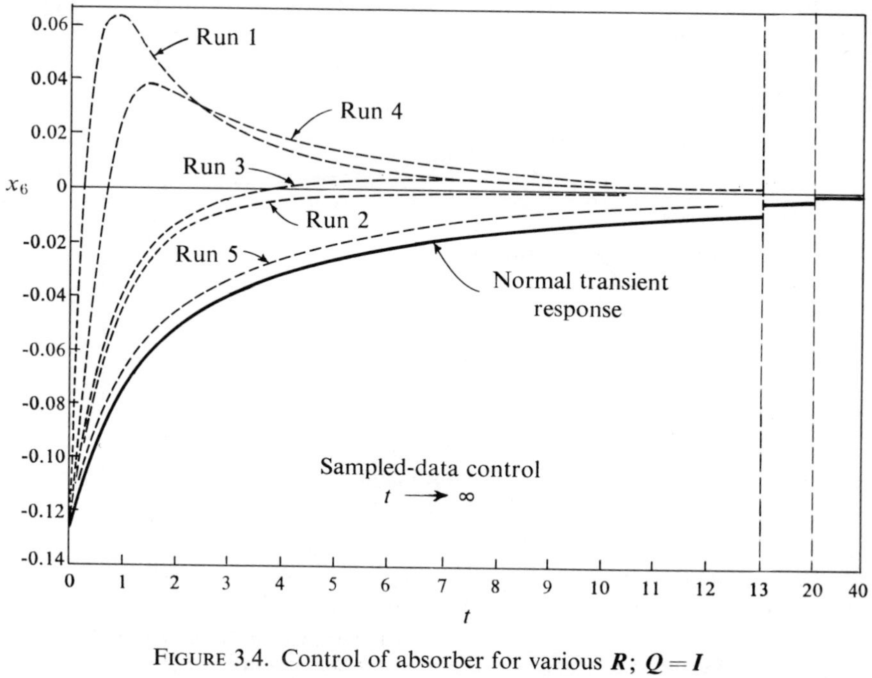

FIGURE 3.4. Control of absorber for various $\boldsymbol{R}$; $\boldsymbol{Q} = \boldsymbol{I}$

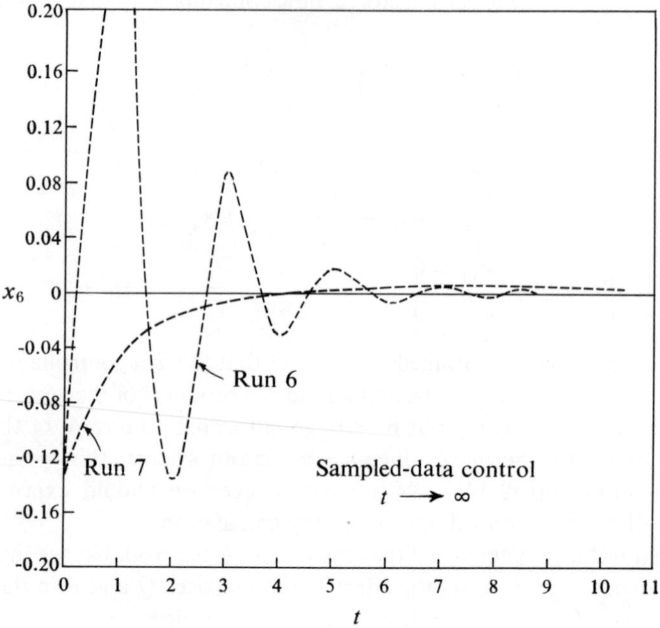

FIGURE 3.5. Control of absorber for various $\boldsymbol{R}$; $\boldsymbol{Q} \neq \boldsymbol{I}$

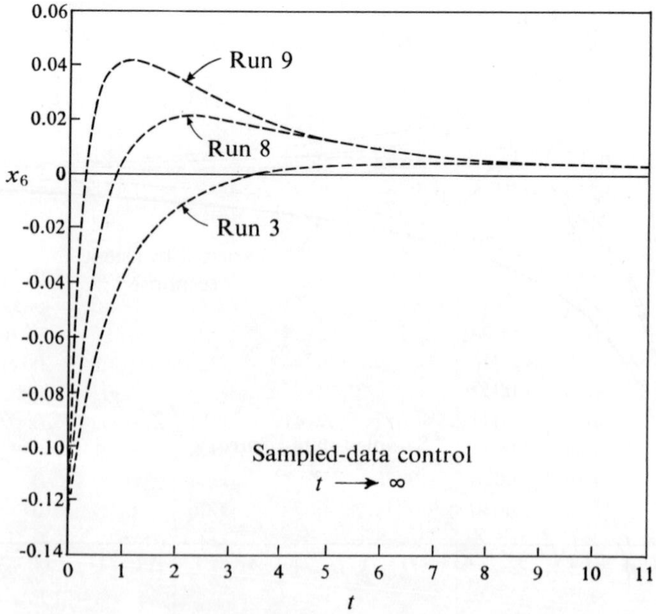

FIGURE 3.6. Control of absorber for changes in both $\boldsymbol{Q}$ and $\boldsymbol{R}$

TABLE 3.3

Sampled-data Optimal Control ($H = I$, $S = 0$)

	Run 1			Run 2			Run 3		
t	x_6	u_1	u_2	x_6	u_1	u_2	x_6	u_1	u_2
0	−.1273	.2181	.3469	−.1273	.2481	.0801	−.1273	.0490	.0891
1	+.0618	.0894	.0810	−.0421	.1064	.0534	−.0386	.0409	.0613
2	+.0370	.0641	.0489	−.0169	.0811	.0379	−.0125	.0346	.0451
3	+.0238	.0459	.0316	−.0080	.0631	.0277	−.0034	.0291	.0343
4	+.0159	.0324	.0210	−.0043	.0491	.0205	+ 0	.0244	.0267
5	+.0107	.0227	.0142	−.0016	.0379	.0154	+.0012	.0202	.0210
6	+.0073	.0159	.0097	−.0016	.0292	.0116	+.0016	.0167	.0167
7	+.0050	.0109	.0066	−.0011	.0223	.0087	+.0015	.0137	.0133
8	+.0034	.0075	.0046	−.0008	.0170	.0066	+.0113	.0112	.0107
9	+.0024	.0052	.0031	−.0006	.0130	.0050	+.0011	.0091	.0086
10	+.0016	.0036	.0021	−.0004	.0099	.0038	+.0009	.0074	.0069
11	+.0011	.0025	.0015	−.0003	.0075	.0029	+.0008	.0060	.0056
12	+.0008	.0017	.0010	−.0002	.0057	.0022	+.0006	.0049	.0045
13	+.0005	.0012	.0007	−.0001	.0043	.0017	+.0005	.0039	.0036
14	0	0	0	−.0001	.0033	.0013	+.0004	.0032	.0029
	$Q = I, R = 0$			$Q = I, R = [-6\ -1]$			$Q = I, R = I$		

	Run 4			Run 5			Run 6		
t	x_6	u_1	u_2	x_6	u_1	u_2	x_6	u_1	u_2
0	−.1273	.0427	.2620	−.1273	.1775	.0119	−.1273	1.0761	1.2588
1	+.0287	.0348	.1110	−.0686	.1281	.0092	+.4166	−.5792	−.7514
2	+.0348	.0284	.0652	−.0452	.0862	.0073	−.1391	.2831	.3538
3	+.0274	.0230	.0438	−.0331	.0696	.0059	+.0878	−.1224	−.1625
4	+.0207	.0183	.0313	−.0255	.0570	.0048	−.0309	.0591	.0766
5	+.0156	.0144	.0230	−.0202	.0468	.0039	+.0187	−.0257	−.0352
6	+.0118	.0113	.0171	−.0162	.0384	.0032	−.0068	.0123	.0166
7	+.0090	.0088	.0129	−.0131	.0315	.0026	+.0040	−.0054	−.0076
8	+.0068	.0068	.0098	−.0106	.0258	.0021	−.0015	.0026	.0036
9	+.0052	.0052	.0075	−.0086	.0211	.0017	+.0009	−.0011	−.0017
10	+.0040	.0040	.0057	−.0070	.0172	.0014	−.0003	.0005	.0080
11	+.0031	.0031	.0044	−.0057	.0141	.0011	+.0002	−.0002	−.0004
12	+.0023	.0024	.0033	−.0047	.0115	.0009	−.0001	.0001	.0002
13	+.0018	.0018	.0026	−.0038	.0094	.0008	0	0	−.0001
14	+.0014	.0014	.0020	−.0031	.0077	.0006	0	0	0
	$Q = I, R = [-1\quad -2]$			$Q = I, R = [-2\quad 1]$			$Q = [-7\ -1\ -1\ -1\ -1\ -7]\ R = 0$		

TABLE 3.3 (continued)

	Run 7			Run 8			Run 9		
t	x_6	u_1	u_2	x_6	u_1	u_2	x_6	u_1	u_2
0	−.1273	.0424	.0737	−.1273	.1158	.2003	−.1273	.1798	.2962
1	−.0446	.0362	.0579	+.0047	.0794	.0996	+.0420	.0933	.0965
2	−.0163	.0305	.0455	+.0204	.0595	.0603	+.0348	.0649	.0536
3	−.0052	.0255	.0360	+.0184	.0455	.0401	+.0237	.0470	.0344
4	−.0005	.0212	.0287	+.0143	.0346	.0280	+.0162	.0339	.0231
5	+.0015	.0175	.0229	+.0107	.0262	.0200	+.0112	.0242	.0159
6	+.0022	.0143	.0184	+.0080	.0196	.0144	+.0078	.0172	.0110
7	+.0023	.0117	.0148	+.0059	.0147	.0105	+.0054	.0121	.0076
8	+.0022	.0096	.0119	+.0044	.0109	.0077	+.0038	.0085	.0053
9	+.0020	.0078	.0096	+.0032	.0081	.0056	+.0026	.0060	.0037
10	+.0017	.0064	.0078	+.0024	.0060	.0042	+.0019	.0042	.0026
11	+.0015	.0052	.0063	+.0017	.0044	.0031	+.0013	.0029	.0018
12	+.0012	.0042	.0051	+.0013	.0033	.0023	+.0009	.0021	.0013
13	+.0010	.0034	.0041	+.0010	.0024	.0017	+.0006	.0014	.0009
14	+.0008	.0028	.0033	+.0007	.0018	.0012	+.0004	.0010	.0006
	$\boldsymbol{Q} = [-7-1-1-1-1-7]$ $\boldsymbol{R} = \boldsymbol{I}$			$\boldsymbol{Q} = 5\boldsymbol{I}$, $\boldsymbol{R} = \boldsymbol{I}$			$\boldsymbol{Q} = 5\boldsymbol{I}$, $\boldsymbol{R} = 0.2\boldsymbol{I}$		

	Run 9a							
t	x_1	x_2	x_3	x_4	x_5	x_6	u_1	u_2
0	−.0306	−.0567	−.0788	−.0976	−.1137	−.1273	1.4525	1.5950
1	+.4499	.0493	−.0570	−.0626	.0607	.5475	−.7330	−.9114
2	−.0717	.0358	−.0062	.0013	.0460	−.1468	−.0065	.1013
3	−.0209	.0002	.0021	.0017	−.0050	−.0067	.0280	.0212
4	.0019	−.0012	.0003	−.0002	−.0010	.0050	.0010	−.0043
5	.0008	0	−.0001	0	.0002	0	−.0009	−.0004
6	0	0	0	0	0	0	0	0

$$\boldsymbol{Q} = \begin{bmatrix} 1.0 & & & \cdots & & 0 \\ & 7.39 & & & & \\ \vdots & & 230.0 & & & \vdots \\ & & & 230.0 & & \\ & & & & 7.39 & \\ 0 & & & \cdots & & 1.0 \end{bmatrix}; \qquad \boldsymbol{R} = \boldsymbol{0}$$

discrete-time case and in Table 3.4 and Figure 3.7 for the continuous-time case. To condense the amount of results, only the composition of plate 6, x_6, of the absorber is shown as a function of time in Tables 3.3 and 3.4 and Figures 3.4 through 3.7.

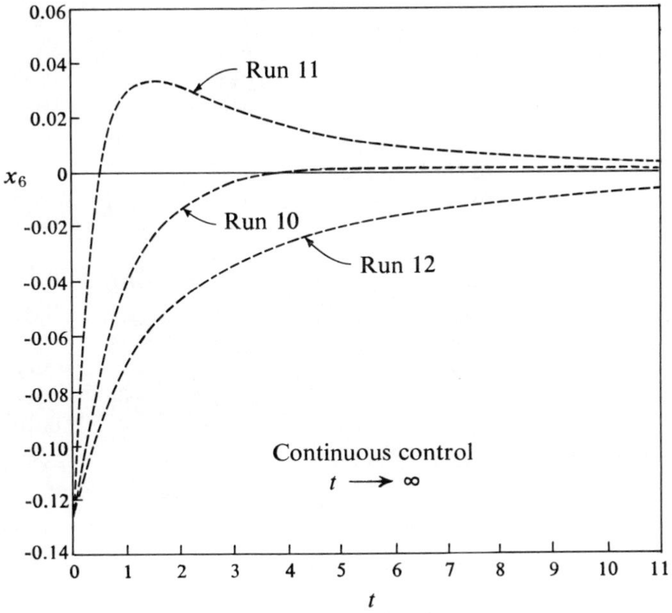

FIGURE 3.7. Control of absorber for various $\boldsymbol{R}$; $\boldsymbol{Q} = \boldsymbol{I}$

As a measure for some form of comparison of the controlled responses, Figure 3.4 also shows the uncontrolled response of x_6 (normal transient response) obtained by applying those inputs at $t = 0$ (and then holding the inputs constant), which brings the system into the origin. The result is, of course, a slow gradual movement toward the origin; even after 20 min a considerable deviation from the final state exists.

Figure 3.4 illustrates the results of optimal sampled-data control of the absorption tower using $\boldsymbol{Q} = \boldsymbol{I}$ and varying the elements of $\boldsymbol{R}$. Thus Run 1 shows the case $\boldsymbol{R} = \boldsymbol{0}$, no penalty on the amount of control used. The result is a very heavy and immediate application of the control variables so that a very rapid rise and overshoot occurs. This overshoot is followed by a gradual decrease toward the origin. Runs 2 through 5 show the result of penalizing the amount of control used. Keeping in mind that $u_2^0(k)$, the gas feed composition, affects x_6 more strongly than $u_1^0(k)$, the liquid feed composition, it can be seen that the responses of Runs 2 and 3 are not too different. However, the use of $\boldsymbol{R} = \boldsymbol{I}$, when compared to $\boldsymbol{R} = \boldsymbol{0}$, restricts the amount of control which is used,

TABLE 3.4

Continuous-Time Optimal Control ($H = I$, $S = 0$)

	Run 10			Run 11		
t	x_6	u_1	u_2	x_6	u_1	u_2
0	−.1273	.0552	.1166	−.1273	.0479	.5588
1	−.0386	.0447	.0741	.0293	.0380	.1533
2	−.0126	.0376	.0524	.0329	.0309	.0777
3	−.0037	.0317	.0392	.0255	.0251	.0502
4	−.0003	.0266	.0301	.0193	.0201	.0352
5	.0010	.0222	.0236	.0146	.0159	.0257
6	.0014	.0183	.0186	.0110	.0125	.0191
7	.0015	.0151	.0148	.0084	.0097	.0143
8	.0014	.0123	.0119	.0064	.0075	.0108
9	.0012	.0100	.0095	.0049	.0058	.0082
10	.0010	.0082	.0077	.0038	.0045	.0063
11	.0008	.0066	.0062	.0029	.0034	.0048
12	.0007	.0054	.0050	.0022	.0026	.0037
13	.0006	.0044	.0040	.0017	.0017	.0025
14	.0005	.0035	.0032	.0012	.0009	.0014
	$Q = I, R = I$			$Q = I, R = [-1 \quad -2]$		

	Run 12			Run 13		
t	x_6	u_1	u_2	x_6	u_1	u_2
0	−.1273	.0616	.0154	−.1273	0	0
1	−.0681	.0508	.0118	−.0733	0	0
2	−.0446	.0436	.0095	−.0508	0	0
3	−.0325	.0379	.0078	−.0378	0	0
4	−.0251	.0328	.0065	−.0311	0	0
5	−.0201	.0284	.0055	−.0258	0	0
6	−.0164	.0245	.0046	−.0218	0	0
7	−.0136	.0210	.0039	−.0187	0	0
8	−.0113	.0180	.0033	−.0162	0	0
9	−.0095	.0154	.0028	−.0142	0	0
10	−.0080	.0131	.0024	−.0124	0	0
11	−.0067	.0112	.0020	−.0109	0	0
12	−.0057	.0095	.0017	−.0096	0	0
13	−.0048	.0076	.0014	−.0085	0	0
14	−.0039	.0055	.0011	−.0075	0	0
	$Q = I, R = [-1 \quad 1]$			$Q = 0, R = I$		

preventing the large overshoot of Run 1. Both Runs 2 and 3 thus yield a smoother response toward the origin. The sequence of Runs 3 and 4 is toward decreasing the weighting on $u_2^0(k)$ and thus corresponds to increasing overshoot. By contrast, Run 5 places a very heavy weighting on $u_2^0(k)$, and as a result the amount of control applied is quite small.

It is rather obvious that this qualitative description of the results points out some of the important trends. By changing the elements in $\boldsymbol{R}$, it is possible to obtain almost any desired optimal response for x_6. Similar statements can, of course, be made for any of the compositions $x_1, x_2, \ldots, x_6$. It should also be noted that without the use of the $\boldsymbol{R}$ matrix, the controls obtained may well be outside of physical bounds. This illustrates the point made previously that an indirect form of state and/or control constraints may be included by a proper selection of the weighting matrices.

In addition to these runs, a series was developed to investigate the effect of changing the weighting elements in $\boldsymbol{Q}$. Thus Table 3.3 shows Runs 6 and 7 with x_1 and x_2 given essentially zero weighting, $\boldsymbol{Q} = [-7\ -1\ -1\ -1\ -1\ -7]$ and with $\boldsymbol{R} = \boldsymbol{0}$ and $\boldsymbol{R} = \boldsymbol{I}$. The response of x_6 is shown in Figure 3.5 for both cases ; when no constraints are placed on the amount of control used ($\boldsymbol{R} = \boldsymbol{0}$), there is a large oscillation in x_6. This follows because $\boldsymbol{Q}$ does not weight x_6, and the optimal control attempts to bring $x_2, \ldots, x_5$ to the origin quickly. By contrast, when $\boldsymbol{R} = \boldsymbol{I}$, the control which can be applied is limited and x_6 takes a smooth, nonoscillatory path to the origin. In another run (not shown), the elements of $\boldsymbol{Q}$ were selected to make only the response of x_1 important ($\boldsymbol{Q} = [-1\ -7\ -7\ -7\ -7\ -7]$) ; in this case x_1 goes to the origin in one sampling period, whereas $x_2, \ldots, x_6$ gradually progress to the origin.

Also shown in Table 3.3 is Run 9a, in which an exponential weighting in $\boldsymbol{Q}$ is applied as one progresses from the ends of the column to the center. This will be detailed further in Chapter 5, Example 5.2 ; for now it suffices to note that this heavy weighting of the center values yields a very fast response. The oscillation shown is, of course, due to the fact that $\boldsymbol{R} = \boldsymbol{0}$.

It is possible to predict in advance the response of the system to certain sets of the weighting matrices. Thus if $\boldsymbol{Q} = 5\boldsymbol{I}$ and $\boldsymbol{R} = 5\boldsymbol{I}$ is used, the response should be identical to that of Run 3 because the scalar quantity 5 can be factored out of the summation which is minimized. Computationally, the results are confirmed completely. When $\boldsymbol{Q}$ alone is raised to $5\boldsymbol{I}$, this is equivalent to $\boldsymbol{Q} = \boldsymbol{I}$ and $\boldsymbol{R} = 0.2\boldsymbol{I}$; when compared to Run 3 this leads to a faster rise and overshoot (Run 8). When $\boldsymbol{Q} = 5\boldsymbol{I}$ and $\boldsymbol{R} = 0.2\boldsymbol{I}$ are used, this result is further emphasized (Run 9). Figure 3.6 shows the plotted results of these latter calculations.

In summary, these sampled-data optimal results point out the versatility of the use of the weighting matrices $\boldsymbol{Q}$ and $\boldsymbol{R}$. Essentially any desired response can be obtained, either for all of the state variables or for only one or more of selected variables, by a proper choice of $\boldsymbol{Q}$ and $\boldsymbol{R}$. This means, of course, that in a real physical system where only one of many dependent variables is important, its response can be optimally controlled with no difficulty.

Some of the important results obtained with the continuous optimal control sequence using the Riccati nonlinear differential equation with a starting value of $\boldsymbol{J}_0 = \boldsymbol{S}$ are shown in Table 3.4 and Figure 3.7. Some general comments, however, are in order regarding the results. First, it is known from the form of the control law that the matrix $\boldsymbol{R}$ can never be the null matrix or the control will become infinite. Thus, $\boldsymbol{R} = \boldsymbol{I}$ or some variation on this was used in all the calculations. Second, the fact that $\boldsymbol{x}_\infty = \boldsymbol{0}$ is an equilibrium point of the system means that for long times of operation the control will always go to the origin. Thus, the value of $\boldsymbol{S}$ used in the performance criterion does not influence the optimal trajectory. This was confirmed computationally by first carrying out a calculation using $\boldsymbol{S} = \boldsymbol{I}$ and then $\boldsymbol{S} = 10\boldsymbol{I}$. The results agreed to all decimal places. If the optimal response is independent of the elements in $\boldsymbol{S}$ and the matrices $\boldsymbol{Q}$ and $\boldsymbol{S}$ are selected to be the null matrices, the results should be a minimum-energy type of control. In the present case, minimum-energy corresponds to $\boldsymbol{u} = \boldsymbol{0}$, and as seen in Run 12 of Table 3.4, this is exactly what the computation yields. The trajectory of x_6 is thus merely the normal transient response shown in Figure 3.4.

From the data shown in Figure 3.7 and in Table 3.4, it can be seen that the results are similar in character and direction to those previously illustrated for the sampled-data case. Once again, a selection of the elements in $\boldsymbol{Q}$ and $\boldsymbol{R}$ can lead to an optimal trajectory for any state or set of states which has essentially any desired shape.

(4) As the next step in the over-all calculation, we shall investigate the effect of time delays on optimal control of the discrete-time systems. The equations of interest have been presented in Section 3.2, where $\alpha =$ integer is interpreted as the amount to delay the application of the control. Two cases previously presented have been analyzed: (1) Run 4 in Table 3.3 with $\boldsymbol{Q} = \boldsymbol{I}$ and $\boldsymbol{R} = [-1\ -2]$ and (2) $\boldsymbol{Q} = \boldsymbol{I}$ and $\boldsymbol{R} = [-6\ -1]$. Both these cases were developed for Table 3.3 assuming no time-delay factor, $\alpha = 0$. Now we desire to show the effect resulting from $\alpha = 1$, $\alpha = 2$, $\alpha = 4$ on the optimal controls and optimal trajectory ($\alpha = 4$ results are not tabulated).

The necessary results of the calculations are shown in Figures 3.8 and 3.9, with the tabulated data for the case $\boldsymbol{Q} = \boldsymbol{I}$ and $\boldsymbol{R} = [-1\ -2]$ shown in Table 3.5. Scanning the optimal controls at $k = 0$ ($t = 0$) in Table 3.5, we can see how the time delay first enters. Figures 3.8 and 3.9 show how an underdamping and an overdamping of the non-time-delay optimal trajectory can be achieved by merely introducing time delay. In the first case a moderate amount of delay, $\alpha = 2$, is actually conducive to a "better" trajectory, but increasing this delay then tends to yield a "poorer" trajectory. Better and poorer are here interpreted qualitatively as indicating how quickly the trajectory reaches the origin. In the second case the time delay always leads to a poorer and poorer trajectory.

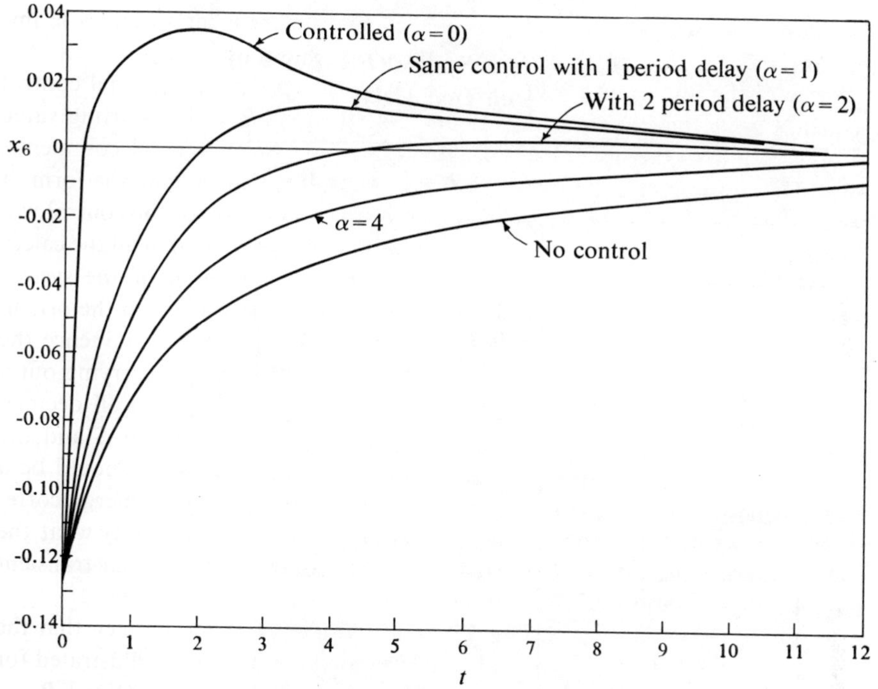

FIGURE 3.8. Control of absorber with delay in control; $\boldsymbol{Q} = \boldsymbol{I}$ and $\boldsymbol{R} = [-1 \ -2]$

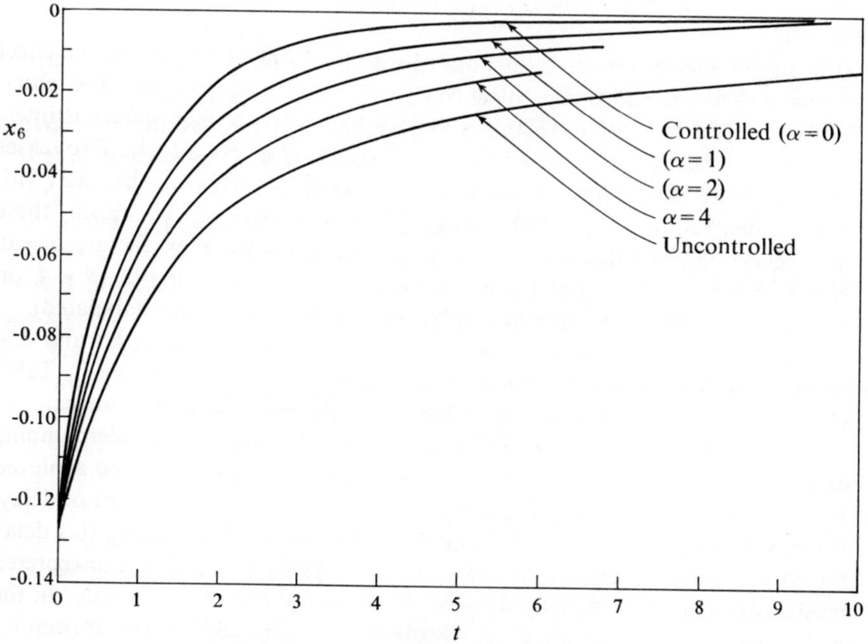

FIGURE 3.9. Control of absorber with delay in control; $\boldsymbol{Q} = \boldsymbol{I}$ and $\boldsymbol{R} = [-6 \ -1]$

TABLE 3.5

Discrete-Time System ($H = I$, $S = 0$) with Time Delay α

$Q = I$, $R = [-1 \quad -2]$

t	x_6	u_1	u_2	x_6	u_1	u_2	x_6	u_1	u_2
0	−.1273	.0427	.2620	−.1273	.0348	.1110	−.1273	.0284	.0652
1	.0287	.0348	.1110	−.0301	.0305	.0833	−.0479	.0255	.0542
2	.0348	.0284	.0652	−.0080	.0260	.0614	−.0191	.0222	.0443
3	.0274	.0230	.0438	.0082	.0219	.0464	−.0070	.0191	.0360
4	.0207	.0183	.0313	.0102	.0181	.0355	−.0016	.0161	.0292
5	.0156	.0144	.0230	.0099	.0148	.0273	.0009	.0135	.0237
6	.0118	.0133	.0171	.0087	.0120	.0212	.0020	.0113	.0193
7	.0090	.0088	.0129	.0073	.0097	.0166	.0023	.0094	.0157
8	.0068	.0068	.0098	.0061	.0078	.0130	.0023	.0077	.0128
9	.0052	.0052	.0075	.0049	.0062	.0102	.0021	.0064	.0105
10	.0040	.0040	.0057	.0040	.0050	.0080	.0019	.0053	.0085
	$\alpha = 0$ (Run 4 in Table 3.3)			$\alpha = 1$			$\alpha = 2$		

Obviously these results are a function of the chosen $\boldsymbol{Q}$ and $\boldsymbol{R}$, but they indicate the wide variation which can be achieved.

(5) In all of the results to this point we have always used the infinite-stage formulation, that is, the case where $\boldsymbol{K}_P$ is a constant $\boldsymbol{K}$. This value of $\boldsymbol{K}$ is then used in the feedback optimal control equation to generate the corresponding optimal control. In the present section, we consider the case of a finite number of stages using the discrete-time formulation with $\mathbf{Q} = \boldsymbol{I}$, $\boldsymbol{R} = \boldsymbol{I}$, $\boldsymbol{S} = \mathbf{0}$, and $\boldsymbol{H} = \boldsymbol{I}$. Since $\boldsymbol{S} = \mathbf{0}$, the computations for $\boldsymbol{J}_P$ and $\boldsymbol{K}_P$ start with $\boldsymbol{J}_0 = \mathbf{0}$. Incidentally, it really does not make any difference what we start with in the iteration for the infinite-stage case ; thus $\boldsymbol{J}_0 = \boldsymbol{Q}$ will yield the same $\boldsymbol{K}$ as $\boldsymbol{J}_0 = \mathbf{0}$ since we are using an iterative procedure. The only difference may be in the number of stages of the iteration required to achieve a constant value for $\boldsymbol{K}$.

The elements of $\boldsymbol{K}_P$ shown in Table 3.1 are still appropriate for the present case except that if we choose to consider only $P = 8$, eight stages of control, $\boldsymbol{K}_8$ is used to generate $\boldsymbol{u}^0(0)$, the optimal control at the start of the process. When $\boldsymbol{x}(1)$ is then generated, $\boldsymbol{K}_7$ is used to calculate $\boldsymbol{u}^0(1)$ and the process continued backward in terms of $\boldsymbol{K}_6, \boldsymbol{K}_5, \ldots, \boldsymbol{K}_1$. Table 3.6 illustrates some of the results obtained.

TABLE 3.6

Discrete-Time System ($H = I$)

	$Q = I, R = I, S = 0$								
t	x_6	u_1	u_2	x_6	u_1	u_2	x_6	u_1	u_2
0	−.1273	.0490	.0891	−.1273	.0486	.0888	−.1273	.0481	.0877
1	−.0386	.0409	.0613	−.0388	.0406	.0609	−.0391	.0403	.0604
2	−.0125	.0346	.0451	−.0128	.0343	.0446	−.0133	.0338	.0440
3	−.0034	.0291	.0343	−.0039	.0288	.0338	−.0045	.0283	.0331
4	0	.0244	.0267	−.0006	.0239	.0261	−.0013	.0233	.0253
5	.0012	.0202	.0210	.0005	.0197	.0203	−.0004	.0190	.0193
6	.0016	.0167	.0167	.0007	.0160	.0158	−.0004	.0151	.0146
7	.0015	.0137	.0133	.0006	.0129	.0122	−.0008	.0117	.0108
8	.0013	.0112	.0107	.0002	.0100	.0083	−.0014	.0087	.0076
9	.0011	.0091	.0086	−.0003	.0078	.0069	−.0022	.0059	.0048
10	.0009	.0074	.0069	−.0008	.0058	.0049	−.0030	.0031	.0023
	$J_0 = 0, P = 25$			$P = 12$			$P = 10$		

t	x_6	u_1	u_2	x_6	u_1	u_2
0	−.1273	.0469	.0859	−.1273	.0441	.0819
1	−.0398	.0394	.0592	−.0414	.0374	.0564
2	−.0143	.0329	.0427	−.0167	.0305	.0395
3	−.0058	.0271	.0315	−.0089	.0243	.0279
4	−.0030	.0219	.0234	−.0068	.0184	.0191
5	−.0024	.0172	.0170	−.0061	.0126	.0119
6	−.0028	.0128	.0119	−.0081	.0067	.0058
7	−.0037	.0087	.0075			
8	−.0049	.0046	.0036			
	$P = 8$			$P = 6$		

As we can see, any $P > 12$ yields results identical to those for the infinite stage. However, as the number of stages of control decreases, it becomes impossible to reach the origin in the finite number of stages. This is exactly what one might have suggested *a priori* without the numerical calculations.

The only difficulty associated with the finite-stage vs. infinite-stage calculations resides in the computer storage required. If the system is of large order and a large number of stages are involved, it may be necessary to store the successive K_P matrices on tape and recover them later. This will increase the computation time markedly.

(6) In part (7) of this example, we shall be considering the effect of using an output relation $y(k) = Hx(k)$ in which H is not the identity matrix I. Thus we need to assure ourselves that with $H \neq I$ the system is observable. In Section 1.9, we showed that a system is observable if the observability matrix V as given by

$$V = [H'A'H' \cdots (A^{n-1})'H']$$

has rank n. In other words, among the nm columns of V, there is a set of n linearly independent vectors. The determination of the rank can be carried out in exactly the same manner as was previously done for the controllability matrix W.

For illustration, we consider the case of A as given previously and H given by

$$H = [0 \quad -7 \quad -7 \quad -7 \quad -7 \quad -1],$$

where the exponents for the diagonal elements are shown as before. We shall note that the rows of H which have only zero elements do not contribute to the rank of V, so instead of the entire matrix H, we simply consider the rows of H which contain nonzero elements (10^{-7} is close to zero). This gives us a smaller matrix,

$$H^* = \begin{bmatrix} 1.0 & 0.0 & 0.0 & 0.0 & 0.0 & 0.0 \\ 0.0 & 0.0 & 0.0 & 0.0 & 0.0 & 0.1 \end{bmatrix},$$

and with this matrix we may construct a modified observability matrix. Here again we shall write the transpose

$$V' = \begin{bmatrix} 1.0000 & .0000 & .0000 & .0000 & .0000 & .0000 \\ .0000 & .0000 & .0000 & .0000 & .0000 & .1000 \\ -1.1731 & .6341 & .0000 & .0000 & .0000 & .0000 \\ .0000 & .0000 & .0000 & .0000 & .0634 & -.1173 \\ 1.7783 & -1.4878 & .4021 & .0000 & .0000 & .0000 \\ .0000 & .0000 & .0000 & .0402 & -.1488 & .1778 \\ -3.0296 & 3.1279 & -1.4151 & .2550 & .0000 & .0000 \\ .0000 & .0000 & .0255 & -.1415 & .3128 & -.3030 \\ 5.5375 & -6.4879 & 3.8053 & -1.1965 & .1617 & .0000 \\ -.0000 & .0162 & -.1196 & .3805 & -.6488 & .5538 \\ -10.6102 & 13.5354 & -9.3368 & 3.9191 & -.9484 & .1025 \\ .0103 & -.0948 & .3919 & -.9337 & 1.3535 & -1.0610 \end{bmatrix},$$

and the dot products of the vectors constituting the columns of V are as follows.

$$\begin{matrix} 1.0000 \\ .0100 \\ 1.7783 \\ .0178 \\ 5.5375 \\ .0554 \\ 21.0300 \\ .2103 \\ 88.6945 \\ .8869 \\ 399.2289 \\ 3.9923 \end{matrix}$$

Proceeding as before, this yields a new observability matrix

$$V^{*\prime} = \begin{bmatrix} .9999 & .0002 & -.0010 & .0023 & -.0034 & .0027 \\ .0027 & -.0252 & .1041 & -.2481 & .3597 & .7180 \\ -1.1729 & .6324 & .0070 & -.0168 & .0244 & -.0191 \\ -.0054 & .0499 & -.2064 & .4918 & -.0788 & -.6142 \\ 1.7774 & -1.4802 & .3709 & .0741 & -.1074 & .0842 \\ .0109 & -.1015 & .4197 & -.5979 & -.0380 & .6418 \\ -3.0266 & 3.1013 & -1.3051 & -.0070 & .3798 & -.2977 \\ -.0227 & .2106 & -.6157 & .6591 & .1208 & -.6723 \\ 5.5285 & -6.4047 & 3.4617 & -.3780 & -1.0247 & .9300 \\ .0480 & -.2824 & .6386 & -.5667 & -.1498 & .5692 \\ -10.5842 & 13.2954 & -8.3449 & 1.5562 & 2.4770 & -2.5825 \\ 0 & 0 & 0 & 0 & 0 & 0 \end{bmatrix},$$

and the dot products of the vectors constituting the columns of V^* are as follows.

$$\begin{matrix} .9999 \\ .7180 \\ 1.7769 \\ .6705 \\ 5.5123 \\ .9576 \\ 20.7155 \\ 1.3251 \\ 85.6271 \\ 1.1576 \\ 373.6604 \\ 0 \end{matrix}$$

Without showing the remaining results, a continuation of this procedure ultimately shows that the original V has rank 6. Since $n = 6$, this means that with the $\boldsymbol{H}$ used for illustration the system is observable. In fact, for all the $\boldsymbol{H}$ used in the next section of this example the system is always observable.

(7) In this section, we shall briefly investigate the effect on the optimal control sequence of using $\boldsymbol{H}$ not equal to $\boldsymbol{I}$. Once again the discrete-time case will be used for illustration with $\boldsymbol{Q} = \boldsymbol{I}$, $\boldsymbol{R} = \boldsymbol{I}$, and $\boldsymbol{S} = \boldsymbol{0}$. The sampling period as before is 1.0 min. In performing the calculations, the only changes which need to be made are to replace $\boldsymbol{Q}$ with $\boldsymbol{H}'\boldsymbol{Q}\boldsymbol{H}$ in all the formulas and to realize that since

$$\boldsymbol{y}(k) = \boldsymbol{H}\boldsymbol{x}(k),$$

the actual output variables are now $\boldsymbol{y}(k)$ and not $\boldsymbol{x}(k)$.

Certain selected results are shown in Table 3.7. As illustration the first run uses $\boldsymbol{H} = [-1\ -7\ -7\ -7\ -7\ -7]$, and thus $\boldsymbol{H}'\boldsymbol{Q}\boldsymbol{H} = [-2\ -14\ -14\ -14\ -14\ -14]$. On this basis this run is equivalent to weighting only $y_1(k)$ in the performance index and being able to measure only $y_1(k)$. Thus we see that only the optimal trajectory for $y_1(k)$ is shown, this being the only measurable output. Furthermore, the control $u_2(k)$, since it applies at the other end of the gas absorber, has only a minor effect on $y_1(k)$, and thus remains quite small. At the same time, we note that if we ran the case $\boldsymbol{Q} = [-2\ -14\ -14\ -14\ -14\ -14]$, $\boldsymbol{R} = \boldsymbol{I}$, $\boldsymbol{S} = \boldsymbol{0}$, $\boldsymbol{H} = \boldsymbol{I}$, we would expect exactly the same results except we would measure $x_1(k)$ and we would also generate the corresponding $x_2(k), \ldots, x_6(k)$. Although not shown here, these results have been confirmed.

Turning to the second run of Table 3.7, we see that here $\boldsymbol{H} = [0\ -7\ -7\ -7\ -7\ -7]$; in other words the output variable is 10 times greater than for the first run, but all other items are equivalent. Furthermore, this means that we weight the $y_1(k)$ very heavily. The results in Table 3.7 for this run confirm the heavy weighting of $y_1(k)$ and also, as before, the relative insignificance of $u_2(k)$.

The next two runs in Table 3.7 illustrate the results associated with letting $y_6(k)$ as well as $y_1(k)$ be output measured variables. Thus, in the first of those two runs $\boldsymbol{H} = [-1\ -7\ -7\ -7\ -7\ -1]$, and we see that the optimal trajectory for $y_1(k)$ and for $u_1(k)$ are essentially the same as for the first run of Table 3.7. By contrast, however, $y_6(k)$ now can be measured and controlled, and thus a strong application of $u_2(k)$ is involved. In the last run the contribution of $y_6(k)$ is decreased by a factor of 10, and the corresponding control, $u_2(\boldsymbol{k})$, is also decreased in a proportionate manner.

Thus we note from these results on varying $\boldsymbol{H}$ that we have another parameter or parameters which can be used to yield different optimal policies. In this case we are able to change the magnitude of the actual state variables as well as differentiate between any of the states.

(8) In all of the work to this point, we have always used a stationary system or a stationary form of the control law. But, as we pointed out in the main

TABLE 3.7

Effect of H on Discrete-Time System ($Q = I$, $R = I$, $S = 0$)

t	y_1	u_1	u_2	y_1	u_1	u_2	y_1	y_6	u_1	u_2
0	−.0306	.0164	.0022	−.3062	.0871	.0060	−.0306	−.1273	.0167	.0358
1	−.0252	.0152	.0019	−.0180	.0533	.0052	−.0251	−.0593	.0153	.0236
2	−.0232	.0142	.0017	−.0088	.0467	.0044	−.0231	−.0358	.0142	.0175
3	−.0220	.0132	.0015	−.0076	.0461	.0038	−.0218	−.0250	.0130	.0137
4	−.0207	.0121	.0014	−.0069	.0368	.0033	−.0204	−.0189	.0118	.0111
5	−.0193	.0109	.0012	−.0062	.0321	.0028	−.0188	−.0149	.0105	.0092
6	−.0176	.0098	.0010	−.0054	.0277	.0024	−.0169	−.0121	.0093	.0077
7	−.0160	.0092	.0009	−.0047	.0238	.0020	−.0151	−.0101	.0081	.0065
8	−.0143	.0087	.0008	−.0041	.0204	.0017	−.0133	−.0084	.0071	.0056
	$H = [-1\ -7\ -7\ -7\ -7\ -7]$			$H = [0\ -7\ -7\ -7\ -7\ -7]$			$H = [-1\ -7\ -7\ -7\ -7\ -1]$			

t	y_1	y_6	u_1	u_2
0	−.0306	−.0127	.0164	.0026
1	−.0252	−.0072	.0152	.0023
2	−.0232	−.0049	.0142	.0020
3	−.0220	−.0037	.0132	.0017
4	−.0207	−.0030	.0121	.0015
5	−.0193	−.0024	.0109	.0013
6	−.0176	−.0020	.0098	.0012
7	−.0159	−.0017	.0087	.0012
8	−.0143	−.0015	.0077	.0009
	$H = [-1\ -7\ -7\ -7\ -7\ -2]$			

discussion in this chapter, we may account for $A = A(t)$ and $B = B(t)$ and/or $Q = Q(t)$, $R = R(t)$ and $S = S(t)$ if the physical system so indicates. In this portion of this numerical example we shall illustrate the features of these types of calculations.

In the first example, we use the continuous-time system with control to be applied over a total of 25 min of total time. As usual, we choose $Q = I$, $R = I$, $S = 0$ and $H = I$ and allow for an explicit time change in A and B; in particular we presuppose that A and B start at time $t = 0$ at the normal values used previously but that at each successive minute interval the elements in each matrix decrease by 1%. The magnitude of this decrease is small and does not cause major changes in the results compared to the constant $\boldsymbol{A}$ and $\boldsymbol{B}$ case but, this does not bother us here. Obviously, the same type of results can be obtained with any explicit time variation in $\boldsymbol{A}$ and $\boldsymbol{B}$.

As a first step in the calculation, we must readjust the final end point since the original (final value) was based upon $\boldsymbol{A}$ and $\boldsymbol{B}$ as constant matrices. This may be readily done since it involves only an integration of the continuous-time system equations with a fixed set of control, $u_1 = 0$ and $u_2 = -0.4167$. Thus, in Table 3.8 we see that $x_1(0)$ and $x_6(0)$ are different from the initial values for the corresponding constant $\boldsymbol{A}$ and $\boldsymbol{B}$ case. Once this has been done, the Riccati calculation may be entered to generate $\boldsymbol{K}_{24}, \boldsymbol{K}_{23}, \ldots, \boldsymbol{K}_1$. Note that in this case we do not necessarily generate the infinite-stage $\boldsymbol{K}$; in fact, the results indicate that the constant $\boldsymbol{K}$ is not approached at any time. Once the $\boldsymbol{K}_P$'s are available, the optimal trajectory and the corresponding control can be generated. These results are shown in Table 3.8 along with the results of Run 10 of Table 3.4 for comparison.

The differences between these two trajectories are not large, but, as pointed out above, large changes could result if $\boldsymbol{A}$ and $\boldsymbol{B}$ changed in a more radical fashion. The main point here is that the time-varying system can be easily handled.

Finally, we consider variations in the control weighting matrices with the form of Equations (3.68), that is,

$$\boldsymbol{Q} = \boldsymbol{Q}_0 e^{2\alpha t}, \qquad \boldsymbol{R} = \boldsymbol{R}_0 e^{2\alpha t}, \qquad \boldsymbol{S} = \boldsymbol{S}_0 e^{2\alpha t},$$

which we call a nonstationary control system. In particular, we choose $t_f = 25.0$ min, $\alpha = 0.05$, and $\boldsymbol{Q}_0 = \boldsymbol{I}$, $\boldsymbol{R}_0 = \boldsymbol{I}$, $\boldsymbol{S}_0 = \boldsymbol{0}$. Thus, in generating the feedback matrices, $\boldsymbol{Q}_{t_f}$ has diagonal elements of 12.182, and $\boldsymbol{R}_{t_f}$ has diagonal elements of 12.182. As we integrate the Riccati equation backward in time, we decrease the elements in $\boldsymbol{Q}$ and $\boldsymbol{R}$ by $e^{-2\alpha T} = 0.90484$ ($T = 1$ min) at each 1-min time interval. As a result, we have a set of time-varying $\boldsymbol{Q}$ and $\boldsymbol{R}$. The result, then, is a very small weighting of the performance index in the beginning followed by an increased weighting as time progresses. Table 3.8 shows the optimal trajectory and controls and, when compared to the stationary case in Table 3.8, exhibits a very rapid and large rise at first. This is then followed by an increased weighting of $\boldsymbol{Q}$ and $\boldsymbol{R}$, yielding a quick response to the origin.

This has illustrated once again the versatility of the control algorithm. As an extension, one can easily conceive of varying only $\boldsymbol{Q}$ or $\boldsymbol{R}$ but not both, and obtaining a different trajectory from that shown.

EXAMPLE 3.2 ▪ In this example, we consider the minimum-time-control of the discrete-time version of the gas absorber. The theory necessary for these calculations was presented in Section 3.7 and consisted first of converting the system equations into a form equivalent to Equations (3.103–3.105). As a second step, these equations are then connected with a linear programming subroutine

TABLE 3.8

Nonstationary cases ($H = I$)

t	x_1	x_6	u_1	u_2	x_1	x_6	u_1	u_2	x_1	x_6	u_1	u_2
0	−.0306	−.1273	.0552	.1166	−.0265	−.1246	.0500	.1109	−.0306	−.1273	.4053	.9861
1	−.0145	−.0386	.0447	.0741	−.0124	−.0384	.0409	.0702	.0279	.0989	.1071	.1909
2	−.0103	−.0126	.0376	.0524	−.0089	−.0129	.0345	.0496	.0219	.0552	.0665	.0392
3	−.0091	−.0037	.0317	.0392	−.0080	−.0040	.0293	.0370	.0151	.0273	.0456	.0245
4	−.0085	−.0037	.0266	.0301	−.0076	−.0006	.0247	.0284	.0102	.0164	.0310	.0186
6	−.0078	−.0003	.0222	.0236	−.0071	+.0008	.0207	.0222	.0068	.0107	.0207	.0126
5	−.0069	+.0010	.0183	.0186	−.0064	+.0012	.0171	.0176	.0045	.0070	.0137	.0082
7	−.0060	+.0014	.0151	.0148	−.0056	+.0013	.0141	.0140	.0030	.0046	.0091	.0054
8	−.0051	+.0015	.0123	.0119	−.0048	+.0012	.0116	.0112	.0200	.0030	.0060	.0035

Continuous-time system

$Q = I, R = I, S = 0$

A, B const (first group); A, B decrease with time (second group)

Nonstationary system

$$Q_{t_f} = \begin{bmatrix} 12.182 & \cdots & 0 \\ \vdots & \ddots & \vdots \\ 0 & \cdots & 12.182 \end{bmatrix}$$

$$R_{t_f} = \begin{bmatrix} 12.182 & \cdots & 0 \\ \vdots & \ddots & \vdots \\ 0 & \cdots & 12.182 \end{bmatrix}$$

Nonstationary control (third group)

(in the present case SHARE program RSMSUB was used). The output of the linear program is the solution for the $(2n + 2Pr + 1)$ unknowns in Equations (3.103–3.105) which follows from minimizing a linear sum of these unknowns. In the present case the only element in this linear sum is the first element g. Once these unknowns are solved for, it is possible to pick out the control vectors $\boldsymbol{u}^{**}$, which are then used with the system Equation (3.93) to generate the optimal transient response of $\boldsymbol{x}(k)$.

We start the discussion with the consideration of the problem in which the controls are bounded from below (lower-bound) only. In terms of the un-normalized control vectors, this means that in Equation (3.97) the $\alpha_i = 0$. In terms of the normalized equations, $\alpha_1 = 0$ but $\alpha_2 = -0.4167$ [(see Equation 1.109)] corresponding to the final equilibrium point being the origin. In the absorber system under consideration, the fact that $\alpha_1 = 0$ and both are not negative is not important. In some systems, however, such a condition might make the origin of the state vector space unreachable for any P, however large.

Table 3.9 lists the main cases investigated in this lower-bound problem, giving the sampling period T, the number of sampling periods P and g, the maximum absolute composition error after P sampling periods. Seven-place accuracy was obtained in the calculations. A 0 entry in Table 3.9 implies a value of g less than 10^{-7}. The computer running time per case on the IBM 7090/94 computer was 10 to 12 sec, including the time needed to calculate the transient response of the composition vector, once the required control had been obtained.

TABLE 3.9

Maximum Composition Deviation for the Absorber with only Lower Bounds on Controls

T, min	P	g
1.0	5	1.8765×10^{-4}
1.0	6	1.7666×10^{-5}
1.0	7	0
1.0	8	0
.5	10	2.9180×10^{-5}
.5	11	0
.5	12	0
.25	14	1.3998×10^{-3}
.25	16	3.4348×10^{-4}
.25	18	9.5348×10^{-5}
.25	19	1.8362×10^{-5}
.25	20	0
.25	24	0

We can see from Table 3.9 that for sampling periods of 1.0, 0.5, and 0.25 min, the minimum number of sampling periods required to reach the desired state is 7, 11, and 20, respectively. Not unexpected is the result that the minimum time required to reach the desired state decreases as the sampling period decreases. Another result is that for a fixed total time, g can be made smaller as the sampling period decreases. This can be seen in Table 3.9 by observing g for the three cases of $P \cdot T = 5$ min. These trends are reasonable since, as P increases (but $P \cdot T$ fixed), there is more freedom allowed in switching the controls, and hence it should be possible to approach nearer to the desired state. For all cases in which g was forced to zero, all but six of the elements of $\boldsymbol{u}^{**}$ were zero. This agrees with the result obtained earlier that at most n controls are not on their bounds when $g = 0$. In Table 3.10 the three time-optimal control sequences are shown, and Figures 3.10 and 3.11 compare the time-optimal responses of x_3 and x_6 with a sampling period of 1 min with the discrete-time run of Table 3.1, $\boldsymbol{Q} = \boldsymbol{I}$, $\boldsymbol{R} = \boldsymbol{0}$, $\boldsymbol{S} = \boldsymbol{0}$, and $\boldsymbol{H} = \boldsymbol{I}$. It can be seen that the minimum time response of each state reaches the origin well in advance of that obtained with the quadratic performance index.

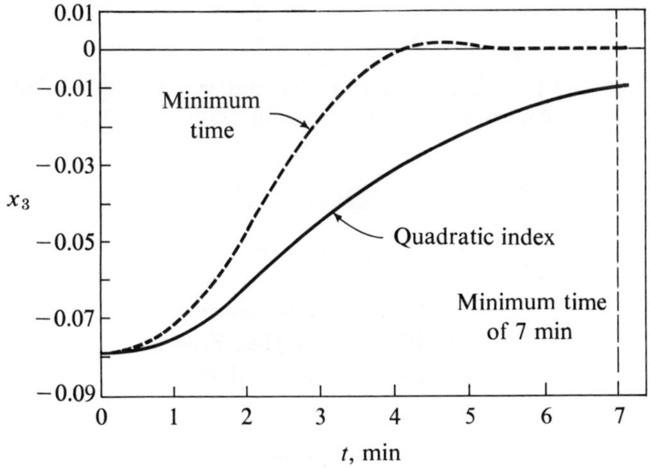

FIGURE 3.10. Comparison of minimum-time and quadratic index control of absorber; sampling period = 1 min.

Figures 3.12 through 3.15 show the minimum-time responses associated with sampling periods of 0.5 and 0.25 min. The states x_1 and x_6 experience larger fluctuations about their final values than do the intermediate compositions. This can be attributed to the proximity of x_1 and x_6 to the controls u_1 and u_2, respectively; in other words, x_1 and x_6 damp the response of x_2 through x_5, u_1, and u_2, but are not themselves damped.

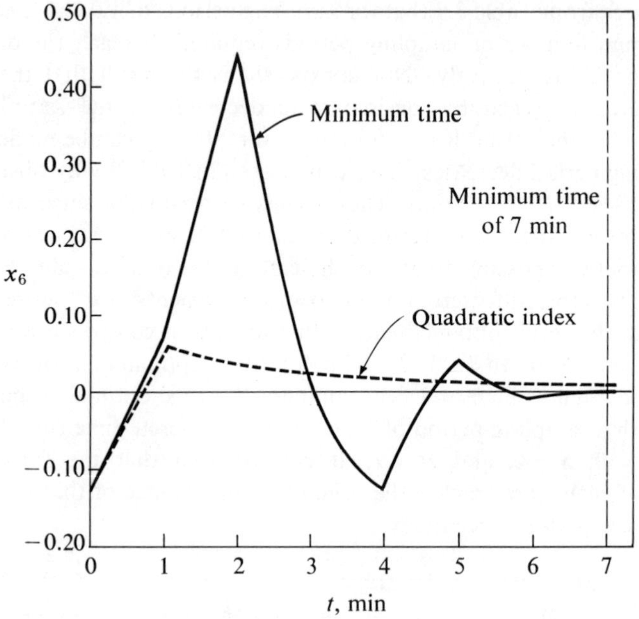

FIGURE 3.11. Comparison of minimum-time and quadratic index control of absorber; sampling period = 1 min.

TABLE 3.10

Minimum-Time Control with Different Sampling Periods. Discrete-Time System

Sampling period: 1 min		
t	u_1	u_2
0	.5156	.3699
1	0	1.1140
2	0	−.4167
3	0	−.4167
4	0	.2236
5	0	−.0349
6	0	.0017

TABLE 3.10 (continued)

Sampling period: 0.5 min

t	u_1	u_2
0	0	3.7615
.5	.6249	−.4167
1.0	0	−.4167
1.5	0	−.4167
2.0	0	.0607
2.5	0	−.4167
3.0	0	−.4167
3.5	0	.0130
4.0	0	.7348
4.5	0	−.4167
5.0	0	.0637

Sampling period: 0.25 min

t	u_1	u_2
0	0	8.1377
.25	1.3370	−.4167
.50	0	−.4167
.75	0	−.4167
1.00	0	−.4167
1.25	0	−.4167
1.50	0	−.4167
1.75	0	−.4167
2.00	0	−.4167
2.25	0	−.4167
2.50	0	−.4167
2.75	0	−.4167
3.00	0	−.4167
3.25	0	1.0340
3.50	0	−.4167
3.75	0	.8284
4.00	0	.3574
4.25	0	−.4167
4.50	0	−.4167
4.75	0	.2277

A second approach to the problem was to consider the x_i's and y_i's in the original absorber system formulation (Section 1.11) to be weight fractions.

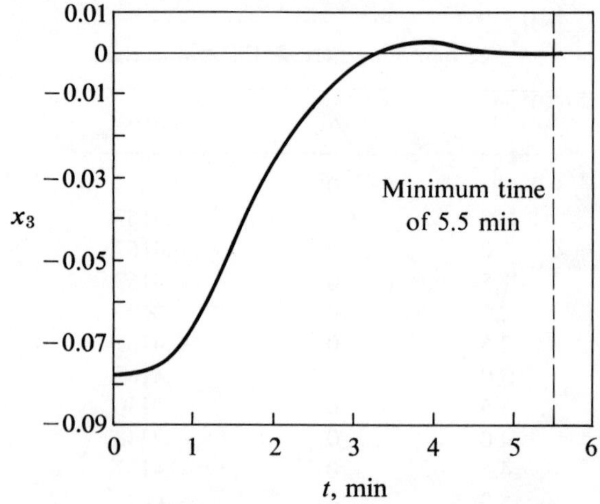

FIGURE 3.12. Minimum-time control of absorber; sampling period = 0.5 min, controls bounded below

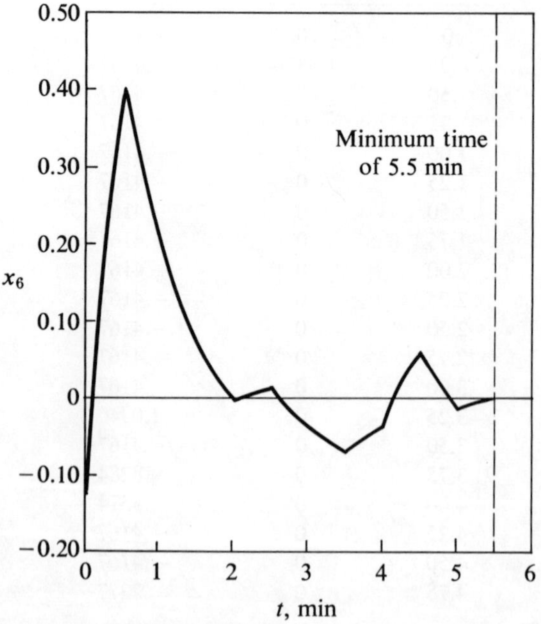

FIGURE 3.13. Minimum-time control of absorber; sampling period = 0.5 min, controls bounded below

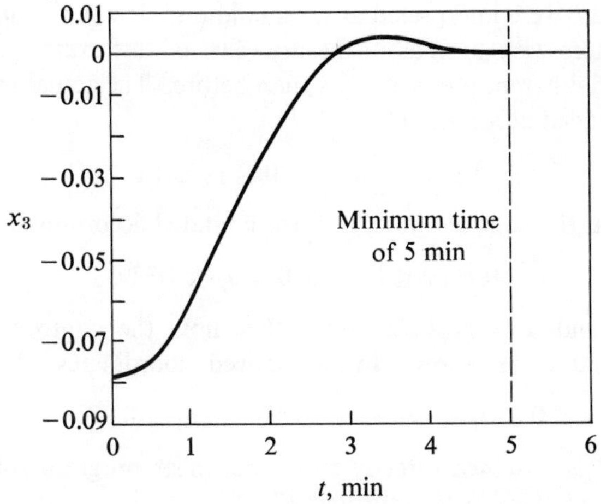

FIGURE 3.14. Minimum-time control of absorber; sampling period = 0.25 min, controls bounded below

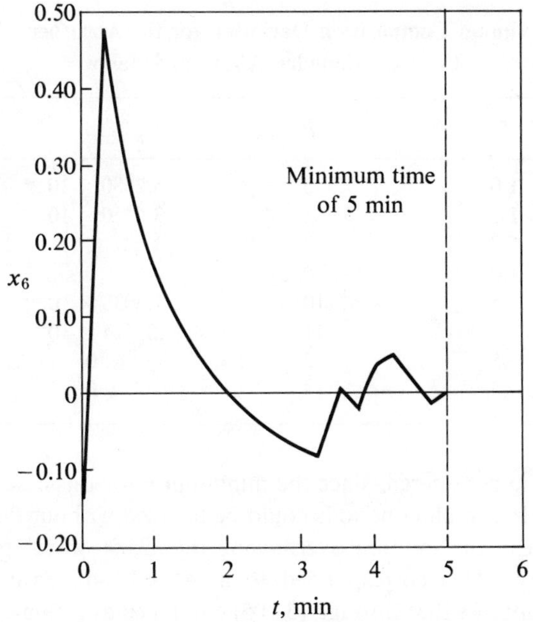

FIGURE 3.15. Minimum-time control of absorber; sampling period = 0.25 min, controls bounded below

This implied that L and G were the total liquid and vapor flow rates, respectively, and that H and h were interpreted as total holdups. The same numerical values of the parameters were used as in the first part of this example, although the parameters had different physical units than before. The actual inlet concentrations were bounded according to

$$0 \leq x_0 \leq 1.0, \qquad 0 \leq y_7 \leq 1.0.$$

This meant that the controls were, in turn, bounded according to

$$0 \leq u_1 \leq 1.0, \qquad 0 \leq u_2 \leq 1.389,$$

since $u_1 = x_0$ and $u_2 = y_7/0.72$. Note that now the controls are bounded from above and from below. In normalized coordinates, this means that

$$0 \leq u_1 \leq 1.0, \qquad -0.4167 \leq u_2 \leq 0.972.$$

As before, $\boldsymbol{u}^{**}$ is obtained directly from the linear program solution for the unknowns in Equations (3.103) through (3.105).

Table 3.11 indicates the principal cases considered. Sampling periods of 1 and 0.5 min were used. Computer storage limitations prevented a 0.25-min sampling

TABLE 3.11

Maximum Composition Deviation for the Absorber with Controls Bounded Above and Below

T	P	g
1.0	5	5.2480×10^{-4}
1.0	6	3.6450×10^{-5}
1.0	7	0
1.0	8	0
.5	10	1.5038×10^{-4}
.5	11	2.5514×10^{-5}
.5	12	0
.5	14	0

period from being considered, since the minimum P for this case was too large. A maximum of 16 sampling periods could be handled without the matrices and vectors involved in the solution overflowing the 32,000-word storage capacity of the computer. This corresponded to a (44×77)-dimensional coefficient matrix in Equations (3.103) through (3.105) combined as a single equation. The minimum times required to reach the desired state were 7 and 6 min for the two different sampling periods, respectively. This compares with 7 and 5.5 min for the problem with only lower bounds on the controls. The time-optimal control sequence is given in Table 3.12. Both Tables 3.10 and 3.12 represent minimum times of 7 min for the 1-min sampling period. The reason for this can be seen by observing the control sequence of Table 3.10, where the controls were bounded below only. All but one control was within the bounds placed on the control of Table 3.12; the one control which exceeded the bound of the other problem did so by a small amount. Thus, when bounds were placed on both sides of the controls, small adjustments could be made in all the controls of Table 3.10, bringing the one inadmissible control down to its upper bound and still transferring the composition vector to its desired state in 7 min.

TABLE 3.12

The Time-Optimal Control and Transient Response of the Absorber with Controls Bounded Above and Below

(Sampling period: 1 min)

t	u_1	u_2	x_1	x_3	x_6
0	.4467	.5453	−.03066	−.07888	−.12732
1	0	.9722	.11713	−.07176	.13899
2	.0185	−.4167	.03144	−.04740	.41602
3	0	−.4167	.01188	−.01716	.00443
4	0	.2321	.00171	−.00001	−.14525
5	0	−.0370	.00008	.00099	.03698
6	0	.0018	.00000	.00003	−.00241
7	0	0	.00000	.00000	.00000

For a sampling period of 0.5 min and only a lower bound on the control, the minimum time was 5.5 min. But the required control sequence (Table 3.10) contained a control which was considerably above the upper bound of the other problem. In meeting the constraint, a radically different control policy evolved (Table 3.13), and the desired state could not be reached in less than a minimum time of 6 min. The transient response of x_6 for this case is shown in Figure 3.16 (p. 223). The response of x_3 is similar to Figure 3.13 and is not shown. The control sequence of Table 3.10 (with a sampling period of 0.25 min) had several large controls, such that, if the problem could have been solved with the controls constrained above, that is, if more storage capacity had been available, one would expect a larger minimum time, as was the case for a 0.5-min sampling period.

For each case listed in Table 3.11 in which $g = 0$ was the result of the linear program, six elements of $\boldsymbol{u}^{**}$ were not on their bounds. This agrees with the theorem stated earlier. It is noted again that for $P \cdot T$ fixed and $g \neq 0$, g

TABLE 3.13

The Time-Optimal Control and Transient Response of the Absorber with Controls Bounded Above and Below

(Sampling period: 0.5 min)

t	u_1	u_2	x_1	x_6	x_6
0	0	.4732	−.03066	−.07888	−.12732
.5	.8625	.9722	−.02872	−.07872	.02131
1.0	0	.9722	.14737	−.07519	.23206
1.5	0	.6404	.07680	−.06343	.36349
2.0	0	−.4167	.03994	−.04761	.37129
2.5	0	−.4167	.01993	−.03043	.12937
3.0	0	−.4167	.00908	−.01517	−.00920
3.5	0	−.4167	.00355	−.00443	−.09454
4.0	0	.0409	.00107	.00112	−.15065
4.5	0	.7341	.00020	.00218	−.07857
5.0	0	−.4167	.00002	.00083	.12824
5.5	0	.0632	.00000	.00004	−.02771
6.0	0	.0000	.00000	.00000	.00000

decreases as T decreases. By comparing corresponding cases in Tables 3.9 and 3.11, it is also seen that the additional constraints have increased g (unless $g = 0$). This is to be expected since additional constraints allow for less freedom in picking a control sequence to drive the compositions to their desired state. The maximum composition deviation, g, is therefore greater.

From a practical point of view, it may be desirable to limit the extreme oscillations of x_6 by placing constraints on it and all the other x_i. This will necessarily increase the minimum time. It may also be advantageous to require that $\dot{\mathbf{x}} = \mathbf{0}$ at the end of the transient response. This restriction would also increase the minimum time. Both of these specifications can, however, be built into the linear programming model, as was pointed out in the main discussion.

Thus we see that the linear programming approach can easily handle the minimum-time control of linear discrete-time systems. The optimal trajectories are quite different from those obtained with the quadratic performance index (Example 3.1), but this is to be expected. As to which method is better than the other, there is no direct answer, other than an engineering one, since it depends on the particular system under investigation.

EXAMPLE 3.3 ▪ In this example, we shall discuss some of the features of the continuous-time solution of the minimum-time control of the gas absorber. The method of Neustadt will be used as developed in Section 3.6. This method involves an initial guess for the adjoint vector $\boldsymbol{\eta}$ such that $\boldsymbol{\eta}'\boldsymbol{x}(0) < 0$ and then an improvement of this first estimate by an iteration procedure until Equation 3.88 is satisfied.

Because of some prior experience with this method, it was decided to simplify the gas-absorber problem such that only one control variable was involved. This may be accomplished by setting the inlet liquid composition $x_0(t)$ equal to zero for all time t. The control $\boldsymbol{u}$ in the Neustadt procedure is then u_2 with $u_1 = 0$ always. All the remaining parameters were left unchanged.

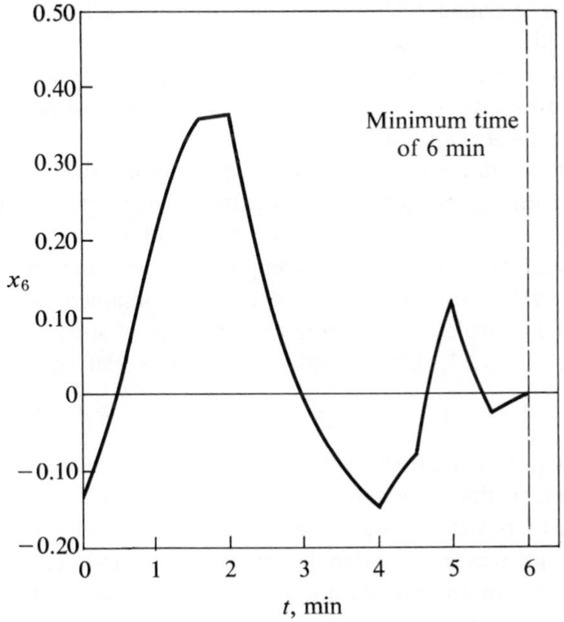

FIGURE 3.16. Minimum-time control of absorber; sampling period = 0.5 min, controls bounded above and below

In the program as run, two quantities had to be monitored with increasing time. These were $d[t_f, \boldsymbol{\eta}, \boldsymbol{x}(0)$, defined as]

$$d[\tau, \boldsymbol{\eta}, \boldsymbol{x}(0)] = \boldsymbol{\eta}'\left[\boldsymbol{x}(0) + \int_0^\tau \exp(-\boldsymbol{A}\lambda)\, \boldsymbol{B}\boldsymbol{u}^0(\lambda)\, d\lambda\right] \tag{3.118}$$

(we have replaced t_f with τ), and the switching function SF, in which, from Equation (3.86),

$$\text{SF} = \boldsymbol{\eta}' \exp(-\boldsymbol{A}\tau)\boldsymbol{B}. \tag{3.119}$$

The integral in Equation (3.118) was evaluated at equal time intervals. As the calculation in time proceeded, SF was monitored until it went through zero; at this point a subroutine iterated Equation (3.119) to find, within a specified tolerance, the value of τ at which the zero occurred. At this point the control $u_2^0(\tau)$ was switched from one bound to the other and the integration continued as before. When $d[\tau, \boldsymbol{\eta}, \boldsymbol{x}(0)]$ went through zero, another subroutine iterated Equation (3.118) to determine (again within a specific tolerance) the value of τ at which the zero occurred. A check was then made to determine whether Equation (3.88),

$$\boldsymbol{x}(0) = -\int_0^{t^{\min}} \exp(\boldsymbol{A}\lambda)\boldsymbol{B}\boldsymbol{u}^0(\lambda)\, d\lambda,$$

held to within a specified tolerance. If not, another $\boldsymbol{\eta}$ had to be picked and the entire procedure repeated.

This then was the over-all calculation procedure. There are, however, many details of interest within the over-all scheme which seem worth discussing here. The matrix $\exp(-\boldsymbol{A}\tau)$ of Equation (3.119) was computed at intervals of $\Delta\tau$ until SF went through zero. The output of the iteration subroutine for SF gave $\exp(-\boldsymbol{A}\tau_{\text{SW}})$, with τ_{SW} being the switching time. The matrix was then evaluated again at equal time intervals (except when an addition τ_{SW} occurred) until $d[\tau, \boldsymbol{\eta}, \boldsymbol{x}(0)]$ went through zero, whereupon the iteration subroutine for d yielded $\exp(-\boldsymbol{A}t^*)$. Initially $\exp(-\boldsymbol{A}\Delta\tau)$ was obtained by a power series expansion in $\boldsymbol{A}\Delta\tau$. Rules for assuring the accuracy of such a series have been presented in Section 1.11. Use was also made of the relation

$$\exp[-\boldsymbol{A}(\tau + \Delta\tau)] = \exp(-\boldsymbol{A}\tau)\exp(-\boldsymbol{A}\Delta\tau)$$

to compute successive matrices without having to evaluate the power series again. However, in finding a zero of SF, successive evaluations of the matrix had to be made by power series expansions. A modified version of the Newton–Raphson technique was employed in this iteration, the modification guaranteeing convergence. Since in any one iteration step, the zero is known to lie between two known values of τ, any estimation of the zero (generated by the Newton–Raphson algorithm) which did not lie in the known interval was rejected in favor of the midpoint of the interval. This procedure always converged to the zero of the switching function.

The vector integral $\int_0^\tau \exp(-\boldsymbol{A}\lambda)\boldsymbol{B}\boldsymbol{u}^0(\lambda)\, d\lambda$ was evaluated at the same intervals of time as the matrix $\exp(-\boldsymbol{A}\tau)$. Since in each time interval $\boldsymbol{u}^0(\lambda)$ [really here $u^0(\lambda)$ since only one control variable is involved] is constant, the integral may be expressed as

$$\int_0^\tau \exp(-\boldsymbol{A}\lambda)\boldsymbol{B}u^0(\lambda)\, d\lambda = \sum_i \left\{\int_{\tau_i}^{\tau_{i+1}} \exp(-\boldsymbol{A}\lambda)\, d\lambda\right\}\boldsymbol{B}u^0(\tau_i)$$

$$= \sum_i \left\{\exp(-\boldsymbol{A}\tau_i)\int_0^{\tau_{i+1}-\tau_i} \exp(-\boldsymbol{A}\lambda)\, d\lambda\right\}\boldsymbol{B}u^0(\tau_j)$$

for equally spaced values of τ_i, $\tau_{i+1} - \tau_i = \Delta\tau$, and the corresponding integral in the summation needed to be evaluated only once. If $\tau_{i+1} - \tau_i \neq \Delta\tau$, as was the case when a switching time was encountered, the integral needed to be evaluated separately for each such case. The matrices exp $(-A\tau_i)$ were available from the computation for the switching function. The integral itself is evaluated by the series expansion, obtained by integrating exp $(-A\Delta\tau)$,

$$\int_0^{\Delta\tau} \exp(-A\lambda)\,d\lambda = \Delta\tau\left[I - \frac{A\Delta\tau}{2!} + \frac{A^2(\Delta\tau)^2}{3!} - \frac{A^3(\Delta\tau)^3}{4!} + \cdots\right].$$

The initial guess on η was taken to be

$$\eta^{(0)} = x(0) \Big/ \sum_{i=1}^{n} |[x(0)]_i| . \tag{3.120}$$

This guaranteed the condition that $\eta^{(0)} - x(0)$ be negative. The method used for improving successive $\eta^{(j)}$'s is known as the accelerated gradient method and is described in reference 79. Basically, it consists of cycles of three steps each in the n-dimensional space of η. In each cycle, the procedure is as follows :

(1) $\eta^{(0)}$ is fixed. At the end of the integration procedure, $t^*[\eta^{(0)}, x(0)]$ is known from Equation (3.89),

$$d\{t^*[\eta^{(0)}, x(0)], \eta^{(0)}, x(0)\} = 0, \tag{3.121}$$

and $\nabla_\eta(0)t^*$ is formed from Equation (3.91),

$$\nabla_\eta(0)t^* = -[\eta^{(0)\prime} \exp[-At^*]Bu^0(t^*)]^{-1}\left[x(0) + \int_0^{t^*} \exp(-A\lambda)Bu^0(\lambda)\,d\lambda\right]\cdot \tag{3.122}$$

Now Equation (3.92),

$$\eta^{(j+1)} = \eta^{(j)} + k\nabla_{\eta^{(j)}}t^*, \tag{3.123}$$

is applied for systematically chosen values of k so as to maximize $t^*[\eta^{(0)}k + k\nabla_{\eta^{(0)}}t^*,\ x(0)]$. Each value of k tried requires another complete integration of the system equations.

(2) The $\eta^{(0)} + k\nabla_{\eta^{(0)}}t^*$ associated with the maximum of t^* will be designated as $\eta^{(1)}$. The procedure of step (1) is repeated so as to maximize $t^*[\eta^{(1)} + \nabla_{\eta^{(1)}}t^*, x(0)]$ with respect to k. Refer to the corresponding $\eta^{(1)} + k\nabla_{\eta^{(1)}}t^*$ as $\eta^{(2)}$.

(3) Now maximize $t^*[\eta^{(0)} + k(\eta^{(2)} - \eta^{(0)}), x(0)]$ with respect to k. The corresponding $\eta^{(0)} + k(\eta^{(2)} - \eta^{(0)})$ is designated as the new $\eta^{(0)}$, and the cycle is complete.

Two techniques were used in trying to find the best k for each of the above steps. At first, the value of t^* associated with each k was stored until the maximum of t^* was found to within some prescribed tolerance, such as $\pm 10^{-6}$. However, the roundoff error, associated with the many matrix manipulations needed per integration of the system equations, frequently obscured the maximum of t^* with respect to k.

A second, more accurate, procedure was therefore adopted. The condition that time t^* be a maximum with respect to k can also be expressed in steps (1), (2), and (3), respectively, as

$$[\nabla_{\eta^{(0)}}t^*]'[\nabla_{\eta^{(k)}}t^*] = 0, \qquad \bar{k} = \eta^{(0)} + k\nabla_{\eta^{(0)}}t^*,$$

$$[\nabla_{\eta^{(1)}}t^*]'[\nabla_{\eta^{(k)}}t^*] = 0, \qquad \bar{k} = \eta^{(1)} + k\nabla_{\eta^{(1)}}t^*,$$

$$[\eta^{(2)} - \eta^{(0)}]'[\nabla_{\eta^{(k)}}t^*] = 0, \qquad \bar{k} = \eta^{(0)} + k(\eta^{(2)} - \eta^{(0)}).$$

It was found that minimizing the magnitude of the above vector products was a better criterion than maximizing t^*. The vector product would still have a significant magnitude, long after t^* had ceased to vary in the sixth significant figure.

With these features in mind, the gas absorber system with the single control variable was introduced into the program; Equation (3.120) was used to select an initial estimate of η. This value then led to $t^*[\eta, x(0)]$ of about 0.52 min. After an hour of running time on the IBM 7094, a value of about 3.14 min for t^* had been obtained. The gradient of t^*, $\nabla_\eta t^*$, was still appreciable, however, and even though convergence was assured, the likelihood of anything resembling rapid convergence was impossible. The reason for this slow convergence can be ascertained from the shape of $t^*\eta$-surface, namely, one with a large number of very flat regions. Roundoff errors in all of the matrix calculations were sufficiently large to obscure the direction of the gradient, thereby causing random stepping in the flat region. Even a double-precision routine was not adequate to keep the ascent up the $t^*\eta$-space moving at a rapid rate. Thus, although progress was ever upward, the path was too slow to permit rapid convergence. On this basis, one must conclude that at least for this system (and others as well [52]) the gap between this mathematical procedure and the actual computer implementation may be too large for practical use at present.

References

BOOKS

1. C. W. Merriam, *Optimization Theory and the Design of Feedback Control Systems*, McGraw-Hill Book Co., 1964.
2. J. R. Ragazzini and G. Franklin, *Sampled-Data Control Systems*, McGraw-Hill Book Co., 1958.
3. J. T. Tou, *Optimum Design of Digital Control Systems*, Academic Press, 1963.
4. J. T. Tou, *Modern Control Theory*, McGraw-Hill Book Co., 1964.

ARTICLES

5. D. S. Adorno, *Inform. and Control*, *5*, 1 (1962).
6. M. Aoki, *Automatica*, *1*, 69 (1962).
7. R. Bellman, I. Glicksberg, and O. Gross, *Quart. Appl. Math.*, *14*, 11 (1956).
8. J. E. Bertram and P. E. Sarachik, "On Optimal Computer Control," *Proc. of First IFAC Congress*, *1*, 419, Butterworths, 1960.
9. M. J. Box, *The Computer Journal*, *8*, 42 (1965).
10. D. W. Bushaw, "Differential Equations with Discontinuous Forcing Term," *Ph.D. Dissertation, Princeton University* (1952).
11. J. A. Cazow, "Optimal Control of a System Subject to Parameter Variation," *JACC Proc.* (1966).
12. J. Chang, *Auto. and Remote Control*, *22*, 1170 (1961).
13. P. Clement, *IEEE Trans. Auto. Control*, *AC-9*, 82 (1964).
14. G. W. Deley and G. Franklin, *J. Basic Eng. 87*, 135 (1965).
15. P. Dorato, *IEEE Trans. Auto. Control*, *AC-8*, 256 (1963).
16. S. E. Dreyfus, *J. Math. Anal. Appl.*, *1*, 228 (1960).
17. J. H. Eaton, *J. Math. Anal. Appl.*, *5*, 329 (1962).
18. J. H. Eaton, *IEEE Trans. Auto. Control*, *AC-10*, 186 (1965).
19. E. J. Fadden and E. G. Gilbert, "Computational Aspects of the Time Optimal Control Problem," in *Computing Methods in Optimization Problems*, Academic Press, 1964.
20. P. L. Falb and D. L. Kleinman, *IEEE Trans. Auto. Control*, *AC-11*, 534 (1966).
21. K. A. Fegley and M. I. Hsu, *IEEE Trans. Auto. Control*, *AC-10*, 114 (1965).
22. R. Fletcher, *The Computer Journal*, *8*, 33 (1965).
23. A. Frank and L. Lapidus, *Chem. Eng. Prog.*, *60*, No. 4 (1964).
24. R. V. Gamkedlidze, *Izv. Akad. Nauk SSSR Ser. Mat.*, *22*, 449 (1958).
25. E. G. Gilbert, "The Application of Hybrid Computers to the Iterative Solution of Optimal Control Problems," in *Computing Methods in Optimization Problems*, Academic Press, 1964.
26. C. A. Harvey and E. B. Lee, *J. Math. Anal. Appl.*, *5*, 258 (1962).
27. C. A. Harvey, *J. Math. Anal. Appl.*, *5*, 245 (1962).
28. C. A. Harvey, *J. Math. Anal. Appl.*, *10*, 334 (1965).
29. Y. C. Ho, *J. Basic. Eng.*, *84*, 33 (1962); *83*, 53 (1961).
30. Y. C. Ho and P. B. Brentani, *J. SIAM Control*, *1*, 319 (1963).
31. Y. C. Ho and S. Baron, *IEEE Trans. Auto. Control*, *AC-10*, 200 (1965).
32. J. M. Holtzmann and S. Horing, *IEEE Trans. Auto. Control*, *AC-10*, 420 (1965).
33. D. Isaacs and C. T. Leondes, *Inform. and Control*, *9*, 393 (1966).
34. C. D. Johnson and J. E. Gibson, *IEEE Trans. Auto. Control*, *AC-8*, 1 (1963).
35. C. D. Johnson and J. E. Gibson, *IEEE Trans. Auto. Control*, *AC-9*, 355 (1964).
36. C. D. Johnson and W. M. Wonham, *J. Basic Eng.*, *87D*, 81 (1965).

37. P. D. Joseph, *IEEE Trans. Auto. Control*, *AC-10*, 281 (1965).
38. R. E. Kalman and R. Koepcke, *Trans. ASME*, *80*, 1820 (1958).
39. R. E. Kalman, *Proc. First Inter. Cong. on Auto Cont., Moscow* (1960).
40. R. E. Kalman, *Bull. Soc. Mat. Maxicana Ser.*, *5*, 102 (1960).
41. R. E. Kalman, *Proc. Natl. Acad. Sci.*, *48*, 596 (1962).
42. R. E. Kalman, T. S. Englar, and R. S. Bucy, "Fundamental Study of Adaptive Control Systems," *RIAS Report ASD-TR-61-27* (April 1962).
43. R. E. Kalman and T. S. Englar, "Optimal Filters and Control Systems," *RIAS Report on ASP* (July 1963).
44. M. Kim, "Optimum Discrete Systems with Amplitude and Energy Constrained Control Function," *JACC Proc.* (1965).
45. R. W. Koepcke, *J. Basic Eng.*, *87D*, 74 (1965).
46. J. D. R. Kramer, "On Control of Linear Systems with Time Lags," *RAND Report P-1948* (March 1960).
47. E. Kreindler, *J. Franklin Inst.*, *274*, 314 (1963).
48. F. Kurzweil, *IEEE Trans. Auto. Control*, *AC-8*, 27 (1963).
49. L. Lapidus, *Chem. Eng. Symp. Series*, *61*, 88 (1965).
50. J. LaSalle, "The Time Optimal Control Problem," *Contributions to the Theory of Nonlinear Oscillations*, *Princeton University Press*, *5*, 1 (1960).
51. E. B. Lee, *J. Math. Anal. Appl.*, *7*, 118 (1963).
52. H. A. Lesser, "The Time-Optimal Control of High Order Linear Systems with Bounded Controls," *Ph.D. Dissertation, Princeton University* (1964).
53. H. Lesser and L. Lapidus, *A.I.Ch.E.J.*, *12*, 143 (1966).
54. D. Luenberger, *IEEE Trans. Auto. Control*, *AC-10*, 202 (1965).
55. A. Nagata, S. Kodoma, and S. Kumagai, *IEEE Trans. Auto. Control*, *AC-10*, 155 (1965).
56. N. E. Nahi, *IEEE Trans. Auto. Control*, *AC-9*, 137 (1964).
57. L. W. Neustadt, *J. Math. Anal Appl.*, *1*, 484 (1960).
58. M. N. Oguztoreli, *J. SIAM Control*, *1*, 290 (1963); *2*, 89 (1964).
59. R. Oldenburger and G. Thompson, *Automatica*, *1*, 177 (1963).
60. B. Pagurek, *IEEE Trans. Auto. Control*, *AC-10*, 178 (1965).
61. B. H. Paiewonsky and P. J. Woodrow, "The Synthesis of Optimal Controls for a Class of Rocket Steering Problems," *Summer Meeting of AIAA* (June 1963).
62. W. A. Porter, *IEEE Trans. Auto. Control*, *AC-10*, 301 (1965).
63. A. I. Propoi, *Auto. and Remote Control*, *2*, 837 (1963).
64. Z. V. Rekasius, *IEEE Trans. Auto. Control*, *AC-9*, 290 (1964); *AC-9*, 370 (1964).
65. P. A. Reynolds and J. A. Cadzow, *IEEE Trans. Auto. Control*, *AC-10*, 209 (1965)
66. E. G. Rynaski, P. A. Reynolds, and W. H. Shed, "Design of Linear Flight Control Systems Using Optimal Control Theory," *Cornell Aero Lab. Report ASD-TDR-63-376* (April 1964).
67. D. R. Snow, *J. SIAM Control*, *2*, 203 (1965).

68. A. Tchamran, *Tech. Report TR-64-2*, Syracuse University (1964).
69. A. Tchamran, *J. Franklin Inst., 280*, 493 (1965).
70. A. Tchamran, "On a Class of Constrained Control Linear Regulator Problems," *JACC Proc.* (1965).
71. H. C. Torng, *J. Franklin Inst., 277*, 28 (1964).
72. F. Tung, *IEEE Trans. Auto. Control, AC-9*, 82 (1964).
73. J. S. Tyler, *IEEE Trans. Auto. Control, AC-10*, 485 (1965).
74. L. Weiss and R. Kalman, "Contributions to Linear System Theory," *RIAS Report 64-9* (April 1964).
75. J. Wing and C. A. Desoer, *J. Franklin Inst., 272*, 208 (1961).
76. J. Wing and C. A. Desoer, *IEEE Trans. Auto. Control, AC-8*, 125 (1963).
77. H. Witsenhausen, *IEEE Trans. Auto. Control, AC-10*, 495 (1965).
78. B. F. Womack and J. N. Dashiell, *IEEE Trans. Auto. Control, AC-10*, 201 (1965).
79. P. Woodrow, "Methods for Locating the Extreme of Multivariate Functions," *Technical Report No. 4, Dept. of Electrical Engineering, Princeton University* (1962).
80. L. A. Zadeh and B. H. Whalen, *IRE Trans. Auto. Control, AC-7*, 45 (1962).

4

Control of Nonlinear Multidimensional Systems

In this chapter, we shall discuss a number of different algorithms which may be used for the dynamic control of nonlinear multidimensional systems or processes. The change of emphasis from linear systems, as detailed in Chapter 3, to nonlinear systems means, as a general rule, that the standard methods such as dynamic programming and the maximum principle cannot be applied in a straightforward manner. Instead, we shall in general turn to the use of iterative procedures which in the limit converge hopefully to the optimal control and trajectory.

In the discussion, we shall first detail the type of problems which shall be encountered and mention briefly certain methods which have been suggested in the literature for overcoming these problems. This will be followed by a discussion of a direct-search method which has proven quite useful for nonlinear control systems, and then the concept of a penalty function will be introduced. The main portions of the chapter, however, are developed according to an outline of the first variation or gradient method and the second variation method. Both of these methods are iterative algorithms suitable for solving some of the most complex control problems. Finally, we present a brief discussion of a number of newer and highly interesting alternative methods.

4.1. Problems associated with control of nonlinear multidimensional systems

Dynamic programming is the first general method which may be proposed for calculating the optimal control and optimal trajectory. Once again, it should be pointed out that this method has the virtue of developing all the optimal trajectories at one time and that the calculation procedure is basically an initial-value one. Unfortunately, dynamic programming has the defect that a system with three or more state variables may lead to storage requirements which are beyond the capabilities of commercial computers. In certain special cases, such as when the system is linear and the performance index has a special form (Chapter 3), the table storage can be dispensed with and the dimensionality is no longer a serious problem. However, in the general case the tables must be developed. A number of different techniques have been proposed [3] to attempt to remove this restriction. The motivation for the desire to use dynamic programming, or some form of it, lies in the fact that constraints on both the control and state variables may be easily handled. In all other methods, these constraints may cause considerable difficulties.

One of the variations on the standard form of dynamic programming that has been proposed involves the introduction of *Lagrangian multipliers* [3] to reduce the effective order of the state variables. A trial-and-error search for the multipliers is then required; however, such a procedure is probably feasible when the dimensionality of the state is three or four (and thus can be reduced to two) but not beyond.

A second procedure which has been suggested for removing the dimensionality barrier of dynamic programming is that of *polynomial approximation* [3]. In this case, any single table is replaced by a suitable orthogonal polynomial made up from appropriate Legendre or Tschebyscheff polynomials. It would then be expected that only the coefficients of this series would be stored instead of the normal dynamic programming tables. Unfortunately, this procedure has one difficulty, at least. For a one-dimensional polynomial approximation (1-state-variable problem) it is necessary to store $B + 1$ values of the coefficients of the polynomial, where B is the degree of the polynomial used. In a two-dimensional polynomial approximation it is necessary to store $(B + 1)^2$ coefficients, and in an n-dimensional polynomial approximation $(B + 1)^n$ coefficients are required. Thus the number of coefficients which must be stored to replace a stage of a dynamic programming table is exponentially related to the dimensionality. For a seven-variable problem, assuming a fourth-degree polynomial, about 78,000 storage locations are required. This number is, of course, much less than the conventional dynamic programming solution of the same problem, but the reduction is not sufficient to make the procedure suitable for general applicability. There are also certain serious questions concerning error accumulation in the use of polynomial approximation which may seriously hinder its use. As a result, the use of either the Lagrangian multipliers or of polynomial approximation seems unsuited as a general procedure for removing the storage problems in dynamic programming. Certain other dynamic programming variants which seem to hold promise will be discussed in later portions of this chapter.

If we turn to the maximum principle in the form of the discrete equations

$$\mathbf{x}(k+1) = \mathbf{h}[\mathbf{x}(k), \mathbf{u}(k)], \qquad \mathbf{z}(k) = \mathbf{g}[\mathbf{x}(k), \mathbf{z}(k+1)], \tag{4.1}$$

and associated boundary conditions $\mathbf{x}(0)$ and $\mathbf{z}(P)$, a two-point boundary value problem must be solved. Only in certain special (but possibly important) cases can this be carried out explicitly. In all other cases a numerical procedure must be used. This may, however, flounder on such items as the instability of the adjoint equations and the insensitivity of the initial adjoint variables $\mathbf{z}(0)$ on the final states $\mathbf{x}(P)$ (see Chapter 3). However, there is no *a priori* reason to completely dispatch this method, even with these difficulties.

As a general rule, each procedure detailed in this chapter involves the assumption of some item in the set of equations of interest; this may be the entire set of control variables, the initial values of the adjoint variables, or some other equivalent quantity. It will then be necessary to devise a means of "improving" the original assumption. "Improved" here means that the new values yield a result closer to the optimal control policy than the original values. If this can be continued, the result, assuming that convergence occurs, will be to generate at least a locally optimal policy. Such questions as whether a global optimum is achieved, what the computation time is, and the amount of computer programming involved will be of major importance in distinguishing between the various methods.

Before we detail these iterative procedures, there are, however, a few comments which are important from an over-all perspective point of view. The over-all system of equations under consideration may be thought of as involving the following three subsets [53]:

(1) the system dynamic equations,
(2) the boundary conditions,
(3) minimization of the Hamiltonian and/or the performance index.

Other auxiliary equations, such as those describing the adjoint variables, may be introduced to aid in the calculation. In one possible iterative procedure, subsets (1) and (3) may be fixed and the iterations converge on the correct subset (2); at this point this can be ascertained as equivalent to introducing the adjoint equation and searching for the correct $\mathbf{z}(0)$, as was done in the continuous-time minimum time problem of Chapter 3. Such a procedure has been termed by Dreyfus [35] an "approximation to the problem," for reasons which will be apparent shortly. This has also been called an "approximation in function space" by Bellman [3]. Alternatively, subsets (1) and (2) can be fixed and the iterations converge on subset (3); this procedure has been termed by

Dreyfus an "approximation to the solution" and an "approximation in policy space" by Bellman. Other possibilities exist, with one of the more interesting being to fix subsets (2) and (3) and to iterate on subset (1).

Furthermore, some of the iteration methods are linear, whereas others are quadratic. The distinction here is that the approximation to the subset which is not optimal is carried out by using linear (first-order) approximations or by using quadratic (second-order) approximations.

4.2. The pair-interchange and associated methods

The iteration methods developed in this section for finding the optimal trajectory can be summarized in over-all concept rather easily. We seek that control vector $\boldsymbol{u}(t)$ for a given system equation and boundary conditions,

$$\dot{\boldsymbol{x}}(t) = \boldsymbol{f}[\boldsymbol{x}(t), \boldsymbol{u}(t)], \qquad \boldsymbol{x}(0) \quad \text{prescribed,}$$

such that the performance index

$$I[\boldsymbol{x}(0), t_f] = \int_0^{t_f} J[\boldsymbol{x}(t), \boldsymbol{u}(t)]\, dt = \int_0^{t_f} J[\boldsymbol{x}(t), u_1(t), u_2(t), \ldots, u_r(t)]\, dt \tag{4.2}$$

is minimized. Let us assume certain functions for $u_1(t), u_2(t), \ldots, u_r(t)$ and call these $u_1^{(0)}(t), u_2^{(0)}(t), \ldots, u_r^{(0)}(t)$ to indicate that they are the starting functions. Obviously, once these values are specified it is possible to use the system equations to generate the $\boldsymbol{x}(t)$, substitute this into $J[\boldsymbol{x}(t), u_1^{(0)}(t), \ldots, u_r^{(0)}(t)]$, and then to calculate $I[\boldsymbol{x}(0), t_f]$. Since this value of the performance index is obtained from the initially assumed set of $\boldsymbol{u}^{(0)}(t)$, we shall call it $I^{(0)}[\boldsymbol{x}(0), t_f]$. Next, we allow $u_1(t)$ to vary, and find that $u_1(t)$ which minimizes

$$I[\boldsymbol{x}(0), t_f] = \int_0^{t_f} J[\boldsymbol{x}(t), u_1(t), u_2^{(0)}(t), u_3^{(0)}(t), \ldots, u_r^{(0)}(t)]\, dt \tag{4.3}$$

with t_f fixed. In other words, we fix $u_2(t), \ldots, u_r(t)$ at the assumed values $u_2^{(0)}(t), \ldots, u_r^{(0)}(t)$ and vary only $u_1(t)$ until that value is found which minimizes $I[\boldsymbol{x}(0), t_f]$. It is, of course, assumed that as $u_1(t)$ varies, $\boldsymbol{x}(t)$ also varies. We call the resulting index $I^{(1)}[\boldsymbol{x}(0), t_f]$, with control vector $\boldsymbol{u}'(t) = [u_1^{(1)}(t)\ u_2^{(0)}(t) \ldots u_r^{(0)}(t)]$. At this point, note that

$$I^{(1)}[\boldsymbol{x}(0), t_f] \leq I^{(0)}[\boldsymbol{x}(0), t_f], \tag{4.4}$$

since at worst the same $u_1(t)$, namely, $u_1^{(0)}(t) = u_1^{(1)}(t)$, can be retained. This procedure is now continued by finding that $u_2(t)$ which minimizes

$$I[\boldsymbol{x}(0), t_f] = \int_0^{t_f} J[\boldsymbol{x}(t), u_1^{(1)}(t), u_2(t), u_3^{(0)}(t), \ldots, u_r^{(0)}(t)]\, dt \tag{4.5}$$

to yield $I^{(2)}[\boldsymbol{x}(0), t_f]$ and $\boldsymbol{u}'(t) = [u_1^{(1)}(t)\ u_2^{(2)}(t)\ u_3^{(0)}(t) \ldots u_r^{(0)}(t)]$. As before,

$$I^{(2)}[\boldsymbol{x}(0), t_f] \leq I^{(1)}[\boldsymbol{x}(0), t_f]. \tag{4.6}$$

Obviously, this algorithm can be continued in the same fashion, searching on each control and yielding monotonic convergence to $I^{(j)}[\boldsymbol{x}(0), t_f]$, where $|I^{(j)}\boldsymbol{x}[(0), t_f] - I^{(j-1)}[\boldsymbol{x}(0), t_f]| < \varepsilon$, an error bound. It is apparent that this procedure is simply an application of finding a minimum along one coordinate direction at a time. However, the question of whether this yields a global optimum or a local optimum is not known. A test of this point is to consider a number of widely different initial decision vectors $\boldsymbol{u}^{(0)}(t)$ and see if the subsequent calculations all converge to the same value of the performance index. If they do converge to the same value, global optimization is probably assured.

We see that in this procedure the system equations and boundary conditions are fixed and the iteration of searching is on values of the performance index. Thus the method falls within the province of the approximation to the solution procedures.

When the minimum value of the performance index is found, one complete optimal trajectory is immediately available. Furthermore, the computer storage required for a multidimensional problem is essentially trivial, since only the last $I^{(j)}[\boldsymbol{x}(0), t_f]$ and the last control function $\boldsymbol{u}^{(j)}(t)$ have to be retained. The extension to a variable t_f can be carried out with no difficulty, and control and state constraints can be incorporated. This last point is easily confirmed by the material to follow.

There are a number of interesting variations on this method which, although not quite so primitive, still retain the advantages of essentially negligible storage and of programming simplicity. The major disadvantage is the possibly long computing times required. One such method is pair interchange as labeled by Jensen [49]; we shall illustrate it with the discrete-time system

$$\boldsymbol{x}(k+1) = \boldsymbol{h}[\boldsymbol{x}(k), u(k)], \qquad \boldsymbol{x}(0) \quad \text{prescribed}$$

with $u(k)$ a scalar for simplicity. In the pair-interchange method, the first step is to guess a nominal (assumed) control sequence, $u^{(0)}(k)$, $k = 0, 1, 2, \ldots, P-1$, each of which must lie at any one of Q values (the control variable in the k-stage is discretized into Q values). The system equations are now evaluated using this assumed control sequence, and the performance index $I^{(0)}[\boldsymbol{x}(0), P]$ results.

Now we fix the controls $u(2), u(3), \ldots, u(P-1)$ at the initially assumed $u^{(0)}(2), u^{(0)}(3), \ldots, u^{(0)}(P-1)$, respectively, and consider variations in $u(0)$ and $u(1)$. Each of these latter control values can assume any of Q values. Taken in combination, they can assume Q^2 values. Let us assume each of the Q^2 pairs and, for each pair, solve the system equations and evaluate the performance index. If $Q = 15$, then $Q^2 = 225$, and 225 trajectories must be evaluated. Of these 225 trajectories, the one which yields the minimum value of the performance index, $I^{(1)}[\boldsymbol{x}(0), P]$, is chosen. Of course,

$$I^{(1)}[\boldsymbol{x}(0), P] \leq I^{(0)}[\boldsymbol{x}(0), P],$$

since, as before, the worst case is to retain the pair $u^{(0)}(0)$ and $u^{(0)}(1)$. The control sequence is now $u^{(1)}(0), u^{(1)}(1), u^{(0)}(2), \ldots, u^{(0)}(P-1)$.

Next consider that the control sequence is fixed, except for the second and third stages, at $u^{(1)}(0), u^{(0)}(3), \ldots, u^{(0)}(P-1)$. Interchange $u(1)$ and $u(2)$ to all Q^2 pairs, and solve the system equations and performance index for all pairs. The best performance index is $I^{(2)}[\boldsymbol{x}(0), P]$, where

$$I^{(2)}[\boldsymbol{x}(0), P] \leq I^{(1)}[\boldsymbol{x}(0), P],$$

and the control sequence is $u^{(1)}(0), u^{(2)}(1), u^{(2)}(2), u^{(0)}(3), \ldots, u^{(0)}(P-1)$. Obviously, this pair interchange can be continued until $u(P-1)$ is reached, and then the entire sequence can be started over and continued until the performance index becomes constant within some error bound. When this occurs, no further improvement in the performance index is possible. Clearly, an extremum has been reached, because any variation in the established control policy does not improve the performance index. Note that this method provides monotonic convergence, the storage required is negligible, and the computer program used to implement the method is quite simple.

If constraints on the control variables exist, the Q allowable mesh points are suitably restricted; thus constrained control presents no difficulty. If $r > 1$, more than one control variable is involved; after iterating on the first control variable over the range $0 \leq k \leq P-1$, the second control variable is iterated in the same fashion over the same range, and so forth. Thus in the multiple-control vector case, there is actually a series of subiterative cycles.

If constraints on the state variables exist, this is equivalent to the problem encountered in dynamic programming. This may be handled by specifying that no control be used which yields a state which is outside the constraints; inadmissible states cannot be tolerated.

More general interchange methods can immediately be suggested. For example, a triplet interchange could be used in which $u(k-1), u(k), u(k+1)$ are scanned simultaneously. Possibly some random procedure could be used, whereby members of the control sequence are randomly changed. Details of these more sophisticated procedures will not be given here, since they are self-apparent.

We have shown the algorithm as proceeding in a forward direction in which the controls are scanned in the order $u(0), u(1), u(2), \ldots$. Actually, the reverse order $u(P-1), u(P-2), u(P-3), \ldots$ could just as easily be used. In this latter form it is possible to see that the method resembles an iterated form of dynamic programming.

4.3. The penalty function for constrained final-time state variables

We have already encountered the case of prescribing certain equality constraints or stopping conditions on some of the final-time state variables. This condition might be expressed as

$$\psi_j(\boldsymbol{x}(t_f), t_f) = 0 \qquad (j = 1, 2, \ldots, m < n) \tag{4.7}$$

or as the vector with m elements,

$$\boldsymbol{\psi}(\boldsymbol{x}(t_f), t_f) = \mathbf{0}. \tag{4.8}$$

We shall refer to these relations as final state equations, and these must, of course, be included as part of the boundary conditions for the system equations. In many cases of interest, this may be done in a rather straightforward fashion by using the *penalty function*.

In the penalty function procedure detailed by Courant [25], Kelley [6], Ho [43–45], Denn [28–31], Okamura [74] and Russell [81], the basic idea is to approximate the constrained minimum problem as an unconstrained problem by defining a new augmented performance function of the final state variables. Thus, we let

$$I[\boldsymbol{x}(0), t_f] = I[\boldsymbol{x}(t_f)] \tag{4.9}$$

represent a final value performance index, and we define the new augmented index as

$$I^*[\boldsymbol{x}(t_f)] = I[\boldsymbol{x}(t_f)] + \boldsymbol{\lambda}'\boldsymbol{\psi}(\boldsymbol{x}(t_f), t_f)$$

or as

$$I^* = I + \boldsymbol{\lambda}'\boldsymbol{\psi} \tag{4.10}$$

to simplify the notation. In Equation (4.10) $\boldsymbol{\lambda}$ is a vector of size $(m \times 1)$ made up of Lagrange multipliers; in other words, we have attached the constraints to the performance index by the multipliers to form an unconstrained index (see Section 2.6). Because we are trying to minimize I^*, the term penalty function evolves from the fact that by adding $\boldsymbol{\lambda}'\boldsymbol{\psi}$ to I, we pay a penalty for not being at the final constraint condition. If we had desired to maximize I, the augmented index would have the equivalent form

$$I^* = I - \boldsymbol{\lambda}'\boldsymbol{\psi},$$

where, instead of the plus sign, the minus sign is used for the penalty function.

Before proceeding to use Equation (4.10), we note that if our system has natural boundary conditions, then the boundary conditions on the adjoint variables are (using the convention in the U.S.A., where the positive derivative is involved)

$$z(t_f) = \left.\frac{\partial I}{\partial \boldsymbol{x}}\right|_{t=t_f}. \tag{4.11}$$

But in the present case,

$$z(t_f) = \left.\frac{\partial I^*}{\partial \boldsymbol{x}}\right|_{t=t_f},$$

and thus

$$z(t_f) = \left[\frac{\partial I}{\partial \boldsymbol{x}} + \frac{\partial}{\partial \boldsymbol{x}}(\boldsymbol{\lambda}'\boldsymbol{\psi})\right]_{t=t_f} \tag{4.12}$$

or

$$z_i(t_f) = \left[\frac{\partial I}{\partial x_i} + \sum_{j=1}^{m} \lambda_j \frac{\partial \psi_j}{\partial x_i}\right]_{t=t_f} \tag{4.13}$$

represents the boundary conditions. Note the correspondence to the boundary conditions defined in the constrained maximum principle (Section 2.6) and the fact that in Equation (4.13) the term $\sum_{j=1}^{m} \lambda_j(\partial\psi_j/\partial x_i)$ will not be zero for $i = 1, 2, \ldots, m$. For $i = m+1, m+2, \ldots, n$, the adjoint boundary conditions will be Equation (4.11).

Now let us try to simplify Equation (4.10). First we select

$$\boldsymbol{\lambda} = \tfrac{1}{2}\boldsymbol{K}\boldsymbol{\psi},$$

where $\boldsymbol{K}$ is a diagonal matrix of size $(m \times m)$. Equation (4.10) now becomes

$$I^* = I + \tfrac{1}{2}(\boldsymbol{K}\boldsymbol{\psi})'\boldsymbol{\psi}$$

or

$$I^* = I + \tfrac{1}{2}\boldsymbol{\psi}'\boldsymbol{K}\boldsymbol{\psi}, \tag{4.14}$$

since $\boldsymbol{K}$ is diagonal and thus symmetric. The part $\boldsymbol{\psi}'\boldsymbol{K}\boldsymbol{\psi}$ is merely a quadratic form representing the weighted sum of squares of the elements of $\boldsymbol{\psi}$.

Equation (4.14) is thus the augmented performance index for the new unconstrained problem. Courant [25] has shown that for $m = 1$ and k_{11} approaching infinity, k_{11} being the single element in $\boldsymbol{K}$, the minimization of Equation (4.14) achieves the true constrained minimum of the original problem ($\boldsymbol{\psi}$ goes to zero). Thus we would expect that in our control problem the use of Equation (4.14) for a selected set of $\boldsymbol{K}$'s, with the diagonal elements in $\boldsymbol{K}$ increasing with each iteration, will enable us to approach the constraints of the final-time states. The use of Equation (4.14) requires on this basis that we use increasingly large positive elements in $\boldsymbol{K}$ as the minimum value of the performance index is approached.

Although excellent results have been obtained with the use of the penalty function for terminal constrained problems by Kelley [6], Kopp and McGill [59], and Denn [28–31], there does exist one serious problem. In attempting to implement its use, we must question ourselves as to the method for increasing the elements of $\boldsymbol{K}$. If the elements are increased too fast, the new controls will tighten up the terminal constraints but leave the unaugmented part of the index, I, essentially unchanged. By contrast, if the elements are not increased fast enough, the specified terminal values will be approached quite slowly. As a result, a certain amount of trial-and-error may be required to achieve a logical sequence of the the elements of $\boldsymbol{K}$.

While we have considered that the terminal constraints are equalities, it is also possible to use inequality constraints [29–31]. Further, although we shall not explicitly detail it here, trajectory constraints, constraints on $\boldsymbol{x}(t)$, can also be included in the penalty function formulation (we shall discuss this point later). Finally, the form of Equation (4.7) may be written more explicitly as

$$\psi_j[\boldsymbol{x}(t_f), t_f] = x_j(t_f) - x_j^d(t_f), \tag{4.15}$$

where $x_j^d(t_f)$ is the explicit, final desired value of the jth state. Equation (4.15) indicates the concern with the deviation of the actual (calculated) value from the desired value. Of course, $x_j^d(t_f)$ could be zero, in which case the origin is the desired terminal state.

The reader will probably recognize that although we have introduced the penalty function as a special concept here, we have already encountered this function in a previous chapter. Thus, in Chapter 3, the quadratic performance index included the final or terminal state term $\|\boldsymbol{x}(t_f)\|_{\boldsymbol{S}}^2$ in addition to the integrated trajectory term. Obviously, this final state term can be viewed as a penalty function in the performance index.

4.4. Approximation-to-the-problem methods

As we have already mentioned, the terminology "approximation to the problem" has been defined by Dreyfus to cover any iterative procedure in which the system equations and the performance index are fixed and the iterations converge on the boundary conditions. To illustrate the explicit workings of this procedure, we shall here use the discrete equations, but it should be evident that the continuous form of the pertinent equations would work just as well.

Let us start the discussion by specifying the equations from Chapter 2 which will be needed. Thus, we use the discrete system equation in the form

$$\boldsymbol{x}(k+1) = \boldsymbol{h}[\boldsymbol{x}(k), \boldsymbol{u}(k)], \tag{4.16}$$

with $\boldsymbol{x}(0)$ *prescribed*, and the discrete adjoint equation

$$\boldsymbol{z}(k) = \frac{\partial \boldsymbol{h}'(k)}{\partial \boldsymbol{x}(k)}\, \boldsymbol{z}(k+1), \tag{4.17}$$

and if we seek to minimize $x_1(P)$, for illustration, the boundary conditions on the adjoint variables are

$$z_1(P) = 1, \qquad z_i(P) = 0 \qquad (i = 2, 3, \ldots, n). \tag{4.18}$$

Conditions for an optimal control reside in choosing $\boldsymbol{u}(k)$ such that $H(k)$ is minimized, where

$$H(k) = \boldsymbol{z}(k)'\boldsymbol{h}[\boldsymbol{x}(k-1), \boldsymbol{u}(k-1)] \tag{4.19}$$

and

$$\boldsymbol{x}(k) = \frac{\partial H(k)}{\partial \boldsymbol{z}(k)} \qquad [\boldsymbol{x}(0) \text{ prescribed}]\,; \tag{4.20}$$

$$\boldsymbol{z}(k) = \frac{\partial H(k)}{\partial \boldsymbol{x}(k)}; \qquad z_1(P) = 1, \qquad z_i(P) = 0 \qquad (i = 2, 3, \ldots, n). \tag{4.21}$$

The minimization of $H(k)$ at each k is obtained, perhaps by putting $\partial H(k)/\partial \boldsymbol{u}(k-1) = \boldsymbol{0}$. In addition, we have the following equation, derived as Equation (2.128),

$$\boldsymbol{z}'(P)\delta\boldsymbol{x}(P) = \boldsymbol{z}'(0)\delta\boldsymbol{x}(0) + \sum_{k=1}^{P}\left[\frac{\partial H(k)}{\partial \boldsymbol{u}(k-1)}\right]'\delta\boldsymbol{u}(k-1) \tag{4.22}$$

or with $\delta\boldsymbol{x}(0) = \boldsymbol{0}$,

$$\boldsymbol{z}'(P)\delta\boldsymbol{x}(P) = \sum_{k=1}^{P}\left[\frac{\partial H(k)}{\partial \boldsymbol{u}(k-1)}\right]'\delta\boldsymbol{u}(k-1). \tag{4.23}$$

With a formulation of this type, we know that we face the solution of a two-point boundary-value problem. The state $\boldsymbol{x}(0)$ is given, but $\boldsymbol{x}(P)$ is completely free since it has not been specified; at the same time $\boldsymbol{z}(P)$ is given, but $\boldsymbol{z}(0)$ is completely free. Thus we have $2n$ difference equations and $2n$ boundary conditions, n corresponding to $\boldsymbol{x}(0)$ and n corresponding to $\boldsymbol{z}(P)$. In dynamic programming we bypass this problem by really prescribing all possible $\boldsymbol{x}(P)$ and stepping backward to generate the $\boldsymbol{x}(0)$ corresponding to any $\boldsymbol{x}(P)$.

To solve the two-point boundary-value problem, we may theoretically proceed in a number of ways. To illustrate, we may guess a final value for $\boldsymbol{x}(P)$, let us say, $\boldsymbol{x}^{(0)}(P)$, so that with $\boldsymbol{z}(P)$ we have $2n$ boundary conditions at a single end of the time-staging intervals. Thus both the system equation (4.16) and the adjoint equation (4.17) may be evaluated *backward* until $\boldsymbol{x}^{(0)}(0)$ and $\boldsymbol{z}^{(0)}(0)$ are calculated. While we are carrying out this simultaneous backward pass, the $\boldsymbol{u}^{(0)}(k)$ may be evaluated at each stage by putting $\partial H(k)/\partial \boldsymbol{u}(k-1) = \boldsymbol{0}$ or by searching in the $H\boldsymbol{u}$-space for the optimum $\boldsymbol{u}$ at each stage. It is important to realize that because the $\boldsymbol{x}^{(0)}(P)$ have been guessed, the value of $\boldsymbol{x}^{(0)}(0)$ calculated will *not* equal $\boldsymbol{x}(0)$, except by chance. If in some manner we can use this deviation between $\boldsymbol{x}^{(0)}(0)$ and $\boldsymbol{x}(0)$ to generate a new set $\boldsymbol{x}^{(1)}(P)$ which in turn will yield $\boldsymbol{x}^{(1)}(0)$ [and the corresponding $\boldsymbol{z}^{(1)}(0)$ and $\boldsymbol{u}^{(1)}(k)$] such that

$$\|\boldsymbol{x}(0) - \boldsymbol{x}^{(0)}(0)\| > \|\boldsymbol{x}(0) - \boldsymbol{x}^{(1)}(0)\|, \tag{4.24}$$

then an iteration scheme is at hand for generating a sequence $\boldsymbol{x}^{(0)}(0)$, $\boldsymbol{x}^{(1)}(0)$, $\ldots$, $\boldsymbol{x}^{(j)}(0)$ such that

$$\|\boldsymbol{x}(0) - \boldsymbol{x}^{(0)}(0)\| > \|\boldsymbol{x}(0) - \boldsymbol{x}^{(1)}(0)\| > \cdots > \|\boldsymbol{x}(0) - \boldsymbol{x}^{(j)}(0)\|$$

until

$$\|\boldsymbol{x}(0) - \boldsymbol{x}^{(j)}(0)\| \leq \varepsilon,$$

where ε is a preassigned error term. In other words, we evolve an iterative process for adjusting $\boldsymbol{x}^{(j)}(P)$ such that as j gets large, $\boldsymbol{x}^{(j)}(0)$ approaches $\boldsymbol{x}(0)$. When this occurs, we have found the optimal control sequence because $\boldsymbol{u}^{(j)}(k)$ is generated at the same time.

It is important to see that, whereas in the limit of large j the solution to the originally specified problem is generated, at each pass the solution to an *unwanted* problem is also generated. Thus $\boldsymbol{x}^{(0)}(P)$ generates a corresponding $\boldsymbol{x}^{(0)}(0)$; but the control achieved during this pass is the optimal control for the problem with initial condition $\boldsymbol{x}^{(0)}(0)$. Each pass in the iteration generates an optimal $\boldsymbol{u}^0(k)$ for the wrong $\boldsymbol{x}(0)$, and thus the wrong problem. In the limit of large j, the unwanted problem solutions converge to the solution of the wanted problem. It is this property of the solution which led to the title *approximation to the problem*.

To use $\boldsymbol{x}^{(0)}(0)$ and $\boldsymbol{x}(0)$ to generate $\boldsymbol{x}^{(1)}(P)$, we may follow the work of Aris [1], Denn [31], or Merriam [7]. From Equation (4.22), with the assumption that the nominal trajectory is sufficiently close to the optimal trajectory so that $\delta\boldsymbol{u}(k-1) = \mathbf{0}$ for $k = 1, 2, \ldots, P$, there follows

$$\boldsymbol{z}'(P)\delta\boldsymbol{x}(P) = \boldsymbol{z}(0)'\delta\boldsymbol{x}(0). \tag{4.25}$$

This may be expanded to

$$\boldsymbol{z}'(P)[\boldsymbol{x}^{(1)}(P) - \boldsymbol{x}^{(0)}(P)] = \boldsymbol{z}(0)'[\boldsymbol{x}(0) - \boldsymbol{x}^{(0)}(0)],$$

or with the first component of $\boldsymbol{x}(P)$ being extremized,

$$x_1^{(1)}(P) = x_1^{(0)}(P) + \boldsymbol{z}(0)'[\boldsymbol{x}(0) - \boldsymbol{x}^{(0)}(0)]. \tag{4.26}$$

But the right-hand side contains only known elements from a backward pass, and we can calculate the new, hopefully improved, $x_1^{(1)}(P)$. Unfortunately, this only improves the single first element in the $\boldsymbol{x}$ vector. If we imbed this problem into n problems with each of the n problems concerned with extremizing a different element of $\boldsymbol{x}(P)$, then a new set of $\boldsymbol{x}^{(1)}(P)$ can be determined. This, of course, involves changing the boundary conditions n times and carrying out the integration n times. If the $\boldsymbol{u}(k)$ obtained is assumed to be the same irrespective of which component is extremized, we may now use Equation (4.26) to generate the new set of $\boldsymbol{x}^{(1)}(P)$. In turn, a new pass through the calculation is now feasible. For an illustration of this type of procedure, see Knapp and Frost [58]. The important point here is that $\delta \boldsymbol{u}(k-1)$ or, alternatively, $\partial H(k)/\partial \boldsymbol{u}(k-1)$ is assumed to be zero in this procedure; that is, we are close to the optimal trajectory. The result is an iterative procedure which involves only simple computer logic and minimal storage requirements.

Alternatively, we might start by guessing $\boldsymbol{z}^{(0)}(0)$ and with the known $\boldsymbol{x}(0)$ evaluate both sets of equations in a forward direction until $\boldsymbol{z}^{(0)}(P)$ and $\boldsymbol{x}^{(0)}(P)$ are evaluated [41]. Using the difference between $\boldsymbol{z}^{(0)}(P)$ and $\boldsymbol{z}(P)$, we might then think of generating a new estimate $\boldsymbol{z}^{(1)}(0)$ and continuing until convergence (hopefully) occurs. At each pass in this procedure, we obtain a stationary solution to an unwanted problem with the wrong final states and the wrong performance index. In fact, if we get $z_1^{(j)}(P), z_2^{(j)}(P), \ldots, z_n^{(j)}(P)$, which are not equal to the prescribed boundary conditions $z_1(P) = 1$, $z_2(P) = 0$, $\ldots$, $z_n(P) = 0$, the performance index which has been minimized is really

$$I[\boldsymbol{x}(0), P] = \boldsymbol{z}^{(j)}(P)'\boldsymbol{x}^{(j)}(P) \tag{4.27}$$

rather than the correct index

$$I[\boldsymbol{x}(0), P] = x_1(P).$$

Given the two procedures above, we suggest that the first one is probably better. In addition to the reasons stated, there exists one further serious problem associated with the second procedure. To illustrate this point, let us consider the system equation in the form

$$\dot{\boldsymbol{x}}(t) = \boldsymbol{A}\boldsymbol{x} + \boldsymbol{B}\boldsymbol{u}, \tag{4.28}$$

and if the forward time integration is stable, $\boldsymbol{A}$ has negative real eigenvalues. The adjoint equation corresponding to Equation (4.28) is given by

$$\dot{\boldsymbol{z}}(t) = -\boldsymbol{A}'\boldsymbol{z}(t).$$

But the eigenvalues of $-\boldsymbol{A}'$ are the negative of those of $\boldsymbol{A}$, and thus the forward integration is unstable. These results carry over in most cases where nonlinear equations are involved; that is, the forward-time integration of the adjoint equations is normally unstable and thus blows up as the integration is carried out. Actually, this instability of the adjoint equations is most pronounced in nonconservative systems, which exchange mass only or heat, etc. In these nonconservative systems, the adjoint variables will show an exponential increase with increasing time.

Other alternative procedures are possible which do not come under the explicit heading of this section, but at least one of these should be presented here in a preliminary way because of the superficial similarity to those above. Further details on this specific method are given in the next section. Thus let us assume

$\boldsymbol{u}^{(0)}(k-1)$, $k = 1, 2, \ldots, P$, and solve the system equations in a forward direction, using $\boldsymbol{x}(0)$ to yield $\boldsymbol{x}^{(0)}(P)$, and the adjoint equations backwards, using $\boldsymbol{z}(P)$ to yield $\boldsymbol{z}^{(0)}(0)$. Once all the $\boldsymbol{x}(k)$ and $\boldsymbol{z}(k)$ are known, we may obtain a new set of controls $\boldsymbol{u}^{(1)}(k-1)$ by carrying out $\partial H(k)/\partial \boldsymbol{u}(k-1) = \mathbf{0}$. This establishes the desired iteration pattern.

A word of caution is needed with respect to using any one of these iteration procedures. This concerns the adjustment of the initial values based on the results of a single iteration pass. As illustration, suppose that we consider the third procedure above and the modified formula

$$\boldsymbol{u}^{(j+1)}(k) = \boldsymbol{u}^{(j-1)}(k) + h[\boldsymbol{u}^{(j)}(k) - \boldsymbol{u}^{(j-1)}(k)], \tag{4.29}$$

where h is a step-size parameter. The expression $\boldsymbol{u}^{(j-1)}(k)$ is the control from the $(j-1)$th iteration, which has generated the new control $\boldsymbol{u}^{(j)}(k)$. The question to be asked is, "Should we use $\boldsymbol{u}^{(j)}(k)$, or should we be a little cautious and not go as far as $\boldsymbol{u}^{(j)}(k)$ would suggest?" We see that for $h = 1$, Equation (4.29) specifies that $\boldsymbol{u}^{(j+1)}(k)$, which may be thought of as the result of answering the question, is to be taken equal to $\boldsymbol{u}^{(j)}(k)$. In other words, for $h = 1$, Equation (4.29) does not affect the calculation procedure since we use the full control suggested by a single iteration cycle. When $|h| \neq 1$, we may use Equation (4.29) to change the results of a single iteration cycle, either to step further or less than suggested by the iteration. The actual details of specifying a specific value of h are largely dependent on the particular system under consideration, and thus we shall not delve further into this point here. Obviously, any of the iteration techniques outlined above can be adjusted in much the same manner.

It is the consensus of experience, however, that, in such indirect methods as the first or second procedure above, a good initial guess on the initial values is a mandatory requirement to make the method work, that is, to converge. Furthermore, the method works best with free final conditions since it may be impossible to select a $\boldsymbol{z}(0)$ such that the trajectory reaches any part of terminal manifold constraints.

While we have used first-order approximations to adjust the boundary conditions, it is possible to turn to more complex approximations. In Section 4.6 we shall point out the salient features of such a second-order approximation termed the neighborhood extremal method [18].

4.5. Approximation-to-the-solution methods

In this section we shall investigate and detail a further *approximation-to-the-solution* method, in which the system equations and the boundary conditions are fixed and an iteration technique developed which converges to the desired performance index. Thus, every suboptimal trajectory will satisfy the system equations and the boundary conditions but not the performance index or the minimum Hamiltonian value. Stated in more specific terms, the method involves a linearization followed by a successive approximation involving the gradient in control space to compute new controls. On this basis the method has been called the *gradient* method, the *projected gradient* method, or even the *first variation* method.

The basic procedures involved are due to Bryson and his co-workers [18, 22–24] and Kelley [6], using the calculus of variations or the maximum principle; to Dreyfus [34, 35], using the concepts of dynamic programming; to Ho [43–45], using the concepts of nonlinear programming; and to Denn [28–32], using the Green's function approach. Actually, all of these formulations result in analogous expressions until constraints are included. It is the inclusion of constraints, be they terminal constraints or control or state constraints, that leads to apparent differences in the formulations. For a simple but interesting discussion of the variational approach, the reader is referred to Douglas and Denn [33].

In general terms, the results of Brown [21], Lee [63], Rosenbrock and Storry [79], and Jensen [49] all show the monotonic convergence of the methods to an optimum performance index. Convergence is basically independent of the initial guess used in the iterative procedure although the rate of convergence, or alternatively computer time, is affected by the initial guess. Of practical importance is the fact that the adjoint equations are always integrated in a stable direction, that is, backward in time, and thus no problems such as were encountered with the "approximation to the problem" technique are involved.

The development used here is to first outline a general procedure for handling the problem of interest. This is followed by a specific development for the continuous and then for the discrete case. Finally, this work is extended to cover the case where control or state constraints are involved.

It is apparent that methods such as the pair-interchange or "approximation to the problem" are brute-force procedures in which the improvement in the controls as the iterations converge is carried out in the simplest manner. In the present procedure an attempt is made to improve the control at each iteration by the calculation of the direction of steepest descent and then stepping in this direction.

We start the discussion with the normal continuous-time model

$$\dot{\boldsymbol{x}}(t) = \boldsymbol{f}[\boldsymbol{x}(t), \boldsymbol{u}(t)] \tag{4.30}$$

and the initial conditions assumed prescribed as $\boldsymbol{x}(0)$. The performance index is taken as

$$I[\boldsymbol{x}(0), t_f] = I[\boldsymbol{x}(t_f), t_f] = I, \tag{4.31}$$

where I will be used to designate the final value index. Let us assume for now that t_f is open and thus not specified. If we define the Hamiltonian H as

$$H = \boldsymbol{z}'\boldsymbol{f} = \boldsymbol{z}'\dot{\boldsymbol{x}}, \tag{4.32}$$

then it follows that for the adjoint variables defined by

$$\dot{z} = -(\partial f'/\partial x)z,$$

we may write

$$\dot{x} = \partial H/\partial z, \qquad \dot{z} = -\partial H/\partial x. \tag{4.33}$$

The boundary conditions are

$$x(0) \qquad \text{prescribed}, \tag{4.34}$$

$$z(t_f) = \left.\frac{\partial I}{\partial x}\right|_{t=t_f}, \tag{4.35}$$

where it is assumed in Equation (4.35) that the $x(t_f)$ is not constrained.

Now we wish to obtain a relationship which shows how I changes when the control is perturbed by an amount $\delta u(t)$. We must keep in mind that a change $\delta u(t)$ will also lead to a change $\delta x(t)$ and in t_f itself, since t_f is not fixed at this point. But we recall that in Chapter 2 we derived Equation (2.116) in the form

$$\delta I = z'(0)\delta x(0) + \int_0^{t_f} z'(\partial f'/\partial u)'\delta u \, dt.$$

If we note that for $x(0)$ prescribed, $\delta x(0) = \mathbf{0}$, this becomes

$$\delta I = \int_0^{t_f} (\partial H/\partial u)'\delta u(t) \, dt, \tag{4.36}$$

where Equation (4.32) has been used to define H. But this equation shows the resulting small perturbation in I due to a small perturbation in $u(t)$. Now if we allow the final time t_f to be free, that is, t_f not fixed, then the final change in I is the incremental change δI due to $u(t)$ plus the change due to a change in t_f. Thus, we write

$$\delta I = \delta I\Big|_{t=t_f} + \left.\frac{dI}{dt}\right|_{t=t_f} \delta t_f. \tag{4.37}$$

But noting that [since I is a function of $x(t_f)$ and t_f]

$$\left.\frac{dI}{dt}\right|_{t=t_f} = \left[\frac{\partial I}{\partial t} + \left(\frac{\partial I}{\partial x}\right)' \frac{\partial x}{\partial t}\right]_{t=t_f} \tag{4.38}$$

and using the nomenclature that $\bar{I}$ refers to the value of the performance index for a specified trajectory (for $u(t)$ specified), Equations (4.36) through (4.38) yield

$$\delta I = I - \bar{I} = \int_0^{\bar{t}_f} \left(\frac{\partial \bar{H}}{\partial u}\right)' \delta u(t) \, dt + \left[\frac{\partial \bar{I}}{\partial t} + \left(\frac{\partial \bar{I}}{\partial x}\right)' \frac{\partial \bar{x}}{\partial t}\right]_{t=\bar{t}_f} \delta t_f$$

or

$$I = \bar{I} + \int_0^{\bar{t}_f} \left(\frac{\partial \bar{H}}{\partial u}\right)' \delta u(t) \, dt + \left[\frac{\partial \bar{I}}{\partial t} + \left(\frac{\partial \bar{I}}{\partial x}\right)' \bar{f}\right]_{t=\bar{t}_f} \delta t_f. \tag{4.39}$$

From Equation (4.39) we see a number of interesting points. First, if the trajectory yielding $\bar{I}$ is the optimal trajectory, then it is necessary that

$$\partial \bar{H}/\partial \boldsymbol{u} = \boldsymbol{0}, \tag{4.40}$$

and therefore

$$\left.\frac{d\bar{I}}{dt}\right|_{t=t_f} = \left[\frac{\partial \bar{I}}{\partial t} + \left(\frac{\partial \bar{I}}{\partial \boldsymbol{x}}\right)' \bar{\boldsymbol{f}}\right]_{t=t_f} = 0. \tag{4.41}$$

In this case, free variations in $\boldsymbol{u}(t)$ and t_f still yield $\delta I = 0$. Second, if the final time t_f is fixed, $\delta t_f = 0$, and only Equation (4.40) is necessary for the trajectory to be an optimal one.

Alternatively, we could have proceeded by expanding I in a Taylor series around the terminal point of the reference trajectory. If only first terms in this expansion are retained, it is possible to show that Equation (4.39) results; this is the basis for the name *first variation*, by which the method is sometimes called.

Before we proceed further with the use of Equation (4.39), it will be instructive if we retreat a few steps to show a quite fundamental variational procedure for obtaining the same results. Let us define the performance index in a very general way,

$$I[\boldsymbol{x}(0), t_f] = \phi[\boldsymbol{x}(t_f), t_f] + \int_0^{t_f} J[\boldsymbol{x}(t), \boldsymbol{u}(t)]\, dt, \tag{4.42}$$

where ϕ is some function of $\boldsymbol{x}(t_f)$ and t_f. Now we ask to minimize I subject to the constraints of the system Equation (4.30); this may be done (as detailed in Section 2.6) by defining the unconstrained index with Lagrange multipliers $\boldsymbol{\lambda}(t)$ such that

$$I = \phi[\boldsymbol{x}(t_f), t_f] + \int_0^{t_f} J[\boldsymbol{x}(t), \boldsymbol{u}(t)]\, dt + \int_0^{t_f} \boldsymbol{\lambda}'[\boldsymbol{f}(\boldsymbol{x}, \boldsymbol{u}) - \dot{\boldsymbol{x}}]\, dt. \tag{4.43}$$

If we let the Hamiltonian be

$$H = \boldsymbol{\lambda}'\boldsymbol{f} + J[\boldsymbol{x}(t), \boldsymbol{u}(t)],$$

then

$$I = \phi[\boldsymbol{x}(t_f), t_f] + \int_0^{t_f} H\, dt - \int_0^{t_f} \boldsymbol{\lambda}'\dot{\boldsymbol{x}}\, dt.$$

Integrating the last integral in this equation by parts, we obtain

$$I = \phi[\boldsymbol{x}(t_f), t_f] + \boldsymbol{\lambda}'(0)\boldsymbol{x}(0) - \boldsymbol{\lambda}'(t_f)\boldsymbol{x}(t_f) + \int_0^{t_f} [H + \dot{\boldsymbol{\lambda}}'\boldsymbol{x}]\, dt. \tag{4.44}$$

Now choosing the simplified case that t_f is specified, we find the variations in I, δI, caused by small perturbations in $\boldsymbol{u}(t)$, $\delta\boldsymbol{u}(t)$, about some reference trajectory,

$$\delta I = \left[\left(\frac{\partial \bar{\phi}}{\partial \boldsymbol{x}}\right)' - \boldsymbol{\lambda}'\right]_{t=t_f} \delta\boldsymbol{x}(t_f) + \int_0^{t_f} \left\{\left(\frac{\partial \bar{H}}{\partial \boldsymbol{x}}\right)' \delta\boldsymbol{x} + \left(\frac{\partial \bar{H}}{\partial \boldsymbol{u}}\right)' \delta\boldsymbol{u} + \dot{\boldsymbol{\lambda}}'\delta\boldsymbol{x}\right\} dt, \tag{4.45}$$

where $\bar{\phi}$ and $\bar{H}$ denote the values of ϕ and H for the reference trajectory. In this equation $\partial\bar{\phi}/\partial\boldsymbol{x}$ and $\partial\bar{H}/\partial\boldsymbol{x}$ are n-dimensional vectors and $\partial\bar{H}/\partial\boldsymbol{u}$ is an r-dimensional vector; also, $\delta\boldsymbol{x}(0) = \boldsymbol{0}$ has been used. But for the reference trajectory to be the optimum (that is, for $\delta I \to 0$), the equation must hold for free variations in $\delta\boldsymbol{x}(t)$ and $\delta\boldsymbol{u}(t)$. Thus, it is sufficient that all of the coefficients vanish, or

$$\dot{\boldsymbol{\lambda}}(t) = -\frac{\partial\bar{H}}{\partial\boldsymbol{x}}, \qquad \boldsymbol{\lambda}(t_f) = \left.\frac{\partial\bar{\phi}}{\partial\boldsymbol{x}}\right|_{t=t_f}, \qquad \frac{\partial\bar{H}}{\partial\boldsymbol{u}} = \boldsymbol{0}.$$

But we now see that $\boldsymbol{\lambda}(t) = \boldsymbol{z}(t) =$ the adjoint state and that the results of Equation (4.39) are confirmed for the case of t_f fixed.

Next, we seek to investigate the behavior of I when the $\boldsymbol{u}(t)$ are constrained by some type of quadratic surface. This is essentially the same problem as was discussed in Section 2.6, and thus we write

$$\delta I = \int_0^{t_f}\left(\frac{\partial\bar{H}}{\partial\boldsymbol{u}}\right)'\delta\boldsymbol{u}(t)\,dt + k\left[\int_0^{t_f}\delta\boldsymbol{u}'\delta\boldsymbol{u}\,dt - r^2\right], \tag{4.46}$$

where all the δu_i are restricted to the same quadratic surface, namely,

$$\int_0^{t_f}\delta\boldsymbol{u}'\delta\boldsymbol{u}\,dt \le r^2.$$

In Equation (4.46), δI includes all terms from Equation (4.39) which do not involve δt_f; in other words, here we are not putting constraints on t_f, nor are we forming an unconstrained index by means of the system equations. To determine $\delta\boldsymbol{u}(t)$, we seek the minimum of the integrand of Equation (4.46) by differentiating with respect to $\delta\boldsymbol{u}(t)$ and setting the result equal to zero. Although minimization of the integrand does not necessarily lead to the minimum of the integral (which we really want), for our present purpose this is good enough. Thus,

$$\delta\boldsymbol{u}(t) = -\frac{1}{2k}\frac{\partial\bar{H}}{\partial\boldsymbol{u}}, \tag{4.47}$$

where we can evaluate k by substituting Equation (4.47) back into the constraint equation to give

$$\frac{1}{2k} = \left[\int_0^{t_f}\frac{1}{r^2}\left(\frac{\partial\bar{H}}{\partial\boldsymbol{u}}\right)'\left(\frac{\partial\bar{H}}{\partial\boldsymbol{u}}\right)dt\right]^{-1/2}.$$

However, we may restrict each δu_i in its own domain, namely,

$$\int_0^{t_f}(\delta u_i)^2\,dt \le r_i^2.$$

Using the latter approach and Equation (4.47), we see that

$$\delta \boldsymbol{u}(t) = -\boldsymbol{K}(\partial \overline{H}/\partial \boldsymbol{u}), \tag{4.48}$$

where $\boldsymbol{K}$ is a diagonal matrix

$$\boldsymbol{K} = \begin{bmatrix} k_{11} & & \cdots & 0 \\ \vdots & k_{22} & & \vdots \\ & & \ddots & \\ 0 & & \cdots & k_{rr} \end{bmatrix},$$

with elements

$$k_{ii} = \left[\int_0^{\bar{t}_f} \frac{1}{r_i^2}\left(\frac{\partial \overline{H}}{\partial u_i}\right)^2 dt\right]^{-1/2}. \tag{4.49}$$

It follows, of course, that if we used the same quadratic surface for each u_i, all the diagonal elements in $\boldsymbol{K}$ would be equal and $\boldsymbol{K}$ could be replaced by a scalar.

Now we are in a position to outline the over-all iterative procedure. First, we note that Equation (4.48) specifies that a change in $\boldsymbol{u}(t)$ is based on the gradient of H, evaluated at the former set of controls which yielded the reference trajectory. Thus, we perform the following steps.

(1) Select an initial control function $\bar{\boldsymbol{u}}(t)$ and integrate the system equations forward in time.

(2) Terminate this trajectory when $d\bar{I}/dt = 0$ or when $\bar{I}$ reaches a minimum point. This fixes the value $t = \bar{t}_f$.

(3) Starting at $t = \bar{t}_f$ and

$$\boldsymbol{z}(t_f) = \left.\frac{\partial \bar{I}}{\partial \boldsymbol{x}}\right|_{t=t_f},$$

integrate the adjoint equations backward. Simultaneously we may evaluate $\delta \boldsymbol{u}(t) = -\boldsymbol{K}(\partial \overline{H}/\partial \boldsymbol{u})$ with an assumed value for $\boldsymbol{K}$. Alternatively, we may determine the elements of $\boldsymbol{K}$ by the use of Equation (4.49).

(4) Once $\delta \boldsymbol{u}(t)$ is known, and since we have $\bar{\boldsymbol{u}}(t)$, we obtain a new $\boldsymbol{u}(t)$ by $\boldsymbol{u}(t) = \bar{\boldsymbol{u}}(t) + \delta \boldsymbol{u}(t)$.

(5) We may now proceed to step (2) and continue the cycle again. Alternatively, if we have merely guessed at the elements of $\boldsymbol{K}$, we may instead select a variety of different $\boldsymbol{K}$, determine different $\delta \boldsymbol{u}(k)$, and integrate forward with each set until $d\bar{I}/dt = 0$. From these sets we select the best $\boldsymbol{K}$, in the sense that it yields the minimum $\bar{I}_{t_f}$. Or we may carry out an interpolation on the $\boldsymbol{K}$'s and resulting $\bar{I}_{t_f}$'s to yield an optimum $\boldsymbol{K}$. Then we return to step (2) and continue. We note that only a *direction of correction* is explicitly determined. The magnitude, $\boldsymbol{K}$, must be guessed or searched for. As a result, the iteration will be first-order to convergence.

(6) The procedure terminates when $\delta \boldsymbol{u}(t)$ goes to zero with the accuracy

desired. This corresponds to the necessary condition that $\partial \bar{H}/\partial \boldsymbol{u} = \mathbf{0}$. Alternatively, the procedure may be terminated when some suitable $\|\partial \bar{H}/\partial \boldsymbol{u}\| = 0$.

As we have already mentioned, this iterative procedure will converge to an optimum control trajectory. However, it should be noted that as the optimal trajectory is approached, $\partial \bar{H}/\partial \boldsymbol{u}$ approaches zero and $\boldsymbol{K}$ approaches infinity in Equation (4.48). As a result, the solution tends to oscillate very near the optimal trajectory, and some changes are required in the calculation procedure at this point. One possible approach to making this change will be given in one of the numerical examples at the end of the chapter.

No consideration has been given to any constraints except those that limit the step size. These may involve only *terminal* values, or they may involve *control* and *state* constraints. Each type of constraint may be handled by the use of the penalty function, augmenting the regular performance index, or by appending the constraints directly to the performance index by a set of Lagrangian multipliers. In the latter case, the complexity of the specific formulation increases significantly.

Perhaps a few words are in order at this point, relating these constrained problems to those occurring when dynamic programming is used. Thus, in the terminal constraint case the state at t_f or the output of stage P must conform to certain preselected bounds. But we recall that in the use of dynamic programming this corresponded to the case where the last stage control was selected not necessarily as optimal but rather to reach the final selected state. For the control or state constrained problem, it will also be recalled that dynamic programming was actually easier to handle than the case without the constraints. Such observations point out the reasons why dynamic programming is such a versatile technique for optimal control calculations, compared, at least, to most other methods. The dimensionality problem, on the other hand, tends to defeat the use of dynamic programming, but it does not discourage to any real degree the gradient procedures detailed here.

Our experience in the use of the gradient method suggests that the algorithm is relatively simple to program for a computer and that the initial conditions used in the iteration are not crucial. Convergence to the optimum is, however, quite slow, especially as the optimum is approached and if the curvature of the function space is small. The method also works best when t_f is fixed and the final state is free (no terminal constraints). Finally, since the minimum condition is satisfied on a pointwise basis, the method tends to yield accurate answers over the entire time domain.

Now we turn to two specific formulations of the gradient method. The first formulation is for a continuous-time system with terminal constraints as due to Bryson [22–24], and the second is the analogous discrete version due to Dreyfus [35]. We start with the linearized form of the *continuous-time system*

$$\delta \dot{\boldsymbol{x}}(t) = \boldsymbol{A}(t)\delta \boldsymbol{x}(t) + \boldsymbol{B}(t)\delta \boldsymbol{u}(t), \tag{4.50}$$

where $\boldsymbol{A}(t)$ and $\boldsymbol{B}(t)$ are matrices with elements obtained by partial differentiation of $\boldsymbol{f}[\boldsymbol{x}(t), \boldsymbol{u}(t)]$. (See Section 2.4.) Implicit here is that we have selected some reference control $\bar{\boldsymbol{u}}(t)$ about which to linearize; that is, $\boldsymbol{A}(t)$ and $\boldsymbol{B}(t)$ are functions of time and also of the selection made for $\bar{\boldsymbol{u}}(t)$. To Equation (4.50) we add the relations

$$I[\boldsymbol{x}(t_f), t_f] \qquad \text{(final-value performance index)}, \tag{4.51}$$

$$\boldsymbol{\psi}[\boldsymbol{x}(t_f), t_f] = \boldsymbol{0} \qquad \text{(terminal final state constraints)}, \tag{4.52}$$

$$\rho[\boldsymbol{x}(t_f), t_f] = 0 \qquad \text{(final time or stopping condition)}, \tag{4.53}$$

which are a final value performance index, terminal final state constraints, and a relationship to determine the final time, respectively. Now the adjoint state may be introduced in the form

$$\dot{\boldsymbol{z}}^I(t) = -\boldsymbol{A}'(t)\boldsymbol{z}^I(t), \tag{4.54}$$

and the boundary conditions

$$\boldsymbol{z}^I(t_f) = (\partial \bar{I}/\partial \boldsymbol{x})_{t=t_f} \tag{4.55}$$

also used. Equivalent to Equation (4.39),

$$\delta I = \int_0^{\bar{t}_f} \boldsymbol{z}^I(t)'\boldsymbol{B}(t)\delta\boldsymbol{u}(t)\, dt + \left[\frac{\partial \bar{I}}{\partial t} + \left(\frac{\partial \bar{I}}{\partial \boldsymbol{x}}\right)'\boldsymbol{f}\right]_{t=\bar{t}_f} \delta t_f. \tag{4.56}$$

The superscript on the adjoint state is used to indicate that this applies to I. In exactly the same manner, if we introduce the adjoint equations

$$\dot{\boldsymbol{Z}}^\psi(t) = -\boldsymbol{A}'(t)\boldsymbol{Z}^\psi(t) \tag{4.57}$$

and

$$\dot{\boldsymbol{z}}^\rho(t) = -\boldsymbol{A}'(t)\boldsymbol{z}^\rho(t), \tag{4.58}$$

with boundary conditions

$$\boldsymbol{Z}^\psi(t_f) = (\partial \bar{\boldsymbol{\psi}}'/\partial \boldsymbol{x})_{t=t_f}, \tag{4.59}$$

$$\boldsymbol{z}^\rho(t_f) = (\partial \bar{\rho}/\partial \boldsymbol{x})_{t=t_f}, \tag{4.60}$$

where $\boldsymbol{Z}^\psi(t)$ is a matrix of dimension $(n \times m)$ [and $\boldsymbol{\psi}$ is taken as $(m \times 1)$] and $\boldsymbol{z}^\rho(t)$ is a $(n \times 1)$ vector, there results

$$\delta\boldsymbol{\psi} = \int_0^{\bar{t}_f} \boldsymbol{Z}^\psi(t)'\boldsymbol{B}(t)\delta\boldsymbol{u}(t)\, dt + \left[\frac{\partial \bar{\boldsymbol{\psi}}}{\partial t} + \left(\frac{\partial \bar{\boldsymbol{\psi}}'}{\partial \boldsymbol{x}}\right)'\boldsymbol{f}\right]_{t=t_f} \delta t_f, \tag{4.61}$$

$$\delta\rho = \int_0^{\bar{t}_f} \boldsymbol{z}^\rho(t)'\boldsymbol{B}(t)\delta\boldsymbol{u}(t)\, dt + \left[\frac{\partial \bar{\rho}}{\partial t} + \left(\frac{\partial \bar{\rho}}{\partial \boldsymbol{x}}\right)'\boldsymbol{f}\right]_{t=t_f} \delta t_f. \tag{4.62}$$

But to satisfy the t_f constraint, it will be necessary that $\delta\rho = 0$; we may then solve for δt_f in Equation (4.62) and substitute into Equations (4.56) and (4.61). This yields

$$\delta I = \int_0^{t_f} \boldsymbol{z}^{I\rho}(t)' \boldsymbol{B}(t) \delta \boldsymbol{u}(t)\, dt \tag{4.63}$$

and

$$\delta \boldsymbol{\psi} = \int_0^{t_f} \boldsymbol{Z}^{\psi\rho}(t)' \boldsymbol{B}(t) \delta \boldsymbol{u}(t)\, dt, \tag{4.64}$$

where $\boldsymbol{z}^{I\rho}(t)$ is of dimension $(n \times 1)$, $\boldsymbol{Z}^{\psi\rho}(t)$ is of dimension $(n \times m)$, and

$$\boldsymbol{z}^{I\rho} = \boldsymbol{z}^{I}(t) - \boldsymbol{z}^{\rho}(t)\left[\left(\frac{\partial \bar{I}}{\partial t} + \left(\frac{\partial \bar{I}}{\partial \boldsymbol{x}}\right)' \boldsymbol{f}\right) \Big/ \left(\frac{\partial \bar{\rho}}{\partial t} + \left(\frac{\partial \bar{\rho}}{\partial \boldsymbol{x}}\right)' \boldsymbol{f}\right)\right]_{t=t_f}, \tag{4.65}$$

$$\boldsymbol{Z}^{\psi\rho} = \boldsymbol{Z}^{\psi}(t) - \boldsymbol{z}^{\rho}(t)\left[\left(\frac{\partial \bar{\psi}}{\partial t} + \left(\frac{\partial \bar{\psi}'}{\partial \boldsymbol{x}}\right)' \boldsymbol{f}\right)' \Big/ \left(\frac{\partial \bar{\rho}}{\partial t} + \left(\frac{\partial \bar{\rho}}{\partial \boldsymbol{x}}\right)' \boldsymbol{f}\right]_{t=t_f}. \tag{4.66}$$

We have now obtained all the necessary conditions showing how small perturbations $\delta\boldsymbol{u}(t)$ produce changes in I and in $\boldsymbol{\psi}$. Because of the final time constraint, however, the influence of $\delta\boldsymbol{u}(t)$ on ρ is not available. The question to be explored now is to devise a procedure for calculating the gradient of I and to determine the step size to be used. Thus, we first illustrate the comparison between the current system and that used for the previous simple system. Regarding the step size to be used, we now have

$$\int_0^{t_f} \delta\boldsymbol{u}'\delta\boldsymbol{u}\, dt = r^2, \tag{4.67}$$

and we wish to extremize δI as given by Equation (4.63) subject to the constraints (4.64) and (4.67). We change the extremizing with constraints to one without constraints by introducing the Lagrange multipliers $\boldsymbol{\lambda}$ and γ such that

$$\delta I = \int_0^{t_f} \boldsymbol{z}^{I\rho}(t)' \boldsymbol{B}(t) \delta \boldsymbol{u}(t)\, dt + \boldsymbol{\lambda}'\left[\delta\boldsymbol{\psi} - \int_0^{t_f} \boldsymbol{Z}^{\psi\rho}(t)' \boldsymbol{B}(t)\delta\boldsymbol{u}(t)\, dt\right]$$
$$+ \gamma\left[r^2 - \int_0^{t_f} \delta\boldsymbol{u}'\delta\boldsymbol{u}\, dt\right]. \tag{4.68}$$

If we now differentiate the integrand with respect to $\delta\boldsymbol{u}(t)$ and set the result equal to zero, we generate that $\delta\boldsymbol{u}(t)$ which will extremize the integrand, that is,

$$\delta\boldsymbol{u}(t) = (1/2\gamma)[\boldsymbol{B}'(t)\boldsymbol{z}^{I\rho}(t) - \boldsymbol{B}'(t)Z^{\psi\rho}(t)\boldsymbol{\lambda}].$$

When this is substituted back into Equations (4.64) and (4.67), the unknowns $\boldsymbol{\lambda}$ and γ may be determined. Equation (4.64) yields

$$2\gamma = (1/r)\left\{\int_0^{t_f} [\boldsymbol{B}'(t)\boldsymbol{z}^{I\rho}(t) - \boldsymbol{B}'(t)\boldsymbol{Z}^{\psi\rho}(t)\boldsymbol{\lambda}]'[\boldsymbol{B}'(t)\boldsymbol{z}^{I\rho}(t) - \boldsymbol{B}'(t)\boldsymbol{Z}^{\psi\rho}(t)\boldsymbol{\lambda}]\, dt\right\}^{1/2}$$

and Equation (4.67) yields

$$\boldsymbol{\lambda} = \left[\int_0^{t_f} \boldsymbol{Z}^{\psi\rho}(t)'\boldsymbol{B}(t)\boldsymbol{B}'(t)\boldsymbol{Z}^{\psi\rho}(t)\, dt\right]^{-1}\left[\int_0^{t_f} \boldsymbol{Z}^{\psi\rho}(t)'\boldsymbol{B}(t)\boldsymbol{B}'(t)\boldsymbol{z}^{I\rho}(t)\, dt - 2\gamma\delta\boldsymbol{\psi}\right],$$

so that γ and $\boldsymbol{\lambda}$ can be evaluated directly. After substituting these items into $\delta\boldsymbol{u}(t)$, we obtain

$$\delta\boldsymbol{u}(t) = \boldsymbol{B}'(t)\{\boldsymbol{z}^{I\rho}(t) - \boldsymbol{Z}^{\psi\rho}(t)\boldsymbol{I}_{\psi\psi}^{-1}\boldsymbol{I}_{\psi\mathrm{I}}\}\left\{\frac{r^2 - \delta\boldsymbol{\psi}'\boldsymbol{I}_{\psi\psi}^{-1}\delta\boldsymbol{\psi}}{I_{\mathrm{II}} - \boldsymbol{I}_{\psi\mathrm{I}}'\boldsymbol{I}_{\psi\psi}^{-1}\boldsymbol{I}_{\psi\mathrm{I}}}\right\}^{1/2} + \boldsymbol{B}'(t)\boldsymbol{Z}^{\psi\rho}(t)\boldsymbol{I}_{\psi\psi}^{-1}\delta\boldsymbol{\psi}, \tag{4.69}$$

and substitution of Equation (4.69) into (4.68) gives

$$\delta I = [\{r^2 - \delta\boldsymbol{\psi}'\boldsymbol{I}_{\psi\psi}^{-1}\delta\boldsymbol{\psi}\}\{I_{\mathrm{II}} - \boldsymbol{I}_{\psi\mathrm{I}}'\boldsymbol{I}_{\psi\psi}^{-1}\boldsymbol{I}_{\psi\mathrm{I}}\}]^{1/2} + \boldsymbol{I}_{\psi\mathrm{I}}'\boldsymbol{I}_{\psi\psi}^{-1}\delta\boldsymbol{\psi}, \tag{4.70}$$

where

$$\begin{aligned} \boldsymbol{I}_{\psi\psi} &= \int_0^{\bar{t}_f} \boldsymbol{Z}^{\psi\rho}(t)'\boldsymbol{B}(t)\boldsymbol{B}(t)'\boldsymbol{Z}^{\psi\rho}(t)\,dt, && (n \times n) \text{ matrix,} \\ \boldsymbol{I}_{\psi\mathrm{I}} &= \int_0^{\bar{t}_f} \boldsymbol{Z}^{\psi\rho}(t)'\boldsymbol{B}(t)\boldsymbol{B}(t)'\boldsymbol{z}^{I\rho}(t)\,dt, && (n \times 1) \text{ vector,} \\ I_{\mathrm{II}} &= \int_0^{\bar{t}_f} \boldsymbol{z}^{I\rho}(t)'\boldsymbol{B}(t)\boldsymbol{B}(t)'\boldsymbol{z}^{I\rho}(t)\,dt, && \text{scalar.} \end{aligned} \tag{4.71}$$

Equations (4.69) through (4.71) contain all the information needed to generate an algorithm for improving an initial guess on the control vector. Although the equations look abstruse, things are not so bad as they seem; all the adjoint equations may be integrated backward since boundary conditions at $t = \bar{t}_f$ are given for each. Once these functions are known, $\boldsymbol{z}^{I\rho}(t)$ and $\boldsymbol{Z}^{\psi\rho}(t)$ can be evaluated since terms in Equations (4.65) and (4.66) such as

$$\left[\frac{\partial \bar{I}}{\partial t} + \left(\frac{\partial \bar{I}}{\partial \boldsymbol{x}}\right)'\boldsymbol{f}\right] \Big/ \left[\frac{\partial \bar{\rho}}{\partial t} + \left(\frac{\partial \bar{\rho}}{\partial \boldsymbol{x}}\right)'\boldsymbol{f}\right]_{t=t_f}$$

are constants. Finally, the $\boldsymbol{I}_{\psi\psi}$, $\boldsymbol{I}_{\psi\mathrm{I}}$ and I_{II} in Equations (4.71) may be calculated since the adjoint variables are known along with $\boldsymbol{B}(t)$.

The actual algorithm for the gradient method applied to the continuous-time system can now be summarized as follows.

(1) Guess $\boldsymbol{u}^{(0)}(t)$ and, using the nonlinear system equations, $\boldsymbol{x}(0)$ prescribed, calculate $\boldsymbol{x}(t)$ until the condition $\rho[\boldsymbol{x}(t_f), t_f] = 0$ is reached. This defines a value of t_f corresponding to the assumed $\boldsymbol{u}^{(0)}(t)$. At this value of t_f, we can also calculate I and $\boldsymbol{\psi}$.

(2) Integrate the adjoint equations backward from t_f to $t = 0$. While doing this, calculate $\boldsymbol{z}^{I\rho}(t)$ and $\boldsymbol{Z}^{\psi\rho}(t)$ and also $\boldsymbol{I}_{\psi\psi}$, $\boldsymbol{I}_{\psi\mathrm{I}}$, and I_{II}.

(3) If values for r and $\delta\boldsymbol{\psi}$ are now selected, Equation (4.69) can be used to generate $\delta\boldsymbol{u}(t)$, and thus from

$$\boldsymbol{u}^{(1)}(t) = \boldsymbol{u}^{(0)}(t) + \delta\boldsymbol{u}(t)$$

a new estimate of the control function is known.

(4) Steps (1) through (3) are repeated until some preassigned error bound on δI is achieved.

As an alternative procedure, we see from Equations (4.69) and (4.70) that when no terminal state constraints exist, $\delta\boldsymbol{\psi} = \mathbf{0}$, these equations become

$$\delta \boldsymbol{u}(t) = \underbrace{r[I_{\mathrm{II}} - \boldsymbol{I}'_{\psi\mathrm{I}}\boldsymbol{I}^{-1}_{\psi\psi}\boldsymbol{I}_{\psi\mathrm{I}}]^{-1/2}}_{a}\underbrace{\boldsymbol{B}'(t)[\boldsymbol{z}^{I_P}(t) - \boldsymbol{Z}^{\psi_P}(t)\boldsymbol{I}^{-1}_{\psi\psi}\boldsymbol{I}_{\psi\mathrm{I}}]}_{b}, \tag{4.72}$$

$$\delta I = r[I_{\mathrm{II}} - \boldsymbol{I}'_{\psi\mathrm{I}}\boldsymbol{I}^{-1}_{\psi\psi}\boldsymbol{I}_{\psi\mathrm{I}}]^{1/2}. \tag{4.73}$$

We may select group b as the gradient vector and group a as the step size in a normal gradient sense. This would be used in conjunction with some modification of the step size to retain the linearization of the over-all equations.

Let us now turn our attention to the *discrete-time system* in the form

$$\boldsymbol{x}(k+1) = \boldsymbol{x}(k) + \boldsymbol{h}[\boldsymbol{x}(k), \boldsymbol{u}(k)]\,\Delta t, \tag{4.74}$$

with $\boldsymbol{x}(0)$ prescribed. We have the standard performance index

$$I[\boldsymbol{x}(0), P], \tag{4.75}$$

which is to be minimized at stage P when the *single* stopping condition or final stage constraint

$$\psi[\boldsymbol{x}(P), P] = 0 \tag{4.76}$$

is satisfied. When the nonoptimal index

$$S[\boldsymbol{x}(k), k]$$

is defined as the value of I at $\psi = 0$, we have shown (Section 2.4) that the following equations result:

$$\frac{\partial S}{\partial \boldsymbol{u}(k)} = \frac{\partial \boldsymbol{h}'}{\partial \boldsymbol{u}(k)} \frac{\partial S}{\partial \boldsymbol{x}(k+1)}\,\Delta t, \tag{4.77}$$

$$\frac{\partial S}{\partial \boldsymbol{x}(k)} = \frac{\partial \boldsymbol{h}'}{\partial \boldsymbol{x}(k)} \frac{\partial S}{\partial \boldsymbol{x}(k+1)}\,\Delta t + \frac{\partial S}{\partial \boldsymbol{x}(k+1)}, \tag{4.78}$$

$$\left.\frac{\partial S}{\partial \boldsymbol{x}}\right|_{k=P} = \left[\frac{\partial I}{\partial \boldsymbol{x}} - \frac{\dot{I}}{\dot{\psi}}\frac{\partial \psi}{\partial \boldsymbol{x}}\right]_{k=P}. \tag{4.79}$$

Let us now develop a gradient procedure based on these equations; at the same time we shall choose the simplest set of formulae we can devise. To start, postulate the gradient improvement (iteration) formula

$$\boldsymbol{u}^{(j+1)}(k) = \boldsymbol{u}^{(j)}(k) + \delta\boldsymbol{u}^{(j)}(k) \tag{4.80}$$

and suggest that the change in $\boldsymbol{u}(k)$ be proportional to the rate at which S changes with $\boldsymbol{u}(k)$. In other words, using Equation (4.77), and dropping the iteration superscript for the moment,

$$\delta\boldsymbol{u}(k) = h\left[\frac{\partial \boldsymbol{h}'}{\partial \boldsymbol{u}(k)} \frac{\partial S}{\partial \boldsymbol{x}(k+1)}\right]\Delta t, \tag{4.81}$$

where h is the proportionality constant. Now if we recognize that to a first-order approximation the total change in I is the sum of all the changes over the entire control sequence, then

$$\delta I = \sum_{k=0}^{P-1} \left(\frac{\partial S}{\partial \boldsymbol{u}(k)} \right)' \delta \boldsymbol{u}(k) = h \sum_{k=0}^{P-1} \left\{ \frac{\partial \boldsymbol{h}'}{\partial \boldsymbol{u}(k)} \frac{\partial S}{\partial \boldsymbol{x}(k+1)} \right\}' \left\{ \frac{\partial \boldsymbol{h}'}{\partial \boldsymbol{u}(k)} \frac{\partial S}{\partial \boldsymbol{x}(k+1)} \right\} \Delta t^2, \tag{4.82}$$

and thus we may solve for h. Substituting this result for h and Equation (4.81) into (4.80), we obtain

$$\boldsymbol{u}^{(j+1)}(k) = \boldsymbol{u}^{(j)}(k)$$
$$+ \left[\left\{ \frac{\partial \boldsymbol{h}'}{\partial \boldsymbol{u}(k)} \frac{\partial S}{\partial \boldsymbol{x}(k+1)} \right\} \delta I \right] \Big/ \sum_{k=0}^{P-1} \left\{ \frac{\partial \boldsymbol{h}'}{\partial \boldsymbol{u}(k)} \frac{\partial S}{\partial \boldsymbol{x}(k+1)} \right\}' \left\{ \frac{\partial \boldsymbol{h}'}{\partial \boldsymbol{u}(k)} \frac{\partial S}{\partial \boldsymbol{x}(k+1)} \right\} \Delta t^2 . \tag{4.83}$$

We are now in a position to outline the discrete gradient algorithm. First, however, note that Equations (4.78) and (4.79) are equivalent to adjoint equations in the sense that $\partial S/\partial \boldsymbol{x}(k)$ is defined by Equation (4.79) at $k = P$ and that Equation (4.78) can be used to calculate $\partial S/\partial \boldsymbol{x}(k)$ in a backward direction. At the same time, a term such as $[\partial \boldsymbol{h}'/\partial \boldsymbol{u}(k)][\partial S/\partial \boldsymbol{x}(k+1)]\, \Delta t$ can also be calculated on the backward pass. Thus we set up the algorithm:

(1) Guess the control sequence $\boldsymbol{u}^{(0)}(0), \boldsymbol{u}^{(0)}(1), \ldots, \boldsymbol{u}^{(0)}(P-1)$.

(2) With these values and $\boldsymbol{x}(0)$, the sequence $\boldsymbol{x}(1), \boldsymbol{x}(2), \ldots, \boldsymbol{x}(P)$ can be evaluated from the system equation.

(3) Starting with the boundary condition at $k = P$, Equation (4.79), $(\partial S/\partial \boldsymbol{x})|_{k=P}$ is evaluated, and then with (4.78), the sequence $\partial S/\partial \boldsymbol{x}(k)$ is generated. At the same time, $[\partial \boldsymbol{h}'/\partial \boldsymbol{u}(k)][\partial S/\partial \boldsymbol{x}(k+1)]$ is also calculated.

(4) A selection for δI is made commensurate with the change desired in the performance index. Note that for steepest descent it is necessary to use $-\delta I$.

(5) All the terms are now available for the right-hand side of Equation (4.83), and a new sequence $\boldsymbol{u}^{(1)}(0), \boldsymbol{u}^{(1)}(1), \ldots, \boldsymbol{u}^{(1)}(P-1)$ can be calculated.

(6) Now the cycle starting with step (2) is continued until finally either no changes in the control sequence are observed or some other criterion is met.

This procedure can be extended to cover the case of multiple-terminal constraints or stopping conditions. Let us assume that in addition to

$$\psi[\boldsymbol{x}(P), P] = 0,$$

we also have

$$\psi_1[\boldsymbol{x}(P), P] = 0. \tag{4.84}$$

Now we have two terminal constraints; this is sufficient to show what is to be done with any number of constraints. The reader will, of course, note the correspondence to the continuous-time case, although a few words will point this out shortly.

First we redefine Equations (4.77) through (4.79) in the following way:

$$\frac{\partial S^I}{\partial \boldsymbol{u}(k)} = \frac{\partial \boldsymbol{h}'}{\partial \boldsymbol{u}(k)} \frac{\partial S^I}{\partial \boldsymbol{x}(k+1)} \Delta t, \tag{4.85}$$

$$\frac{\partial S}{\partial \boldsymbol{x}(k)} = \frac{\partial \boldsymbol{h}'}{\partial \boldsymbol{x}(k)} \frac{\partial S^I}{\partial \boldsymbol{x}(k+1)} \Delta t + \frac{\partial S^I}{\partial \boldsymbol{x}(k+1)}, \tag{4.86}$$

$$\left.\frac{\partial S^I}{\partial \boldsymbol{x}}\right|_{k=P} = \left[\frac{\partial I}{\partial \boldsymbol{x}} - \frac{\dot{I}}{\dot{\psi}} \frac{\partial \psi}{\partial \boldsymbol{x}}\right]_{k=P}, \tag{4.87}$$

where $\partial S^I/\partial \boldsymbol{x}$ indicates the effect of a change in $\boldsymbol{x}$ on the value of I at the final time. But if we interpret $\partial S^{\psi_1}/\partial \boldsymbol{x}$ as indicating the effect of a change in $\boldsymbol{x}$ on the final value of ψ_1, then by an analogous derivation we find

$$\frac{\partial S^{\psi_1}}{\partial \boldsymbol{u}(k)} = \frac{\partial \boldsymbol{h}'}{\partial \boldsymbol{u}(k)} \frac{\partial S^{\psi_1}}{\partial \boldsymbol{x}(k+1)} \Delta t, \tag{4.88}$$

$$\frac{\partial S^{\psi_1}}{\partial \boldsymbol{x}(k)} = \frac{\partial \boldsymbol{h}'}{\partial \boldsymbol{x}(k)} \frac{\partial S^{\psi_1}}{\partial \boldsymbol{x}(k+1)} \Delta t + \frac{\partial S^{\psi_1}}{\partial \boldsymbol{x}(k+1)}, \tag{4.89}$$

$$\left.\frac{\partial S^{\psi_1}}{\partial \boldsymbol{x}}\right|_{k=P} = \left[\frac{\partial \psi_1}{\partial \boldsymbol{x}} - \frac{\dot{\psi}_1}{\dot{\psi}} \frac{\partial \psi}{\partial \boldsymbol{x}}\right]_{k=P}. \tag{4.90}$$

Now, if we assume that

$$\delta \boldsymbol{u}(k) = h_1 \frac{\partial S^I}{\partial \boldsymbol{u}(k)} + h_2 \frac{\partial S^{\psi_1}}{\partial \boldsymbol{u}(k)}, \tag{4.91}$$

and in analogy to Equation (4.82),

$$\delta I = \sum_{k=0}^{P-1} \left(\frac{\partial S^I}{\partial \boldsymbol{u}(k)}\right)' \delta \boldsymbol{u}(k), \tag{4.92}$$

$$\delta \psi_1 = \sum_{k=0}^{P-1} \left(\frac{\partial S^{\psi_1}}{\partial \boldsymbol{u}(k)}\right)' \delta \boldsymbol{u}(k), \tag{4.93}$$

we obtain two simultaneous equations in h_1 and h_2,

$$\delta I = h_1 \left\{\sum_{k=0}^{P-1} \left(\frac{\partial S^I}{\partial \boldsymbol{u}(k)}\right)' \sum_{k=0}^{P-1} \frac{\partial S^I}{\partial \boldsymbol{u}(k)}\right\} + h_2 \left\{\sum_{k=0}^{P-1} \left(\frac{\partial S^I}{\partial \boldsymbol{u}(k)}\right)' \frac{\partial S^{\psi_1}}{\partial \boldsymbol{u}(k)}\right\}, \tag{4.94}$$

$$\delta \psi_1 = h_1 \left\{\sum_{k=0}^{P-1} \left(\frac{\partial S^I}{\partial \boldsymbol{u}(k)}\right)' \frac{\partial S^{\psi_1}}{\partial \boldsymbol{u}(k)}\right\} + h_2 \left\{\sum_{k=0}^{P-1} \left(\frac{\partial S^{\psi_1}}{\partial \boldsymbol{u}(k)}\right)' \sum_{k=0}^{P-1} \frac{\partial S^{\psi_1}}{\partial \boldsymbol{u}(k)}\right\}. \tag{4.95}$$

Solving Equations (4.94) and (4.95) for h_1 and h_2 and substituting into Equation (4.91) then leads to an equation for $\delta \boldsymbol{u}(k)$; once the improvements desired for $-\delta I$ and $-\delta\psi_1$ are specified, Equation (4.91) can be used to generate the next improved set of controls.

It should be kept in mind that Equation (4.74), the original discrete-time equation, is based on the use of a small value of Δt. Thus, the results of a computation of the type above can only be considered as accurate in the limit as Δt becomes small.

It may also be seen that Equation (4.84) could have been written in terms of a vector of m constraints,

$$\boldsymbol{\psi}_1[\boldsymbol{x}(P), P] = \boldsymbol{0},$$

with the result that Equations (4.94) and (4.95) would include $m + 1$ unknowns $h_1, h_2, \ldots, h_{m+1}$. (Equation (4.95) will then be a vector equation equivalent to m scalar equations.) Thus, any number of terminal constraints $m < n$ can be easily handled by using this formulation.

Although the continuous-time and discrete-time formulations seem, at first glance, to be quite different, this is not true. In fact, it is possible to show the direct connections between the two. To illustrate this point briefly, we note first that Equations (4.78) and (4.86) become equivalent to (4.54) (the adjoint equation) in the limit as $\Delta t \to 0$. In other words, the difference here is only due to the continuous or discrete nature of the equations. Second, Equation (4.82) in the form

$$\delta I = \sum_{k=0}^{P-1} \left(\frac{\partial S}{\partial \boldsymbol{u}(k)}\right)' \delta \boldsymbol{u}(k)$$

is equivalent to Equation (4.56) with $\delta t_f = 0$ and integration replaced by summation. This follows by noting the correspondence of $\boldsymbol{z}^I(t)$ to $\partial S/\partial \boldsymbol{x}(k+1)$ and $\boldsymbol{B}(t)$ to $[\partial \boldsymbol{h}'/\partial \boldsymbol{u}(k)]'$. Finally, we point out that Equations (4.81) or (4.91) result from a direct analysis of the continuous-time formulation. Thus, if we write Equation (4.68) in the form

$$\delta I = \int_0^{t_f} \{\boldsymbol{z}^{I\rho}(t)'\boldsymbol{B}(t)\delta\boldsymbol{u}(t) - \boldsymbol{\lambda}'\boldsymbol{Z}^{\psi\rho}(t)'\boldsymbol{B}(t)\delta\boldsymbol{u}(t) - \gamma\delta\boldsymbol{u}(t)'\delta\boldsymbol{u}(t)\}\, dt + \boldsymbol{\lambda}'\delta\boldsymbol{\psi} + \gamma r^2$$

and wish to extremize δI with respect to $\delta \boldsymbol{u}$, we could, as a first approximation, extremize the integrand. Differentiation of the integrand with respect to $\delta \boldsymbol{u}$ gives

$$\boldsymbol{B}'(t)\boldsymbol{z}^{I\rho}(t) - \boldsymbol{B}'(t)\boldsymbol{Z}^{\psi\rho}(t)\boldsymbol{\lambda} - 2\gamma\delta\boldsymbol{u}(t) = \boldsymbol{0}.$$

Therefore,

$$\delta\boldsymbol{u}(t) = \frac{1}{2\gamma}[\boldsymbol{B}'(t)\boldsymbol{z}^{I\rho}(t) - \boldsymbol{B}'(t)\boldsymbol{Z}^{\psi\rho}(t)\boldsymbol{\lambda}],$$

and since γ is a constant and $\boldsymbol{\lambda}$ is a constant vector, we may write

$$\delta \boldsymbol{u}(t) = h_1 \boldsymbol{B}'(t)\boldsymbol{z}^{I\rho}(t) + \boldsymbol{B}'(t)\boldsymbol{Z}^{\psi\rho}(t)\boldsymbol{h}_2 .$$

Now noting that for the discrete system $\boldsymbol{B}'(t)$ is replaced by $\partial \boldsymbol{h}'/\partial \boldsymbol{u}(k)$ and $\boldsymbol{z}$ is replaced by $\partial S/\partial \boldsymbol{x}(k+1)$, and if $\boldsymbol{\psi}$ is not a vector but a scalar ψ_1, $\boldsymbol{h}_2 = h_2$, the equation becomes

$$\delta \boldsymbol{u}(k) = h_1 \frac{\partial \boldsymbol{h}'}{\partial \boldsymbol{u}(k)} \frac{\partial S^I}{\partial \boldsymbol{x}(k+1)} + h_2 \frac{\partial \boldsymbol{h}'}{\partial \boldsymbol{u}(k)} \frac{\partial S^{\psi_1}}{\partial \boldsymbol{x}(k+1)} .$$

By rescaling h_1 and h_2, Equation (4.91) results. When $\boldsymbol{\psi}$ is not involved at all (no terminal constraints), $\boldsymbol{h}_2 = \boldsymbol{0}$, and the result is Equation (4.81). In the discrete formulation, h_1 and $\boldsymbol{h}_2$ are evaluated explicitly. However, in the continuous-time formulation, the actual forms of γ and $\boldsymbol{\lambda}$ are calculated and substituted back to yield Equation (4.69).

As we can easily see from the discrete formulation, the terminal constraint problem is handled by the projected-gradient method by solving sets of simultaneous equations. By contrast, it is possible to use a penalty-function approach, in which the augmented performance index I^* of the form of (4.14),

$$I^* = I + \tfrac{1}{2}\boldsymbol{\psi}'\boldsymbol{K}\boldsymbol{\psi},$$

is specified. The minimum of I^* is now sought without requiring any terminal constraints to be satisfied but rather by paying a penalty for deviation from the desired terminal values. Obviously, we now have the problem of appropriately adjusting the elements of $\boldsymbol{K}$ as mentioned in Section 4.3 rather than handling the simultaneous equations. This penalty-function approach has been detailed by Kelley [6], Denn [29], and Kopp and McGill [59], and in particular Kelley has suggested a convenient scheme for adjusting the elements in $\boldsymbol{K}$ as the iterations proceed.

At this time it is not clear which method, the projected-gradient or the penalty-function, is better to use. Although certain results have been obtained (see Denn [29]), these are not conclusive. At the same time, we point out the work of Rosenbaum [78], in which an interesting variation of the projected gradient is developed which greatly increases the convergence rate.

Let us now briefly explore the variations required to handle the control- or state-constrained cases. The problem here is to add conditions of the form

$$\boldsymbol{c}(\boldsymbol{x}, \boldsymbol{u}) \leq \boldsymbol{0}$$

to the previous formulation. Obviously, the approach used could involve a penalty function or a projected gradient. In the penalty-function approach, the work of Kelley [6] and Denn [29] explicitly shows how to handle the problem. As illustration, if we are concerned only with state constraints, new variables of the form

$$\dot{x}_i(t) = c_i^2 H(c_i) \tag{4.96}$$

are introduced with initial condition $x_i(0) = 0$. The c_i are the elements in $\boldsymbol{c}$, and H is the unit step function,

$$H = \begin{cases} 0, & c_i < 0, \\ 1, & c_i \geq 0. \end{cases} \tag{4.97}$$

It then follows that

$$x_i(t_f) = \int_0^{t_f} c_i^2 H(c_i)\, dt, \tag{4.98}$$

and a new augmented index is

$$I^{**} = I^* + \tfrac{1}{2} \sum k_{ii}^* x_i(t_f)^2. \tag{4.99}$$

In other words, the state constraints are handled by the penalty function by setting up new variables which convert the problem to a terminal-state type of formulation. Once again, the k_{ii}^* must be adjusted suitably as the calculation proceeds.

Turning now to the gradient-projection method for handling these types of constraints, we shall illustrate the procedure with control constraints. The analogous case for the state situation is developed by Bryson [24] and Denn [29]. Thus we note that when the constraint is reached, $\boldsymbol{c} = \boldsymbol{0}$ and

$$(\partial \boldsymbol{c}'/\partial \boldsymbol{x})'\delta \boldsymbol{x}(t) + (\partial \boldsymbol{c}'/\partial \boldsymbol{u})'\delta \boldsymbol{u}(t) = \boldsymbol{0}; \tag{4.100}$$

the linearized system Equation (4.50) in the form

$$\delta \dot{\boldsymbol{x}}(t) = (\partial \boldsymbol{f}'/\partial \boldsymbol{x})'\delta \boldsymbol{x}(t) + (\partial \boldsymbol{f}'/\partial \boldsymbol{u})'\delta \boldsymbol{u}(t)$$

becomes

$$\delta \dot{\boldsymbol{x}}(t) = \left\{ \left(\frac{\partial \boldsymbol{f}'}{\partial \boldsymbol{x}}\right)' - \left(\frac{\partial \boldsymbol{f}'}{\partial \boldsymbol{u}}\right)' \left[\left(\frac{\partial \boldsymbol{c}'}{\partial \boldsymbol{u}}\right)\left(\frac{\partial \boldsymbol{c}'}{\partial \boldsymbol{u}}\right)' \right]^{-1} \left(\frac{\partial \boldsymbol{c}'}{\partial \boldsymbol{u}}\right)\left(\frac{\partial \boldsymbol{c}'}{\partial \boldsymbol{x}}\right)' \right\} \delta \boldsymbol{x}(t). \tag{4.101}$$

Equation (4.101) is now the linearized system equation which must be satisfied if the trajectory is on the constraint $\boldsymbol{c} = \boldsymbol{0}$. Equivalent to the adjoint equations,

$$\dot{\boldsymbol{z}}(t) = -\frac{\partial \boldsymbol{f}'}{\partial \boldsymbol{x}}\, \boldsymbol{z}(t) \qquad (\boldsymbol{c} < \boldsymbol{0})$$

when not on the constraints; we now find that

$$\dot{\boldsymbol{z}}(t) = -\left\{ \frac{\partial \boldsymbol{f}'}{\partial \boldsymbol{x}} - \left(\frac{\partial \boldsymbol{c}'}{\partial \boldsymbol{x}}\right)\left(\frac{\partial \boldsymbol{c}'}{\partial \boldsymbol{u}}\right)' \left[\left(\frac{\partial \boldsymbol{c}'}{\partial \boldsymbol{u}}\right)\left(\frac{\partial \boldsymbol{c}'}{\partial \boldsymbol{u}}\right)' \right]^{-1} \left(\frac{\partial \boldsymbol{f}'}{\partial \boldsymbol{u}}\right) \right\} \boldsymbol{z}(t) \qquad (\boldsymbol{c} = \boldsymbol{0}) \tag{4.102}$$

when on a constraint. Furthermore, instead of

$$\partial H/\partial \boldsymbol{u} = \boldsymbol{0} \qquad (\boldsymbol{c} < \boldsymbol{0})$$

determining the optimal control, we now have that

$$[(\partial \boldsymbol{c}'/\partial \boldsymbol{u})(\partial \boldsymbol{c}'/\partial \boldsymbol{u})']^{-1}(\partial H/\partial \boldsymbol{u}) > \boldsymbol{0} \qquad (\boldsymbol{c} = \boldsymbol{0})$$

must be satisfied for optimal control. Obviously, $\boldsymbol{c} = \boldsymbol{0}$ is used at any time to actually specify the control itself when on a constraint. In other words, if

$c_j = u_j - u_j^d$, where u_j^d is the constraint on the jth control, $u_j = u_j^d$ is used. As a result, we have two sets of system and adjoint equations which are handled depending on $\boldsymbol{c}$. The actual implementation in a gradient procedure can now be carried out, but we shall not do so here because of the complexity of the results.

4.6. Second-variation method

The procedure to be discussed in this section is a natural evolution of the first-order linearizations of Section 4.5. In Section 4.5 we linearized the equations by truncating after all linear terms; thereby the second-order and higher-order terms were ignored. It is well known that the use of a linear approximation in a gradient search procedure is an excellent means for arriving at the neighborhood of the optimum point quickly and from almost any initial starting point. Near the optimum point, however, the linear approximation becomes deficient, and it is necessary to turn to a second-order approximation to finally achieve the optimum itself. The basic philosophy of the present *second-variation* method is much the same, because the technique is best used by first allowing the gradient method to reach close to the optimal trajectory and then switching to the second-order method for refinement. This point is more fully detailed in Example 4.5.

The pioneer work in this area has been carried out by Bryson and coworkers [18], Kelley and coworkers [55–57], Merriam [7, 69], and Jaswinski [47, 48]. In addition, Mitter [72] and Breakwell and Ho [19] have added to the work in this field. We shall first detail the approach given by Merriam and then point out in broader terms the connection between the second variation and the linear-quadratic Problem of Chapter 3. This will allow us to put the method into a neat package which can include a number of other proposed procedures, namely the *neighborhood extremal* and *quasilinearization* algorithms. We shall see that these methods determine both the *direction of correction* and the *magnitude* of the step size. Thus, the over-all iteration algorithm to convergence will be second-order. Terminal constraints may be included via the penalty-function approach or included directly in the formulation, as was done in Section 5 of this Chapter. The inclusion of trajectory control and state constraints seems only feasible via penalty functions.

The second-variation method can most simply be detailed by using the standard continuous-time model

$$\dot{\boldsymbol{x}}(t) = \boldsymbol{f}[\boldsymbol{x}(t), \boldsymbol{u}(t)], \tag{4.103}$$

with $\boldsymbol{x}(0)$ prescribed. No terminal constraints are to be imposed on $\boldsymbol{x}(t_f)$, although we specify the final time t_f. We consider the performance index to be minimized in the form

$$I[\boldsymbol{x}(0), t_f] = I = \int_0^{t_f} J(\boldsymbol{x}, \boldsymbol{u}, t)\, dt. \tag{4.104}$$

Since the performance index as given by Equation (4.104) is subject to the system constraints of Equation (4.103), we shall consider the minimization of the unconstrained performance index

$$I^* = I + \int_0^{t_f} \mathbf{z}'(\mathbf{f} - \dot{\mathbf{x}})\, dt, \tag{4.105}$$

where $\mathbf{z}$ is a vector of n Lagrange multipliers, that is,

$$I^* = \int_0^{t_f} [J(\mathbf{x}, \mathbf{u}, t) + \mathbf{z}'(\mathbf{f} - \dot{\mathbf{x}})]\, dt. \tag{4.106}$$

The problem is to construct an iteration algorithm such that

$$I^{*(j+1)} = \int_0^{t_f} [J^{(j+1)} + \mathbf{z}'^{(j+1)}(\mathbf{f}^{(j+1)} - \dot{\mathbf{x}}^{(j+1)})]\, dt \tag{4.107}$$

converges in a desirable way. The superscript $(j+1)$ is used to indicate the stage of iteration, and we wish to have

$$I^{*(0)} > I^{*(1)} > \cdots > I^{*(j)} > I^{*(j+1)} > \cdots. \tag{4.108}$$

In this section, we shall use the *second-variation method* to establish an iteration algorithm which ensures rapid convergence to the minimum value of I^*. We start by expressing the values of the functions at stage $(j+1)$ in terms of the jth iteration by means of a Taylor's series expansion. By retaining only the terms up to the second order, we get (J is a function of $\mathbf{x}$ and $\mathbf{u}$)

$$\begin{aligned} J^{(j+1)} \approx J^{(j)} &+ \left(\frac{\partial J^{(j)}}{\partial \mathbf{x}^{(j)}}\right)' \delta\mathbf{x}^{(j)} + \left(\frac{\partial J^{(j)}}{\partial \mathbf{u}^{(j)}}\right)' \delta\mathbf{u}^{(j)} \\ &+ \tfrac{1}{2}\delta\mathbf{x}^{(j)'} \frac{\partial^2 J^{(j)}}{\partial \mathbf{x}^{(j)2}} \delta\mathbf{x}^{(j)} + \delta\mathbf{u}^{(j)'} \frac{\partial^2 J^{(j)}}{\partial \mathbf{u}^{(j)}\, \partial \mathbf{x}^{(j)}} \delta\mathbf{x}^{(j)} + \tfrac{1}{2}\delta\mathbf{u}^{(j)'} \frac{\partial^2 J^{(j)}}{\partial \mathbf{u}^{(j)2}} \delta\mathbf{u}^{(j)} \end{aligned} \tag{4.109}$$

where

$$\delta\mathbf{x}^{(j)} = \mathbf{x}^{(j+1)} - \mathbf{x}^{(j)}, \qquad \delta\mathbf{u}^{(j)} = \mathbf{u}^{(j+1)} - \mathbf{u}^{(j)}. \tag{4.110}$$

In addition,

$$\frac{\partial^2 J}{\partial \mathbf{x}^2} = \begin{bmatrix} \dfrac{\partial^2 J}{\partial x_1^2} & \dfrac{\partial^2 J}{\partial x_1\, \partial x_2} & \cdots & \dfrac{\partial^2 J}{\partial x_1\, \partial x_n} \\ \vdots & & & \vdots \\ \dfrac{\partial^2 J}{\partial x_n\, \partial x_1} & & \cdots & \dfrac{\partial^2 J}{\partial x_n^2} \end{bmatrix};$$

$$\frac{\partial^2 J}{\partial \mathbf{u}\, \partial \mathbf{x}} = \begin{bmatrix} \dfrac{\partial^2 J}{\partial u_1\, \partial x_1} & \cdots & \dfrac{\partial^2 J}{\partial u_1\, \partial x_n} \\ \vdots & & \vdots \\ \dfrac{\partial^2 J}{\partial u_r\, \partial x_1} & \cdots & \dfrac{\partial^2 J}{\partial u_r\, \partial x_n} \end{bmatrix}, \tag{4.111}$$

where the superscript (j) has been omitted for clarity. We thus see that

$$\delta \boldsymbol{u}' \frac{\partial^2 J}{\partial \boldsymbol{u}\, \partial \boldsymbol{x}}\, \delta \boldsymbol{x} = \sum_{i=1}^{n} \sum_{j=1}^{r} \frac{\partial^2 J}{\partial u_j\, \partial x_i}\, \delta u_j \delta x_i, \tag{4.112}$$

but we prefer to use the matrix notation for conciseness. Next, we define the special Hamiltonian

$$\overline{H} = \boldsymbol{z}'\boldsymbol{f} \tag{4.113}$$

and expand $\overline{H}$ at the $(j+1)$st iteration up to the second-order terms as a function of $\overline{H}$ at the jth iteration (note that $\overline{H}$ is a function of $\boldsymbol{x}$, $\boldsymbol{u}$, and $\boldsymbol{z}$ and that $\partial^2 \overline{H}/\partial \boldsymbol{z}^2 = \boldsymbol{0}$),

$$\begin{aligned} \overline{H}^{(j+1)} = \overline{H}^{(j)} &+ \left(\frac{\partial \overline{H}^{(j)}}{\partial \boldsymbol{x}^{(j)}}\right)' \delta \boldsymbol{x}^{(j)} + \left(\frac{\partial \overline{H}^{(j)}}{\partial \boldsymbol{u}^{(j)}}\right)' \delta \boldsymbol{u}^{(j)} + \left[\frac{\partial \overline{H}^{(j)}}{\partial \boldsymbol{z}^{(j)}}\right]' \delta \boldsymbol{z}^{(j)} \\ &+ \tfrac{1}{2} \delta \boldsymbol{x}^{(j)\prime} \frac{\partial^2 \overline{H}}{\partial \boldsymbol{x}^{(j)2}}\, \delta \boldsymbol{x}^{(j)} + \delta \boldsymbol{u}^{(j)\prime} \frac{\partial^2 \overline{H}^{(j)}}{\partial \boldsymbol{u}^{(j)}\, \partial \boldsymbol{x}^{(j)}}\, \delta \boldsymbol{x}^{(j)} \\ &+ \tfrac{1}{2} \delta \boldsymbol{u}^{(j)\prime} \frac{\partial^2 \overline{H}^{(j)}}{\partial \boldsymbol{u}^{(j)2}}\, \delta \boldsymbol{u}^{(j)} + \delta \boldsymbol{u}^{(j)\prime} \frac{\partial^2 \overline{H}^{(j)}}{\partial \boldsymbol{u}^{(j)}\, \partial \boldsymbol{z}^{(j)}}\, \delta \boldsymbol{z}^{(j)} + \delta \boldsymbol{x}^{(j)\prime} \frac{\partial^2 \overline{H}^{(j)}}{\partial \boldsymbol{x}^{(j)}\, \partial \boldsymbol{z}^{(j)}}\, \delta \boldsymbol{z}^{(j)}. \end{aligned} \tag{4.114}$$

Next, we turn to the nonlinear system equations and note that if we linearize these equations (Taylor-series expansions to first order), the result is

$$\delta \dot{\boldsymbol{x}}^{(j)} = (\partial \boldsymbol{f}^{(j)\prime}/\partial \boldsymbol{x}^{(j)})'\, \delta \boldsymbol{x}^{(j)} + (\partial \boldsymbol{f}^{(j)\prime}/\partial \boldsymbol{u}^{(j)})'\, \delta \boldsymbol{u}^{(j)} \tag{4.115}$$

with $\delta \boldsymbol{x}(0) = \boldsymbol{0}$ since the initial conditions are constant. This last equation may be rearranged by noting that

$$\dot{\boldsymbol{x}}^{(j+1)} = \delta \dot{\boldsymbol{x}}^{(j)} + \boldsymbol{f}^{(j)}. \tag{4.116}$$

Thus Equation (4.115) can be written as

$$\dot{\boldsymbol{x}}^{(j+1)} = \boldsymbol{f}^{(j)} + \frac{\partial^2 \overline{H}^{(j)}}{\partial \boldsymbol{z}^{(j)}\, \partial \boldsymbol{x}^{(j)}}\, \delta \boldsymbol{x}^{(j)} + \frac{\partial^2 \overline{H}^{(j)}}{\partial \boldsymbol{z}^{(j)}\, \partial \boldsymbol{u}^{(j)}}\, \delta \boldsymbol{u}^{(j)}. \tag{4.117}$$

Furthermore, let us write

$$\boldsymbol{z}^{(j+1)} = \boldsymbol{z}^{(j)} + \boldsymbol{P}^{(j)} \delta \boldsymbol{x}^{(j)},$$

so that (the Riccati transformation)

$$\delta \boldsymbol{z}^{(j)} = \boldsymbol{P}^{(j)} \delta \boldsymbol{x}^{(j)}, \tag{4.118}$$

where the matrix $\boldsymbol{P}$ is defined by

$$\boldsymbol{P} = \begin{bmatrix} \dfrac{\partial z_1}{\partial x_1} & \cdots & \dfrac{\partial z_1}{\partial x_n} \\ \vdots & & \vdots \\ \dfrac{\partial z_n}{\partial x_1} & \cdots & \dfrac{\partial z_n}{\partial x_n} \end{bmatrix} = \left(\frac{\partial \boldsymbol{z}'}{\partial \boldsymbol{x}}\right)' \tag{4.119}$$

and is symmetric; that is, $\partial z_i/\partial x_j = \partial z_j/\partial x_i$. Of course $\boldsymbol{P}$ is unknown explicitly at this point. To simplify the notation, we shall omit the superscript (j) in subsequent development.

If we now define the normal Hamiltonian function

$$H = J + \boldsymbol{z}'\boldsymbol{f},$$

then the above expansions can be substituted into Equation (4.107) to yield

$$I^{*(j+1)} = I^* + \int_0^{t_f} \left\{\left(\frac{\partial H}{\partial \boldsymbol{x}}\right)' \delta\boldsymbol{x} + \left(\frac{\partial H}{\partial \boldsymbol{u}}\right)' \delta\boldsymbol{u} + \frac{1}{2}\,\delta\boldsymbol{x}'\,\frac{\partial^2 H}{\partial \boldsymbol{x}^2}\,\delta\boldsymbol{x} + \delta\boldsymbol{u}'\,\frac{\partial^2 H}{\partial \boldsymbol{u}\,\partial \boldsymbol{x}}\,\delta\boldsymbol{x} \right.$$
$$\left. + \frac{1}{2}\,\delta\boldsymbol{u}'\,\frac{\partial^2 H}{\partial \boldsymbol{u}^2}\,\delta\boldsymbol{u} + \delta\boldsymbol{u}'\,\frac{\partial \boldsymbol{f}'}{\partial \boldsymbol{u}}\,\boldsymbol{P}\delta\boldsymbol{x} + \delta\boldsymbol{x}'\,\frac{\partial \boldsymbol{f}'}{\partial \boldsymbol{x}}\,\boldsymbol{P}\delta\boldsymbol{x} - \boldsymbol{z}'\delta\dot{\boldsymbol{x}} - \delta\boldsymbol{x}'\boldsymbol{P}\delta\dot{\boldsymbol{x}}\right\} dt. \tag{4.120}$$

To this point, we have not used the canonical equations which are necessary for an optimal trajectory. To use this information, we shall go through a dynamic programming analysis leading to the Hamilton–Jacobi equation. This analysis is identical to that given in Chapter 2 leading to Equation (2.139). This, in turn, will lead to the canonical equations and, in addition, can be used for further manipulations. First, we define

$$H^0 = \min_{\boldsymbol{u}} \left[J(\boldsymbol{x}, \boldsymbol{u}, t) + \boldsymbol{z}'\boldsymbol{f}\right] = \min_{\boldsymbol{u}} [H], \tag{4.121}$$

and

$$I^0(\boldsymbol{x}, t) = \min_{\boldsymbol{u}} \int_t^{t_f} J(\boldsymbol{x}, \boldsymbol{u}, \lambda)\, d\lambda, \tag{4.122}$$

with the adjoint variable being related to I^0 by

$$\boldsymbol{z} = \partial I^0/\partial \boldsymbol{x}. \tag{4.123}$$

But from the principle of optimality in dynamic programming, it follows that

$$I^0(\boldsymbol{x}, t) = \min_{\boldsymbol{u}} \left[\int_t^{t+\Delta t} J(\boldsymbol{x}, \boldsymbol{u}, \lambda)\, d\lambda + \int_{t+\Delta t}^{t_f} J(\boldsymbol{x}, \boldsymbol{u}, \lambda)\, d\lambda\right]$$
$$= \min_{\boldsymbol{u}} \left[\int_t^{t+\Delta t} J(\boldsymbol{x}, \boldsymbol{u}, \lambda)\, d\lambda + I^0(\boldsymbol{x} + \dot{\boldsymbol{x}}\Delta t, t + \Delta t)\right].$$

As Δt approaches zero,

$$I^0(\boldsymbol{x}, t) = \min_{\boldsymbol{u}} \left[J(\boldsymbol{x}, \boldsymbol{u}, t)\Delta t + I^0(\boldsymbol{x}, t) + \left(\frac{\partial I^0}{\partial \boldsymbol{x}}\right)' \dot{\boldsymbol{x}}\Delta t + \frac{\partial I^0}{\partial t}\Delta t \right];$$

that is,

$$J^0(\boldsymbol{x}, \boldsymbol{u}^0, t) + (\partial I^0/\partial \boldsymbol{x})'\dot{\boldsymbol{x}} + (\partial I^0/\partial t) = 0, \tag{4.124}$$

which may be written as

$$\partial I^0/\partial t + H^0 = 0. \tag{4.125}$$

Equation (4.125) is the Hamilton–Jacobi partial differential equation.

The partial differentiation of Equation (4.125) with respect to $\boldsymbol{x}$ yields

$$\frac{\partial H^0}{\partial \boldsymbol{x}} + \frac{\partial^2 I^0}{\partial \boldsymbol{x}\, \partial t} = \boldsymbol{0}$$

or

$$\frac{\partial H^0}{\partial \boldsymbol{x}} + \frac{\partial \boldsymbol{z}}{\partial t} = \boldsymbol{0}. \tag{4.126}$$

However, the total time derivative of $\boldsymbol{z}$ is

$$\dot{\boldsymbol{z}} = \frac{\partial \boldsymbol{z}}{\partial t} + \left(\frac{\partial \boldsymbol{z}'}{\partial \boldsymbol{x}}\right)' \dot{\boldsymbol{x}} = -\frac{\partial J^0}{\partial \boldsymbol{x}} - \frac{\partial(\boldsymbol{z}'\boldsymbol{f})}{\partial \boldsymbol{x}} + \left(\frac{\partial \boldsymbol{z}'}{\partial \boldsymbol{x}}\right)' \dot{\boldsymbol{x}}, \tag{4.127}$$

since

$$(\partial J/\partial \boldsymbol{u}) + (\partial/\partial \boldsymbol{u})(\boldsymbol{z}'\boldsymbol{f}) = \boldsymbol{0} \tag{4.128}$$

due to the optimality condition. Expanding Equation (4.127), we get the adjoint equation, namely,

$$\dot{\boldsymbol{z}} = -(\partial J/\partial \boldsymbol{x}) - (\partial \boldsymbol{f}'/\partial \boldsymbol{x})\boldsymbol{z}. \tag{4.129}$$

If we follow the same series of steps for $\boldsymbol{P}$, noting that $\boldsymbol{P} = \partial \boldsymbol{z}'/\partial \boldsymbol{x}$, there also results

$$\dot{\boldsymbol{P}} = -(\partial^2 H/\partial \boldsymbol{x}^2) - \{\boldsymbol{P}(\partial \boldsymbol{f}'/\partial \boldsymbol{x})' + (\partial \boldsymbol{f}'/\partial \boldsymbol{x})\boldsymbol{P}\} + \boldsymbol{K}\boldsymbol{R}, \tag{4.130}$$

where

$$\boldsymbol{K} = -\partial \boldsymbol{u}'/\partial \boldsymbol{x} \tag{4.131}$$

and

$$\boldsymbol{R} = (\partial^2 H/\partial \boldsymbol{u}\, \partial \boldsymbol{x}) + (\partial \boldsymbol{f}'/\partial \boldsymbol{u})\boldsymbol{P}. \tag{4.132}$$

Equation (4.130) will be recognized as the Riccati equation encountered in Chapter 3. To evaluate $\boldsymbol{K}$, we note from Equation (4.128) that

$$(\partial J/\partial \boldsymbol{u}) + (\partial \boldsymbol{f}'/\partial \boldsymbol{u})\boldsymbol{z} = \boldsymbol{0},$$

so that differentiating with respect to $\boldsymbol{x}$ gives

$$\left(\frac{\partial \boldsymbol{u}'}{\partial \boldsymbol{x}}\right)\frac{\partial^2 J}{\partial \boldsymbol{u}^2} + \frac{\partial^2 J}{\partial \boldsymbol{x}\,\partial \boldsymbol{u}} + \left(\frac{\partial \boldsymbol{u}'}{\partial \boldsymbol{x}}\right)\sum_{i=1}^{n} z_i \frac{\partial^2 f_i}{\partial \boldsymbol{u}^2} + \sum_{i=1}^{n} z_i \frac{\partial^2 f_i}{\partial \boldsymbol{x}\,\partial \boldsymbol{u}} + \frac{\partial \boldsymbol{z}'}{\partial \boldsymbol{x}}\left(\frac{\partial \boldsymbol{f}'}{\partial \boldsymbol{u}}\right)' = \boldsymbol{0}, \quad (4.133)$$

that is,

$$(\partial \boldsymbol{u}'/\partial \boldsymbol{x})(\partial^2 H/\partial \boldsymbol{u}^2) = -\boldsymbol{R}'$$

and

$$\boldsymbol{K} = \boldsymbol{R}'(\partial^2 H/\partial \boldsymbol{u}^2)^{-1}. \quad (4.134)$$

On the basis of these new relationships, we may now write Equation (4.120) in the form

$$I^{*(j+1)} = I^* + \int_0^{t_f} \{\tfrac{1}{2}\delta \boldsymbol{u}'\boldsymbol{T}\delta \boldsymbol{u} + \boldsymbol{s}'\delta \boldsymbol{u} + \tfrac{1}{2}\delta \boldsymbol{x}'\boldsymbol{K}\boldsymbol{R}\delta \boldsymbol{x} + \delta \boldsymbol{u}'\boldsymbol{R}\delta \boldsymbol{x}\}\, dt, \quad (4.135)$$

where

$$\boldsymbol{T} = \partial^2 H/\partial \boldsymbol{u}^2, \quad (4.136)$$

$$\boldsymbol{s} = \partial H/\partial \boldsymbol{u}. \quad (4.137)$$

Let us now step back for a moment to see what all these manipulations and transformations have yielded. Starting from the nonlinear system equation and the performance index, we have used the canonical equations to yield a linear system equation, Equation (4.115), and a quadratic-type performance index, Equation (4.135). At the same time, it is necessary that the matrix $\boldsymbol{P}$ satisfy Equation (4.130). The new performance index obviously includes quadratic terms in $\delta \boldsymbol{u}$ and $\delta \boldsymbol{x}$, a mixed term in $\delta \boldsymbol{u}$ and $\delta \boldsymbol{x}$, and a term involving $\partial H/\partial \boldsymbol{u}$. To obtain the new index, we used all the necessary conditions except the minimization of the Hamiltonian; that is, we did not use $\partial H/\partial \boldsymbol{u} = \boldsymbol{0}$. If we can now solve this new problem, the result will be the solution of our original nonlinear problem (for a further discussion on this point see later parts of this section).

In order that the solution be obtained for this new problem (or the iterations converge), it is necessary that

$$I^{*(j+1)} - I^{*(j)} < 0. \quad (4.138)$$

This implies that the integral on the right-hand side of Equation (4.135) be less than zero. To assure this point and to speed the convergence, we consider the minimization of the integral

$$v(\delta \boldsymbol{x}, t) = \int_t^{t_f} \{ \qquad \qquad \} \, d\lambda, \quad (4.139)$$

where the term in brackets is the integrand of Equation (4.135). This minimization is to be carried out by the proper choice of $\delta \boldsymbol{u}$ such that

$$v^0(\delta \boldsymbol{x}, t) = \min_{\delta \boldsymbol{u}} v(\delta \boldsymbol{x}, t). \quad (4.140)$$

Since $v(\delta\boldsymbol{x}, t)$, as given by Equation (4.139), is quadratic in $\delta\boldsymbol{x}$, we may write the minimum of $v(\delta\boldsymbol{x}, t)$ as a quadratic expression,

$$v^0(\delta\boldsymbol{x}, t) = q(t) + [\boldsymbol{q}(t)]'\delta\boldsymbol{x} + \delta\boldsymbol{x}'\boldsymbol{Q}(t)\delta\boldsymbol{x}, \tag{4.141}$$

where

$$\begin{aligned} q(t) &= \text{scalar function of } t, \\ \boldsymbol{q}(t) &= (n \times 1) \text{ vector function of } t, \\ \boldsymbol{Q}(t) &= (n \times n) \text{ matrix function of } t \text{ (symmetric)}, \end{aligned}$$

and $q(t_f) = 0$, $\boldsymbol{q}(t_f) = \boldsymbol{0}$, $\boldsymbol{Q}(t_f) = \boldsymbol{0}$. From Equation (4.141),

$$\partial v^0(\delta\boldsymbol{x}, t)/\partial t = \dot{q}(t) + [\dot{\boldsymbol{q}}(t)]'\delta\boldsymbol{x} + \delta\boldsymbol{x}'\dot{\boldsymbol{Q}}(t)\delta\boldsymbol{x}, \tag{4.142}$$

and

$$[\partial v^0(\delta\boldsymbol{x}, t)]/\partial\boldsymbol{x} = \boldsymbol{q}(t) + 2\boldsymbol{Q}(t)\delta\boldsymbol{x}. \tag{4.143}$$

Now minimization of $v(\delta\boldsymbol{x}, t)$ as given by Equation (4.139) yields

$$\begin{aligned} &\tfrac{1}{2}\delta\boldsymbol{u}^{0\prime}\boldsymbol{T}\delta\boldsymbol{u}^0 + \boldsymbol{s}'\delta\boldsymbol{u}^0 + \delta\boldsymbol{u}^{0\prime}\boldsymbol{R}\delta\boldsymbol{x} + \tfrac{1}{2}\delta\boldsymbol{x}'\boldsymbol{K}\boldsymbol{R}\delta\boldsymbol{x} \\ &\qquad + [\boldsymbol{q}'(t) + 2\delta\boldsymbol{x}'\boldsymbol{Q}(t)]\delta\dot{\boldsymbol{x}} + \dot{q}(t) + [\dot{\boldsymbol{q}}(t)]'\delta\boldsymbol{x} + \delta\boldsymbol{x}'\dot{\boldsymbol{Q}}(t)\delta\boldsymbol{x} = 0, \end{aligned} \tag{4.144}$$

where

$$\delta\boldsymbol{u}^0 = -\boldsymbol{T}^{-1}\left\{\boldsymbol{s} + \boldsymbol{R}\delta\boldsymbol{x} + \frac{\partial\boldsymbol{f}'}{\partial\boldsymbol{u}}[\boldsymbol{q}(t) + 2\boldsymbol{Q}(t)\delta\boldsymbol{x}]\right\} \tag{4.145}$$

and

$$\delta\dot{\boldsymbol{x}} = (\partial\boldsymbol{f}'/\partial\boldsymbol{x})'\delta\boldsymbol{x} + (\partial\boldsymbol{f}'/\partial\boldsymbol{u})'\delta\boldsymbol{u}. \tag{4.146}$$

When the optimal control as given by Equation (4.145) is substituted into Equation (4.144) and the coefficients of $\delta\boldsymbol{x}$ and $\delta\boldsymbol{x}'\delta\boldsymbol{x}$ along with the terms not containing $\delta\boldsymbol{x}$ are put equal to zero (to satisfy the identity for any $\delta\boldsymbol{x}$), there results

$$\begin{aligned} \dot{q} = \tfrac{1}{2}\{&\boldsymbol{s}'\boldsymbol{T}^{-1}\boldsymbol{s} + \boldsymbol{s}'\boldsymbol{T}^{-1}(\partial\boldsymbol{f}'/\partial\boldsymbol{u})\boldsymbol{q} + \boldsymbol{q}'(\partial\boldsymbol{f}'/\partial\boldsymbol{u})\boldsymbol{T}^{-1}\boldsymbol{s} \\ &+ \boldsymbol{q}'(\partial\boldsymbol{f}'/\partial\boldsymbol{u})'\boldsymbol{T}^{-1}(\partial\boldsymbol{f}'/\partial\boldsymbol{u})\boldsymbol{q}\}, \end{aligned} \tag{4.147}$$

$$\begin{aligned} \dot{\boldsymbol{q}} = \boldsymbol{R}'\boldsymbol{T}^{-1}\boldsymbol{s} + \boldsymbol{R}'\boldsymbol{T}^{-1}(\partial\boldsymbol{f}'/\partial\boldsymbol{u})'\boldsymbol{q} - (\partial\boldsymbol{f}'/\partial\boldsymbol{x})'\boldsymbol{q} + 2\boldsymbol{Q}[&(\partial\boldsymbol{f}'/\partial\boldsymbol{u})'\boldsymbol{T}^{-1}\boldsymbol{s} \\ &+ (\partial\boldsymbol{f}'/\partial\boldsymbol{u})\boldsymbol{T}^{-1}(\partial\boldsymbol{f}'/\partial\boldsymbol{u})\boldsymbol{q}], \end{aligned} \tag{4.148}$$

$$\dot{\boldsymbol{Q}} = 2\{\boldsymbol{Q}(\partial\boldsymbol{f}'/\partial\boldsymbol{u})'\boldsymbol{T}^{-1}\boldsymbol{R} + \boldsymbol{Q}(\partial\boldsymbol{f}'/\partial\boldsymbol{u})'\boldsymbol{T}^{-1}(\partial\boldsymbol{f}'/\partial\boldsymbol{u})\boldsymbol{Q} - \boldsymbol{Q}(\partial\boldsymbol{f}'/\partial\boldsymbol{x})'\}. \tag{4.149}$$

At this point, we note that the matrix $\boldsymbol{Q}$ contributes only insignificantly to the control. Furthermore, $\boldsymbol{Q}$ appears as a second-order term itself. Therefore, to facilitate programming on the digital computer, we shall discard these $[n(n + 1)]/2$

equations and put $\boldsymbol{Q}$ equal to zero. Also, Equation (4.147) is not required for the evaluation of control. Therefore, Equation (4.148) will take the form

$$\dot{\boldsymbol{q}} = \boldsymbol{R}'\boldsymbol{T}^{-1}\boldsymbol{s} + \boldsymbol{R}'\boldsymbol{T}^{-1}(\partial \boldsymbol{f}'/\partial \boldsymbol{u})\boldsymbol{q} - (\partial \boldsymbol{f}'/\partial \boldsymbol{x})'\boldsymbol{q}, \tag{4.150}$$

and the change in control simplifies to

$$\delta \boldsymbol{u}^0 = -\boldsymbol{T}^{-1}[\boldsymbol{s} + \boldsymbol{R}\delta\boldsymbol{x} + (\partial \boldsymbol{f}'/\partial \boldsymbol{u})\boldsymbol{q}]. \tag{4.151}$$

To prevent overstepping in the control adjustment and to maintain the validity of the approximations used, Merriam has suggested the introduction of a constant, ε, where $0 < \varepsilon \leq 1$, into Equation (4.151) to give

$$\delta \boldsymbol{u}^0 = -\varepsilon \boldsymbol{T}^{-1}[\boldsymbol{s} + (\partial \boldsymbol{f}'/\partial \boldsymbol{u})\boldsymbol{q}] - \boldsymbol{T}^{-1}\boldsymbol{R}\delta\boldsymbol{x}. \tag{4.152}$$

Now we are in a position to detail the second-variation algorithm.

(1) Some initial guess is made for $\boldsymbol{u}(t)$.

(2) Equations (4.103) and (4.104) are integrated forward from $t = 0$ to $t = t_f$; that is, $(n + 1)$ equations are integrated forward in time, namely

$$\dot{\boldsymbol{x}} = \boldsymbol{f}(\boldsymbol{x}, \boldsymbol{u}) \qquad \text{and} \qquad \dot{I} = J(\boldsymbol{x}, \boldsymbol{u}, t).$$

(3) While the integration is carried out, the values of $\boldsymbol{x}$ are retained in the computer memory at small time intervals to approximate the continuous system.

(4) The adjoint Equation (4.129), plus the additional Equations (4.130) and (4.150) are integrated backward; that is, $2n + [n(n + 1)]/2$ equations are integrated backward in time from t_f to 0.

(5) During the backward integration, the values of $\boldsymbol{T}$, $\boldsymbol{s}$, $\boldsymbol{q}$, and $\boldsymbol{R}$ are stored in the computer memory.

(6) The new value of control is calculated from Equation (4.152), that is,

$$\boldsymbol{u}^{(j+1)} = \boldsymbol{u}^{(j)} - \left(\varepsilon \boldsymbol{T}^{-1}\left(\boldsymbol{s} + \frac{\partial \boldsymbol{f}'}{\partial \boldsymbol{u}}\boldsymbol{q}\right)\right)^{(j)} - (\boldsymbol{T}^{-1}\boldsymbol{R})^{(j)}(\boldsymbol{x}^{(j+1)} - \boldsymbol{x}^{(j)}), \tag{4.153}$$

and steps (2) through (6) are carried out again.

(7) This iteration is continued until no further change in $\boldsymbol{u}$ is noticed or until the performance index does not change (the former is more sensitive).

As a side point, we note that if the performance index increases during some iteration, the parameter ε is halved and the iteration continued. In addition, the matrices $\boldsymbol{P}$ and $\boldsymbol{T}$ must be positive-definite to assure convergence to at least a local minimum. The entire method is illustrated in detail in Example 4.5 of Section 4.8. At present, we simply state that the extra time required to integrate the additional equations is more than offset by the very rapid convergence.

Actually, the algorithm as just presented seems quite complicated, and little motivation was presented for its derivation. It thus seems appropriate to outline further material on the second variation, with special emphasis being placed on connecting this with some of the material in Chapter 3. To do this, we start with System 1 below (the linear system with a quadratic performance index),

$$\dot{\boldsymbol{x}}(t) = \boldsymbol{A}\boldsymbol{x}(t) + \boldsymbol{B}\boldsymbol{u}(t),$$
$$I[\boldsymbol{x}(0), t_f] = I = \tfrac{1}{2}\int_0^{t_f}\{\|\boldsymbol{x}(t)\|_{\boldsymbol{Q}}^2 + \|\boldsymbol{u}(t)\|_{\boldsymbol{R}}^2\}\, dt, \qquad \text{(System 1)}$$

and repeat some of the material already presented in Chapter 3. Note that we desire to select $\boldsymbol{u}(t)$ so as to minimize I subject to the system equation. We ignore here the boundary conditions on $\boldsymbol{x}(t)$, any terminal values in the state such as a term $\boldsymbol{x}(t_f)'\boldsymbol{s}\boldsymbol{x}(t_f)$ in the performance index, and consider the final time t_f to be fixed explicitly. Actually, the terminal values and a variable t_f can be included in our analysis, but it merely tends to complicate the equations and thus cover up the simple features we wish to emphasize. In particular the inclusion of the terminal values will change some of the boundary conditions we will use.

For System 1, we define the Hamiltonian

$$H = \boldsymbol{z}'[\boldsymbol{A}\boldsymbol{x} + \boldsymbol{B}\boldsymbol{u}] + \tfrac{1}{2}[\boldsymbol{x}'\boldsymbol{Q}\boldsymbol{x} + \boldsymbol{u}'\boldsymbol{R}\boldsymbol{u}], \tag{4.154}$$

where we have set $z_0 = 1$, and it follows immediately that

$$\partial H/\partial \boldsymbol{u} = \boldsymbol{B}'\boldsymbol{z} + \boldsymbol{R}\boldsymbol{u}, \qquad \partial H/\partial \boldsymbol{x} = \boldsymbol{Q}\boldsymbol{x} + \boldsymbol{A}'\boldsymbol{z}, \qquad \partial^2 H/\partial \boldsymbol{u}^2 = \boldsymbol{R},$$
$$\frac{\partial^2 H}{\partial \boldsymbol{x}^2} = \boldsymbol{Q}, \qquad \frac{\partial^2 H}{\partial \boldsymbol{x}\,\partial \boldsymbol{u}} = \boldsymbol{0}, \qquad \frac{\partial^2 H}{\partial \boldsymbol{u}\,\partial \boldsymbol{x}} = \boldsymbol{0}. \tag{4.155}$$

From the necessary conditions for optimal control, $\partial H/\partial \boldsymbol{u} = \boldsymbol{0}$, there results the feedback law of Chapter 3, namely,

$$\boldsymbol{u}^0 = -\boldsymbol{R}^{-1}\boldsymbol{B}'\boldsymbol{z}. \tag{4.156}$$

When this optimal law is substituted into the canonical equations, we obtain the free canonical equations

$$\dot{\boldsymbol{x}}(t) = \frac{\partial H}{\partial \boldsymbol{z}} = \boldsymbol{A}\boldsymbol{x} - \boldsymbol{B}\boldsymbol{R}^{-1}\boldsymbol{B}'\boldsymbol{z},$$
$$\dot{\boldsymbol{z}}(t) = -\frac{\partial H}{\partial \boldsymbol{x}} = -\boldsymbol{Q}\boldsymbol{x} - \boldsymbol{A}'\boldsymbol{z}, \tag{4.157}$$

or in more concise notation

$$\begin{bmatrix}\dot{\boldsymbol{x}}(t)\\ \dot{\boldsymbol{z}}(t)\end{bmatrix} = \begin{bmatrix}\boldsymbol{C} & \boldsymbol{D}\\ \boldsymbol{E} & -\boldsymbol{C}'\end{bmatrix}\begin{bmatrix}\boldsymbol{x}(t)\\ \boldsymbol{z}(t)\end{bmatrix} \tag{4.158}$$

where $\boldsymbol{C} = \boldsymbol{A}$; $\boldsymbol{D} = -\boldsymbol{B}\boldsymbol{R}^{-1}\boldsymbol{B}'$; and $\boldsymbol{E} = -\boldsymbol{Q}$. We also recall that to explicitly find $\boldsymbol{u}^0$ it was necessary to assume a linear relationship between $\boldsymbol{z}$ and $\boldsymbol{x}$ in Equation (4.156) (see Equation (3.55) with $\boldsymbol{S} = \boldsymbol{0}$); this led to the Riccati equation, whose final condition at $t = t_f$ was the null matrix.

Now we turn to a new system which is a slight variant on System 1, namely,

$$\dot{x}(t) = \bar{A}x(t) + Bu(t),$$
$$I[x(0), t_f] = I = \tfrac{1}{2}\int_0^{t_f} \{\|x(t)\|_{\bar{Q}}^2 + \|u(t)\|_R^2 + 2x(t)'Fu(t)\}\, dt. \qquad \text{(System 2)}$$

System 2 contains a cross-product term in the performance index with F an $(n \times r)$ matrix; in all other respects it is identical to System 1 except that we allow for a different $A(\bar{A})$ and $Q(\bar{Q})$. We proceed in exactly the same manner as with System 1 to yield the equivalent of Equations (4.154) through (4.157),

$$H = z'[\bar{A}x + Bu] + \tfrac{1}{2}[x'\bar{Q}x + u'Ru + 2x'Fu], \qquad (4.154)'$$

$$\begin{aligned} \partial H/\partial u &= B'z + Ru + F'x, \qquad \partial H/\partial x = \bar{Q}x + \bar{A}'z + Fu, \\ \partial^2 H/\partial u^2 &= R, \qquad \partial^2 H/\partial x^2 = \bar{Q}, \qquad \partial^2 H/\partial u\, \partial x = F', \end{aligned} \qquad (4.155)'$$

$$u^0 = -R^{-1}[B'z + F'x], \qquad (4.156)'$$

$$\begin{aligned} \dot{x}(t) &= (\bar{A} - BR^{-1}F')x - BR^{-1}B'z, \\ \dot{z}(t) &= [-\bar{Q} + FR^{-1}F']x + [-\bar{A}' + FR^{-1}B']z. \end{aligned} \qquad (4.157)'$$

The form of Equation (4.158) remains the same, except that for System 2

$$\begin{aligned} C &= \bar{A} - BR^{-1}F', \\ D &= -BR^{-1}B', \\ E &= -\bar{Q} + FR^{-1}F'. \end{aligned} \qquad (4.158)'$$

As expected, the results of System 2 are identical to those of System 1 when $F = 0$ is used.

Actually, System 1 can be obtained from System 2 by a simple change of variable. Thus, if we let

$$u = \bar{u} - R^{-1}F'x$$

in System 2, then we obtain System 1 in terms of $\bar{u}$.

Now the reader may ask, "What have we shown with all these manipulations?" The answer to this question will become apparent as soon as we introduce System 3 and carry out some suitable operations on it:

$$\dot{x}(t) = f[x(t), u(t)],$$
$$I[x(0), t_f] = I = \int_0^{t_f} J[x, u]\, dt. \qquad \text{(System 3)}$$

Note that System 3 uses a nonlinear system equation and a generalized integrated performance index.

For this case, we define the Hamiltonian as

$$H = z'\dot{x} + J[x, u], \qquad (4.159)$$

and define an augmented performance index I^* by attaching the constraint system equations by adjoint variables $\boldsymbol{z}(t)$:

$$I^* = I + \int_0^{t_f} (H - \boldsymbol{z}'\dot{\boldsymbol{x}})\, dt. \tag{4.160}$$

Now we do two things. First we linearize the nonlinear system equations, and second we consider a perturbation in I^* due to the perturbation $\delta\boldsymbol{u}(t)$ in $\boldsymbol{u}(t)$; in the latter case we carry out the expansion of H in the integral of Equation (4.160) to second-order terms. The perturbations are assumed to be *weak* perturbations such that $\delta\boldsymbol{u}(t)$ and the resulting $\delta\boldsymbol{x}(t)$ are both small or bounded. If the perturbations are carried out around the optimal trajectory and control, the resulting trajectories must remain in the *neighborhood* of the optimal trajectory. From these two changes we get [see Equation (4.115)]

$$\delta\dot{\boldsymbol{x}}(t) = (\partial\boldsymbol{f}'/\partial\boldsymbol{x})'\delta\boldsymbol{x} + (\partial\boldsymbol{f}'/\partial\boldsymbol{x})'\delta\boldsymbol{u}, \tag{4.161}$$

$$\begin{aligned}\delta I^* &= \int_0^{t_f} \left\{ \left[\left(\frac{\partial H}{\partial \boldsymbol{x}} \right)' + \dot{\boldsymbol{z}}' \right] \delta\boldsymbol{x} + \left(\frac{\partial H}{\partial \boldsymbol{u}} \right)' \delta\boldsymbol{u} \right\} dt \\ &\quad + \int_0^{t_f} \frac{1}{2} \left[\delta\boldsymbol{x}' \frac{\partial^2 H}{\partial \boldsymbol{x}^2} \delta\boldsymbol{x} + \delta\boldsymbol{u}' \frac{\partial^2 H}{\partial \boldsymbol{u}^2} \delta\boldsymbol{u} + 2\delta\boldsymbol{x}' \frac{\partial^2 H}{\partial \boldsymbol{x}\,\partial \boldsymbol{u}} \delta\boldsymbol{u} \right] dt. \end{aligned} \tag{4.162}$$

But if we now apply the necessary conditions for a first-order extremum (we generate an extremal curve),

$$\partial H/\partial\boldsymbol{u} = \boldsymbol{0}, \qquad \dot{\boldsymbol{z}}(t) = -\partial H/\partial\boldsymbol{x},$$

then Equation (4.162) becomes

$$\delta I^* = \frac{1}{2} \int_0^{t_f} \left[\delta\boldsymbol{x}' \frac{\partial^2 H}{\partial \boldsymbol{x}^2} \delta\boldsymbol{x} + \delta\boldsymbol{u}' \frac{\partial^2 H}{\partial \boldsymbol{u}^2} \delta\boldsymbol{u} + 2\delta\boldsymbol{x}' \frac{\partial^2 H}{\partial \boldsymbol{x}\,\partial \boldsymbol{u}} \delta\boldsymbol{u} \right] dt \tag{4.163}$$

or in more concise terms

$$\delta I^* = \frac{1}{2} \int_0^{t_f} [\delta\boldsymbol{x}' \; \delta\boldsymbol{u}'] \begin{bmatrix} \dfrac{\partial^2 H}{\partial \boldsymbol{x}^2} & \dfrac{\partial^2 H}{\partial \boldsymbol{x}\,\partial \boldsymbol{u}} \\ \dfrac{\partial^2 H}{\partial \boldsymbol{u}\,\partial \boldsymbol{x}} & \dfrac{\partial^2 H}{\partial \boldsymbol{u}^2} \end{bmatrix} \begin{bmatrix} \delta\boldsymbol{x} \\ \delta\boldsymbol{u} \end{bmatrix} dt. \tag{4.164}$$

It is important to emphasize the features of the material just covered. Starting with the full nonlinear problem and a general performance index, we have carried out a linearization of the system equations and carried terms in the index to second order. By then applying the necessary conditions for a minimum, the result is Equations (4.161) and (4.163) [or (4.164)]. This resulting set of equations must now be solved for $\delta\boldsymbol{u}^0$. As stated, this is termed the *accessory minimum problem* (see Breakwell and Ho [19], Mitter [72], Lee [64], and Athans and Falb [2]). It is apparent that every extremal yields an accessory minimum problem or, stated in a different fashion, the search for the optimal conditions starts with a determination of extremals.

The solution to this accessory minimum problem can be obtained immediately by comparing the System 2 equations with (4.161) and (4.163). We see that Equations (4.154)′ to (4.157)′ [and 4.158)′] all hold for the accessory minimization problem if we note the following correspondence.

System 2	Accessory Problem
$\bar{\boldsymbol{Q}}$	$\dfrac{\partial^2 H}{\partial \boldsymbol{x}^2}$
$\boldsymbol{R}$	$\dfrac{\partial^2 H}{\partial \boldsymbol{u}^2}$
$\boldsymbol{F}$	$\dfrac{\partial^2 H}{\partial \boldsymbol{x}\,\partial \boldsymbol{u}}$
$\bar{\boldsymbol{A}}$	$\left(\dfrac{\partial \boldsymbol{f}'}{\partial \boldsymbol{x}}\right)'$
$\boldsymbol{B}$	$\left(\dfrac{\partial \boldsymbol{f}'}{\partial \boldsymbol{u}}\right)'$
I	δI^*

Thus, we see that by a proper interpretation of the various matrices, the necessary conditions for solution of the linear system with a quadratic performance index are equivalent to those for solving the nonlinear problem via the accessory minimum problem.

Actually, this explicit correspondence leaves a few important points out. To show these, let us return to System 1 for a moment. For this case $\partial^2 H/\partial \boldsymbol{u}\,\partial \boldsymbol{x}$, $\partial^2 H/\partial \boldsymbol{x}\,\partial \boldsymbol{u} = \boldsymbol{0}$, $\partial^2 H/\partial \boldsymbol{x}^2 = \boldsymbol{Q}$ = positive semidefinite and $\partial^2 H/\partial \boldsymbol{u}^2 = \boldsymbol{R}$ = positive-definite. The requirement on $\boldsymbol{R}$ assures us of a nontrivial solution since $\boldsymbol{R}^{-1}$ exists. Further, the matrix of weighting elements in Equation (4.164) is positive-semidefinite because of $\boldsymbol{Q}$. But this means that δI^* in (4.164) is always nonnegative when System 1 is used; this is merely another way of saying that any perturbation about the optimal trajectory always leads to an increase in δI^*. This is sufficient to guarantee that for System 1 at least a locally minimum value of I is obtained. We may extend this idea directly to System 3 (or 2) and require that $\partial^2 H/\partial \boldsymbol{u}^2$ be positive-definite (equivalent to $\boldsymbol{R}$) and that

$$\frac{\partial^2 H}{\partial \boldsymbol{x}^2} - \frac{\partial^2 H}{\partial \boldsymbol{x}\,\partial \boldsymbol{u}}\left(\frac{\partial^2 H}{\partial \boldsymbol{u}^2}\right)^{-1}\frac{\partial^2 H}{\partial \boldsymbol{u}\,\partial \boldsymbol{x}}$$

be positive-semidefinite (equivalent to $\boldsymbol{Q}$). We may summarize these results by stating the necessary and sufficient conditions for the solution of the accessory minimum problem to have at least a local minimum as follows:

(1) the canonical equations
(2) $\partial H/\partial \boldsymbol{u} = \boldsymbol{0}$,
(3) $\partial^2 H/\partial \boldsymbol{u}^2$ be positive definite,
(4) $\dfrac{\partial^2 H}{\partial \boldsymbol{x}^2} - \dfrac{\partial^2 H}{\partial \boldsymbol{x}\,\partial \boldsymbol{u}}\left(\dfrac{\partial^2 H}{\partial \boldsymbol{u}^2}\right)^{-1}\dfrac{\partial^2 H}{\partial \boldsymbol{u}\,\partial \boldsymbol{x}}$ be positive semi-definite.

Statement 3 is the strengthened Legendre-Clebsh condition of the calculus of variations. Statement 4 is directly related to the controllability of the system equations; that is $(\partial \boldsymbol{f}'/\partial \boldsymbol{x})'$ and $(\partial \boldsymbol{f}'/\partial \boldsymbol{u})'$ must form a controllable pair in the nomenclature of Section 1.9. If they do not, then the Riccati equation may become unbounded (recall the solution of System 1); this in turn is related to the question of conjugate points (see Mitter [72], Lee [64], and Breakwell and Ho [19]). The point is that statement 4 is sufficient to guarantee that the system is controllable and that no conjugate points exist or that the Riccati equation is stable (bounded).

Let us now turn our attention to a specific procedure for implementing these ideas. This has been called the "successive sweep method" by McReynolds and Bryson [68]; the method is equivalent to that previously presented in this section. We shall carry out the analysis with no terminal constraints and with a fixed t_f to simplify the discussion. The important point here is that in an iterative procedure to obtain the optimal control the first necessary condition is that $\partial \bar{H}/\partial(\delta \boldsymbol{u}) \neq \boldsymbol{0}$, and Equations (4.156)′ and (4.157)′ will have the form

$$\delta \boldsymbol{u} = -\left(\frac{\partial^2 H}{\partial \boldsymbol{u}^2}\right)^{-1}\left[\frac{\partial \boldsymbol{f}'}{\partial \boldsymbol{u}}\,\delta \boldsymbol{z} + \frac{\partial^2 H}{\partial \boldsymbol{u}\,\partial \boldsymbol{x}}\,\delta \boldsymbol{x} - \frac{\partial \bar{H}}{\partial(\delta \boldsymbol{u})}\right], \tag{4.165}$$

$$\delta \dot{\boldsymbol{x}} = \boldsymbol{C}\delta \boldsymbol{x} + \boldsymbol{D}\delta \boldsymbol{z} + \left(\frac{\partial \boldsymbol{f}'}{\partial \boldsymbol{u}}\right)'\left(\frac{\partial^2 H}{\partial \boldsymbol{u}^2}\right)^{-1}\frac{\partial \bar{H}}{\partial(\delta \boldsymbol{u})}, \qquad [\delta \boldsymbol{x}(0) = \boldsymbol{0}], \tag{4.166}$$

$$\delta \dot{\boldsymbol{z}} = \boldsymbol{E}\delta \boldsymbol{x} - \boldsymbol{C}'\delta \boldsymbol{z} - \frac{\partial^2 H}{\partial \boldsymbol{x}\,\partial \boldsymbol{u}}\left(\frac{\partial^2 H}{\partial \boldsymbol{u}^2}\right)^{-1}\frac{\partial \bar{H}}{\partial(\delta \boldsymbol{u})}, \qquad [\delta \boldsymbol{z}(t_f) = \boldsymbol{0}], \tag{4.167}$$

where $\boldsymbol{C}$, $\boldsymbol{D}$, and $\boldsymbol{E}$ are as given for the accessory minimum problem and $\bar{H}$ is the Hamiltonian for the accessory minimum problem. Now we introduce the linear equation (compare to (3.48)),

$$\delta \boldsymbol{z}(t) = \boldsymbol{J}(t)\delta \boldsymbol{x}(t) + \boldsymbol{g}(t), \tag{4.168}$$

where $\boldsymbol{J}$ is a matrix function and $\boldsymbol{g}$ is a vector function of t only. Note the similarity to Equation (4.118). In fact, Equation (4.168) is the Riccati transformation [82] and is used to decouple the two-point boundary-value problem. Differentiation of Equation (4.168) yields

$$\delta\dot{z}(t) = \dot{J}(t)\delta x(t) + J(t)\delta\dot{x}(t) + \dot{g}(t), \tag{4.169}$$

and substituting Equation (4.168) into (4.166) gives

$$\delta\dot{x}(t) = (C + DJ)\delta x + Dg + \left(\frac{\partial f'}{\partial u}\right)'\left(\frac{\partial^2 H}{\partial u^2}\right)^{-1}\frac{\partial \overline{H}}{\partial(\delta u)}. \tag{4.170}$$

Thus Equation (4.169) becomes

$$\delta\dot{z}(t) = (\dot{J} + JC + JDJ)\delta x + JDg + J\left(\frac{\partial f'}{\partial u}\right)'\left(\frac{\partial^2 H}{\partial u^2}\right)^{-1}\frac{\partial \overline{H}}{\partial(\delta u)} + \dot{g}. \tag{4.171}$$

Now equating Equations (4.171) and (4.167) yields

$$(\dot{J} + JC + JDJ)\delta x + JDg + J\left(\frac{\partial f'}{\partial u}\right)'\left(\frac{\partial^2 H}{\partial u^2}\right)^{-1}\frac{\partial \overline{H}}{\partial(\delta u)} + \dot{g}$$
$$= (E - C'J)\delta x - C'g - \frac{\partial^2 H}{\partial x\,\partial u}\left(\frac{\partial^2 H}{\partial u^2}\right)^{-1}\frac{\partial \overline{H}}{\partial(\delta u)}. \tag{4.172}$$

But if Equation (4.172) must hold for any $\delta x(t)$, it is necessary that the coefficients become zero, and thus

$$\dot{J} = -C'J - JC - JDJ + E \qquad [J(t_f) = 0], \tag{4.173}$$

$$\dot{g} = -(C' + JD)g - J\left(\frac{\partial f'}{\partial u}\right)'\left(\frac{\partial^2 H}{\partial u^2}\right)^{-1}\frac{\partial \overline{H}}{\partial(\delta u)} - \frac{\partial^2 H}{\partial x\,\partial u}\left(\frac{\partial^2 H}{\partial u^2}\right)^{-1}\frac{\partial \overline{H}}{\partial(\delta u)},$$
$$g(t_f) = 0, \tag{4.174}$$

and from Equations (4.165) and (4.168),

$$\delta u = -\left(\frac{\partial^2 H}{\partial u^2}\right)^{-1}\left[\left(\frac{\partial^2 H}{\partial u\,\partial x} + \frac{\partial f'}{\partial u}J\right)\delta x + \frac{\partial f'}{\partial u}g - \frac{\partial \overline{H}}{\partial(\delta u)}\right]. \tag{4.175}$$

Note that Equation (4.173) is the Riccati equation of the type encountered in Chapter 3. This equation would be expected as part of the solution of the accessory minimization problem.

Now we are in a position to outline the specific algorithm. It takes the following steps:

(1) Make an initial guess at the control function $u(t)$, and using the system equation calculate $x(t)$ at small time intervals and store them in computer memory.

(2) Integrate the adjoint equation backward from $t = t_f$ to $t = 0$. During this pass, evaluate $\partial H/\partial u$, $\partial^2 H/\partial u^2$, $(\partial^2 H/\partial u^2)^{-1}$, $\partial^2 H/\partial u\,\partial x$, and $\partial^2 H/\partial x^2$.

(3) At the same time as step (2), Equations (4.173) and (4.174) may be integrated backward. In addition, the equation

$$\partial \bar{H}/\partial(\delta \boldsymbol{u}) = k_{11}(\partial H/\partial \boldsymbol{u}) \tag{4.176}$$

may be evaluated, where k_{11} is a step-size parameter.

(4) Calculate $\delta \boldsymbol{u}$ from Equation (4.175) and repeat the entire cycle until $\partial H/\partial \boldsymbol{u} = \boldsymbol{0}$. When this attained, the optimal trajectory is known. A careful comparison of this algorithm and that previously outlined for the second variation will show the identical features. Further, we note that major portions of the ASP program mentioned in Chapter 3 can be used to solve the current problem.

The *neighboring extremal* method of Breakwell, et al [18] represents a variation on the method just discussed, in which the free canonical equations are used with $\partial \bar{H}/\partial(\delta \boldsymbol{u}) = \boldsymbol{0}$ [see Equations (4.165) through (4.167)]. Since these equations are linear and the conditions $\delta \boldsymbol{x}(0)$ and $\delta \boldsymbol{z}(t_f)$ are known, the authors develop a procedure for guessing at $\boldsymbol{z}(0)$ and, by solving the free canonical equations, generate an improvement $\delta \boldsymbol{z}(0)$. This is continued until the correct $\boldsymbol{z}(0)$ is obtained for the original nonlinear problem. This may be viewed as a second-order extension of those methods discussed in Section 4.4 of this Chapter.

For further interesting details on this method, the reader is referred to the above-listed articles. Of particular importance is the discussion of conjugate points, a condition whereby the Riccati equation is unbounded and does not converge to a local optimum and the discussion on how to ensure that $\partial^2 H/\partial \boldsymbol{u}^2$ is positive.

4.7. Alternative methods of interest

In the previous sections of this chapter, we have presented a number of methods for handling the nonlinear control problem. These particular methods have been detailed because they are currently in favor with many investigators. However, there also exist a number of alternative approaches, which may or may not turn out to be superior to the methods discussed. Thus, the function of the current section is to point out the broad features of certain of these alternative methods.

In particular, we shall mention the work of Larson [60, 61] and of Daly [26] as variations on the dynamic programming approach; the work of Lasdon [62], which involves the optimization of subsets of the over-all system; the use of nonlinear programming; and finally a technique called quasi-linearization. It should be pointed out that the cursory treatment given to these various methods does not imply a lack of confidence in them but rather a lack of experience in the versatility of their usage.

We have already pointed out the manifold advantages to the use of dynamic programming for optimal control calculations, namely, the generation of entire families of optimal trajectories subject to terminal and to trajectory control and state constraints. Unfortunately, the storage requirements as a function of the number of state variables limit the usefulness of the method. It would thus seem obvious that if some variation on the procedure given in Chapter 2 can be used to overcome the state-dimensionality problem, it might open the entire area of optimal control calculations. One such variation is due to Larson [60, 61] and is called *dynamic programming with continuous independent variable.* In normal dynamic programming the continuous-time system model

$$\dot{\boldsymbol{x}}(t) = \boldsymbol{f}[\boldsymbol{x}(t), \boldsymbol{u}(t)] \tag{4.177}$$

is rewritten in discrete form as

$$\boldsymbol{x}(t + \Delta t) = \boldsymbol{h}[\boldsymbol{x}(t), \boldsymbol{u}(t), \Delta t]. \tag{4.178}$$

When Δt is fixed at some value, Equation (4.178) may be considered as

$$\boldsymbol{x}(k+1) = \boldsymbol{h}[\boldsymbol{x}(k), \boldsymbol{u}(k)] \qquad (k = 0, 1, 2, \ldots). \tag{4.179}$$

With this discrete equation, the dynamic programming algorithm is used to generate the optimal tables, with each table spaced Δt time units apart. Larson suggested, however, adding one more degree of freedom to the calculation by allowing Δt to float freely and to be determined subject to certain criteria in the calculation; in fact, the Δt is determined as the time required for at least one state variable to change by one increment. In other words, instead of fixing Δt and varying the states as in conventional dynamic programming, one of the states is fixed and the time interval is calculated to give a certain change in this particular state. The important feature here is that only neighborhood points need be considered in building up the dynamic programming tables.

To point out some of the features, we shall use a simple example, namely, a single state and control variable connected by the system equation

$$\dot{x}(t) = Ku(t), \qquad x(0) \qquad \text{prescribed.} \tag{4.180}$$

In addition, there exists some performance index which we can take as

$$I[x(0), t_f] = I[x(t_f), t_f]. \tag{4.181}$$

First, we note that we may write Equation (4.180) in the form

$$\delta x(t)/\delta t = Ku(t)$$

or as

$$\delta t = |\delta x(t)/Ku(t)|. \tag{4.182}$$

It follows that for some conveniently fixed value of $\delta x(t)$, a corresponding δt can be calculated which satisfies the system equation in discrete form.

Now let us break the two-dimensional region xt_f into a set of rectangular blocks with each block covering an area $j\,\delta x$ of x by T units of t, where j is a small integer and T is considerably larger than the values of δt determined by

Equation 4.182. A typical such block is shown in Figure 4.1, which is bounded by 5 δx to 8 δx in the state side and is $1T$ long. This block is one of the entire series of blocks which completely cover the xt_f-domain. Ignoring for the moment the calculations leading into this block, we see in Figure 4.1 that there are a number of vectors $\boldsymbol{p}(0), \ldots, \boldsymbol{p}(3)$ (indicated by the small circles) which define the optimal trajectory calculation up to the current block. Each vector has elements x, t, u^0, I^0; in other words, each point indicates the state, the time, the optimal control to use, and the resulting optimal performance index. Now we seek to continue the calculation backward to generate a sequence of new optimal points.

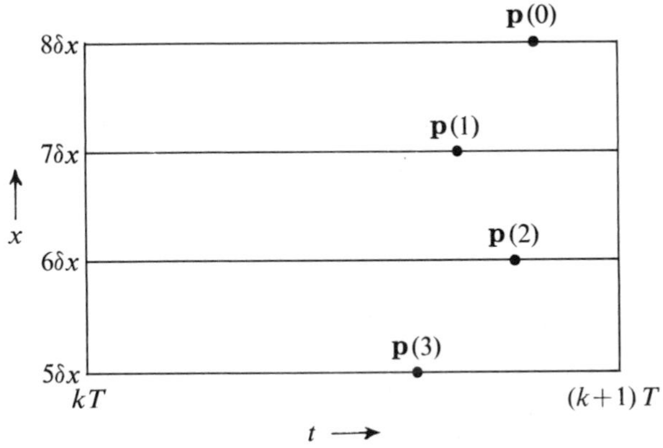

FIGURE 4.1. Two-dimensional block with initial set of optimal points

To start, we pick $\boldsymbol{p}(2)$, since of the points within the block (not on the boundary) it has the largest time associated with it; call this point $\boldsymbol{p}^*$ with time t^*. We now desire to calculate a new optimal point at the state of $\boldsymbol{p}^*$ but at a time $t < t^*$ [a state on the same line, 6 δx, but to the left of $\boldsymbol{p}(2)$]. Before determining this new point, we must specify the allowable controls which, for simplicity, we take as

$$u(t) = \begin{cases} u(1), \\ u(-1). \end{cases} \tag{4.183}$$

Equation (4.183) merely says that the allowable control is only $u(1)$ or $u(-1)$; any number of allowable controls could be used here, but it would only complicate the discussion. But from Equation (4.182) we see that

$$\delta t(1) = \left| \frac{\delta x}{Ku(1)} \right|, \tag{4.184}$$

$$\delta t(-1) = \left| \frac{\delta x}{Ku(-1)} \right|, \tag{4.185}$$

where $\delta t(1)$ corresponds to using the control $u(1)$ and $\delta t(-1)$ corresponds to using $u(-1)$. Immediately we can say that if the control $u(1)$ is applied to the state corresponding to $\boldsymbol{p}^*$ at the time $t(1) = t[\boldsymbol{p}(1)] - \delta t(1)$, the result will be a trajectory ending after $\delta t(1)$ units at $\boldsymbol{p}(1)$; the same type of result holds for $u(-1)$ and $t(-1)$, as shown in Figure 4.2. Both new circled points have the same state as $\boldsymbol{p}^*$, with the one starting at the time $t(1)$ passing to the state $\boldsymbol{p}(1)$ in $\delta t(1)$ time units, and the other starting at the time $t(-1)$ passing to the state $\boldsymbol{p}(3)$ in $\delta t(-1)$ time units. Obviously, each changes the state by one increment, but the changes occur over different time increments.

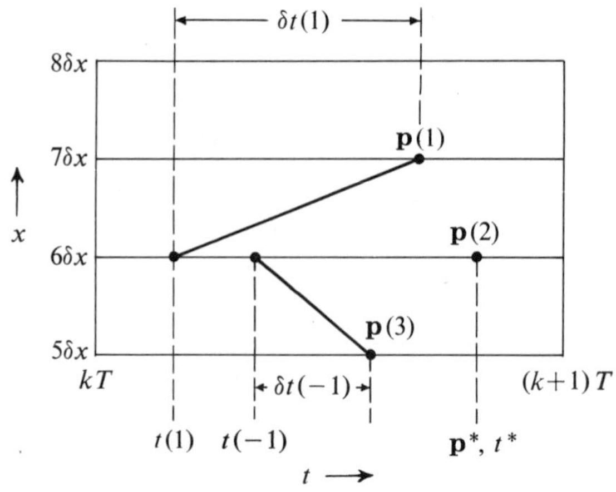

FIGURE 4.2. Generation of a new optimal point

The question now to be answered is, "Which point is better?" This may be settled by evoking the principle of optimality, that is, determining whether the "cost" of going from the state at $t(-1)$ to $\boldsymbol{p}(3)$ plus the cost of going from $\boldsymbol{p}(3)$ to the state at t_f (as given by $I[\boldsymbol{p}(3)]$) is less than or greater than the corresponding path $t(1)$ to $\boldsymbol{p}(1)$ to the state at t_f. Once this calculation has been carried out we find, for example, that the state at $t(1)$ is better; this is a new optimal point at the state $\boldsymbol{p}^*$ and time $t(1)$.

Now we repeat the same type of calculation, but on the $7\,\delta x$ line since it now has the largest time increment of the three points $\boldsymbol{p}(1)$, $\boldsymbol{p}(3)$, and $\boldsymbol{p}[t(1)]$. This is continued until at least one optimal point has been computed at each state, but in the block to the left of the current block. When this occurs, the current block is done and we are ready to process the new block (the one to the left of the current one) in exactly the same manner.

In this way we use block after block until time zero is finally reached. We now have a complete set of optimal points which may be used in a forward direction to recover the optimal trajectory. The start of the entire calculation would, of course, be merely to take the right-most block and to specify $I[\mathbf{x}(t_f), t_f]$ at each state within the block.

It is important to note that when one block is completed, all the optimal points generated within that block can be removed from the main computer memory and sent to any auxiliary storage desired, that is, a tape unit. In fact, at no time do we need to retain any more storage than when we enter the computations of a block (as we generate a new point, we can remove the old optimal point from the main computer memory). The feature here is that large values of δt are used with small increments in the state variable (only 2 δx in the present case) rather than for small values of δt and a large number of δx, as in conventional dynamic programming.

It is this type of procedure which, when applied to higher dimensional problems, makes the method so promising in terms of lowered storage requirements. Thus Larson details the three-stage variable problem with 100 levels in each state; by conventional dynamic programming the storage requirements are $(100)^3 = 10^6$ storage locations. By contrast, the method of the continuous independent variables requires storage only in the hundreds.

Obviously, our discussion here has been much too brief to really appreciate the computational procedure. The interested reader should consult the primary references above. However, it should be pointed out that the method requires approximately the same computational time as in conventional dynamic programming (for problems where conventional dynamic programming can be used); it is the storage saving which is important and *not* the computing time. At the same time, the chemical engineer who is frequently confronted with systems with a fixed number of physical stages (not time stages) should realize that such a physical situation is not amenable to the current approach. In other words, one cannot specify fractional stages, as the present method requires.

There does exist one further important difference between the current method and conventional dynamic programming. In conventional dynamic programming, the interpolations are carried out in the state direction, that is, interpolation is always between states for a fixed time value. By contrast the present method interpolates in the time direction while holding the state fixed. In an xt-diagram, this can be interpreted as either interpolating in a vertical or a horizontal direction. It would thus be expected that certain functions would be handled with one method better than with the other; the inverse situation also applies. However, to date, little experience has been gained with the current method, and it is impossible to predict the applicability of the method.

As another variation on the standard dynamic programming procedure, we mention the work of Daly [26] called *conformal grid updating*. This method involves a rotation of the state coordinate system under investigation to include those trajectories which are physically realizable, plus a refinement of the grid spacing to improve the trajectory. In other words, a very rough loose grid of points is used to first obtain a normal dynamic programming trajectory (the number of points $x_1, x_2, \ldots, x_N$ is kept quite small). Once this trajectory is known, it is possible to transform the bounds on the states to follow the curvature of the approximately optimal trajectory. Within these new bounds, an equivalent set of state points can be located.

Now, if the dynamic programming analysis is repeated for the new set of points, the grid may thereby be distorted again in order that it continue to conform to the shape of the best known estimate of the optimal policy. The upper and lower boundaries of the grid will always be defined such that the estimated optimal path is midway between them. For a grid of a given resolution, a situation is reached beyond which further distortion of the grid is unnecessary.

At this point, the resolution of the grid is increased. Since it is known that the grid conforms to the shape of the best known optimal policy, in increasing the resolution of the grid, it is reasonable to simply consider as new boundaries a set of states only half as far from the best known optimum path as the old ones were.

This procedure is continued to any desired resolution of grid. The result obtained is then the optimal trajectory within the constraints of the grid resolution used. In this way, only a limited number of discrete values of any state variable need be used, although the dynamic programming algorithm is repeated over and over. Computational experience with two- and three-variable problems using this method has been quite promising.

Another interesting and possibly quite important technique is due to Lasdon [62] and is called multilevel optimization. Lasdon developed the material primarily for steady-state staged systems but Takahara [85] has indicated the necessary extensions to time-operating control systems of the type we have been considering here. The basic hypothesis behind the multilevel approach is quite simple, and yet quite elegant. Given a normal type of time-staged control system, the first level of the computation is to break or cut the time stages into independent subsystems; a new performance index is then defined for each subsystem. On this basis each subsystem may be optimized, that is, the optimal control selected corresponding to the new performance index.

Obviously, it is now necessary to devise some algorithm for matching the inputs and outputs from the subsystems so that in the limit the output from stage k is the input to stage $k + 1$. Lasdon calls this portion of the over-all technique the second level of computation and develops the necessary iterative procedure. The algorithm itself is quite simple, and it can be shown to converge in a global sense and to be amenable to handling all types of inequality constraints.

As can be visualized by this brief discussion, the multilevel procedure bears certain similarities to dynamic programming in the sense that a "single" time stage is handled rather than all p time stages simultaneously. This work may prove quite fruitful for handling the nonlinear control problem of the present chapter.

In Chapter 3 we illustrated the versatility of using the linear programming concept for evaluating the optimal control of linear systems with constrained control and even constrained states. The resulting procedure led to the use of available computer programs and was able to generate optimal trajectories with a minimum of computer time. In this case, the problem was to extremize the performance index subject to the linear system equations and any other system constraints. If, instead, the system equations are nonlinear, one may visualize the problem as extremizing the performance index subject to the nonlinear system equations and the system constraints. But this latter formulation is what is usually called a *nonlinear programming* problem; since there are available computer programs for such problems, it seems natural to consider the use of this technique.

To date, this approach has been applied by Ho [43–45], Ringlee [75], and Rosen [76]. Thus, Rosen has shown that if the constraints and the system equations taken together determine a closed, convex, and bounded set, and if the controls are linear in the system equation, the nonlinear programming algorithm will yield the minimum value of I; furthermore, he has shown that certain conditions may be stated which are both necessary and sufficient so that the control resulting is the optimal control.

As illustration, Rosen used a discrete system with four state variables and with variable coefficients (nonautonomous) having the following features:

(1) $I = \mathbf{x}'(t_f)\mathbf{x}(t_f)$,

(2) terminal state constraints, $x_3(t_f) = x_4(t_f) = 0$,

(3) state constraints, $|x_4(t)| \leq \frac{1}{2}$, $0 \leq t \leq t_f$,

(4) control constraints, $|u(t)| \leq 1$.

This is similar to a system used by Ho, except that Ho treated an autonomous system. As the reader can see, this system includes most of the difficulties that we had considered in previous sections. The solution obtained by Rosen required about 2 min of computing time on an IBM 7090, an extremely short period for the problem under consideration. There is no question that this approach will prove most feasible for a variety of problems.

The final method that we wish to briefly mention is called *quasi-linearization* by Bellman and Kalaba [4] or alternatively the *generalized Newton–Raphson* method by McGill, Kopp, and Kenneth [59, 67] (see also [66, 84]). This procedure bears a marked resemblance to the second variation method, except that an additional degree of freedom is obtained in the calculation by not requiring that the differential and adjoint constraint equations be satisfied until the iteration converges. Viewed in another context, the method is an extension of the Newton–Raphson method for finding the root of a scalar function $f(x)$ [67]. In the scalar formulation, the root is found for $f(x) = 0$ by iterating an equation such as

$$\frac{df(x^{(j)})}{dx}[x^{(j+1)} - x^{(j)}] + f[x^{(j)}] = 0, \tag{4.186}$$

where j indicates the iteration step. In the present case, we have a continuous-time vector system

$$\dot{\boldsymbol{x}}(t) = \boldsymbol{f}[\boldsymbol{x}(t), \boldsymbol{u}(t)], \tag{4.187}$$

with boundary conditions such as

$$\begin{aligned} x_i(0) &= a_i \qquad (i = 1, 2, \ldots, m), \\ x_i(t_f) &= b_i \qquad (i = m+1, \ldots, n). \end{aligned} \tag{4.188}$$

Equation (4.188) comprises partial initial state specification and a set of terminal constraints, the sum specifying n conditions. Let us assume that we have the jth approximation to the optimal trajectory $\boldsymbol{x}(t)$; the $(j+1)$st approximation is then obtained by expanding Equation (4.187) in a Taylor series and retaining only the linear terms in analogy to Equation (4.186), that is,

$$\dot{x}_i^{(j+1)} \approx f_i(\boldsymbol{x}^{(j)}, \boldsymbol{u}^{(j)}) + \sum_{k=1}^{n} \left[(x_k^{(j+1)} - x_k^{(j)}) \left. \frac{\partial f_i}{\partial x_k} \right|_{\boldsymbol{x}=\boldsymbol{x}^{(j)}} \right] \qquad (i = 1, 2, \ldots, n). \tag{4.189}$$

But Equation (4.189) now represents a set of linear ordinary differential equations (linear in $x_i^{(j+1)}$), and thus the solution can be obtained as the sum of the particular solution plus the sum of weighted homogeneous solution. To obtain this solution, we set $f_i(\boldsymbol{x}^{(j)}, \boldsymbol{u}^{(j)}) = 0$ and $x_i^{(j)} = 0$, solve Equation (4.189) n times subject to $x_k^{(j+1)}(0) = 1$, $x_i(0) = 0$, $i \neq k$, where $k = 1, 2, \ldots, n$; the result is n homogeneous solutions. We denote these homogeneous solutions as h_i^k, $k = 1, 2, \ldots, n$. The particular solution, denoted as p_i, is obtained by solving Equation (4.189) with $x_i^{(j+1)} = 0$. The weighting constants for the homogeneous solutions are then found by solving the algebraic equations

$$p_i(0) + \sum_{k=1}^{n} c_k h_i^k(0) = a_i \qquad (i = 1, 2, \ldots, m),$$

$$p_i(t_f) + \sum_{k=1}^{n} c_k h_i^k(t_f) = b_i \qquad (i = m+1, \ldots, n).$$

This procedure thus yields a new trajectory $\boldsymbol{x}^{(j+1)}(t)$ and if continued, convergence yields the optimal trajectory $\boldsymbol{x}^0(t)$. As an initial approximation, one may take (from among many possibilities)

$$x_i^{(0)}(t) = \begin{cases} a_i & (i = 1, 2, \ldots, m), \\ b_i & (i = m+1, \ldots, n). \end{cases}$$

Actually, as detailed above there is no way to really know if the trajectory obtained is the optimal one and, further, to recover the control which yields the optimal trajectory. Thus, we define the Hamiltonian and the adjoint equations; when these are carried along with the main calculation, we may use $\partial H/\partial \boldsymbol{u} = \boldsymbol{0}$ as the criterion for the unconstrained optimal trajectory and to recover $\boldsymbol{u}^0(t)$.

It is important to note that in terms of the specifications in Section 4.1, quasi-linearization essentially fixes the boundary condition and the performance index or the minimum Hamiltonian condition and iterates on the system dynamic equations [fixes subsets (2) and (3) and iterates on subset (1)]. Convergence to the optimal trajectory is second-order. Numerical results applied to chemical engineering problems are shown by Lee [64] and Rothenberger [80]. McGill and Kenneth [67] give perhaps the clearest and most detailed discussion of the algorithm.

The work of Rothenberger illustrates some of the advantages and disadvantages of quasi-linearization. On the positive side, the method seems capable of handling moderate dimensionality in the state and including, via penalty functions, state trajectory constraints. The initial guess used in the iteration is not crucial and the algorithm converges quickly and with a minimum of computer time. On the negative side, however, there is a tendency for the linearized systems to exhibit a decided spread in eigenvalues. This, in turn, leads to marked instabilities in the adjoint equations; this effect is most pronounced when t_f is large. When this instability occurs, even the most sophisticated methods for solving the linear equations eventually make convergence of the quasi-linearization algorithm impossible.

As mentioned above, the quasi-linearization algorithm bears a marked resemblance to those previously developed for the second variation. To show this, we start with the necessary conditions and linearize around a nominal $\bar{\boldsymbol{x}}(t)$ and $\bar{\boldsymbol{u}}(t)$ (see Mitter [72] and Schley and Lee [82]):

$$\delta\dot{\boldsymbol{x}} = \left(\frac{\partial \boldsymbol{f}'}{\partial \boldsymbol{x}}\right)'\delta\boldsymbol{x} + \left(\frac{\partial \boldsymbol{f}'}{\partial \boldsymbol{u}}\right)'\delta\boldsymbol{u} + \bar{\boldsymbol{f}} - \dot{\bar{\boldsymbol{x}}}; \qquad \delta\boldsymbol{x}(0) = \boldsymbol{0}, \tag{4.190}$$

$$\delta\dot{\boldsymbol{z}} = -\frac{\partial^2 \overline{H}}{\partial \boldsymbol{x}^2}\delta\boldsymbol{x} - \frac{\partial^2 \overline{H}}{\partial \boldsymbol{x}\,\partial \boldsymbol{u}}\delta\boldsymbol{u} - \frac{\partial \bar{\boldsymbol{f}}'}{\partial \boldsymbol{x}}\delta\boldsymbol{z} - \frac{\partial \overline{H}}{\partial \boldsymbol{x}} - \dot{\bar{\boldsymbol{z}}}; \qquad \delta\boldsymbol{z}(t_f) = \boldsymbol{0},$$

$$\frac{\partial \overline{H}}{\partial \boldsymbol{u}} + \frac{\partial^2 \overline{H}}{\partial \boldsymbol{u}^2}\delta\boldsymbol{u} + \frac{\partial^2 \overline{H}}{\partial \boldsymbol{u}\,\partial \boldsymbol{x}}\delta\boldsymbol{x} + \frac{\partial \boldsymbol{f}'}{\partial \boldsymbol{u}}\delta\boldsymbol{z} = \boldsymbol{0}. \tag{4.191}$$

The reader may wish to confirm that, except for not satisfying the system and adjoint equations, Equations (4.190) and (4.191) are equivalent to those in the second variation method. On this basis, it might prove computationally more feasible to use the Riccati transformation to solve this problem than the method outlined above. In fact, this may tend to remove some of the disadvantages of the method just mentioned.

4.8. Numerical examples

In this section we shall illustrate the use of the various techniques detailed in Sections 4.1 through 4.7 for solving multidimensional nonlinear control systems. In general, we shall follow the order used in presenting the different methods.

EXAMPLE 4.1 ▪ In this first example, we shall detail a simple combinatorial problem which automatically requires the use of an iteration sequence. The problem has been called the *routing problem* by Bellman [3, 9], although the concepts can be extended to many topological networks consisting of interconnecting nodes. The problem has also been used by Bellman and Kalaba [10] to define the kth best policies or, alternatively, an appropriate series of suboptimal policies.

We consider a set of P cities with every two cities linked by a connecting road. Associated with every ith and jth city is a positive scalar number t_{ij} representing the time to travel along the connecting road from city i to city j. Because of road conditions, t_{ij} need not be proportional to the length of the road, and furthermore t_{ij} need not be equal to t_{ji}; that is, it may require different time to travel from city i to city j than in the reverse direction. Starting at any of the cities, we ask to find that route to the Pth city which requires the minimum amount of time.

As a simple extension on this problem, we also could specify that certain cities are not connected. But this merely implies that the connection i to j is inadmissible, and for this particular combination we set t_{ij} equal to a very large number. Computationally, this will preclude the path i to j.

Obviously, there are only a finite number of paths possible for the P cities, and one might suggest a direct or enumerative approach in which all of the possible paths are scanned. For P a large number, however, this is impossible because of the fantastic number of possible combinations. Instead, we turn to dynamic programming which has proved worth while previously in replacing the direct enumeration problems. Thus we define

$I^0(i, P) =$ the time required to travel from the ith city to the Pth city by an optimal (minimum routing time) path

or, to simplify the nomenclature,

$$I^0(i, P) = I_i^0.$$

It is immediately apparent that

$$I_P^0 = 0, \tag{4.192}$$

since it requires zero time to start at the Pth city and travel to the Pth city.

Now we observe that if we start at the ith city and choose to go directly to the jth city, the remainder of the route, j to P, must be selected so as to minimize the remaining time. Stated in equation form, this means that

$$I_i^0 = \min_{j \neq i} \{t_{ij} + I_j^0\} \qquad (i = 1, 2, \ldots, P-1). \tag{4.193}$$

At this point it looks as if we have the dynamic programming recurrence relationship, Equation (4.193), and a starting point, Equation (4.192), and thus we may proceed to use same in the normal fashion. Unfortunately, a little reflection indicates that this is not true because I_i^0 actually exists on both sides of Equation (4.193). In other words, the trip from city j to P may involve passage through city i; but the path from city i is what the left-hand side of Equation (4.193) involves. Thus I_i^0 is implied in I_j^0. If the problem has been phrased to preclude a path back to itself,

$$I_i^0 = \min_{i<j} \{t_{ij} + I_j^0\},$$

then this difficulty would not occur (this nonreturn to the ith city is analogous to our normal type of sequential control problem). We also note that because we have chosen the t_{ij} to be all positive constants, we prevent the possibility of an internal looping between some of the cities which might prevent ever getting to city P. It should be relatively obvious to the chemical engineer that the main problem formulated is equivalent to recycle in a process system.

Since the unknown function occurs on both sides of the recurrence relationship, this relationship is of little use to us in its explicit form; instead, we must turn to some iterative variation. Bellman has suggested two such procedures which we shall detail below; Bentley and Cooke [12] have extended the analysis considerably.

In each iterative procedure suggested by Bellman, the recurrence relationship is rewritten in the form

$$\begin{aligned} I_i^{(k)} &= \min_{j \neq i}[t_{ij} + I_j^{(k-1)}], \\ I_P^{(k)} &= 0 \qquad (i = 1, 2, \ldots, P-1), \end{aligned} \tag{4.194}$$

where (k) indicates the iterative step; $I_i^{(0)}$ will represent the initial estimates in the iteration, and it is the particular choice of these starting values which differentiates the two methods. In each case, he has shown that the sequence $I_i^{(k)}$ will converge to a unique I_i^0 in monotonic fashion.

As a first selection of the initial estimates, we may take

$$\begin{aligned} I_i^{(0)} &= t_{iP}, \\ I_P^{(0)} &= 0 \qquad (i = 1, 2, \ldots, P-1). \end{aligned} \tag{4.195}$$

This implies that we start the sequence by going directly from city i to city P. The use of Equation (4.194) next generates the optimal paths with one intermediate city between i and P, then two intermediate cities, and so on as $k = 0, 1, 2, \ldots$. It can be seen that the method assumes an initial set of times which are not optimal, but which are physically realizable, and then proceeds to improve these times. Thus, at each stage it yields a nonoptimal solution to the original problem; as such it fits into the category of "approximation to the solution," as defined by Dreyfus, or "approximation in policy space," as defined by Bellman.

Alternatively, we may select as initial estimates the set of equations

$$I_i^{(0)} = \min_{j \neq i} t_{ij}, \qquad I_P^{(0)} = 0 \qquad (i = 1, 2, \ldots, P-1). \tag{4.196}$$

This method evaluates the best path of length k starting at city i and then improves the same by increasing k. It can be seen here that each step in the iteration gives an optimal solution to a problem shorter than the original one (a solution to an unwanted problem). Thus it fits into the category of "approximation to the problem," as defined by Dreyfus, or "approximation in function space," as defined by Bellman.

The reader will observe that in the present problem the solution automatically requires an iterative procedure. Furthermore, the two procedures which are detailed to solve the problem are those which we have indicated as important in this chapter.

EXAMPLE 4.2 ▪ The pair-interchange and associated methods will be illustrated here, using three different system models. These systems exhibit a progressive increase in order of mathematical complexity. Analogous results have been obtained for a variety of other systems, but to minimize the amount of discussion, only three of the total will be used here.

The first system to be handled is the three-stage extraction unit of Section 1.11 with equations

$$\begin{aligned} x(k) &= x(k-1) - v(k)y(k) \qquad (k = 1, 2, 3), \\ p(k) &= p(k-1) + v(k)[y(k) - \lambda], \end{aligned} \tag{4.197}$$

with $x(0)$ prescribed and

$$p(0) = 0. \tag{4.198}$$

Here $v(1)$, $v(2)$, and $v(3)$ are to be selected so as to maximize $p(3)$. To make the problem partially realistic, we do not assume linear equilibrium at each stage between x and y, but rather we use the nonlinear equilibrium data of Table 1.2. Furthermore, to have a reference to check the answers, we first solve the problem using dynamic programming. Thus, following Example 2.2 of Chapter 2, we write the recurrence relationships for this problem as

$$I^0[x(0), R+1] = \max_{v(1)} \{v(1)[y(1) - \lambda] + I^0[x(1), R]\}, \tag{4.199}$$

with $I^0[x(0), 0] = 0$. As parameters in the solution we shall use $x(0) = 0.150$ and $\lambda = 0.05$.

To solve this problem by dynamic programming, we first discretize $x(k)$ and $v(k)$. In this case, we discretize $x(k)$ in 0.01 increments to cover the over-all interval of 0.0 to 0.20; in an equivalent manner $v(k)$ is discretized in 0.01 increments to cover the over-all interval of 0.0 to 1.0. To calculate a value of $y(k)$ corresponding to a specific $x(k)$, or vice versa, linear interpolation in the tabulated equilibrium data is used.

With these preliminaries in hand, we consider the last stage (stage 3) and for each of the 21 different possible $x(k)$ use Equation (4.199) with $R = 0$ to generate the best control $v^0(k)$, the output from this stage $x(k+1)$, and also $p(k)$. This, of course, means that for each $x(k)$ we use each of the 101 $v(k)$'s and pick that $v(k)$ which is the best one, and denote it by $v^0(k)$. Once stage 3 has been handled, we move back to include stage 2 plus stage 3 and then finally to stage 1 plus stages 2 and 3, using in each case Equation (4.199) to evaluate the control policy for all 21 different $x(k)$. The results of these calculations are shown in Table 4.1; the discrete states and the corresponding optimal $v^0(k)$ and $p(k)$ for each state are also shown.

TABLE 4.1

Dynamic Programming Three-Stage Optimal Table

$x(0)$	$p(k)$	$v^0(k)$	$p(k)$	$v^0(k)$	$p(k)$	$v^0(k)$
0	0	.0000	0	.0000	0	.0000
.0100	0	.0000	0	.0000	0	.0000
.0200	0	.0000	0	.0000	0	.0000
.0300	.0017	.0500	.0014	.0700	.0009	.0900
.0400	.0049	.0800	.0042	.1000	.0032	.1700
.0500	.0090	.1400	.0081	.1600	.0064	.2500
.0600	.0142	.1300	.0128	.1600	.0100	.3100
.0700	.0197	.1600	.0181	.2100	.0142	.3700
.0800	.0257	.2000	.0237	.2500	.0188	.3900
.0900	.0319	.2300	.0296	.3000	.0239	.4400
.1000	.0384	.2400	.0357	.3400	.0292	.4800
.1100	.0450	.2800	.0419	.3800	.0348	.5300
.1200	.0518	.3200	.0483	.4200	.0406	.5900
.1300	.0585	.3600	.0548	.4600	.0464	.6700
.1400	.0654	.3900	.0614	.4900	.0522	.7400
.1500	.0723	.4300	.0680	.5300	.0581	.7800
.1600	.0792	.4900	.0748	.5900	.0641	.8200
.1700	.0862	.5200	.0815	.6500	.0703	.8600
.1800	.0932	.5500	.0883	.6800	.0765	.9000
.1900	.1002	.5900	.0951	.7100	.0829	.9500
.2000	.1073	.6500	.1020	.7500	.0892	1.0000
	Stage 1		Stage 2		Stage 3	

Once the tables are developed as a result of the backward dynamic programming pass (stage 3 to stage 1), we make a forward pass to pick up the explicit optimal values. Since the feed to stage 1 is $x(0) = 0.150$, we enter the state column at this value and read off immediately $p(3) = 0.0723$ and $v^0(1) = 0.430$ (columns two and three). For $x(0) = 0.150$ and $v^0(1) = 0.430$, Equation (4.197) then yields an output from stage 1 of $x(1) = 0.0799$ as feed to stage 2.

Now we enter the state column at $x(1) = 0.0799$ and read off from columns four and five the corresponding $p(2) = 0.0236$ and $v^0(2) = 0.2496$; linear interpolation is used at this point to pick up $p(2)$ and $v^0(2)$. In turn, these yield an output of $x(2) = 0.0501$, which, when used as feed to stage 3, yields $p(1) = 0.0064$ and $v^0(3) = 0.2506$ from columns six and seven. The output from stage 3 is then calculated as $x(3) = 0.0316$.

In summary, the dynamic programming algorithm has yielded the following.

(feed) $x(0) = .150$	$v^0(1) = .430$	$p(3) = .0723$
$x(1) = .0799$	$v^0(2) = .2496$	$p(2) = .0236$
$x(2) = .0501$	$v^0(3) = .2506$	$p(1) = .0064$
$x(3) = .0316$		

Because of the nonlinear equilibrium relationship, we see that the optimal control is *not* $v^0(1) = v^0(2) = v^0(3)$.

With these numbers in hand as check values, we now turn to an iterative algorithm for solving the same problem. This algorithm uses the following steps:

(1) Given $x(0) = 0.150$, guess numerical values for $v^{(0)}(1)$, $v^{(0)}(2)$, $v^{(0)}(3)$.

(2) With these initial values, calculate $x^{(0)}(1)$, $x^{(0)}(2)$, and $x^{(0)}(3)$ and then $p^{(0)}(1)$, $p^{(0)}(2)$, and $p^{(0)}(3)$.

(3) With $v^{(0)}(2)$ and $v^{(0)}(3)$ fixed, scan the discretized $v(k)$ in stage 1 to find that $v(1)$ which maximizes $p(3)$. The result is a new set $v^{(1)}(1)$, $v^{(0)}(2)$, and $v^{(0)}(3)$; a new set of states $x^{(1)}(1)$, $x^{(1)}(2)$; and $x^{(1)}(3)$, and a new profit set $p^{(1)}(1)$, $p^{(1)}(2)$, and $p^{(1)}(3)$.

(4) With $v^{(1)}(1)$ and $v^{(0)}(3)$ fixed, scan the discrete $v(k)$ in stage 2 to find that $v^{(1)}(2)$ which maximizes $p(2)$. This yields the set $v^{(1)}(1)$, $v^{(1)}(2)$, and $v^{(1)}(3)$.

(5) Now with $v^{(1)}(1)$ and $v^{(1)}(2)$ fixed, scan the discrete controls in stage 3 to find that $v^{(1)}(3)$ which maximizes $p(1)$.

This completes a single pass of the iteration algorithm; we now return to step (2) and continue the iteration to yield a further set of improved controls. This is continued until the controls become constant within a preselected tolerance. The over-all iteration pattern is recognized as the explicit use of Equations (4.2) through (4.6).

Table 4.2 shows the results of such a calculation, using as initial estimates $v^{(0)}(1) = 0.990$, $v^{(0)}(2) = 0.500$, and $v^{(0)}(3) = 0.0$. It can be seen that only five passes are required to achieve the equivalent results obtained by dynamic programming. The method itself is very fast computationally and requires an almost trivial amount of computer storage.

As a second illustration, we consider the standard gas-absorption system and seek to find the optimal control and trajectory using the pair-interchange method. This system represents an increase in state dimensionality over the three-stage extraction system of 6 to 1 (each time stage now has 6 state variables, whereas in the extraction there is only 1 state variable per stage) and has two control variables rather than one. Even though the system is linear, we shall not take

TABLE 4.2

Extraction Iteration Sequence

	$v(1)$	$v(2)$	$v(3)$	$x(1)$	$x(2)$	$x(3)$	$p(3)$	$p(2)$	$p(1)$
Initial guess	.990	.500	0	.0449	.0199	.0199	—	—	—
Iteration 1	.510	.370	.150	.0713	.0380	.0278	.0672	.0148	.0027
Iteration 2	.420	.300	.230	.0812	.0495	.0305	.0712	.0237	.0055
Iteration 3	.420	.260	.250	.0812	.0502	.0313	.0720	.0244	.0064
Iteration 4	.430	.250	.250	.0799	.0501	.0315	.0722	.0237	.0064
Iteration 5	.430	.250	.250	.0799	.0501	.0315	.0723	.0237	.0064

advantage of this fact but instead treat the system as if it were nonlinear. The system equations are

$$\dot{\boldsymbol{x}}(t) = \boldsymbol{A}\boldsymbol{x}(t) + \boldsymbol{B}\boldsymbol{u}(t), \qquad \boldsymbol{x}(0) \text{ prescribed,} \tag{4.200}$$

with $\boldsymbol{A}$, $\boldsymbol{B}$ and $\boldsymbol{x}(0)$ given in Section 1.11, and we wish to minimize the quadratic performance index

$$I[\boldsymbol{x}(0), t_f] = \boldsymbol{x}(t_f)'\boldsymbol{S}\boldsymbol{x}(t_f) + \int_0^{t_f} [\boldsymbol{x}(t)'\boldsymbol{Q}\boldsymbol{x}(t) + \boldsymbol{u}(t)'\boldsymbol{R}\boldsymbol{u}(t)]\, dt. \tag{4.201}$$

In accordance with the strategy set down for the pair-interchange method, Section 4.2, we first select a nominal set of the control variables,

$$\boldsymbol{u}^{(0)}(t) = \begin{bmatrix} u_1^{(0)}(t) \\ u_2^{(0)}(t) \end{bmatrix};$$

once these values are chosen, the system Equations (4.200) are integrated numerically, using a fourth-order Runge-Kutta-Gill subroutine for first-order ordinary differential equations. Control $u_1(t)$ is allowed to assume any of Q_1 discrete values, and control $u_2(t)$ is allowed to assume any of Q_2 discrete values in the actual calculation, and these are held constant for a sampling period. Thus, although we write the system equations in the continuous form above, in actual usage we really use a discrete form; that is, because of the method of integration, which does not use the benefit of linearity, Equation (4.200) is really used in the form

$$\boldsymbol{x}(k+1) - \boldsymbol{x}(k) = \boldsymbol{f}[\boldsymbol{x}(k), \boldsymbol{u}(k)]\Delta t, \tag{4.202}$$

where in this case $\boldsymbol{f} = \boldsymbol{A}\boldsymbol{x}(k) + \boldsymbol{B}\boldsymbol{u}(k)$. For linear systems, we would normally integrate (4.200) over a small time interval, in which case $\boldsymbol{f} = \boldsymbol{\Phi}\boldsymbol{x}(k) + \boldsymbol{\Delta}\boldsymbol{u}(k)$. In the same sense, because the applied control is held constant for a sampling period, the integral in Equation (4.201) is replaced by an equivalent sum over P terms. Alternatively, we may replace Equations (4.202) and (4.201) by

$$\boldsymbol{x}(k+1) = \boldsymbol{x}(k) + [\boldsymbol{A}\boldsymbol{x}(k) + \boldsymbol{B}\boldsymbol{u}(k)]T \tag{4.203}$$

and

$$x_7(k+1) = x_7(k) + [\boldsymbol{x}(k+1)'\boldsymbol{Q}\boldsymbol{x}(k+1) + \boldsymbol{u}'(k)\boldsymbol{R}\boldsymbol{u}(k)]T, \tag{4.204}$$

where the new variable $x_7(k)$ represents the cumulative sum of the performance index and $\boldsymbol{S}$ has been taken as the null matrix. Now we seek to minimize $x_7(P)$, which serves as a final-value performance index; T is the sampling period.

The actual calculation proceeds exactly as outlined in Section 4.2. First, with $u_2(k)$ held at its nominal values, $u_2^{(0)}(k)$, $u_1^{(0)}(0)$, and $u_1^{(0)}(1)$ are scanned to find the best set from among the allowable $Q_1 \cdot Q_1$ set of controls. "Best" here means that set which yields the minimum value of $I[\boldsymbol{x}(0), t_f]$ or $x_7(P)$. Second, $u_1^{(1)}(0)$ is fixed at its newly improved value, and $u_1^{(1)}(1)$ and $u_1^{(0)}(2)$ are adjusted in the same manner. Third, this is continued for all the double combinations of $u_1^{(0)}(k)$; then with $u_1^{(1)}(k)$ fixed at the improved values, the procedure is repeated with $u_2^{(0)}(k)$ using the Q_2 values each time. This completes one iteration cycle. The entire cycle is then repeated until some preselected criterion is met.

To illustrate the results of such a calculation, we select first the case of $\boldsymbol{Q} = \boldsymbol{I}$, $\boldsymbol{R} = \boldsymbol{0}$, $\boldsymbol{S} = \boldsymbol{0}$ and choose a sampling period of $T = 1$ min, an integration time of 0.1 min in the Runge-Kutta-Gill routine, and use $P = 15$ total stages. This allows us to compare the current results with those previously illustrated in Chapter 3. In fact, for the optimal response for this case, our previous results indicate $I^0[\boldsymbol{x}(0), 15] = 0.04617$. Now we select the nominal policy

$$u_1^{(0)}(k) = 0, \qquad u_2^{(0)}(k) = -0.100 \qquad (k = 0, 1, 2, \ldots, 14),$$

and allow the following discrete controls.

$u_1(k)$	$u_2(k)$
.0	−.100
.005	−.105
.010	−.110
.020	−.120
.030	−.130
.040	−.140
.050	−.160
.070	−.180
.090	−.240
.110	−.280
.150	−.330
.200	−.350
.220	−.370
.250	−.400
—	−.480

Note that here $Q_1 = 14$ and $Q_2 = 15$, and we refer to this as a (14, 15) allowable control mesh. For this sequence, the results of the pair-interchange method on the performance index are shown in Table 4.3.

TABLE 4.3

Pair Interchange on Absorption System

$Q = I$, $R = 0$, $S = 0$	
Iteration Step	Performance Index
0	.15671
1	.06958
2	.04928
3	.04713
4	.04686
5	.04684

In five iterations the pair-interchange method has converged to a value quite close to that obtained by the method of Chapter 3, namely, 0.04684 and 0.04617, respectively. The resulting trajectories, although not shown, are also in agreement with the previous results.

The defect in the present method is, of course, the large amount of computing time required. For the current problem, the pair-interchange method requires about 15 times as much computer time to achieve the answer as does the method of Chapter 3. However, this result must be tempered to point out that in the pair-interchange calculation, no use was made of the linearity of the system equations and, in fact, a nonlinear system of the same dimension would probably require about the same calculation time.

To proceed further with this calculation, we now raise the question of the effect of the number of points in the allowable control mesh. In other words, what effect does the amount of discretizing of the control have on the final result. In Table 4.4 we show some further results for (4, 9), (6, 11), and (13, 14) allowable control meshes with the deleted values taken out roughly from the entire range of the (14, 15) case. We see that as a more refined control is allowed, the performance index does approach that value obtained from the Chapter 3 results; in the latter case an essentially infinite allowable control mesh was used. We do not actually expect to reach the value of 0.04617 due to the approximation introduced by discretization of the continuous-time system.

Equivalent results were also obtained for the case $Q = I$, $R = I$, and $S = 0$, with an optimal performance index being obtained after five iterations with a (11, 15) allowable control mesh. Although we have concentrated here on the performance index, we should point out that the resulting control and state trajectories are essentially identical to those shown in Chapter 3.

As a final item here, we point out one virtue of the pair-interchange method, namely, that the control is necessarily constrained in the sense that only control

TABLE 4.4

Pair Interchange on Absorption System

$Q = I, \ R = 0, \ S = 0$

Allowable Control Mesh	Performance Index
(4, 9)	.0623
(6, 11)	.0569
(13, 14)	.0470
(14, 15)	.0468

values within the bounds of the allowable control mesh are considered. If the resulting trajectory includes control values at the upper and lower values, it is a simple feature to extend the mesh if desired. In other words, the physical constraints on the control do not in any way hinder the use of the method; in fact, as in dynamic programming, the constraints really aid the computational aspects by limiting the range of variables.

As a final illustration of the pair-interchange method, we use the second nonlinear system of Section 1.11. This system has the complexity of large state dimension (7 state variables), three control variables, and considerable coupled nonlinearities. On this basis it provides a most severe test for the feasibility of the pair-interchange computation method.

In brief terms, the continuous-time system equations are of the form

$$\dot{\boldsymbol{x}}(t) = \boldsymbol{f}[\boldsymbol{x}(t), \boldsymbol{u}(t), \boldsymbol{v}(t)], \tag{4.205}$$

with the explicit form given by Equations (1.137). The control vector contains the three elements $\boldsymbol{u}'(t) = [F_2 \ F_3 \ \bar{I}]$, where F_2 and F_3 are the flow rates of components 2 and 3 and $\bar{I}$ denotes the light intensity. The performance index has the form (1.142)

$$I(\boldsymbol{x}(0), t_f) = \int_0^{t_f} J(x_1, \ldots, x_7)\, dt, \tag{4.206}$$

relating the integrated input and output variables of the reactor. We illustrate the calculations for a given initial state $\boldsymbol{x}(0)$ (1.140) and with $I[\boldsymbol{x}(0), t_f]$ to be maximized.

Once again, we may write the system in discrete terms as

$$\boldsymbol{x}(k+1) = \boldsymbol{x}(k) + \boldsymbol{h}[\boldsymbol{x}(k), \boldsymbol{u}(k), \boldsymbol{v}(k), T] \tag{4.207}$$

and include the performance index by a new variable $x_8(k)$, such that

$$x_8(k+1) = x_8(k) + J(\boldsymbol{x}(k+1), \boldsymbol{u}(k), T). \tag{4.208}$$

Now $x_8(k+1)$ serves as the final-value performance index.

In all the computations to be described, t_f is arbitrarily taken as 12 min with a sampling period of 1.2 min. Thus, there are 10 stages of discrete control to be applied. As before, the Runge-Kutta-Gill routine was used to integrate the system equations. The choice of 12 min for t_f was taken as a compromise between an extended time and a short time; this tends to reduce the computation time involved. An obvious extension of the results to be presented here would be to vary the sampling period and to vary the over-all time.

Two different cases are examined, using the pair-interchange method. In the first, the assumed initial nominal trajectory was taken to be a step change in all of the control variables to the optimal steady-state values corresponding to $F_1 = 6.00$ (see Section 1.11). No constraints on the control variables other than those necessitated by a discrete approach were used in this first case. In the second case, not only was a step change in control variables assumed as an initial nominal policy, but oscillatory and random policies were also assumed as a first approximation. Furthermore, in the second case the control variables were constrained to lie at the second steady state detailed in Section 1.11, Equation (1.141), for the last three stages.

Considering the first case, we start with the nominal assumed policy that

$$F_2(k) = u_1(k) = 7.00, \qquad F_3(k) = u_2(k) = 1.75, \qquad \bar{I}(k) = u_3(k) = 0.900$$
$$(k = 0, 1, \ldots, 9),$$

and an allowable control mesh of 11 values for each control. This will be referred to as the (11, 11, 11) allowable control mesh case with the explicit discrete values shown below.

$u_1(k)$	$u_2(k)$	$u_3(k)$
3.00	.75	.60
4.00	1.00	.70
5.00	1.75	.75
6.00	2.50	.80
7.00	3.00	.85
8.00	4.00	.90
9.00	5.00	.95
10.00	6.00	1.00
12.00	7.00	1.05
14.00	8.00	1.10
16.00	10.00	1.15

Based upon the assumed control policy, as illustration, there result the states and the value of the performance index at final time t_f, or stage $k = 9$. This serves as the beginning of the iterations.

$$x_1(t_f) = .2820,$$

$$x_2(t_f) = .2580,$$

$$x_3(t_f) = .05286, \qquad I[\mathbf{x}(0), t_f] = 17.588 = x_8(t_f),$$

$$x_5(t_f) = .1422, \qquad t_f = 12.0 \text{ min.}$$

$$x_6(t_f) = .08143,$$

$$x_7(t_f) = .07055,$$

Now the pair-interchange method is initiated with the first iteration being to scan $u_1(k)$, the second iteration being to scan $u_2(k)$, etc. Shown in Table 4.5 are the changes in $I[\mathbf{x}(0), t_f]$ and the results for $\mathbf{x}(t_f)$ after 10 total iterations. Convergence of the iterative cycle has occurred in these 10 steps.

TABLE 4.5

Pair-Interchange on CSTR

Initial Guess: $I[\mathbf{x}(0), t_f] = 17.588$		
Iteration 1:		18.146
Iteration 2:		18.845
Iteration 3:		18.858
Iteration 4:		18.862
Iteration 5:		18.863
Iteration 6:		18.864
Iteration 7:		18.865
Iteration 8:		18.868
Iteration 9:		18.868
Iteration 10:	$x_1(t_f) =$	.20039
	$x_2(t_f) =$	.2374
	$x_3(t_f) =$	.1699
	$x_4(t_f) =$	.05412
	$x_5(t_f) =$	.2530
	$x_6(t_f) =$	.05459
	$x_7(t_f) =$	.03056
	$I[\mathbf{x}(0), t_f] =$	18.870

It is important to note that this calculation is with a fixed final time t_f but a free right-hand end on the final state. Because of the choice of t_f, the system does not reach the final equilibrium state $\mathbf{x}_e$ of Equation (1.141).

Although this iteration may be continued, the 10 steps are sufficient for our needs here, and we need not attempt to extend the computation.

The second case treated, where the control variables over the last three stages were held constant at the final steady states corresponding to $F_1 = 6.00$ [$\boldsymbol{x}_e$ of Equation (1.141)], is of further interest. Here we have an almost fixed right-hand end on the final state, and computations were carried out which show, quite clearly, the effect of both the allowable control-mesh size and different assumed initial control policies.

To show the effect of varying the mesh size of the allowable control (Q_j for each control), a series of computations was made with the starting nominal control:

$$u_1(k) = 7.00, \qquad u_2(k) = 1.75, \qquad u_3(k) = .90 \qquad (k = 0, 1, 2, \ldots, 9).$$

A further constraint that $u_1(k)$, $u_2(k)$, and $u_3(k)$ be always held constant at the nominal values in stages $k = 7$, 8, and 9 was also imposed. Four different allowable control-mesh sizes were used, namely (5, 5, 5), (7, 7, 7), (9, 9, 9), and (11, 11, 11), with the explicit values shown in Table 4.6. In each case, the result is that each iteration improves the value of the performance index; a rapid rise

TABLE 4.6

Allowable-Control-Mesh Sizes

(5, 5, 5)		
u_1	u_2	u_3
5.00	1.00	.60
6.50	1.50	.80
7.00	1.75	.90
7.50	2.00	1.00
8.50	2.50	1.20

(7, 7, 7)		
u_1	u_2	u_3
5.50	1.00	.600
6.50	1.50	.800
7.00	1.75	.900
7.50	2.00	1.00
8.00	2.50	1.10
8.50	3.00	1.20
9.00	3.50	1.40

TABLE 4.6 (continued)

(9, 9, 9)		
u_1	u_2	u_3
5.50	1.00	.60
6.50	1.50	.80
7.00	1.75	.90
7.50	2.00	1.00
8.00	2.50	1.10
8.50	3.00	1.20
9.00	3.50	1.40
10.00	4.00	1.60
12.00	4.50	1.90

(11, 11, 11)		
u_1	u_2	u_3
5.00	1.00	.60
5.50	1.50	.80
6.50	1.75	.90
7.00	2.00	1.00
7.50	2.25	1.05
8.00	2.50	1.10
8.50	3.00	1.15
9.00	3.50	1.20
10.00	4.00	1.40
11.00	4.50	1.60
12.00	5.00	1.90

occurs and is followed by an asymptotic approach to a constant value. The asymptotic value approached for each different allowable control mesh is, however, different. In fact, after 10 iterations, we have the following.

Mesh Size	Performance index	Computation time, min
(5, 5, 5)	17.781	5
(7, 7, 7)	17.847	11
(9, 9, 9)	17.868	16
(11, 11, 11)	17.875	20

The final states for the (11, 11, 11) case are as follows.

$$x_1(t_f) = .2727 \qquad x_5(t_f) = .1984$$

$$x_2(t_f) = .2412 \qquad x_6(t_f) = .08249$$

$$x_3(t_f) = .06265 \qquad x_7(t_f) = .05731$$

$$x_4(t_f) = .08522$$

The effect of increasing the allowable control mesh is clearly evident from these calculations where the finer mesh leads to a better (higher) value of the performance index. Here is a case of trading computation time for accuracy in the sense that too coarse an allowable control mesh leads to less accuracy. Note that the optimal performance index is 17.89 in the constrained control case, as compared to 18.83 in the unconstrained control case. A verbal interpretation is that in the constrained case, the reactor is "starved" in the last three time stages. The explicit iterations leading to the optimal trajectories are given in Table 4.7 for the (11, 11, 11) mesh. Note that only seven iterations were needed here.

TABLE 4.7

Iteration of Optimal Controls for Case of (11, 11, 11)

Iteration 0

$u_1(k) = 7.00$

$u_2(k) = 1.75 \qquad (k = 0, 1, 2, \ldots, 9)$

$u_3(k) = 0.90$

Stage k	Iteration 1, $u_1(k)$	Iteration 2, $u_2(k)$	Iteration 3, $u_3(k)$
0	5.5	3.0	1.10
1	6.5	1.5	1.10
2	6.5	2.0	.9
3	7.0	2.25	.9
4	7.5	2.5	.9
5	7.6	4.0	.9
6	10.0	5.0	.9
7	7.0	1.75	.9
8	7.0	1.75	.9
9	7.0	1.75	.9

TABLE 4.7 (continued)

Stage k	Iteration 4, $u_1(k)$	Iteration 5, $u_2(k)$	Iteration 6, $u_3(k)$	Iteration 7, $u_1(k)$
0	5.5	3.0	1.10	5.5
1	8.0	1.5	1.15	7.5
2	7.5	2.5	.9	7.0
3	8.0	2.25	.9	8.0
4	8.5	2.5	.9	8.5
5	9.0	4.0	.9	9.0
6	11.0	5.0	.9	11.0
7	7.0	1.75	.9	7.0
8	7.0	1.75	.9	7.0
9	7.0	1.75	.9	7.0
		Final Set of Controls		

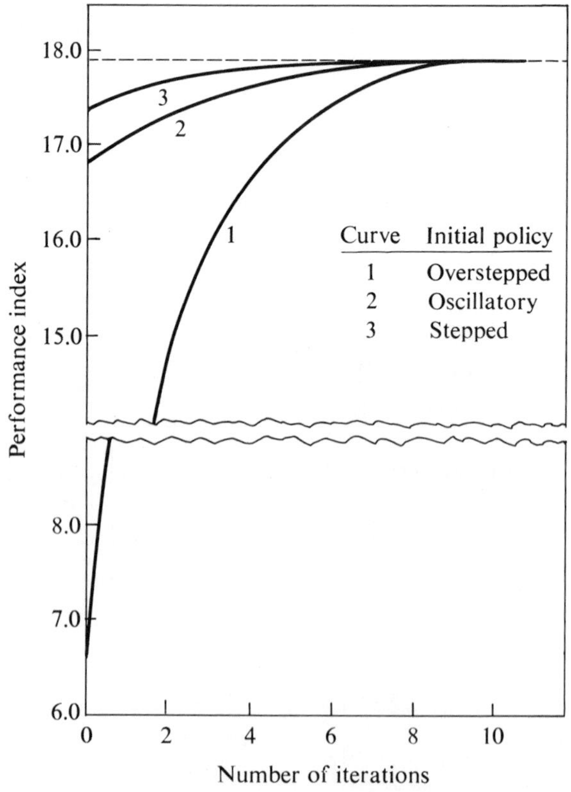

FIGURE 4.3. Effect of different initial policies on control of CSTR

To determine whether the global optimum (as opposed to a relative optimum) is achieved, several different nominal control policies were used as starting points. The assumed nominal policies used are shown in Table 4.8 and the results in Figure 4.3. All computations used the (11, 11, 11) allowable control mesh of the first part of this computation. After 10 iterations, the performance index

TABLE 4.8

Differing Nominal Policies for the CSTR Constrained Case

Curve 1. Assumed Nominal Policy*

Stage (k)	$u_1(k)$	$u_2(k)$	$u_3(k)$
0	16.00	10.00	1.10
1	16.00	10.00	1.10
2	16.00	10.00	1.10
3	16.00	10.00	1.10
4	16.00	10.00	1.10
5	16.00	10.00	1.10
6	16.00	10.00	1.10
7	7.00	1.75	.900
8	7.00	1.75	.900
9	7.00	1.75	.900

Curve 2. Assumed Nominal Policy*

Stage (k)	$u_1(k)$	$u_2(k)$	$u_3(k)$
0	3.00	5.00	1.00
1	5.00	4.00	.95
2	7.00	2.50	.90
3	9.00	1.75	.70
4	7.00	1.00	.80
5	5.00	3.00	.90
6	3.00	4.00	.85
7	7.00	1.75	.900
8	7.00	1.75	.900
9	7.00	1.75	.900

Curve 3. Assumed Nominal Policy*

$u_1(k) = 7.00$	$k = 0, 1, \ldots, 9$
$u_2(k) = 1.75$	$k = 0, 1, \ldots, 9$
$u_3(k) = 0.90$	$k = 0, 1, \ldots, 9$

* See Figure 4.3.

associated with Curve 1 was 17.863, with Curve 2 it was 17.864, and with Curve 3 it was 17.875. These results, which exhibit convergence to an equivalent value of the performance index, tend to substantiate the computational results. Also, the same resulting trajectory was obtained with these different initial policies so that it can be assumed that the global optimum was achieved.

The computer storage required for both the absorber and the CSTR in implementing the pair-interchange method was of the order of a few thousand, so that high dimensionality poses no difficulties in this sense. By way of contrast, had dynamic programming been employed, the CSTR problem would have required a vast amount of storage, and the absorber problem, with no advantage taken of the linearity, would have required about the same.

In summary, it may be concluded that the pair-interchange and associated methods work quite well for representative large-dimensional chemical processes since they provide the same results for the absorber problem as previously obtained by a different method and provide convergence to a global optimum for the CSTR problem from different initial nominal policies.

EXAMPLE 4.3 ▪ In this example, we shall illustrate the results of the gradient or "approximation to the solution" method of Section 4.5. The linear gas absorber and the nonlinear reactor will be used as illustrative examples for the computational discussion.

In its simplest form, the gradient method relies on Equations (4.74) through (4.83), which may be summarized for no stopping conditions or terminal constraints as the system equation

$$\boldsymbol{x}(k+1) = \boldsymbol{x}(k) + \boldsymbol{h}[\boldsymbol{x}(k), \boldsymbol{u}(k)]\,\Delta t, \qquad \boldsymbol{x}(0) \text{ prescribed}, \tag{4.209}$$

and the following nonoptimal return (or adjoint) equations:

$$\frac{\partial S}{\partial \boldsymbol{u}(k)} = \frac{\partial \boldsymbol{h}'}{\partial \boldsymbol{u}(k)} \frac{\partial S}{\partial \boldsymbol{x}(k+1)}\,\Delta t, \tag{4.210}$$

$$\frac{\partial S}{\partial \boldsymbol{x}(k)} = \frac{\partial \boldsymbol{h}'}{\partial \boldsymbol{x}(k)} \frac{\partial S}{\partial \boldsymbol{x}(k+1)}\,\Delta t + \frac{\partial S}{\partial \boldsymbol{x}(k+1)}, \tag{4.211}$$

$$\left.\frac{\partial S}{\partial \boldsymbol{x}}\right|_{k=P} = \left.\frac{\partial I}{\partial \boldsymbol{x}}\right|_{k=P}. \tag{4.212}$$

The gradient itself is improved by the equation

$$\boldsymbol{u}^{(j+1)}(k) = \boldsymbol{u}^{(j)}(k) + \frac{\{[\partial \boldsymbol{h}'/\partial \boldsymbol{u}(k)][\partial S/\partial \boldsymbol{x}(k+1)]\}\delta I}{\sum_{k=0}^{P-1}([\partial \boldsymbol{h}'/\partial \boldsymbol{u}(k)][\partial S/\partial \boldsymbol{x}(k+1)])'([\partial \boldsymbol{h}'/\partial \boldsymbol{u}(k)][\partial S/\partial \boldsymbol{x}(k+1)])\,\Delta t}, \tag{4.213}$$

following an initial assumption on $\boldsymbol{u}^{(0)}(k)$.

In actually carrying out the calculations detailed here, two simple modifications were found necessary. First, we note that as the optimal trajectory is approached both the numerator and the denominator of the second term on the right-hand side of Equation (4.213) approach zero. This, of course, follows from the fact [Equation (4.210)] that at the optimal condition $\partial S/\partial \boldsymbol{u}(k) = \mathbf{0}$. Furthermore, the denominator will approach zero faster than the numerator. As a result, as the optimal trajectory is approached, instabilities and oscillations in the control will result unless care is taken. In the present case, as the optimum is approached the square on the denominator term (note that the denominator is a scalar product) is removed; this empirical approach seems to work moderately well to prevent excessive oscillation of the control.

As a second modification, we note that in Equation (4.213) we must specify δI as an indication of the degree of improvement on the control. When the optimum trajectory is approached, *a priori* specification of δI may not be simply made, since this would lead to an overstepping of the optimum. Thus the procedure adopted is to note the value of the performance index after an iteration; when the value increases (if we are minimizing the index), the control sequence is redetermined after halving δI.

As we can see by these modifications, the gradient method presents certain difficulties in actually reaching the optimum trajectory. By contrast, it would be expected to be able to move from a nonoptimal trajectory to the neighborhood of the optimal trajectory with no difficulty.

With these features in mind, we turn to the gas absorber to detail the computational results. First, however, we note from Equations (4.209) through (4.213) that we must formulate explicitly the terms $\partial \boldsymbol{h}'/\partial \boldsymbol{x}(k)$ and $\partial \boldsymbol{h}'/\partial \boldsymbol{u}(k)$. This may be done most easily by noting that our discrete system equations are

$$x_m(k+1) = x_m(k) + \left[\frac{d}{e}\, x_{m-1}(k) - \left(\frac{d+1}{e}\right) x_m(k) + \frac{1}{e}\, x_{m+1}(k)\right] \Delta t, \qquad (4.214)$$

for $m = 1, 2, \ldots, 6$. These equations are obtained directly from Equation (1.103). Furthermore, if we write the performance index as a 7th state variable, then

$$x_7(k+1) = x_7(k) + [\boldsymbol{x}(k+1)'\boldsymbol{Q}\boldsymbol{x}(k+1)], \qquad (4.215)$$

where $\boldsymbol{x}(k+1)$ is a vector with the six elements $x_1, x_2, \ldots, x_6$. In Equation (4.215), we have used $\boldsymbol{R} = \mathbf{0}$ to simplify the subsequent manipulations. Now, since

$$h_m[\boldsymbol{x}(k), \boldsymbol{u}(k)] = \left[\frac{d}{e}\, x_{m-1}(k) - \left(\frac{d+1}{e}\right) x_m(k) + \frac{1}{e}\, x_{m+1}(k)\right],$$

we note that

$$\frac{\partial \boldsymbol{h}'}{\partial \boldsymbol{u}(k)} = \left[\frac{d}{e}\, \frac{1}{e}\right]. \qquad (4.216)$$

This is seen to be independent of the state or control variables. By contrast, using Equations (4.209) and (4.215), we may write

$$h_7 = x_7(k) + q_{11}x_1(k+1)^2 + q_{22}x_2(k+1)^2 + \cdots + q_{66}x_6(k+1)^2, \quad (4.217)$$

where $q_{11}, q_{22}, \ldots, q_{66}$ are the main diagonal elements of $\boldsymbol{Q}$. It thus follows that

$$h_7 = x_7(k) + q_{11}\left\{x_1(k) + \left[\frac{d}{e}\, x_0(k) - \left(\frac{d+1}{e}\right)x_1(k) + \frac{1}{e}\, x_2(k)\right]\Delta t\right\}^2$$
$$+ \cdots + q_{66}\left\{x_6(k) + \left[\frac{d}{e}\, x_5(k) - \frac{(d+1)}{e}\, x_6(k) + \frac{1}{e}\, x_7(k)\right]\Delta t\right\}^2,$$

and as example,

$$\frac{\partial h_7}{\partial x_3(k)} = \frac{2q_{22}\,\Delta t^2}{e}\left\{x_2(k) + \left[\frac{d}{e}\, x_1(k) - \left(\frac{d+1}{e}\right)x_2(k) + \frac{1}{e}\, x_3(k)\right]\Delta t\right\} + 2q_{33}\,\Delta t^2$$
$$\times\left[1 - \frac{d+1}{e}\,\Delta t\right]\left\{x_3(k) + \left[\frac{d}{e}\, x_2(k) - \frac{(d+1)}{e}\, x_3(k) + \frac{1}{e}\, x_4(k)\right]\Delta t\right\}$$
$$+ \frac{2dq_{44}\,\Delta t^2}{e}\left\{x_4(k) + \left[\frac{d}{e}\, x_3(k) - \left(\frac{d+1}{e}\right)x_4(k) + \frac{1}{e}\, x_5(k)\right]\Delta t\right\}. \quad (4.218)$$

The other derivatives $\partial h_7/\partial x_1(k), \ldots, \partial h_7/\partial x_6(k)$ follow in an analogous manner. These derivatives are functions of the state variables as contrasted to $\partial \boldsymbol{h}'/\partial \boldsymbol{u}(k)$.

Now we are in a position to detail the specific calculations. In particular, for the gas absorber we select $\boldsymbol{Q} = \boldsymbol{I}$, $\boldsymbol{R} = \boldsymbol{0}$, a sampling period of $\Delta t = T = 1$ min, an integration time of 0.1 min in the Runge-Kutta-Gill routine, and use $P = 15$ total stages. As in Example 4.2, we select the normalized initial controls

$$u_1^{(0)}(k) = 0, \qquad u_2^{(0)}(k) = -.100, \qquad k = 0, 1, 2, \ldots, 14,$$

and consider the three different sets for δI listed below.

Set 1	Set 2	Set 3
$\delta I_1 = -.001$	$\delta I_1 = -.003$	$\delta I_1 = -.005$
$\delta I_2 = -.003$	$\delta I_2 = -.005$	$\delta I_2 = -.007$

The δI's are negative, of course, because we desire to minimize the performance index. There are two δI's, one for each control variable, and the controls are iterated one at a time in an alternating fashion.

Figure 4.4 shows the performance index vs. the number of iterations for the different δI sets. Table 4.9 details the explicit values for Set 2. The performance indices for all three cases converge to approximately 0.0475, which compares favorably with previous results of Example 4.2, namely, 0.0468. Sets 2 and 3 required about 1.5 min of 7094 computation time, with 40 iterations; Set 1 required about 2 min, with 57 iterations. After approximately the first 15 iterations, all the curves are seen to assume approximately the same slope. This follows from the fact that after about 15 iterations, the δI in Sets 2 and 3 were automatically reduced to approximately those of Set 1.

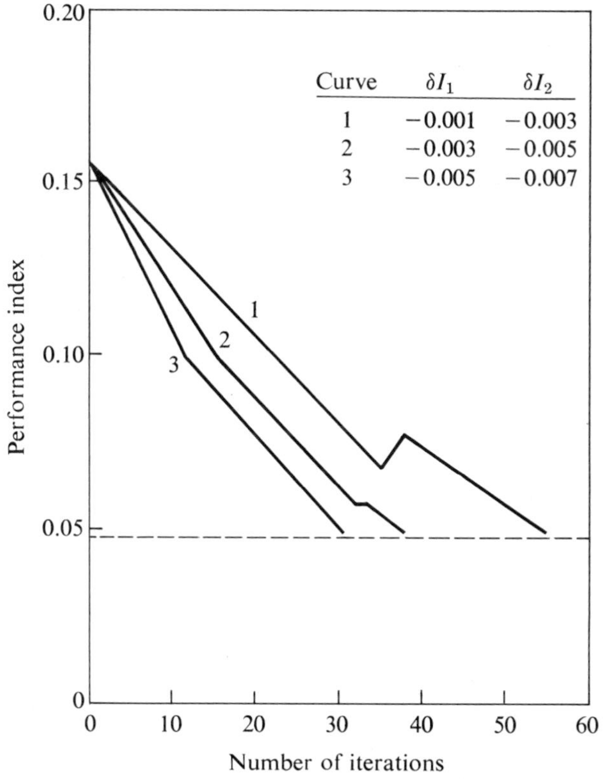

FIGURE 4.4. Effect of varying δI for the absorber system

The peak appearing in Set 1 at about the 35th iteration is where the denominator in Equation (4.213) has become quite small and led to an overstepped control. The algorithm corrected this by taking the square root of the denominator of Equation (4.213). A slight oscillatory behavior of all three sets near the optimum results from slightly overstepping the optimal control and readjusting it. Furthermore, computations with $\boldsymbol{Q} = \boldsymbol{I}$ and $\boldsymbol{R} = \boldsymbol{I}$ yielded analogous results and compared favorably with the results in Example 4.2.

TABLE 4.9

Performance Index vs. Number of Iterations for Set $\delta I_1 = -0.003$, $\delta I_2 = -0.005$

Iteration	Index
0	.15663
2	.14862
4	.14037
6	.13254
8	.12509
10	.11802
12	.11131
14	.10492
16	.09884
18	.09304
20	.08751
22	.08221
24	.07712
26	.07218
28	.06739
30	.06264
32	.05794
34	.05506
36	.05167
38	.04929
40	.04804
42	.04802

(Oscillation from here on)

It is of interest to note that although the pair-interchange method required about 13 min of computation time vs. the 1 to 2 min here, the number of iterations is in the inverse manner, namely, 5 to 6 for the pair-interchange and 40 for the gradient method. Considering the details of each method, this is a completely expected result.

Now we turn to the nonlinear reactor problem. In this system the differentials $\partial \mathbf{h}'/\partial \mathbf{x}(k)$ and $\partial \mathbf{h}'/\partial \mathbf{u}(k)$ are functions of the state and control variables. As illustration, the balance for variable 1 is written as

$$x_1(k+1) = x_1(k) + h_1[\mathbf{x}(k), \mathbf{u}(k)]\, \Delta t,$$

where

$$h_1[\mathbf{x}(k), \mathbf{u}(k)] = F_1 - Fx_1 - k_1x_1x_2 - k_4x_1x_6\bar{I}^{1/2}.$$

But this means that (using $F = F_1 + F_2 + F_3$)

$$\partial h_1/\partial x_1(k) = -(F_1 + F_2 + F_3) - k_1x_2(k) - k_4x_6(k)\bar{I}^{1/2}$$

or with $u_1(k) = F_2$, $u_2(k) = F_3$, and $u_3(k) = \bar{I}$,

$$\partial h_1/\partial x_1(k) = -(F_1 + u_1(k) + u_2(k)) - k_1 x_2(k) - k_4 x_6(k) u_3(k)^{1/2}.$$

In the same sense,

$$\partial h_1/\partial u(k) = -x_1(k).$$

Similar differentials are found for the other components, but these will not be detailed here. The main point is the dependence of the partial derivatives on the state and controls.

A series of preliminary calculations were carried out to explore and establish a good set of δI_i's. It was found that $\delta I_1 = 0.03$, $\delta I_2 = 0.02$, and $\delta I_3 = 0.005$ (note the plus sign since we are maximizing I) produced convergence to a performance index of 18.81 after about 120 iterations from an assumed initial control sequence.

Once these δI_i's were established, computations were carried out using different assumed initial or nominal control policies. These are shown in Table 4.10 and the results are plotted on Figure 4.5. As before, these results are for $P = 10$ time stages with a total time of 12 min.

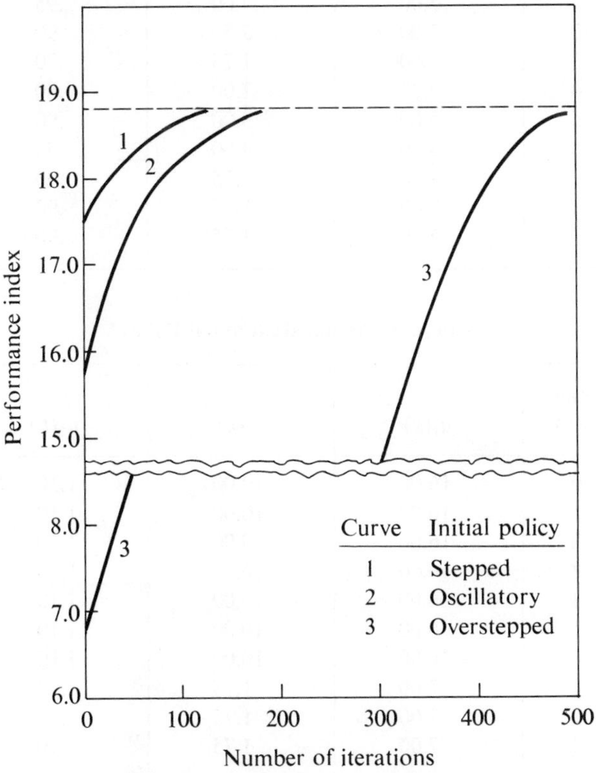

FIGURE 4.5. Effect of different initial policies on the control of CSTR

TABLE 4.10

Different Assumed Nominal Policies for Optimal Control of the CSTR by the Gradient Technique

Curve 1. Assumed Nominal Policy*

$u_1(k) = 7.00$	$k = 0, 1, 2, \ldots, 9$
$u_2(k) = 1.75$	$k = 0, 1, 2, \ldots, 9$
$u_3(k) = .90$	$k = 0, 1, 2, \ldots, 9$

Curve 2. Assumed Nominal Policy*

Stage (k)	$u_1(k)$	$u_2(k)$	$u_3(k)$
0	3.00	5.00	1.00
1	5.00	4.00	.95
2	7.00	2.50	.90
3	9.00	1.75	.70
4	7.00	1.00	.80
5	5.00	3.00	.90
6	3.00	4.00	.85
7	7.00	1.75	.90
8	7.00	1.75	.90
9	7.00	1.75	.90

Curve 3. Assumed Nominal Policy*

Stage (k)	$u_1(k)$	$u_2(k)$	$u_3(k)$
0	16.00	10.00	1.10
1	16.00	10.00	1.10
2	16.00	10.00	1.10
3	16.00	10.00	1.10
4	16.00	10.00	1.10
5	16.00	10.00	1.10
6	16.00	10.00	1.10
7	7.00	1.75	.90
8	7.00	1.75	.90
9	7.00	1.75	.90

* See FIGURE 4.5.

All three nominal policies lead to maximum performance indices of about 18.81. This is slightly lower than the results obtained with the pair-interchange method and is probably due to the behavior of Equation (4.213) as the optimum is approached. At the same time, the state and control variables approached those obtained by the pair-interchange method. Computation times of about 2, 4, and 9 min (on the IBM 7094) were needed for cases 1, 2, and 3, respectively. Of final interest is the fact that even for a 7-state variable nonlinear problem, the total computer storage required was of the order of a few thousand. Thus high state dimensionality poses no difficulty with this method.

EXAMPLE 4.4 ▪ In this example, we illustrate a slight variation on the methods of Example 4.3. The main difference is the method used to successively improve the control estimates. Thus, following the material at the end of Section 4.4, we write the system equations in the normal discrete form and introduce the adjoint vector $\boldsymbol{z}(k)$ such that

$$\boldsymbol{z}(k) = [\partial \boldsymbol{h}'/\partial \boldsymbol{x}(k)]\boldsymbol{z}(k+1),$$

with boundary conditions

$$z_i(P) = 0, \qquad z_{n+1}(P) = 1, \qquad (i = 1, \ldots, n).$$

Here $n + 1$ is the extra state variable introduced to account for the performance index. Finally, we introduce the Hamiltonian $H(k)$ such that

$$H(k) = \boldsymbol{z}(k)'\boldsymbol{h}[\boldsymbol{x}(k-1), \boldsymbol{u}(k-1)]. \tag{4.219}$$

The procedure to be used is to guess at the initial set of controls $\boldsymbol{u}^{(0)}(k)$; once these are known, the system equations may be integrated forward, using the prescribed initial conditions $\boldsymbol{x}(0)$. This yields the corresponding $\boldsymbol{x}^{(0)}(k)$. With these $\boldsymbol{x}^{(0)}(k)$ and the known boundary conditions on the adjoint variables, the adjoint variables may be integrated backward in time. At each stage, however, the Hamiltonian may be extremized by calculating H vs. $\boldsymbol{u}(k)$ using an allowable control mesh of 0, 0.01, 0.02, . . ., 1.00 to scan the H $\boldsymbol{u}(k)$ space. This, then, yields us an improved set of the $\boldsymbol{u}(k)$, which we call $\boldsymbol{u}^{(1)}(k)$.

At this point we have an improved set of the control variables, but rather than just use these values, we use instead only a certain fraction of the change indicated. In other words, we actually use $\boldsymbol{u}^{(2)}(k)$ obtained from the formula

$$\boldsymbol{u}^{(2)}(k) = \boldsymbol{u}^{(0)}(k) + \bar{\boldsymbol{K}}[\boldsymbol{u}^{(1)}(k) - \boldsymbol{u}^{(0)}(k)], \tag{4.220}$$

where $\bar{\boldsymbol{K}}$ is a diagonal matrix with elements $\bar{k}_{11}, \ldots, \bar{k}_{rr}$.

To illustrate the results of this type of calculation, we shall use the gas-absorber system with an initial guess on the controls as given in the early part of Example 4.2. The same number of time stages, $P = 15$, and of weighting parameters, $\boldsymbol{Q} = \boldsymbol{I}$, $\boldsymbol{R} = \boldsymbol{0}$, $\boldsymbol{S} = \boldsymbol{0}$, are used as before. Furthermore, we use a variety of different $\bar{K}$ to show the effect of this parameter. Incidentally, we note that $\bar{K} = I$ yields the discrete maximum principle formulation. The necessary explicit forms of the equations used are equivalent to those already shown with the gradient method.

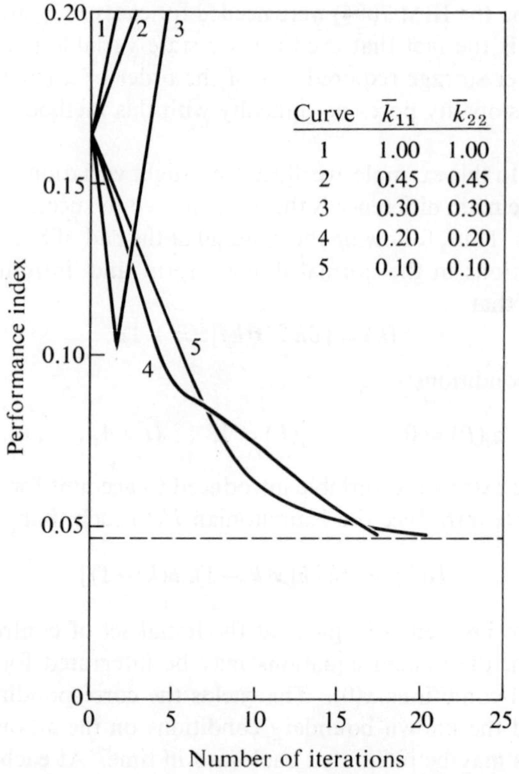

FIGURE 4.6. Effect of $\bar{k}_{ii}$ on the absorber system

Figure 4.6 shows the results of such a calculation with five different sets of $\bar{k}_{11}$ and $\bar{k}_{22}$. Convergence in the case of $\bar{k}_{11} = 0.2$, $\bar{k}_{22} = 0.2$ took 15 iterations to go from a value of the performance index of 0.1566 to 0.04645. This corresponds favorably to the previous results obtained on this system, and the controls and the resulting optimum trajectory agree quite well also.

It is important to note in Figure 4.6 that the cases $\bar{k}_{11} = \bar{k}_{22} = 1.0$, $\bar{k}_{11} = \bar{k}_{22} = 0.45$, and $\bar{k}_{11} = \bar{k}_{22} = 0.30$ all diverge from the optimal trajectory. This implies, of course, that the standard form of the discrete maximum principle, $\bar{k}_{11} = \bar{k}_{22} = 1.0$, does not yield convergence. Other results obtained by the present authors tend to confirm this point.

A series of runs was also made with the nonlinear reactor system. The equivalent type approach as above was used with an allowable control mesh of

$$u_1(k) = 0.50\,j + 3.00, \qquad j = 1, \ldots, 30,$$
$$u_2(k) = 0.25\,j + 0.25, \qquad j = 1, \ldots, 40,$$
$$u\ (k) = 0.05\,j + 0.60, \qquad j = 1, \ldots, 30,$$

and $\bar{k}_{11} = \bar{k}_{22} = \bar{k}_{33} = 0.20$. Figure 4.7 shows the results obtained by using the starting nominal controls of Table 4.11. As we can see, convergence occurred in all cases; about 20 iterations were required to yield a performance index of approximately 18.84. These results compare quite favorably with those obtained previously on this system.

TABLE 4.11

Assumed Nominal Policies

Curve 1*	
$u_1(k) = 7.00$	$k = 0, \ldots, 9$
$u_2(k) = 1.75$	$k = 0, \ldots, 9$
$u_3(k) = .90$	$k = 0, \ldots, 9$
Curve 2*	
$u_1(k) = 7.00$	$k = 0, \ldots, 9$
$u_2(k) = 1.75$	$k = 0, \ldots, 9$
$u_3(k) = .75$	$k = 0, \ldots, 9$
Curve 3*	
$u_1(k) = 7.00$	$k = 0, \ldots, 9$
$u_2(k) = 1.75$	$k = 0, \ldots, 9$
$u_3(k) = 1.10$	$k = 0, \ldots, 9$
Curve 4*	
$u_1(k) = 7.00$	$k = 0, \ldots, 9$
$u_2(k) = 1.00$	$k = 0, \ldots, 9$
$u_3(k) = .90$	$k = 0, \ldots, 9$
Curve 5*	
$u_1(k) = 7.00$	$k = 0, \ldots, 9$
$u_2(k) = 3.50$	$k = 0, \ldots, 9$
$u_3(k) = .90$	$k = 0, \ldots, 9$

* See Figure 4.7.

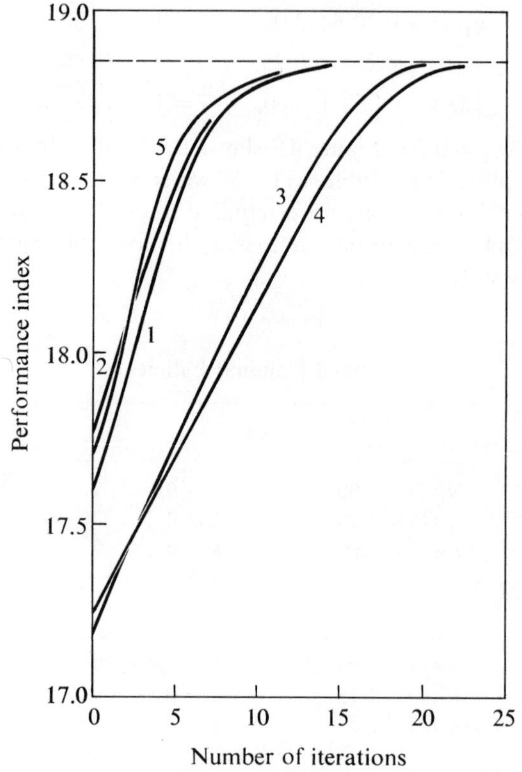

FIGURE 4.7. Effect of different initial policies on control of CSTR

EXAMPLE 4.5 ▪ In this example, we shall illustrate the features of the second variation method detailed in Section 4.6. The nonlinear exothermic CSTR of (1.125) and (1.126) is used to highlight the computational aspects of the method. At the same time, equivalent results will be illustrated for the first variation or gradient method of Section 4.5. This comparison of the two methods will serve to point out the strong features of the second-variation approach. In addition, a brief mention will be made of results obtained on applying the second-variation method to the linear absorber with a quadratic performance index of (1.103). In this special case, one-step convergence is *a priori* predicted, and the computations confirm this point.

The state equations for the CSTR are given by Equations (2.246) and (2.247), that is,

$$\dot{T} = -(T + 0.25) + (C + 0.5) \exp\left(\frac{25T}{T + 2}\right) - u_1(T + 0.25), \quad (4.221)$$

$$\dot{C} = 0.5 - C - (C + 0.5)\exp\left(\frac{25\,T}{T+2}\right), \tag{4.222}$$

where u_1 is the control action which has a minimum value of 0 when the valve is completely closed. For the moment we shall assume that u_1 is not bounded from above, but we shall try to keep it from becoming too large by a suitable weighting in the performance index.

The performance index which we wish to minimize is

$$I[\mathbf{x}(0), t_f] = I = \int_0^{0.78} \{(T^2 + C^2) + r(u_1 - 1)^2\}\,dt, \tag{4.223}$$

where r is a constant weighting factor. For initial conditions, we shall choose $T(0) = 0.05$ and $C(0) = 0.0$. It is noted that $T = 0$, $C = 0$, $u_1 = 1$ defines an *unstable* steady state at which we wish to maintain the system. This means that the initial policy must be chosen wisely to apply the second-variation method. Otherwise, instability will arise.

To start the major part of our discussion, we desire to put the problem into standard normalized form and derive all the necessary explicit equations for the second-variation method. Thus we define the control action

$$u = u_1 - 1. \tag{4.224}$$

In this form, then,

$$J[\mathbf{x}(t), \mathbf{u}(t)] = J = T^2 + C^2 + ru^2 \tag{4.225}$$

and

$$\frac{\partial J}{\partial \mathbf{x}} = \begin{bmatrix} \dfrac{\partial J}{\partial T} \\[2ex] \dfrac{\partial J}{\partial C} \end{bmatrix} = \begin{bmatrix} 2T \\ 2C \end{bmatrix}, \tag{4.226}$$

$$\frac{\partial \mathbf{f}'}{\partial \mathbf{x}} = \begin{bmatrix} \dfrac{\partial f_1}{\partial T} & \dfrac{\partial f_2}{\partial T} \\[2ex] \dfrac{\partial f_1}{\partial C} & \dfrac{\partial f_2}{\partial C} \end{bmatrix}$$

$$= \begin{bmatrix} -2 + (C + 0.5)\dfrac{50}{(T+2)^2}\exp\left(\dfrac{25\,T}{T+2}\right) - u, & -(C + 0.5)\dfrac{50}{(T+2)^2}\exp\left(\dfrac{25\,T}{T+2}\right) \\[2ex] \exp\left(\dfrac{25\,T}{T+2}\right), & -1 - \exp\left(\dfrac{25\,T}{T+2}\right) \end{bmatrix}. \tag{4.227}$$

Therefore, the adjoint equation may be written as

$$\dot{z} = \begin{bmatrix} \dot{z}_1 \\ \dot{z}_2 \end{bmatrix} = -\begin{bmatrix} 2T \\ 2C \end{bmatrix} - \begin{bmatrix} -2 + (C+0.5)\dfrac{50}{(T+2)^2}\exp\left(\dfrac{25\,T}{T+2}\right) - u, & -(C+0.5)\dfrac{50}{(T+2)^2}\exp\left(\dfrac{25\,T}{T+2}\right) \\ \exp\left(\dfrac{25\,T}{T+2}\right), & -1 - \exp\left(\dfrac{25\,T}{T+2}\right) \end{bmatrix} \begin{bmatrix} z_1 \\ z_2 \end{bmatrix}. \tag{4.228}$$

Further manipulations of interest are

$$\frac{\partial^2 J}{\partial \mathbf{x}^2} = \begin{bmatrix} 2 & 0 \\ 0 & 2 \end{bmatrix}, \tag{4.229}$$

$$\frac{\partial^2 f_1}{\partial \mathbf{x}^2} = \begin{bmatrix} \dfrac{\partial^2 f_1}{\partial T^2} & \dfrac{\partial^2 f_1}{\partial T\,\partial C} \\ \dfrac{\partial^2 f_1}{\partial C\,\partial T} & \dfrac{\partial^2 f_1}{\partial C^2} \end{bmatrix}$$

$$= \begin{bmatrix} (C+0.5)\left(\dfrac{2500}{(T+2)^4} - \dfrac{100}{(T+2)^3}\right)\exp\left(\dfrac{25\,T}{T+2}\right), & -\dfrac{50}{(T+2)^2}\exp\left(\dfrac{25\,T}{T+2}\right) \\ \dfrac{50}{(T+2)^2}\exp\left(\dfrac{25\,T}{T+2}\right), & 0 \end{bmatrix}, \tag{4.230}$$

$$\frac{\partial^2 f_2}{\partial \mathbf{x}^2} = \begin{bmatrix} -(C+0.5)\left(\dfrac{2500}{(T+2)^4} - \dfrac{100}{(T+2)^3}\right)\exp\left(\dfrac{25\,T}{T+2}\right), & -\dfrac{50}{(T+2)^2}\exp\left(\dfrac{25\,T}{T+2}\right) \\ -\dfrac{50}{(T+2)^2}\exp\left(\dfrac{25\,T}{T+2}\right), & 0 \end{bmatrix}. \tag{4.231}$$

Since [Equation (4.132)]

$$\boldsymbol{R} = \frac{\partial^2 J}{\partial \boldsymbol{u}\, \partial \boldsymbol{x}} + \frac{\partial \boldsymbol{f}'}{\partial \boldsymbol{u}} \boldsymbol{P} + \sum_{i=1}^{n} z_i \frac{\partial^2 f_i}{\partial \boldsymbol{u}\, \partial \boldsymbol{x}} \quad \text{and} \quad \frac{\partial^2 f_1}{\partial \boldsymbol{u}\, \partial \boldsymbol{x}} = \left[\frac{\partial^2 f_1}{\partial u\, \partial T}, \frac{\partial^2 f_1}{\partial u\, \partial C}\right] = [-1 \quad 0],$$

it follows that

$$\begin{aligned} \boldsymbol{R} &= [-(T+0.25)\ 0]\begin{bmatrix} P_{11} & P_{12} \\ P_{12} & P_{22} \end{bmatrix} + z_1[-1 \quad 0] \\ &= [-(T+0.25)P_{11} - z_1,\ -(T+0.25)P_{12}]. \end{aligned} \tag{4.232}$$

Since [Equation (4.136)]

$$\boldsymbol{T} = \frac{\partial^2 J}{\partial \boldsymbol{u}^2} = \sum_{i=1}^{n} z_i \frac{\partial^2 f_i}{\partial \boldsymbol{u}^2},$$

then

$$\boldsymbol{T} = 2r \qquad \text{(a scalar).} \tag{4.233}$$

From this information, we can evaluate the differential equation [see Equation (4.130)]

$$\begin{aligned} \dot{\boldsymbol{P}} &= \begin{bmatrix} \dot{P}_{11} & \dot{P}_{12} \\ \dot{P}_{21} & \dot{P}_{22} \end{bmatrix} \\ &= -\begin{bmatrix} 2 & 0 \\ 0 & 2 \end{bmatrix} - z_1 \frac{\partial^2 f_1}{\partial \boldsymbol{x}^2} - z_2 \frac{\partial^2 f_2}{\partial \boldsymbol{x}^2} - \left\{\boldsymbol{P}\left(\frac{\partial \boldsymbol{f}'}{\partial \boldsymbol{x}}\right)' + \left(\frac{\partial \boldsymbol{f}'}{\partial \boldsymbol{x}}\right)\boldsymbol{P}\right\} + \frac{1}{2r} \boldsymbol{R}'\boldsymbol{R}. \end{aligned} \tag{4.234}$$

Also, in this example, $\boldsymbol{s}$ is a scalar:

$$\boldsymbol{s} = 2ru - z_1(T + 0.25) = s, \tag{4.235}$$

and with the above, we can evaluate [see Equation (4.150)]

$$\dot{\boldsymbol{q}} = \begin{bmatrix} \dot{q}_1 \\ \dot{q}_2 \end{bmatrix} = \frac{s}{2r}\begin{bmatrix} R_{11} \\ R_{12} \end{bmatrix} + \frac{1}{2r}\begin{bmatrix} R_{11} \\ R_{12} \end{bmatrix}[-(T+0.25),\ 0]\begin{bmatrix} q_1 \\ q_2 \end{bmatrix} - \left(\frac{\partial \boldsymbol{f}'}{\partial \boldsymbol{x}}\right)'\begin{bmatrix} q_1 \\ q_2 \end{bmatrix}. \tag{4.236}$$

The final conditions are $t_f = 0.78$, $\boldsymbol{z}(0.78) = \boldsymbol{0}$, $\boldsymbol{P}(0.78) = \boldsymbol{0}$, and $\boldsymbol{q}(0.78) = \boldsymbol{0}$.

Now we are in a position to perform a calculation on the CSTR. Equations (4.228), (4.234), and (4.236) are to be integrated backward from $t_f = 0.78$, using known values of T, C, and u. The values of T and C are obtained by a forward integration (from $t = 0$) of Equations (4.221) and (4.222), and u is obtained by the iteration formula

$$u^{(j+1)} = u^{(j)} - \left[\frac{\varepsilon}{2r}\left(s + \frac{\partial \boldsymbol{f}'}{\partial \boldsymbol{u}} \boldsymbol{q}\right)\right]^{(j)} - \frac{\boldsymbol{R}}{2r}[\boldsymbol{x}^{(j+1)} - \boldsymbol{x}^{(j)}], \tag{4.237}$$

where

$$x = \begin{bmatrix} T \\ C \end{bmatrix}.$$

On this basis, the computational features are quite straightforward. All that is needed is an initial guess of the control $u^{(0)}$ to start the iteration. It is, however, important that the initial guess be as good as possible, that is, close enough to the optimal values; otherwise, the iteration may not converge and instability might be encountered.

As an illustration of a careful selection of an initial policy, we shall choose the bang-bang control as obtained for time optimal control of the CSTR in Chapter 2 (Example 2.3 of Section 2.8). This is not the answer to the current problem, but is probably quite close. We thus choose $u = 1.0$ for the time interval (0, 0.47), $u = -1.0$ for the time interval (0.47, 0.76), and $u = 0.0$ for the time interval (0.76, 0.78). At the same time, we select $r = 0.1$.

An interesting parameter in the computation is the step-size factor ε, which determines the magnitude of the step taken in each iteration stage j. Thus, we have selected a series of values of ε and carried out the computation for each value. The results are tabulated in Table 4.12, where it is seen that with $\varepsilon = 1.0$,

TABLE 4.12

Effect of the Size of ε on Rate of Convergence.
Step Size in Integration = 0.0025

Iteration Number	Value of I		
	$\varepsilon = 1.0$	$\varepsilon = 0.5$	$\varepsilon = 0.25$
0	.0781	.0781	.0781
1	.0439	.0380	.0544
2	.0295	.0295	.0419
3	.0271	.0273	.0351
4	.0266	.0268	.0314
5	.0266	.0266	.0292
6	.0266	.0266	.0281
7	.0266	.0266	.0274
8	.0266	.0266	.0271
9	.0266	.0266	.0269
10	.0266	.0266	.0268
11	.0266	.0266	.0267
12	.0266	.0266	.0266
13	.0266	.0266	.0266

the minimum for the performance index I is obtained in only 4 iterations, whereas with $\varepsilon = 0.25$, 12 iterations are required. The step size for integrations of the various differential equations was taken as 0.0025 for all these cases. It is apparent from the definition for ε, that for rapid convergence ε should be made as large as possible. In the present case, it is seen that the results confirm this point, with the value of $\varepsilon = 1.0$ yielding the fastest convergence. Of course, a value of $\varepsilon > 1.0$ will cause the system to diverge.

TABLE 4.13

Effect of the Size of ε on Rate of Convergence.
Step Size in Integration = 0.01

Iteration Number	Value of I			
	$\varepsilon = 1.0$	$\varepsilon = 0.4$	$\varepsilon = 0.2$	$\varepsilon = 0.1$
0	.0782	.0782	.0782	.0782
1	.0420	.0438	.0588	.0681
2	.0298	.0328	.0469	.0599
3	.0272	.0289	.0395	.0534
4	.0267	.0275	.0349	.0482
5	.0267	.0270	.0319	.0440
6	.0267	.0268	.0300	.0407
7	.0266	.0267	.0288	.0380
8	.0266	.0267	.0280	.0358
9	.0266	.0267	.0275	.0341
10	.0267	.0267	.0272	.0326
11		.0267	.0270	.0315
12		.0267	.0269	.0306
13		.0267	.0268	.0298
14		.0267	.0268	.0292
15		.0266	.0267	.0284

Table 4.13 shows similar results obtained for a larger step size in integration of the various differential equations (0.01 instead of 0.0025) and the values of the performance index I from Table 4.13 are plotted in Figure 4.8 to give a visual picture of the rate of convergence. Once again, $\varepsilon = 1.0$ yields fastest convergence rate as compared to any other ε used. In addition, the number of iterations for an integration interval of 0.0025 and 0.01 is the same. Thus, in all subsequent computations, 0.01 is used to minimize computer time. However, with $\varepsilon = 1.0$, after 10 iterations the performance index increases, and then the ε must be cut down. As a result, the selection $\varepsilon = 0.4$ and integration interval = 0.01 is used from here on.

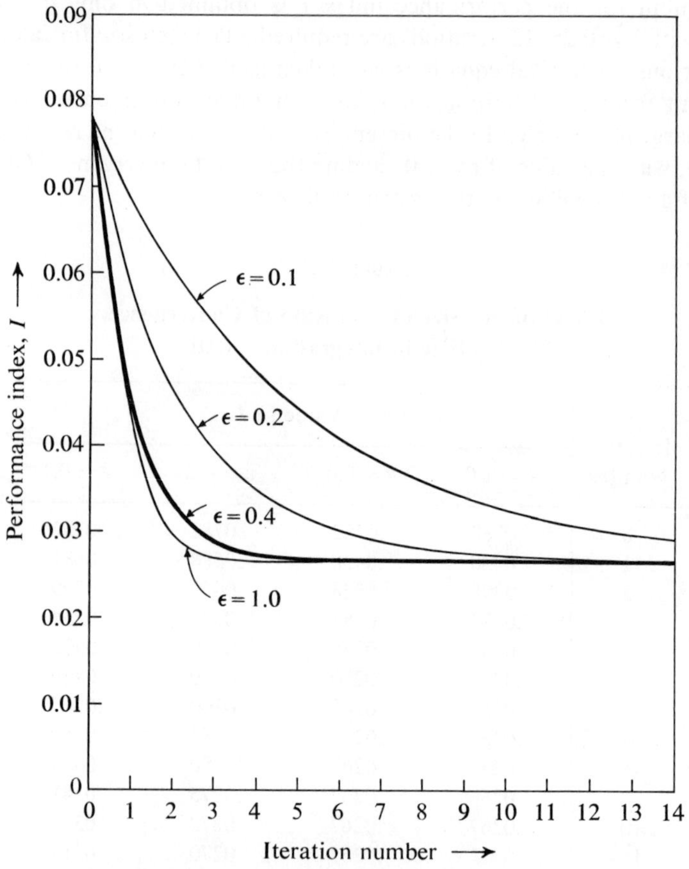

FIGURE 4.8. Effect of the size of ε on the rate of convergence

All of these results were obtained with the carefully chosen initial control policy corresponding to the time-optimal results of Section 2.8. This ensured convergence of the second variation method. If instead we choose some other initial policy, the iteration will probably diverge. To bypass this problem and to start the second variation method with a good initial policy, it might be suggested that the first variation or gradient method be used for the first few iterations. This, of course, makes use of the feature of the gradient method to go quickly from almost any initial policy to the neighborhood of the optimum. If the second variation then starts with this near-optimum policy, the chances are excellent that convergence will occur. This feature is shown for two different initial policies in Figures 4.9 and 4.10. Each initial policy has been shown, by calculations not detailed here, to diverge from the optimal policy when the second variation is used at the start. The first variation method is used for the

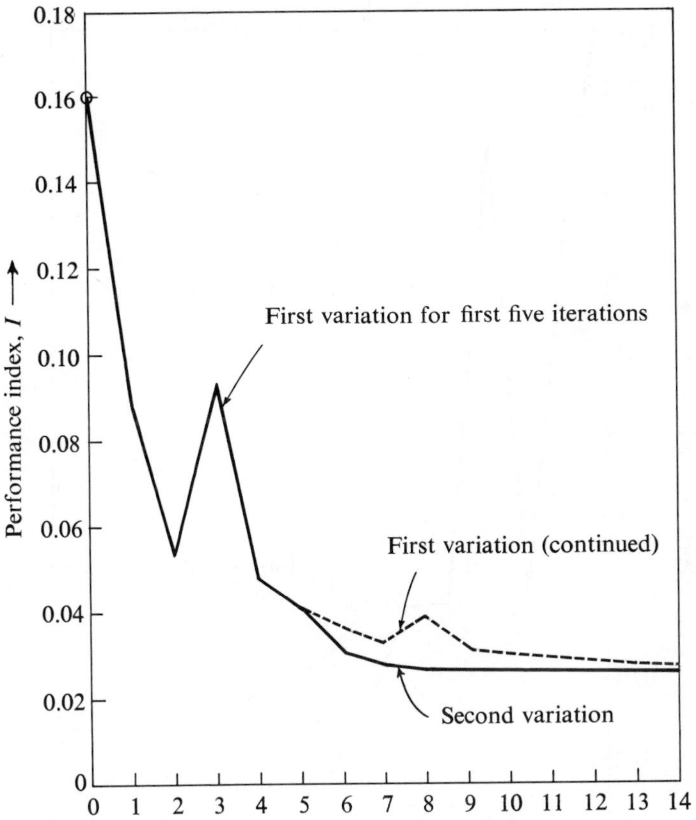

FIGURE 4.9. First- and second-variation control; initial policy, $u = 0.5$ for $t = 0, 0.76$ and $u = 0.0$ for $t = 0.76, 0.78$

first five iterations, and then the second variation method is used until convergence results. The dotted curves show the result of a complete application of the first variation method. The combined method, as expected, is considerably better than either method used singly.

This example illustrates in a most effective manner the versatility and importance associated with the combined use of the first and second variations. Although the time per iteration is greater for the combined method than the first method, 2.4 sec vs. 1.5 sec on the IBM 7094, this is not a serious restriction. Of further importance is the fact that after even 50 iterations of the first variation alone, convergence is not completely reached. By contrast, fewer than 10 iterations of the combined method yields complete convergence. This can most easily be seen in Figure 4.11.

Let us now consider briefly the linear absorber system with quadratic performance index discussed in detail in Chapter 3 and in Examples 4.2 through 4.4

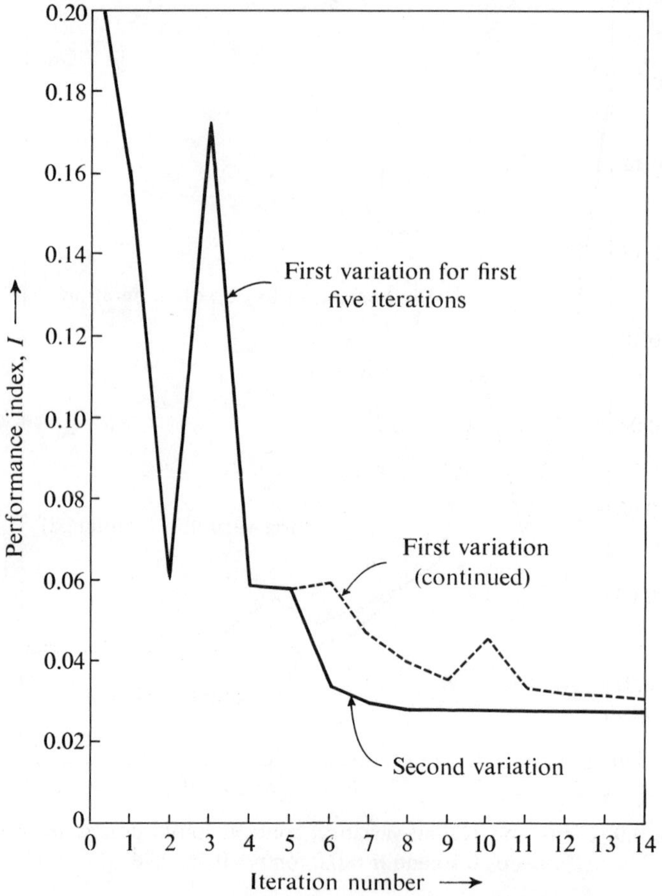

FIRST 4.10. First- and second-variation control initial policy; $u = 0.0$ for $t = 0, 0.78$

of this chapter. For such a system, no approximations are introduced in the expansion of $I^{(j+1)}$ since J is quadratic in $\boldsymbol{x}$ and $\boldsymbol{u}$.

We shall not detail the equations here for transforming the absorber problem to the second variation form, but merely mention that with the performance index

$$I = \int_0^{10.0} [\boldsymbol{x}'\boldsymbol{Q}\boldsymbol{x} + \boldsymbol{u}'\boldsymbol{R}\boldsymbol{u}]\, dt,$$

convergence to a minimum in I and to the optimal policy did occur in one step. In this calculation, $\boldsymbol{Q} = \boldsymbol{I}$, $\boldsymbol{R} = \boldsymbol{I}$, $t_f = 10.0$, and $\varepsilon = 1.0$. Furthermore, using two widely different initial control policies, we obtained the performance index

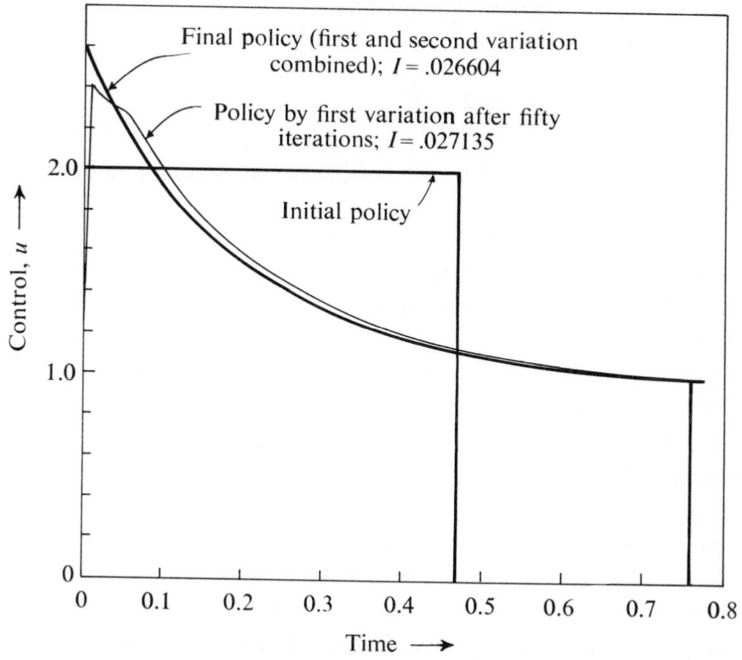

FIGURE 4.11. Comparison of final policy for first and second variations

of $I^0 = 0.12586$ in *one step* with an integration interval of 0.01. This value of the index and the resulting trajectory and control were equivalent to the results obtained in Examples 4.2 through 4.4 of this chapter for the case $\boldsymbol{Q} = \boldsymbol{I}$, $\boldsymbol{R} = \boldsymbol{I}$, and $\boldsymbol{S} = \boldsymbol{0}$. The computation time per iteration was 1 min on the IBM 7094.

References

BOOKS

1. R. ARIS, *Discrete Dynamic Programming*, Blaisdell Publishing Co., 1964.
2. M. ATHANS and P. L. FALB, *Optimal Control*, McGraw-Hill Book Co. 1966.
3. R. BELLMAN, *Applied Dynamic Programming*, Princeton University Press, 1962.
4. R. BELLMAN and R. KALABA, *Quasilinearization and Nonlinear Boundary-Value Problems*, Elsevier, 1965.
5. R. L. GRAVES and P. WOLFE, (Editors), *Recent Advances in Mathematical Programming*, McGraw-Hill Book Co., 1963.
6. H. J. KELLEY, "Method of Gradients" in *Optimization Techniques*, G. Leitmann, Ed., Academic Press, 1962.

7. C. W. Merriam, *Optimization Theory and the Design of Feedback Control Systems*, McGraw-Hill Book Co., 1964.

ARTICLES

8. B. Baker, "Iterative Algorithms for Nonlinear Multistage Optimization," *B.S. Thesis, Princeton University* (1965).
9. R. Bellman, *Quart. Appl. Math.*, *16*, 87 (1958).
10. R. Bellman and R. Kalaba, *J. SIAM*, *8*, 582 (1960).
11. R. E. Bellman, H. N. Kagiwada, and R. E. Kalaba, *IEEE Trans. Auto. Control*, *AC-10*, 199 (1965).
12. D. L. Bentley and K. L. Cooke, *J. Math. Anal. Appl.*, *10*, 269 (1965).
13. L. D. Berkovitz, *J. Math. Anal. Appl.*, *3*, 145 (1961).
14. L. D. Berkovitz, *J. Math. Anal. Appl.*, *5*, 488 (1962).
15. L. D. Berkovitz and S. E. Dreyfus, *J. Math. Anal Appl.*, *10*, 275 (1965).
16. S. P. Bingulac, *IEEE Trans. Auto Control*, *AC-10*, 208 (1965).
17. J. V. Breakwell, *J. SIAM*, *7*, 215 (1959).
18. J. V. Breakwell, J. L. Speyer, and A. E. Bryson, *J. SIAM Control*, *1*, 193 (1963).
19. J. V. Breakwell and Y. Ho, *Int. J. Eng. Sci.*, *2*, 265 (1965).
20. J. V. Breakwell, F. Tung, and R. R. Smith, *AIAA J.*, *3*, 907 (1965).
21. R. E. Brown, "Some Numerical Aspects of Steepest Descent Trajectory Optimization," *AIAA Paper*, 64–662 (August 1964).
22. A. E. Bryson, W. F. Denham, F. J. Carroll, and K. Mikami, *JAS*, *29*, 420 (1961).
23. A. E. Bryson and W. Denham, *J. Appl. Mech.*, *29*, 247 (1962).
24. A. E. Bryson, W. F. Denham, and S. E. Dreyfus, *AIAA J.*, *1*, 2544 (1963).
25. E. Courant, "Lectures on Calculus of Variations," *New York University* (1945–46).
26. W. N. Daly, "Dynamic Programming and Optimization of Transient Control,' *B.S. Thesis*, *Princeton University* (1965).
27. W. F. Denham and A. E. Bryson, *AIAA J.*, *2*, 25 (1964).
28. M. Denn, *A.I.Ch.E. J.*, *11*, 367 (1965).
29. M. Denn, *IEC Fund.*, *4*, 231, 240 (1965).
30. M. Denn and R. Aris, *Chem. Eng. Sci.*, *20*, 373 (1965).
31. M. Denn and R. Aris, *IEC Fund.*, *4*, 7, 213, 248 (1965).
32. M. Denn and R. Aris, *ZAMP*, *16*, 290 (1965).
33. J. M. Douglas and M. M. Denn, *Ind. Eng. Chem.*, *57*, 19 (November 1965).
34. S. E. Dreyfus, *J. Math. Anal. Appl.*, *4*, 297 (1962); *5*, 30 (1962).
35. S. E. Dreyfus, "Variational Problems with State Variable Inequality Constraints," *RAND Report P-2605-1* (August 1963).
36. R. C. Durbeck and L. S. Lasdon, "Control Model Simplification Using a Two-Level Decomposition Technique," *JACC Proceedings* (1965).

37. B. S. Goh, *J. SIAM Control*, *4*, 309 (1966).

38. R. G. Gottlieb, "Rapid Convergence to Optimum Solutions Using a Min-H Strategy," *JACC Proceedings* (1966).

39. L. A. Gould and W. Kipiniak, *AIEE Trans.*, *Part I*, 734 (1961).

40. R. G. Graham, *AIAA J.*, *3*, 154 (1965).

41. M. Handelsman, *AIAA J.*, *4*, 1077 (1966).

42. M. A. Hanson, *J. Math. Anal. Appl.*, *8*, 84 (1964).

43. Y. Ho, *J. Basic Eng.*, *84*, 33 (1962).

44. Y. Ho, *J. Math. Anal. Appl.*, *5*, 216 (1962).

45. Y. Ho and P. G. Brentani, *J. SIAM Control*, *1*, 319 (1963).

46. R. Jackson, *Chem. Eng. Sci.*, *20*, 405 (1965).

47. A. H. Jazwinski, *AIAA J.*, *2*, 1371 (1964).

48. A. H. Jazwinski, *AIAA J.*, *3*, 925 (1965).

49. T. Jensen, "Dynamic Control of Large Dimension Nonlinear Chemical Processes," *Ph.D. Dissertation, Princeton University* (1964).

50. S. A. Jurovics and J. E. McIntyre, *ARS J.*, *32*, 1354 (1964).

51. R. E. Kalaba, "Some Aspects of Quasilinearization" in *Nonlinear Differential Equations and Nonlinear Mechanics*, J. La Salle and S. Lefschetz, Academic Press, 1963.

52. N. Kallay, *IEEE Trans. Auto. Control*, *AC-7*, 10 (1962).

53. R. E. Kalman, "Control Theory and Applications," *Proceedings IBM Scientific Computing Symposium* (1966).

54. H. J. Kelley, *J. SIAM*, *9*, 514 (1961).

55. H. J. Kelley, R. E. Kopp, and H. G. Moyer, *Preprint 63-415 at AIAA Astrodynamics Conference* (August 1963).

56. H. J. Kelley, *AIAA J.*, *2*, 1380 (1964).

57. H. J. Kelley, *IEEE Trans. Auto Control*, *AC-9*, 375 (1964).

58. C. M. Knapp and P. A. Frost, *IEEE Trans. Auto Control*, *AC-10*, 189 (1965).

59. R. E. Kopp and R. McGill, "Several Trajectory Optimization Techniques I" in *Computing Methods in Optimization Problems*, Academic Press, 1964.

60. R. E. Larson, *IEEE Trans. Auto. Control*, *AC-10*, 135 (1965).

61. R. E. Larson, *J. Math. Anal. Appl.*, *11*, 519 (1965).

62. L. S. Lasdon, "A Multi-Level Technique for Optimization," *Case Inst. of Tech. Report SRC-50-C-64-19* (April 1964).

63. E. S. Lee, *A.I.Ch.E. J.*, *10*, 309 (1964).

64. E. S. Lee, *Chem. Eng. Sci.*, *21*, 183 (1966).

65. I. Lee, *Inform. and Cont.*, *8*, 689 (1965).

66. R. S. Long, *AIAA J.*, *3*, 1351, 1937 (1965).

67. R. McGill and P. Kenneth, *AIAA J.*, *2*, 176 (1964).

68. S. R. McReynolds and A. E. Bryson, "A Successive Sweep Method for Solving Optimal Programming Problems," *presented at 1965 JACC* (June 1965).

69. C. W. MERRIAM, *J. SIAM Control*, *2*, 1 (1964).
70. C. W. MERRIAM, *Inform. and Control*, *8*, 215 (1965).
71. M. D. MESAROVIC, J. D. PEARSON, and Y. TAKOHARA, "A Multilevel Structure for a Class of Linear Dynamic Optimization Problems," *JACC Proceedings* (1965).
72. S. K. MITTER, *Automatica*, *3*, 135 (1966).
73. H. G. MOYER and G. PINKHAM, "Several Trajectory Optimization Techniques. II" in *Computing Methods in Optimization Problems*, Academic Press, 1964.
74. K. OKAMURA, *J. SIAM Control*, *2*, 317 (1965).
75. R. J. RINGLEE, *IEEE Trans. Auto. Control*, *AC-10*, 28 (1965).
76. J. B. ROSEN, "Optimal Control and Convex Programming," *Proceedings IBM Scientific Computing Symposium* (1966).
77. J. B. ROSEN, *J. SIAM*, *8*, 181 (1960); *9*, 514 (1961).
78. R. ROSENBAUM, *AIAA J.*, *1*, 1703 (1963).
79. H. H. ROSENBROCK and C. STORRY, "On the Computation of the Optimal Temperature Profile in a Tubular Reaction Vessel" in Computing Methods in Optimization Problems, Academic Press, 1964.
80. B. F. ROTHENBERGER, "Quasilinearization as a Numerical Method," *Ph.D. Dissertation*, *Princeton University* (1965).
81. D. L. RUSSELL, *J. SIAM Control*, *2*, 409 (1965).
82. C. H. SCHLEY and I. LEE, "Optimal Control Computation by the Newton-Raphson Method and the Riccati Transformation," *JACC Proceedings* (1966).
83. R. T. STANCIL, *AIAA J.*, *2*, 1365 (1964).
84. R. J. SYLVESTER and F. MEYER, *J. SIAM*, *13*, 586 (1965).
85. Y. TAKAHARA, "Multi-Level Approach to Dynamic Optimization," *Case Inst. of Tech. Report SRC 59-A-64-21* (May 1964).
86. P. WOLFE, *Econometrica*, *27*, 382 (1958).

5

Stability and Control of Linear Systems

In this chapter, our main emphasis will be to apply Liapunov's second (direct) method to construct an algorithm which yields the necessary and sufficient conditions for asymptotic stability of linear systems. Besides providing stability information, Liapunov's second method will be shown to be also effective in formulating the solution to the optimal control problem. This is done by minimizing the ratio of the derivative of the Liapunov function with respect to time to the Liapunov function. On this basis one is reassured that the final state equilibrium point is approached as fast as possible. The use of this method to calculate the feedback matrix leads to the familiar steady-state Riccati equation, which was obtained by the maximum principle in Chapter 3.

Although the emphasis is on linear systems in this Chapter, we shall also consider general (and hence nonlinear) systems. In this case the application of Liapunov's second method will be used to generate the optimal control via an iteration procedure. The actual consideration of stability of nonlinear systems is postponed until Chapter 6, where this feature can be considered in detail. The recent reviews of Brockett [16], Lefferts [31], Lefschetz [32], Nesbit [36], Schultz [42], and Szego [46] are instructive for the reader in the areas covered by Chapters 5 and 6.

5.1. Stability of linear stationary systems

Although most of the systems encountered in practice are nonlinear in nature, it must be emphasized that a nonlinear system can always be linearized near a singularity or steady-state point, and if the linearized system is unstable, then also the corresponding nonlinear system is itself unstable. On the other hand, if the linearized system is found to be stable, then also the related nonlinear system is stable even if only locally or in a small region bounding the point. We have already discussed in Chapter 1 the procedure for linearizing a nonlinear system in order to investigate the behavior close enough to a singular point. We have also outlined some systems which by themselves are linear; for example, the linear absorber and the liquid-liquid countercurrent extraction train.

We shall therefore begin our discussion here with the consideration of the simplest case, namely, an autonomous unforced linear system described by the vector-matrix differential Equations (1.20) and (1.25), that is,

$$\dot{\boldsymbol{x}} = \boldsymbol{A}\boldsymbol{x}, \tag{5.1}$$

where $\boldsymbol{A}$ is a constant $n \times n$ matrix called the coefficient matrix, and $\boldsymbol{x}$ is the state vector with n state variables. The solution to this equation has been detailed in Section 1.3, where we wrote the solution in the form of an infinite series given by Equation (1.22), namely,

$$\boldsymbol{x}(t) = \boldsymbol{\Phi}(t)\boldsymbol{x}(0) = \sum_{i=0}^{\infty} \frac{(\boldsymbol{A}t)^i}{i!}\,\boldsymbol{x}(0).$$

Presently, however, we shall construct an alternative solution in terms of the eigenvalues of $\boldsymbol{A}$.

It is well known that the solution to a linear ordinary differential equation, such as Equation (5.1), can be expressed in the form of a sum of exponentials. One such set may be written as

$$\boldsymbol{x} = \boldsymbol{c}e^{\lambda t}, \tag{5.2}$$

where $\boldsymbol{c}$ is a constant column vector of n elements and λ is as yet an undetermined scalar. Differentiating Equation (5.2) with respect to time, we get

$$\dot{\boldsymbol{x}} = \lambda\boldsymbol{c}e^{\lambda t}. \tag{5.3}$$

Substitution of Equation (5.3) into Equation (5.1) gives

$$\lambda\boldsymbol{c}e^{\lambda t} = \boldsymbol{A}\boldsymbol{x}, \tag{5.4}$$

and using Equation (5.2), we shall have

$$[\boldsymbol{A} - \lambda\boldsymbol{I}]\boldsymbol{c}e^{\lambda t} = \boldsymbol{0}, \tag{5.5}$$

where $\boldsymbol{I}$ is the unit matrix of dimension n. In order that the solution to Equation (5.5) be nontrivial, the coefficients of $\boldsymbol{c}$ must vanish; that is, the determinant of the coefficient matrix of $\boldsymbol{c}$ must be zero,

$$\det(\boldsymbol{A} - \lambda \boldsymbol{I}) = 0. \tag{5.6}$$

Let us now expand this nth order determinant to obtain the *characteristic equation*, which may be written in the general polynomial form as

$$f(\lambda) = a_0\lambda^n + a_1\lambda^{n-1} + \cdots + a_{n-1}\lambda + a_n = 0. \tag{5.7}$$

The solution to Equation (5.7) yields the n eigenvalues, $\lambda_1, \lambda_2, \ldots, \lambda_n$, of the matrix $\boldsymbol{A}$. Since the solution to Equation (5.1) is given by the form (5.2), where the eigenvalues appear in the exponential, we see that if the real part of any eigenvalue is positive, the corresponding solution will become unbounded for a sufficiently large value of t. Similarly, if the real part of an eigenvalue is negative, the term on the right-hand side of Equation (5.2) corresponding to that eigenvalue will approach zero. Thus, it is natural to arrive at the following important conclusions.

(1) If *all* roots of the characteristic equation have only negative real parts, the system is asymptotically stable.

(2) If $\mathrm{Re}(\lambda_i) = 0$ for some i and the rest $\mathrm{Re}(\lambda_j) < 0$, the system is said to be *critical.* However, it is evident that such a system does not possess *structural stability* since a small change in any of the parameters of the system could lead to instability. For practical purposes, thus, the system could be considered to be unstable.

(3) If $\mathrm{Re}(\lambda_i) > 0$ for any i, the system is unstable.

In order to determine whether all the eigenvalues, λ_i, have negative real parts, it is not necessary to solve Equation (5.7). The determination of the signs of the real parts of the eigenvalues may be carried out conveniently by either the *Routh–Hurwitz analytical method* or the *Nyquist numerical method* without explicitly solving for the eigenvalues. Both these methods give conditions which indicate the presence or absence of positive real parts.

Let us develop the proof of the Routh–Hurwitz criterion after Hurwitz [22]. Consider the polynomial of degree n which we shall write in the form

$$f(x) = a_0x^n + a_1x^{n-1} + \cdots + a_n, \tag{5.8}$$

where a_0 will always be taken as positive and all the coefficients a_i's will be assumed to be real. Let us denote the n roots of $f(x)$ by $x_1, x_2, \ldots, x_n$, so that Equation (5.8) may be rewritten as

$$f(x) = a_0(x - x_1)(x - x_2) \ldots (x - x_n). \tag{5.9}$$

The problem is now to determine conditions so that the roots $x_1, x_2, \ldots, x_n$ have only negative real parts.

Suppose we now map the x_i's on a plane with the imaginary part plotted vs. the real part. Then, in order that all x_i's have negative real parts, the points must be in the left-hand side of the plane. From Cauchy's principle [7] it is known that if a contour integral is formed, the only contribution to the integral results from poles that are surrounded by the contour. We, therefore, consider a contour C taken along the imaginary axis and around a semicircle of radius R in the left half-plane, as shown in Figure 5.1. If R is sufficiently large, all x_i's with negative real parts will lie within C. Furthermore,

$$\frac{1}{2\pi i}\oint_C \frac{dx}{x - x_i} = \begin{cases} 1 & \text{if} \quad \text{Re}\,(x_i) < 0, \\ 0 & \text{if} \quad \text{Re}\,(x_i) > 0, \end{cases} \tag{5.10}$$

since only the x_i's within the contour contribute to the integral. Here we shall consider the following integral integrated along the above-mentioned contour

$$M = \frac{1}{2\pi i}\oint_C \left(\frac{1}{x - x_1} + \frac{1}{x - x_2} + \cdots + \frac{1}{x - x_n}\right) dx, \tag{5.11}$$

and conclude that if $M = n$, the total number of roots of $f(x)$, then all the roots have negative real parts. We shall determine the conditions to make $M = n$ which will guarantee that *all* the x_i's lie in the left half-plane.

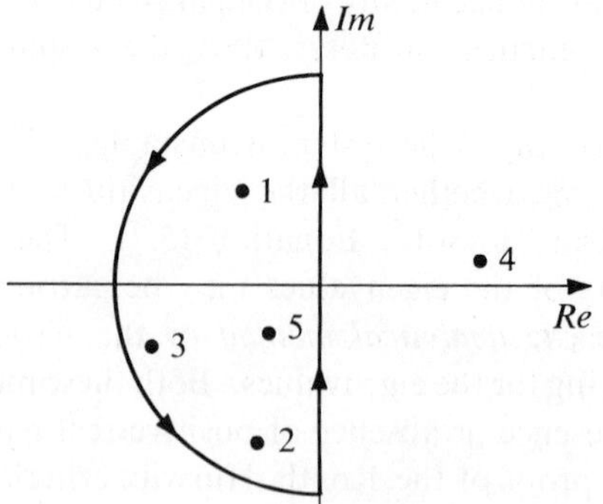

FIGURE 5.1. Illustration of the contour C for integration. The points 1, 2, 3 and 5 are within the region surrounded by the contour; the point 4 is outside.

From Equation (5.9), we note that

$$\frac{1}{x - x_1} + \frac{1}{x - x_2} + \cdots + \frac{1}{x - x_n} = \frac{f'(x)}{f(x)}. \tag{5.12}$$

We can further write Equation (5.12) as

$$\frac{f'(x)}{f(x)} = \frac{d}{dx}[\log f(x)] = \frac{d}{dx}[\log|f(x)| + i\arg f(x)]. \tag{5.13}$$

Therefore we can replace Equation (5.11) by

$$M = \frac{1}{2\pi i}\oint_C \frac{d}{dx}[\log|f(x)| + i\arg f(x)]\,dx. \tag{5.14}$$

Since $\log|f(x)|$ is single-valued, the only contribution to the contour integral comes from the argument, and thus

$$M = 1/2\pi\,\Delta\arg f(x), \tag{5.15}$$

where $\Delta\arg f(x)$ is the change in the argument of $f(x)$ after contour integration.

Now let us find an expression for $\Delta\arg f(x)$ on the semicircular part of the contour C. From Equation (5.8), we may factor out a_0x^n to give

$$f(x) = a_0x^n\left[1 + \frac{a_1x^{-1}}{a_0} + \cdots + \frac{a_nx^{-n}}{a_0}\right]. \tag{5.16}$$

Let

$$x = Re^{i\theta}, \tag{5.17}$$

and substitute into Equation (5.16) to give

$$f(x) = a_0R^ne^{in\theta}\left[1 + \frac{a_1}{a_0R}e^{-i\theta} + \cdots + \frac{a_n}{a_0R^n}e^{-in\theta}\right].$$

If R is chosen to be large, it follows that

$$f(x) = a_0R^ne^{in\theta}[1 + 0(1/R)]. \tag{5.18}$$

Now letting R approach ∞, and noting that θ changes by π in traversing the semicircle, we obtain the change in the argument *on the semicircular part of C*, namely,

$$\Delta\arg f(x) = n\pi. \tag{5.19}$$

Next, we find an expression for $\Delta\arg f(x)$ on the imaginary axis. Note that if $f(x)$ is multiplied by an arbitrary complex constant, the change in $\arg f(x)$ is not altered. Letting $x = -iz$, we consider $i^nf(-iz)$ as the real variable, where z varies from $+\infty$ to $-\infty$. This is equivalent to having x vary from $-i\infty$ to $+i\infty$. Thus, if we separate the real and imaginary parts by writing

$$i^nf(-iz) = U(z) + iV(z) \tag{5.20}$$

and define

$$R(z) \equiv V(z)/U(z) \equiv \tan(\pi\phi), \tag{5.21}$$

we see that

$$\pi\phi = \tan^{-1} R(z) = \arg\,[i^n f(-iz)]. \tag{5.22}$$

It is easy to observe that the change in arg $f(x)$ as x varies from $-i\infty$ to $+i\infty$ on the imaginary axis is equal to the increase in $\pi\phi$ as z varies from $+\infty$ to $-\infty$. This increase will be denoted by $\pi\Delta\phi$. The total contribution to the contour integral will be this increase in ϕ plus the change in the arg $f(x)$ along the semicircle. Hence,

$$M = (n + \Delta\phi)/2, \tag{5.23}$$

and it is evident that *all* the roots lie in the left half-plane ($M = n$) if and only if

$$\Delta\phi = n. \tag{5.24}$$

Using Equation (5.8), we note that

$$\begin{aligned} i^n f(-iz) &= i^n[a_0(-1)^n i^n z^n + a_1(-1)^{n-1} i^{n-1} z^{n-1} + a_2(-1)^{n-2} i^{n-2} z^{n-2} + \cdots + a_n \\ &= a_0(-1)^n i^{2n} z^n + a_1(-1)^{n-1} i^{2n-1} z^{n-1} \\ &\quad + a_2(-1)^{n-2} i^{2n-2} z^{n-2} + \cdots + a_n \\ &= (a_0 z^n - a_2 z^{n-2} + \cdots) + i(a_1 z^{n-1} - a_3 z^{n-3} + \cdots), \end{aligned}$$

and therefore,

$$R(z) = \frac{a_1 z^{n-1} - a_3 z^{n-3} + \cdots}{a_0 z^n - a_2 z^{n-2} + \cdots}. \tag{5.25}$$

The problem is thus reduced to the determination of the change in $\tan^{-1} R(z)$ as z goes from $+\infty$ to $-\infty$. Since $R(z)$ is a real function of the real variable z, it can also be graphed. By considering this graph, we can readily deduce the following general conclusions:

(1) $\Delta\phi = 0$ if $R(z)$ has no poles.
(2) Between two poles, ϕ changes by $+1$, -1, or 0.
(3) $\Delta\phi = n$ if and only if $R(z)$ has n poles.
(4) $\Delta\phi = n$ if and only if the roots of $U(z)$ and $V(z)$ are real and interlocking (between two roots of V there is a root of U, and conversely).
(5) $\Delta\phi = n$ if and only if R has n distinct poles and $c_i > 0$, $i = 1, 2, \ldots, n$, where c_i is defined by the expansion of $R(z)$ in the neighborhood of a pole at a_i,

$$R(z) = c_i/(z - a_i) + \cdots. \tag{5.26}$$

(6) $\Delta\phi$ is decreased by 2 for every c_i which is negative.
(7) $\Delta\phi$ is decreased by 1 for every pole which is absent.
(8) $\Delta\phi$ is decreased by 1 for every common root of $U(z)$ and $V(z)$.
(9) $\Delta\phi$ is decreased by 2λ for every pole of order 2λ.

(10) $\Delta\phi$ is decreased by $2\lambda + 1 \pm 1$ for every pole of order $2\lambda + 1$, the sign being opposite to the sign of D_i in the expansion

$$R(z) = \frac{D_i}{(z - a_i)^{2\lambda+1}} + \cdots. \tag{5.27}$$

The main feature of this derivation is the introduction of the quadratic form defined by

$$Q = \frac{1}{2\pi i} \oint_{\Gamma} R(z)[\theta(z)]^2 \, dz, \tag{5.28}$$

where

$$\theta(z) = y_1 + y_2 z + \cdots + y_n z^{n-1}.$$

The quantities $y_1, y_2, \ldots, y_n$ are arbitrary, real parameters. The function $R(z)$ is now continued into the complex z-plane and the contour Γ is chosen sufficiently large to enclose all the poles of R, which in general, may lie off the real axis.

Upon integration, we see that Q has the form

$$Q = \sum_{i,j=1}^{n} b_{ij} y_i y_j = \boldsymbol{y}'\boldsymbol{B}\boldsymbol{y}, \tag{5.29}$$

where $\boldsymbol{B}$ is the matrix of the quadratic form, $\boldsymbol{y}$ is a column vector, and $\boldsymbol{y}'$ is its transpose. It is clear that by appropriate redefinition, if necessary, $\boldsymbol{B}$ can always be chosen symmetric. It is known that any real, symmetric matrix can be diagonalized, that is, there exists a real orthogonal matrix $\boldsymbol{A}$, such that

$$\boldsymbol{A}\boldsymbol{B}\boldsymbol{A}' = \begin{bmatrix} \lambda_1^2 &&&&&&&& \\ & \lambda_2^2 &&&&&&& \\ && \ddots &&&&&& \\ &&& \lambda_p^2 &&&&& \\ &&&& -\lambda_{p+1}^2 &&&& \\ &&&&& \ddots &&& \\ &&&&&& -\lambda_r^2 && \\ &&&&&&& 0 & \\ &&&&&&&& \ddots \\ &&&&&&&&& 0 \end{bmatrix} = \boldsymbol{D}, \tag{5.30}$$

a diagonal matrix.

The number of nonzero characteristic values, r, is equal to the rank of $\boldsymbol{B}$; the number of these nonzero characteristic values which are positive is called the index, p, of $\boldsymbol{B}$.

Now we introduce a new vector $\boldsymbol{v}$ by the linear transformation

$$\boldsymbol{v} = \boldsymbol{A}\boldsymbol{y}, \tag{5.31}$$

so that

$$\boldsymbol{y} = \boldsymbol{A}^{-1}\boldsymbol{v} = \boldsymbol{A}'\boldsymbol{v}. \tag{5.32}$$

Then

$$Q = \boldsymbol{y}'\boldsymbol{B}\boldsymbol{y} = (\boldsymbol{A}'\boldsymbol{v})'\boldsymbol{B}(\boldsymbol{A}'\boldsymbol{v}) = \boldsymbol{v}'(\boldsymbol{A}\boldsymbol{B}\boldsymbol{A}')\boldsymbol{v} = \boldsymbol{v}'\boldsymbol{D}\boldsymbol{v}.$$

Thus, it follows that

$$Q = \lambda_1^2 v_1^2 + \lambda_2^2 v_2^2 + \cdots + \lambda_p^2 v_p^2 - \lambda_{p+1}^2 v_{p+1}^2 - \cdots - \lambda_r^2 v_r^2. \tag{5.33}$$

If $p = n = r$, then Q is said to be positive-definite. The necessary and sufficient conditions for this to be the case are that $B_\nu > 0$, $\nu = 1, 2, \ldots, n$, where B_ν is the determinant of the leading principal minor of $\boldsymbol{B}$,

$$B_\nu = \begin{vmatrix} b_{11} & \cdots & b_{1\nu} \\ \vdots & & \vdots \\ b_{\nu 1} & \cdots & b_{\nu\nu} \end{vmatrix}. \tag{5.34}$$

Now let us return to the definition of Q as a contour integral and evaluate it by residues. Since $\theta^2(z)$ is analytic, the only poles inside Γ are those of $R(z)$. At a simple pole on the real axis, the residue is $c_i[\theta(a_i)]^2$, which has the form $\pm A_i^2$, where A_i is a real linear combination of the y's and the sign is the same as the sign of c_i. Because the poles of $R(z)$ are determined by the roots of the polynomial $U(z)$, the poles of $R(z)$ off the real axis will occur in complex conjugate pairs. The contribution to Q from the residues of such a pair will be equal to

$$\begin{aligned} c_j[\theta(a_j)]^2 + c_j^*[\theta(a_j^*)]^2 &= (A_j + iB_j)^2 + [A_j - iB_j]^2 \\ &= 2A_j^2 - 2B_j^2, \end{aligned} \tag{5.35}$$

where A_j and B_j are real linear combinations of the y's. Similar results can be obtained for poles of higher multiplicity. For a pole on the real axis of order 2λ, the residue will consist of λ positive squares and λ negative squares; if the order is $2\lambda + 1$, there will be λ positive squares and λ negative squares, with the sign of the last term determined by the sign of D_i in Equation (5.26). Similar results hold for multiple poles off the real axis.

The difference between the positive squares and the negative squares in Q is called the *signature* of Q,

$$s = p - q = 2p - r, \tag{5.36}$$

and we find that

$$\Delta\phi = s. \tag{5.37}$$

The number of roots of $f(x)$ in the left half-plane is then obtained from the relation

$$M = \tfrac{1}{2}(n + \Delta\phi) = \tfrac{1}{2}(n + s). \tag{5.38}$$

The main result of interest here is that *all* the roots of $f(x)$ lie in the left half-plane if and only if Q is a positive-definite quadratic form ($p = s = r = n$). This is equivalent to the condition that the matrix $\boldsymbol{B}$ is positive-definite.

To express this condition in terms of the coefficients of the polynomial $f(x)$, we must evaluate the determinants of the leading principal minors of $\boldsymbol{B}$ in terms of $a_0, a_1, \ldots, a_n$. We expand $R(z)$ at ∞:

$$R(z) = \frac{a_1 z^{n-1} - a_3 z^{n-3} + \cdots}{a_0 z^n - a_2 z^{n-2} + \cdots} = \frac{b_1}{z} + \frac{b_2}{z^2} + \frac{b_3}{z^3} + \cdots. \tag{5.39}$$

Then

$$R(z)[\theta(z)]^2 = \sum_{k=1}^{\infty} \frac{b_k}{z^k} \sum_{l,m=1}^{n} y_l y_m z^{l+m-2} = \sum_{k=1}^{\infty} \left(\sum_{l,m=1}^{n} b_k y_l y_m z^{l+m-2-k} \right), \tag{5.40}$$

and immediately

$$(\mathrm{Res})_\infty = \sum_{l,m=1}^{n} b_{l+m-1} y_l y_m = Q = \boldsymbol{y}'\boldsymbol{B}\boldsymbol{y}, \tag{5.41}$$

where

$$\boldsymbol{B} = \begin{bmatrix} b_1 & b_2 & b_3 & \cdots & b_n \\ b_2 & b_3 & b_4 & \cdots & b_{n+1} \\ \vdots & & & & \vdots \\ b_n & b_{n+1} & b_{n+2} & \cdots & b_{2n-1} \end{bmatrix}, \tag{5.42}$$

and the necessary and sufficient conditions that $\boldsymbol{B}$ be positive-definite are that

$$B_\nu = \begin{vmatrix} b_1 & \cdots & b_\nu \\ \vdots & & \vdots \\ b_\nu & \cdots & b_{2\nu-1} \end{vmatrix} > 0, \qquad \text{for} \quad \nu = 1, 2, \ldots, n, \tag{5.43}$$

and it is found that the set of inequalities (5.43) is precisely equivalent to the set of inequalities

$$H_\mu > 0, \qquad \mu = 1, 2, \ldots, n, \tag{5.44}$$

where

$$H_\mu = \begin{vmatrix} a_1 & a_3 & a_5 & \cdots & a_{2\mu-1} \\ a_0 & a_2 & a_4 & & a_{2\mu-2} \\ 0 & a_1 & a_3 & & a_{2\mu-3} \\ 0 & a_0 & a_2 & \cdots & a_{2\mu-4} \\ \vdots & & & & \vdots \\ 0 & 0 & 0 & \cdots & a_{\mu+1} \\ 0 & 0 & 0 & \cdots & a_\mu \end{vmatrix}$$

is the *Hurwitz determinant* of degree μ.

As a consequence we may state the Hurwitz criterion: "All roots of the polynomial of degree n

$$f(x) = a_0 x^n + a_1 x^{n-1} + \cdots + a_{n-1}x + a_n,$$

with $a_0 > 0$, have negative real parts if and only if $H_\mu > 0$, $\mu = 1, 2, \ldots, n$." In other words, if we construct the following determinants

$$\Delta_1 = a_1, \qquad \Delta_2 = \begin{vmatrix} a_1 & a_3 \\ a_0 & a_2 \end{vmatrix}, \qquad \Delta_3 = \begin{vmatrix} a_1 & a_3 & a_5 \\ a_0 & a_2 & a_4 \\ 0 & a_1 & a_3 \end{vmatrix}, \ldots,$$

$$\Delta_{n-1} = \begin{vmatrix} a_1 & a_3 & a_5 & \cdots & 0 \\ a_0 & a_2 & a_4 & & 0 \\ 0 & a_1 & a_3 & \cdots & 0 \\ \vdots & & & & \vdots \\ 0 & 0 & 0 & \cdots & a_{n-1} \end{vmatrix}, \qquad \Delta_n = a_n \Delta_{n-1},$$

and (a) all a_i are positive, and (b) all the determinants are positive, then the system (5.1) is asymptotically stable.

A great shortcoming of the application of the Routh–Hurwitz criterion is the absence of the idea of the relative stability of the system; if the system is found to be stable, it is not apparent "how stable" it is. In other words, without detailed evaluation of the determinants no information is given whether the system remains stable if a parameter is changed in the describing equation; if the system is found to be unstable, the Routh–Hurwitz criterion does not provide immediately a stabilization procedure. The Nyquist criterion, on the other hand, accomplishes the same end graphically and, in addition, provides information concerning the relative stability. Since the Nyquist method has been presented in detail in many books [2, 5], it will not be outlined here. However, the Routh–Hurwitz criterion does provide a rapid and convenient means of stability determination, and its use is outlined in the next section.

5.2. Two-dimensional system, phase-plane representation

Although the physical systems usually encountered are multidimensional, there is some virtue in considering in some detail a system describable by only two state variables. First, a detailed study of such a system can give valuable insight into the behavior of more complex systems. This follows from the fact that it illustrates effectively how the state variables are coupled together to yield a wide variety of possible trajectories for even such a seemingly simple system. Second, it is essential that some background be developed for the study of stability of nonlinear systems in the following chapter, and the examination of a simple linear system appears appropriate for this purpose.

We shall therefore consider a system described by two first-order ordinary linear differential equations in the form

$$\dot{x} = ax + by, \qquad \dot{y} = cx + dy, \tag{5.45}$$

where x and y are state-variables and a, b, c, and d are constants. The origin defined by $x = 0$, $y = 0$ is called the *singular point*, since it is where both $\dot{x}$ and $\dot{y}$ vanish simultaneously. It is desired to investigate the nature of this singular point for different values of a, b, c, and d. In other words, we wish to know the nature of the trajectories approaching or leaving the origin. The notation of either approaching or leaving the origin is equivalent, depending on whether time is measured in a positive or negative direction.

By differentiating the first equation with respect to time, we can eliminate y,

$$\ddot{x} = a\dot{x} + b\left[cx + d\left(\frac{\dot{x} - ax}{b}\right)\right],$$

which we may write as

$$[D^2 - (a + d)D + (ad - bc)]x = 0, \tag{5.46}$$

where $D = d/dt$ is the differential operator.

To determine the stability of this system, we may use the Routh–Hurwitz criterion of Section 5.1. The coefficients of the characteristic equation are immediately identified as

$$a_0 = 1, \qquad a_1 = -(a + d), \qquad a_2 = (ad - bc), \tag{5.47}$$

and to have all these coefficients positive (the first condition) it is necessary that $(a + d) < 0$ and $(ad - bc) > 0$. Also, the determinants as defined by

$$\Delta_1 = a_1 = -(a + d), \qquad \Delta_2 = \begin{vmatrix} a_1 & 0 \\ a_0 & a_2 \end{vmatrix} = -(a + d)(ad - bc), \tag{5.48}$$

must be positive. At this point, it might be instructive to draw attention to the redundancy of the Routh–Hurwitz criterion, as has been observed by Gantmacher [4] and has been again drawn to the reader's attention by Zadeh and Desoer [13]. It is quite obvious that if all the coefficients of the characteristic equation are positive, and if the determinants of odd-order are positive, then those of even-order are also positive, and vice versa. Therefore, in the above case it would have been sufficient to demand only that a_0, a_1, a_2, and Δ_1 be positive. (Even this is a bit redundant, since $\Delta_1 = a_1$.) We shall not go into detail here on this matter, but will mention only that there exists a more efficient test for stability that does not involve redundancy.

We, therefore, have the important result that the two conditions

$$(a + d) < 0, \qquad (ad - bc) > 0 \tag{5.49}$$

ensure that the roots of the characteristic equation have only negative real parts and that the system as described by Equation (5.45) is asymptotically stable. Once we have this stability information, it is useful to know the nature of the trajectories in the vicinity of the origin. For this reason, we shall arbitrarily take (1, 0) as a starting point and integrate Equation (5.46) with the initial conditions

$$x(0) = 1, \qquad \left[\frac{dx}{dt} - ax\right]_{t=0} = 0. \tag{5.50}$$

The general solution of Equation (5.46) is

$$x = Ae^{\lambda_1 t} + Be^{\lambda_2 t}, \tag{5.51}$$

where A, B are arbitrary constants to be determined from the initial conditions, and

$$\lambda_1 = \tfrac{1}{2}\{(a + d) + \sqrt{(a + d)^2 - 4(ad - bc)}\},$$

$$\lambda_2 = \tfrac{1}{2}\{(a + d) - \sqrt{(a + d)^2 - 4(ad - bc)}\}.$$

By using the initial condition as given by Equations (5.50), A and B can be evaluated, and y can also be readily obtained. The results are

$$x = \frac{\exp\left[\frac{1}{2}(a + d)t\right]}{\alpha}\left[(a - d)\sinh \tfrac{1}{2}\alpha t + \alpha \cosh \tfrac{1}{2}\alpha t\right], \tag{5.52}$$

$$y = (2c/\alpha)\exp\left[\tfrac{1}{2}(a + d)t\right]\sinh \tfrac{1}{2}\alpha t, \tag{5.53}$$

where

$$\alpha = \lambda_1 - \lambda_2 = \sqrt{(a + d)^2 - 4(ad - bc)} = \sqrt{(a - d)^2 + 4bc}. \tag{5.54}$$

We shall use Equations (5.52) and (5.53) again in Chapter 6, but now let us look at the form of the general solution as given by Equation (5.51). We note that if $(ad - bc) > 0$, the signs of λ_1 and λ_2 are determined by the sign of $(a + d)$. If, however, $(ad - bc) < 0$, then $\lambda_1 > 0$, regardless of the value of $(a + d)$. This reaffirms the conclusions about stability as determined by the Routh–Hurwitz criterion and expressed by the inequalities (5.49). We therefore have the following two cases:

CASE 1. $(ad - bc) < 0$. The singularity is a *saddle point* which is always unstable. (A saddle point can be thought of as a stagnation point in fluid dynamics, where the streamlines represent the trajectories.)

CASE 2. $(ad - bc) > 0$. This case can be really subdivided further. (a) If $(a + d)^2 - 4(ad - bc) < 0$, α as defined by Equation (5.54) is imaginary, and the solutions as expressed by Equations (5.52) and (5.53), for example, are sinusoidal. This singularity is called a *focus*, and it is obvious that it is stable only if $(a + d) < 0$. (b) If $(a + d)^2 - 4(ad - bc) \geq 0$, α is real and the solutions are hyperbolic, as given by Equations (5.52) and (5.53), for example. This singularity is called a *node*, which, again, is stable if $(a + d) < 0$.

If the reader is unfamiliar with the nature of the trajectories for the saddle point, focus, and the node, it is recommended that any of the various books on nonlinear mechanics be examined, such as those written by Andronov and Chaikin [1], Cunningham [3], Gibson [5], Ku [8], Malkin [10], Minorsky [11], or Saaty and Bram [12]. The papers of Perlmutter and associates [15, 20] and Aris [37, 48] are also of interest. We would now like to draw the reader's attention to the case of the focus, and especially to the time required to perform one cycle in the phase plane. If we define the angle measured in the phase plane by

$$\psi = \tan^{-1}(y/x), \tag{5.55}$$

then it follows directly from Equation (5.54) that when α is imaginary,

$$\psi = \phi_0 + [\operatorname{sgn}(c - b)][\tfrac{1}{2}\sqrt{-(a - d)^2 - 4bc}]t, \tag{5.56}$$

or the time for one cycle is

$$T = 4\pi/\sqrt{-(a - d)^2 - 4bc}. \tag{5.57}$$

Once we know the type of singularity and the period of a cycle in the case of a focus, the phase portrait can be readily obtained. The classical construction methods such as the isocline method, where slopes dy/dx are calculated and drawn at different points, the δ-method or Pell's method have largely been replaced by the advent of the computer technology. Now the equations can be directly integrated and plotted by an analog or a digital computer. It must be emphasized that in spite of the dimensionality limitations, the phase plane representation is even convenient for some higher-order systems where the projections of the trajectories in space on a plane can give a good visual picture of the behavior of the whole system. In the consideration of nonlinear systems, the knowledge of the related linearized systems is essential. In nonlinear systems there are additional complications resulting from the possibility of multiple singular points and the possibility of limit-cycle behavior. These are detailed in Chapter 6.

5.3. Liapunov function for linear continuous-time stationary systems

In Section 2.5 we outlined in some detail Liapunov's second method for determining the stability of a system, and we illustrated the method of approach to the consideration of a second-order linear system. In this section we would like to expand on that development by considering a multidimensional linear continuous-time stationary system which is described by the unforced differential equation

$$\dot{\boldsymbol{x}} = \boldsymbol{A}\boldsymbol{x}, \tag{5.58}$$

where $\boldsymbol{x}$ is an n-dimensional vector and $\boldsymbol{A}$ is a constant $n \times n$ matrix. To control such a system a control term is added, but for the moment let us consider the uncontrolled system as described by Equation (5.58).

For a Liapunov function we shall take a quadratic form

$$V(\boldsymbol{x}) = \boldsymbol{x}'\boldsymbol{Q}\boldsymbol{x}, \tag{5.59}$$

where the matrix $\boldsymbol{Q}$ is chosen to be a constant positive-definite symmetric $n \times n$ matrix so that $V(\boldsymbol{x})$ will be positive-definite. If the system is asymptotically stable, we can choose $\boldsymbol{Q}$ in such a manner that the derivative of $V(\boldsymbol{x})$ is negative-definite. Then we can express this as

$$\dot{V}(\boldsymbol{x}) = -\boldsymbol{x}'\boldsymbol{C}\boldsymbol{x}, \tag{5.60}$$

where $\boldsymbol{C}$ is a constant positive-definite symmetric $n \times n$ matrix. By differentiating Equation (5.59), we obtain

$$\dot{V}(\boldsymbol{x}) = \dot{\boldsymbol{x}}'\boldsymbol{Q}\boldsymbol{x} + \boldsymbol{x}'\boldsymbol{Q}\dot{\boldsymbol{x}} = \boldsymbol{x}'(\boldsymbol{A}'\boldsymbol{Q} + \boldsymbol{Q}\boldsymbol{A})\boldsymbol{x}. \tag{5.61}$$

Therefore,

$$\boldsymbol{A}'\boldsymbol{Q} + \boldsymbol{Q}\boldsymbol{A} = -\boldsymbol{C}. \tag{5.62}$$

Now let us recall the fundamental theorem of Liapunov as outlined in Section 2.5, namely,

If a positive-definite function can be found such that its time derivative is negative-definite, then the system is asymptotically stable.

If such positive-definite symmetric matrices $\boldsymbol{Q}$ and $\boldsymbol{C}$ can be found to satisfy Equation (5.62), then these conditions for Liapunov's theorem on asymptotic stability are satisfied, that is, there exists a positive-definite scalar function of the state such that its derivative with respect to time is negative-definite. Hence, under these conditions the system is asymptotically stable.

If the eigenvalues of A are nonzero and none of the sums $\lambda_i + \lambda_j$ $(i, j = 1, 2, \ldots, n)$ vanishes, Equation (5.62) gives a system of unique linear equations for the $[n(n+1)]/2$ unknown elements q_{ij} of $\boldsymbol{Q}$. The matrix $\boldsymbol{Q}$ can be determined by the solution of the linear simultaneous equations, and it will be positive-definite if and only if A has eigenvalues with negative real parts. This can be proved either by the reduction of the matrix to triangular form, as done by Hahn [21], or by the concept of Kronecker product method, as formulated by Bellman [14].

To construct a solution of Equation (5.62) in integral form, let us consider the integral

$$V[\boldsymbol{x}(t)] - V[\boldsymbol{x}(0)] = \int_0^t \dot{V}(\boldsymbol{x})\,dt, \tag{5.63}$$

which, with the help of Equation (5.60), may be written as

$$V[\boldsymbol{x}(t)] - V[\boldsymbol{x}(0)] = -\int_0^t \boldsymbol{x}'\boldsymbol{C}\boldsymbol{x}\,dt. \tag{5.64}$$

If the system is asymptotically stable, $\boldsymbol{x}(t)$ approaches $\boldsymbol{0}$ as $t \to \infty$, and thus Equation (5.64) gives

$$0 - \boldsymbol{x}'(0)\boldsymbol{Q}\boldsymbol{x}(0) = -\int_0^\infty \boldsymbol{x}'\boldsymbol{C}\boldsymbol{x}\,dt. \tag{5.65}$$

However, the solution to Equation (5.58) can be expressed as Equation (1.21):

$$\boldsymbol{x}(t) = \exp(\boldsymbol{A}t)\boldsymbol{x}(0), \tag{5.66}$$

and since

$$\boldsymbol{x}'(t) = \boldsymbol{x}'(0)\exp(\boldsymbol{A}'t), \tag{5.67}$$

we can substitute Equations (5.66) and (5.67) into the right-hand side of Equation (5.65) to give

$$\boldsymbol{x}'(0)\boldsymbol{Q}\boldsymbol{x}(0) = \boldsymbol{x}'(0)\left\{\int_0^\infty [\exp(\boldsymbol{A}'t)]\boldsymbol{C}[\exp(\boldsymbol{A}t)]\,dt\right\}\boldsymbol{x}(0). \tag{5.68}$$

But since $\boldsymbol{x}(0)$ is arbitrary, it follows that

$$\boldsymbol{Q} = \int_0^\infty \exp(\boldsymbol{A}'t)\boldsymbol{C}\exp(\boldsymbol{A}t)\,dt \tag{5.69}$$

is an integral solution of Equation (5.62) provided that the eigenvalues of A all have negative real parts.

To show that Equation (5.69) is truly a solution of Equation (5.62), we shall substitute the expression for $\boldsymbol{Q}$ as given by Equation (5.69) in the left-hand side of Equation (5.62). This yields

$$\begin{aligned} A'Q + QA &= \int_0^\infty [A' \exp(A't)C \exp(At) + \exp(A't)C \exp(At)A]\, dt \\ &= \int_0^\infty \frac{d}{dt} [\exp(A't)C \exp(At)]\, dt = -C, \end{aligned}$$

which is the right-hand side of Equation (5.62) provided that all the eigenvalues of $\boldsymbol{A}$ have negative real parts.

In the present work we shall not be concerned with critical cases where some of the eigenvalues have vanishing real parts and the rest have negative real parts, since in most physical systems the parameters are not defined precisely enough to warrant such accurate analysis. Such systems are said to be *structurally unstable*, since a little change in some parameters can change the vanishing real part to a positive real part and the system will become unstable.

For linear stationary systems, then, the problem of stability determination is reduced to ascertaining a positive-definite solution $\boldsymbol{Q}$ for Equation (5.62). If such a solution can be found, the system is asymptotically stable because a Liapunov function which is positive-definite and has a negative-definite derivative will also then have been found. Due to the nature of the linear system, the stability will be global.

As we saw above, from a choice of the matrix $\boldsymbol{C}$ we can determine the matrix $\boldsymbol{Q}$. However, in practice the reverse procedure is used, in which the matrix $\boldsymbol{Q}$ is chosen arbitrarily to satisfy some physical intuition about the problem; Equation (5.62) is then used to ensure that the choice has been appropriate. We try to have $\boldsymbol{Q}$ as simple as possible, and most frequently we choose a diagonal matrix (such as the identity matrix). Then the Liapunov function is easily interpreted as some measure of distance from the equilibrium point.

But now we want to turn to the controlled system, that is,

$$\dot{x} = Ax + Bu, \tag{5.70}$$

and raise the question of how the added control term complicates the situation. It is quite obvious that with the applied control, the desired singular point is reached sooner and a stable system remains stable. The choice of the control vector $\boldsymbol{u}$ to get the "best" response depends on the choice of the Liapunov function, V, and as we shall point out in Section 5.5, one approach is to choose $\boldsymbol{u}$ so that the ratio $\dot{V}/V$ is minimized to maximize the rate of approach to the origin.

5.4. Liapunov function for linear discrete-time stationary system

Up to now in this chapter, we have been considering continuous-time systems. The construction of a Liapunov function for a discrete-time system is quite analogous, and we shall just briefly draw this similarity to the reader's attention.

Let us consider a system described by the standard unforced difference equation

$$\boldsymbol{x}(k+1) = \boldsymbol{\Phi x}(k), \tag{5.71}$$

where $\boldsymbol{x}(k)$ is an n-dimensional state vector and $\boldsymbol{\Phi}$ is a constant $n \times n$ matrix. The sampling time T has been omitted for convenience. To construct a Liapunov function for this system, we again seek a quadratic form

$$V[\boldsymbol{x}(k)] = \boldsymbol{x}'(k)\boldsymbol{Q}\boldsymbol{x}(k) \tag{5.72}$$

which will be positive-definite, since $\boldsymbol{Q}$ is chosen to be a positive-definite symmetric matrix. Again, $\boldsymbol{Q}$ is usually selected to be a diagonal matrix such as the identity matrix.

The forward difference of $V[\boldsymbol{x}(k)]$ (analogous to the first derivative in the continuous case) is

$$\Delta V[\boldsymbol{x}(k)] = V[\boldsymbol{x}(k+1)] - V[\boldsymbol{x}(k)], \tag{5.73}$$

$$\begin{aligned} \Delta V[\boldsymbol{x}(k)] &= \boldsymbol{x}'(k+1)\boldsymbol{Q}\boldsymbol{x}(k+1) - \boldsymbol{x}'(k)\boldsymbol{Q}\boldsymbol{x}(k) \\ &= \boldsymbol{x}'(k)[\boldsymbol{\Phi}'\boldsymbol{Q}\boldsymbol{\Phi} - \boldsymbol{Q}]\boldsymbol{x}(k). \end{aligned} \tag{5.74}$$

To make $\Delta V[\boldsymbol{x}(k)]$ negative-definite (for stability), we choose $\boldsymbol{Q}$ such that

$$\boldsymbol{\Phi}'\boldsymbol{Q}\boldsymbol{\Phi} - \boldsymbol{Q} = -\boldsymbol{P}, \tag{5.75}$$

where $\boldsymbol{P}$ is a positive-definite symmetric matrix. If such a positive-definite function $V[\boldsymbol{x}(k)]$ whose forward difference is negative-definite can be found, the system will be asymptotically stable. In other words, for asymptotic stability of the system, Equation (5.75) must have a unique solution.

As was the case for the continuous system, with control we may write the system equation as

$$\boldsymbol{x}(k+1) = \boldsymbol{\Phi x}(k) + \boldsymbol{\Delta}(k), \tag{5.76}$$

where the vector $\boldsymbol{\Delta}(k)$ containing the control has been added. In choosing the appropriate control, one approach is to try to minimize $\Delta V[\boldsymbol{x}(k)]$ as given in Equation (5.73), which becomes, for Equation (5.76),

$$\Delta V(\boldsymbol{x}(k)) = [(\boldsymbol{\Phi}'\boldsymbol{Q}\boldsymbol{\Phi} - \boldsymbol{Q})\boldsymbol{x}(k) + 2\boldsymbol{\Phi}'\boldsymbol{Q}\boldsymbol{\Delta}]'\boldsymbol{x}(k) + \boldsymbol{\Delta}'\boldsymbol{Q}\boldsymbol{\Delta}. \tag{5.77}$$

This approach is discussed in some detail in Section 5.5 and is illustrated in Section 5.9.

5.5. Nonuniqueness of Liapunov function and application to control

We have already mentioned that one significant advantage of the Liapunov direct method over the conventional energy considerations is the freedom in choosing the trial functions. This is of special help when there exists some intuitive feeling as to the behavior of the system but, at the same time, it is hard to express this in rigorous mathematical formulation. From experience, one may then suggest some trial function which might be a suitable Liapunov function for the system. To show the freedom of choice of the trial functions, let us consider again the linear stationary continuous unforced system described by

$$\dot{\boldsymbol{x}} = \boldsymbol{A}\boldsymbol{x}. \tag{5.78}$$

This time, let us choose as a trial function

$$V_2(\boldsymbol{x}) = \dot{\boldsymbol{x}}'\boldsymbol{Q}\dot{\boldsymbol{x}}, \tag{5.79}$$

where $\boldsymbol{Q}$ is again a positive-definite symmetric matrix. Our aim is to show that this new function is also a suitable Liapunov function if all eigenvalues of $\boldsymbol{A}$ have negative real parts.

First, let us calculate the derivative of $V_2(x)$,

$$\dot{V}_2(\boldsymbol{x}) = \ddot{\boldsymbol{x}}'\boldsymbol{Q}\dot{\boldsymbol{x}} + \dot{\boldsymbol{x}}'\boldsymbol{Q}\ddot{\boldsymbol{x}}, \tag{5.80}$$

$$\dot{V}_2(\boldsymbol{x}) = \dot{\boldsymbol{x}}'\boldsymbol{A}'\boldsymbol{Q}\dot{\boldsymbol{x}} + \dot{\boldsymbol{x}}'\boldsymbol{Q}\boldsymbol{A}\dot{\boldsymbol{x}}, \tag{5.81}$$

$$\dot{V}_2(\boldsymbol{x}) = \dot{\boldsymbol{x}}'(\boldsymbol{A}'\boldsymbol{Q} + \boldsymbol{Q}\boldsymbol{A})\dot{\boldsymbol{x}}. \tag{5.82}$$

However, from Equation (5.62), we see that the quantity in the parentheses can be put equal to $-\boldsymbol{C}$. Therefore,

$$\dot{V}_2(\boldsymbol{x}) = -\dot{\boldsymbol{x}}'\boldsymbol{C}\dot{\boldsymbol{x}}, \tag{5.83}$$

where

$$\boldsymbol{C} = -(\boldsymbol{A}'\boldsymbol{Q} + \boldsymbol{Q}\boldsymbol{A}), \tag{5.84}$$

is a positive-definite symmetric matrix if all eigenvalues of $\boldsymbol{A}$ have negative real parts. At this point, we should emphasize that for nonlinear systems different stability regions can be obtained with the use of different Liapunov functions, and the effort is directed toward finding Liapunov functions that give the largest region of stability. This point will be considered again in Chapter 6.

For a linear system, stability is always global, so that the use of different Liapunov functions does not give any additional information regarding the size of the region. However, when we consider the two Liapunov functions $\boldsymbol{x}'\boldsymbol{Q}\boldsymbol{x}$ and $\dot{\boldsymbol{x}}'\boldsymbol{Q}\dot{\boldsymbol{x}}$ for the above system, we note that if the former is used

$$\frac{\dot{V}(\boldsymbol{x})}{V(\boldsymbol{x})} = -\frac{\boldsymbol{x}'\boldsymbol{C}\boldsymbol{x}}{\boldsymbol{x}'\boldsymbol{Q}\boldsymbol{x}}, \tag{5.85}$$

and if the latter is used

$$\frac{\dot{V}_2(\boldsymbol{x})}{V_2(\boldsymbol{x})} = -\frac{\dot{\boldsymbol{x}}'\boldsymbol{C}\dot{\boldsymbol{x}}}{\dot{\boldsymbol{x}}'\boldsymbol{Q}\dot{\boldsymbol{x}}} = -\frac{\boldsymbol{x}'\boldsymbol{A}'\boldsymbol{C}\boldsymbol{A}\boldsymbol{x}}{\boldsymbol{x}'\boldsymbol{A}'\boldsymbol{Q}\boldsymbol{A}\boldsymbol{x}}. \tag{5.86}$$

These two ratios as given by Equations (5.85) and (5.86) are equal if $\boldsymbol{A}$ is an identity matrix or if $\boldsymbol{C} = \boldsymbol{Q}$, but in general these ratios are not equal. Yet each of these ratios gives a good idea of the rate at which the equilibrium point is approached. Equation (5.85) gives the rate of approach to equilibrium in $\boldsymbol{x}$-space, and Equation (5.86) gives the rate in $\dot{\boldsymbol{x}}$-space where the "distance" in each case is weighted by the matrix $\boldsymbol{Q}$.

Since the Liapunov function is some measure of the distance of the state of the system from the desired state, it is natural to choose the control in such a way as to make the time derivative of the Liapunov function negative and numerically as large as possible if the desired state is to be approached rapidly. Although this choice does not in general lead to time-optimal control, it does provide a systematic way of choosing the control so that stability is ensured at each stage, and for the particular Liapunov function, the choice leads to the "best" control sequence. This criterion for optimization was used by Koepcke and Lapidus [26] to devise control for discrete systems and, as an example, the control of an extraction train was considered (see also Stevens and Wanninger [44]).

To illustrate the method of approach, let us consider the discrete case, namely, the extraction train whose dynamics can be described by Equation (1.122):

$$\boldsymbol{z}(k+1) = \boldsymbol{\Phi}(k)\boldsymbol{z}(k) + \boldsymbol{\Delta}(k), \tag{5.87}$$

where $\boldsymbol{\Phi}(k)$ is the coefficient matrix and $\boldsymbol{\Delta}(k)$ is a vector containing the control variables. In this particular case of the extraction train, $\boldsymbol{\Phi}$ contains also the control variables and therefore the coefficient matrix is variable. The desired state to be reached is $\boldsymbol{z} = \boldsymbol{0}$.

We shall choose a suitable Liapunov function which represents some distance from the origin by letting

$$V[\boldsymbol{z}(k)] = \boldsymbol{z}'(k)\boldsymbol{Q}\boldsymbol{z}(k), \tag{5.88}$$

where $\boldsymbol{Q}$ is a positive-definite symmetric matrix. Then the forward difference of $V[\boldsymbol{z}(k)]$ is

$$\Delta V[\boldsymbol{z}(k)] = V[\boldsymbol{z}(k+1)] - V[\boldsymbol{z}(k)] = \boldsymbol{z}'(k+1)\boldsymbol{Q}\boldsymbol{z}(k+1) - \boldsymbol{z}'(k)\boldsymbol{Q}\boldsymbol{z}(k). \tag{5.89}$$

With the help of the system dynamics, Equation (5.87), this becomes

$$\Delta V[\boldsymbol{z}(k)] = \boldsymbol{z}'(k)[\boldsymbol{\Phi}'\boldsymbol{Q}\boldsymbol{\Phi} - \boldsymbol{Q}]\boldsymbol{z}(k) + 2\boldsymbol{\Delta}'\boldsymbol{Q}\boldsymbol{\Phi}\boldsymbol{z}(k) + \boldsymbol{\Delta}'\boldsymbol{Q}\boldsymbol{\Delta}. \tag{5.90}$$

If we let

$$\begin{aligned} \boldsymbol{P} &= \boldsymbol{\Phi}'\boldsymbol{Q}\boldsymbol{\Phi} - \boldsymbol{Q} &&= \text{a matrix}, \\ \boldsymbol{s} &= 2\boldsymbol{\Phi}'\boldsymbol{Q}\boldsymbol{\Delta} &&= \text{a vector}, \\ R &= \boldsymbol{\Delta}'\boldsymbol{Q}\boldsymbol{\Delta} &&= \text{a scalar}, \end{aligned} \tag{5.91}$$

Equation (5.90) may be written in a more compact way as

$$\Delta V[\boldsymbol{z}(k)] = [\boldsymbol{P}\boldsymbol{z}(k) + \boldsymbol{s}]'\boldsymbol{z}(k) + R. \tag{5.92}$$

A possible procedure to determine the optimum control vector, $\boldsymbol{u}^0$, would be to differentiate Equation (5.92) with respect to the control vector $\boldsymbol{u}(k)$, set the result to zero, and then solve for $\boldsymbol{u}^0(k)$. This will minimize $\Delta V[\boldsymbol{z}(k)]$. In general, however, this approach is unfruitful, since this would mean determining the derivative of both $\boldsymbol{\Phi}$ and $\boldsymbol{\Delta}$ with respect to $\boldsymbol{u}$, which usually has constraints placed upon it; that is,

$$b_j \leq u_j \leq c_j .$$

To circumvent these problems, the $\boldsymbol{u}$'s can be limited to a finite set selected by some means, such as bounded by constraints, and various values of $\Delta V[\boldsymbol{z}(k)]$ can be calculated from Equation (5.92); this is done for each combination of the u_j's, since now $\boldsymbol{P}$, $\boldsymbol{s}$, and R are uniquely determined. Starting with $\boldsymbol{z}(0)$ the set of u_j's denoted by $\boldsymbol{u}^0(0)$ is chosen which minimizes $\Delta V[\boldsymbol{z}(k)]$ for this interval. The $\boldsymbol{z}(1)$ resulting from this choice is evaluated from the system dynamics Equation (5.87). This procedure is continued to yield $\boldsymbol{u}^0(1)$, $\boldsymbol{z}(2)$, $\boldsymbol{u}^0(2)$, $\boldsymbol{z}(3)$, etc., until the desired state $\boldsymbol{z} = \boldsymbol{0}$ has been reached within given tolerance.

This procedure was used successfully by Lapidus and Koepcke [26] in the consideration of the time-optimal control of an extraction train. We shall outline this example in detail, with one and two control variables, in Section 5.9. In addition, we shall illustrate the application of the method to a stationary case where $\boldsymbol{\Phi}$ is constant.

It should be emphasized that this procedure is applicable for control with or without constraints. As a matter of fact, control with constraints is easier to handle because the constraints reduce the size of the table for the possible control values. Also, constraints may be placed on the state variables without any added complications, and the problem becomes even simpler since the values of control variables which produce responses in state variables outside the constraints do not have to be considered.

Furthermore, this method handles the *nonstationary* problem, where the control is inside $\boldsymbol{\Phi}$, and which is only slightly more difficult than the stationary case, where $\boldsymbol{\Phi}$ is constant. The number of state variables is no problem, and 10 state variables could be handled quite easily for either the nonstationary or stationary case. This should be compared with dynamic programming, where the increase in the number of state variables can make the problem insoluble. By using Liapunov's method, we are assured of stability at each stage of calculation, and one can actually feel the way the system is approaching the steady state.

To further illustrate the application of Liapunov's method for control synthesis, let us consider the system as described by the linear vector equation

$$\dot{\boldsymbol{x}} = \boldsymbol{A}\boldsymbol{x} + \boldsymbol{B}\boldsymbol{u}. \tag{5.93}$$

Suppose the control variables are bounded by the inequalities

$$|u_j| \leq K_j \qquad (j = 1, 2, \ldots, r), \tag{5.94}$$

and we wish to choose the control $\boldsymbol{u}$ in such a way that the origin is approached in minimum time. We choose a positive-definite form for the Liapunov function, namely,

$$V(\mathbf{x}) = V = \boldsymbol{x}'\boldsymbol{Q}\boldsymbol{x}, \tag{5.95}$$

where $\boldsymbol{Q}$ is a positive-definite symmetric matrix. The derivative is

$$\dot{V} = \boldsymbol{x}'[\boldsymbol{A}'\boldsymbol{Q} + \boldsymbol{Q}\boldsymbol{A}]\boldsymbol{x} + \boldsymbol{u}'\boldsymbol{B}'\boldsymbol{Q}\boldsymbol{x} + \boldsymbol{x}'\boldsymbol{Q}\boldsymbol{B}\boldsymbol{u}, \tag{5.96}$$

and we wish to make $\dot{V}$ as negative as possible to approach the origin most quickly. Hence, we choose the control

$$u_j = -K_j \operatorname{sgn}(\boldsymbol{B}'\boldsymbol{Q}\boldsymbol{x})_j \qquad (j = 1, 2, \ldots, r) \tag{5.97}$$

to minimize $\dot{V}$ as defined by Equation (5.96).

It should be noted that the control as defined by Equation (5.97) is bang-bang, which is to be expected for such a system as shown in Chapters 2 and 3. This method is applicable whether the uncontrolled system is stable or unstable, and if K_j is sufficiently large, a stable operation is always assured.

If there are no constraints on the control, the control could be chosen to ensure exponential stability. To illustrate this, let us choose the control as

$$\boldsymbol{u} = -k\boldsymbol{B}^{-1}\boldsymbol{x}, \tag{5.98}$$

provided that the inverse of $\boldsymbol{B}$ exists. If $\boldsymbol{B}$ is not square, we could choose

$$\boldsymbol{u} = -k\boldsymbol{G}\boldsymbol{x},$$

where the matrix $\boldsymbol{G}$ is chosen so that

$$\boldsymbol{B}\boldsymbol{G} = \boldsymbol{I}.$$

With this substitution, Equation (5.96) becomes

$$\dot{V} = \boldsymbol{x}'[\boldsymbol{A}'\boldsymbol{Q} + \boldsymbol{Q}\boldsymbol{A}]\boldsymbol{x} - 2k\boldsymbol{x}'\boldsymbol{Q}\boldsymbol{x}. \tag{5.99}$$

If the system without control is neutrally stable,

$$\boldsymbol{A}'\boldsymbol{Q} + \boldsymbol{Q}\boldsymbol{A} = \boldsymbol{0}$$

and

$$\dot{V} = -2kV, \tag{5.100}$$

which could be integrated to give

$$V = V_0 \exp(-2kt), \tag{5.101}$$

that is,

$$\|\boldsymbol{x}(t)\|_{\boldsymbol{Q}} = \|\boldsymbol{x}(0)\|_{\boldsymbol{Q}} \exp(-kt), \tag{5.102}$$

and the origin is approached asymptotically.

Furthermore, if the system itself is stable without the control, then with control

$$\|x(t)\|_Q \leq \|x(0)\|_Q \exp(-kt). \tag{5.103}$$

If, however, the system is unstable without control, the constant k could be chosen sufficiently large so that exponential stability could still be assured. We could, for example, choose k such that

$$A'Q + QA \leq kQ, \tag{5.104}$$

which will then give

$$\|x(t)\|_Q \leq \|x(0)\|_Q \exp\left(-\frac{kt}{2}\right), \tag{5.105}$$

and exponential stability is still assured.

5.6. Improvement of linear control system

Suppose that without control, a particular system is asymptotically stable. The question arises whether some added control actually improves the performance of the system in the sense of reducing the cost of the error and the cost of control combined. It is not hard to visualize a situation where the cost of the control would be greater than the savings obtained by the reduction of the error. This problem was considered by LaSalle [29] using Liapunov's second method.

Suppose that with control, the system is described by the linear vector equation

$$\dot{x} = Ax + Bu, \tag{5.106}$$

which is the same equation we have just been considering; A is an $n \times n$ matrix, B is an $n \times r$ matrix and u is the r-dimensional control vector where $r \leq n$.

To decide whether the added control (Bu) is really worthwhile, we shall consider the savings from the reduction of error as opposed to the cost of the control. We therefore formulate a performance index of the form

$$I[x(0), t_f] = \int_0^{t_f} (x'Cx + u'Ru)\, dt, \tag{5.107}$$

where C and R are positive-definite symmetric matrices. In previous sections, we have used the notation Q instead of C in the performance index. Here we shall reserve Q for the weighting of the error expressed by the Liapunov function, as has been done in the previous sections in this chapter. In Equation (5.107) the first term represents the cost of the error, and the second, of control. We would like to know the conditions under which $I[x(0), t_f]$ will be reduced by a nonzero control vector u.

Let the Liapunov function for the system be

$$V(x) = x'Qx, \tag{5.108}$$

where Q is positive-definite symmetric matrix and satisfies the equation

$$A'Q + QA = -C, \tag{5.109}$$

where C is the positive-definite matrix encountered in Equation (5.107). From Equation (5.108), calculate the derivative of the Liapunov function

$$\dot{V}(x) = \dot{x}'Qx + x'Q\dot{x} \tag{5.110}$$

and substitute from Equation (5.106) and Equation (5.109)

$$\dot{V}(x) = -x'Cx + u'B'Qx + x'QBu. \tag{5.111}$$

Now let

$$B'Qx = -\tfrac{1}{2}Pu \tag{5.112}$$

to define a linear control law, since from Equation (5.112) it is seen that

$$u = -2P^{-1}B'Qx.$$

Substitution of Equation (5.112) into (5.111) gives

$$\dot{V}(x) = -x'Cx - u'Pu. \tag{5.113}$$

Now let us suppose that the system starts from a point away from the equilibrium point. With control, the equilibrium point is approached faster since $\dot{V}(x)$ is smaller due to the addition of the negative control term $-u'Pu$. (It is noted that $V(x)$ as defined by Equation (5.108) is some measure of the distance from the origin.)

We have therefore the following two cases to consider and compare (with $t_f = \infty$):

CASE 1. Without control

$$\dot{V}(x) = -x'Cx,$$

$$0 - V[x(0)] = -\int_0^\infty x'Cx\,dt,$$

so that

$$V[x(0)] = \int_0^\infty x'Cx\,dt. \tag{5.114}$$

CASE 2. With control

$$\dot{V}(x) = -x'Cx - u'Pu,$$

$$0 - V[x(0)] = -\int_0^\infty (x'Cx + u'Pu)\,dt,$$

$$V[x(0)] = \int_0^\infty (x'Cx + u'Pu)\,dt. \tag{5.115}$$

Comparing Equations (5.114) and (5.115), we see that the effect of the control is to reduce the cost of the error by $\int_0^\infty \boldsymbol{u}'\boldsymbol{P}\boldsymbol{u}\,dt$. However, at the same time, we pay $\int_0^\infty \boldsymbol{u}'\boldsymbol{R}\boldsymbol{u}\,dt$ for the control. Now, if $\boldsymbol{P} - \boldsymbol{R}$ is positive-definite, the systems performance will have improved, since the performance index has been reduced by $\int_0^\infty \boldsymbol{u}'(\boldsymbol{P} - \boldsymbol{R})\boldsymbol{u}\,dt$. An obvious choice for $\boldsymbol{P}$ is thus

$$\boldsymbol{P} = k\boldsymbol{R}, \tag{5.116}$$

with $k > 1$ to ensure that the added control will improve the performance.

5.7. Stability of linear time-dependent equations

In Section 5.1 we noted that for a linear stationary system of the form

$$\dot{\boldsymbol{x}} = \boldsymbol{A}\boldsymbol{x}, \tag{5.117}$$

where $\boldsymbol{A}$ is a constant matrix, the necessary and sufficient condition for stability (asymptotic) is the requirement that every eigenvalue of $\boldsymbol{A}$ should have a negative real part. But suppose that $\boldsymbol{A}$ is not constant but varies with time. In other words, suppose that the system is described by

$$\dot{\boldsymbol{x}} = \boldsymbol{A}(t)\boldsymbol{x}, \tag{5.118}$$

where the matrix $\boldsymbol{A}$ is a function of time. Then stability is *not* ensured by having the real part of each eigenvalue of $\boldsymbol{A}(t)$ less than some negative constant; that is,

$$\operatorname{Re}(\lambda_i) \le -\varepsilon < 0 \qquad (i = 1, 2, \ldots, n) \tag{5.119}$$

does not ensure stability of the system as described by Equation (5.118). For example, if we consider a two-dimensional system for which the coefficient matrix is

$$\boldsymbol{A}(t) = \begin{bmatrix} -1 - 9\cos^2 6t + 12\sin 6t\cos 6t, & 12\cos^2 6t + 9\sin 6t\cos 6t \\ -12\sin^2 6t + 9\sin 6t\cos 6t, & -(1 + 9\sin^2 6t + 12\sin 6t\cos 6t) \end{bmatrix},$$

the eigenvalues are -1 and -10 for all t, yet the system is unstable.

Although the condition of negative real parts as expressed by Equation (5.119) is not in itself sufficient to ensure stability, yet it will do so if the variation of $\boldsymbol{A}(t)$ is sufficiently slow. The question of how slow is slow enough arises immediately. However, before attempting to answer this question explicitly, we shall follow the analysis by Rosenbrock [40] to show that for the system (5.118) with condition (5.119), the trivial solution $\boldsymbol{x} = \boldsymbol{0}$ is asymptotically stable if $|a_{ij}| < a$ and $|\dot{a}_{ij}| < \delta$, where a and δ are some constants. In other words, we shall show that the trivial solution of the equation $\dot{\boldsymbol{x}} = \boldsymbol{A}(t)\boldsymbol{x}$ is asymptotically stable if the rate of change of the elements $a_{ij}(t)$ of $\boldsymbol{A}(t)$ is sufficiently slow.

For the analysis, we first assume that for all $t \geq 0$ Equation (5.119) is satisfied, that is,

$$\operatorname{Re}(\lambda_i) \leq -\varepsilon < 0 \qquad (i = 1, 2, \ldots, n).$$

Let us consider the quadratic form

$$V(\boldsymbol{x}) = \boldsymbol{x}'\boldsymbol{P}(t)\boldsymbol{x} \tag{5.120}$$

and the matrix $\boldsymbol{R}(t)$

$$\boldsymbol{R}(t) = \boldsymbol{P}(t) - \varepsilon_1 \boldsymbol{I}, \tag{5.121}$$

where the symmetric matrix $\boldsymbol{P}(t)$ and the constant ε_1 will be defined later. Then, differentiation of Equation (5.120) gives

$$\begin{aligned} V(\boldsymbol{x}) &= \dot{\boldsymbol{x}}'\boldsymbol{P}(t)\boldsymbol{x} + \boldsymbol{x}'\dot{\boldsymbol{P}}(t)\boldsymbol{x} + \boldsymbol{x}'\boldsymbol{P}(t)\dot{\boldsymbol{x}} = \boldsymbol{x}'[\boldsymbol{A}'(t)\boldsymbol{P}(t) + \boldsymbol{P}(t)\boldsymbol{A}]\boldsymbol{x} + \boldsymbol{x}'\dot{\boldsymbol{P}}(t)\boldsymbol{x} \\ &= \boldsymbol{x}'[\boldsymbol{A}'(t)\boldsymbol{R}(t) + \boldsymbol{R}(t)\boldsymbol{A}(t)]\boldsymbol{x} + \varepsilon_1 \boldsymbol{x}'[\boldsymbol{A}'(t) + \boldsymbol{A}(t)]\boldsymbol{x} + \boldsymbol{x}'\dot{\boldsymbol{P}}(t)\boldsymbol{x}. \end{aligned} \tag{5.122}$$

Let

$$\boldsymbol{A}'(t)\boldsymbol{R}(t) + \boldsymbol{R}(t)\boldsymbol{A}(t) = -\boldsymbol{C}(t), \tag{5.123}$$

where $\boldsymbol{C}(t)$ is a positive-definite symmetric matrix. Equation (5.123) can then be solved for $\boldsymbol{R}(t)$ (as we had solved for $\boldsymbol{Q}$ in Section 5.3) to give

$$\boldsymbol{R}(t) = \int_0^\infty \exp\,[\boldsymbol{A}'(t)t]\boldsymbol{C}(t) \exp\,[\boldsymbol{A}(t)t]\; dt. \tag{5.124}$$

This matrix $\boldsymbol{R}(t)$ so defined will be positive-definite.

Now suppose that $\boldsymbol{C}$ is a constant matrix. Then Equation (5.123) can be differentiated to give

$$\boldsymbol{A}'(t)\dot{\boldsymbol{R}}(t) + \dot{\boldsymbol{R}}(t)\boldsymbol{A}(t) = -[\dot{\boldsymbol{A}}'(t)\boldsymbol{R}(t) + \boldsymbol{R}(t)\dot{\boldsymbol{A}}(t)], \tag{5.125}$$

and this equation can also be solved for $\dot{\boldsymbol{R}}(t)$, giving

$$\dot{\boldsymbol{R}}(t) = \int_0^\infty \exp\,[\boldsymbol{A}'(t)t][\dot{\boldsymbol{A}}'(t)\boldsymbol{R}(t) + \boldsymbol{R}(t)\dot{\boldsymbol{A}}(t)] \exp\,[\boldsymbol{A}(t)t]\; dt. \tag{5.126}$$

However, by definition $\dot{\boldsymbol{R}}(t) = \dot{\boldsymbol{P}}(t)$, so that

$$\dot{\boldsymbol{P}}(t) = \int_0^\infty \exp\,[\boldsymbol{A}'(t)t][\dot{\boldsymbol{A}}'(t)\boldsymbol{R}(t) + \boldsymbol{R}(t)\dot{\boldsymbol{A}}(t)] \exp\,[\boldsymbol{A}(t)t]\; dt. \tag{5.127}$$

Equation (5.127) shows that each element of $\dot{p}_{ij}$ of $\dot{\boldsymbol{P}}(t)$ is a continuous function of $\dot{a}_{ij}$ and r_{ij}. Equation (5.125) with constant $\boldsymbol{C}$, shows that each element r_{ij} of $\boldsymbol{R}$ is a continuous function of a_{ij}.

Now let $|a_{ij}| < a$ and $|\dot{a}_{ij}| < \varepsilon_2$ for all i, j. Let the greatest value of the continuous function $|\dot{p}_{ij}|$ be $\eta(\varepsilon_2)$. Then η is a continuous function of ε_2, and $\eta(0) = 0$. It follows that ε_2 can be chosen sufficiently small to ensure that $\dot{\boldsymbol{P}} - \boldsymbol{I}$ is negative-definite. Also, we can choose ε_1 so that $\varepsilon_1[\boldsymbol{A}'(t) + \boldsymbol{A}(t)] - \boldsymbol{I}$ is negative-definite.

Then, if we select $\boldsymbol{C} = 3\boldsymbol{I}$ and ε_1 and ε_2 as described, $\dot{V}(\boldsymbol{x}, t)$ will be negative-definite. Furthermore, since $\boldsymbol{R}(t)$ is positive-definite, $\boldsymbol{P}(t)$ will also be positive-definite [Equation (5.123)], and therefore $V(\boldsymbol{x}, t)$ as defined by Equation (5.120) is positive-definite. Also, if we let ρ be the largest value of $|r_{ij}|$ in the region $|a_{ij}| < a$, then

$$V(\boldsymbol{x}, t) = \boldsymbol{x}'[\boldsymbol{R}(t)]\boldsymbol{x} + \varepsilon_1 \boldsymbol{x}'\boldsymbol{x} < (\varepsilon_1 + n^2\rho)\boldsymbol{x}'\boldsymbol{x}.$$

Therefore, under these conditions V is a Liapunov function for the time-varying system, and the trivial solution $\boldsymbol{x} = \boldsymbol{0}$ is asymptotically stable (in the large due to linearity).

Let us now consider a particular form of $\boldsymbol{A}(t)$ given by

$$\boldsymbol{A}(t) = \begin{bmatrix} 0 & 1 & 0 & \cdots & 0 \\ 0 & 0 & 1 & \cdots & 0 \\ \vdots & & & & \vdots \\ -a_1(t) & -a_2(t) & -a_3(t) & \cdots & -a_n(t) \end{bmatrix}, \tag{5.128}$$

which corresponds to the nth-order differential equation

$$x^{(n)} + a_n(t)x^{(n-1)} + \cdots + a_2(t)\dot{x} + a_1(t)x = 0. \tag{5.129}$$

With this special form of $\boldsymbol{A}(t)$, the eigenvalues are uniquely related to the coefficients $a_i(t)$ of Equation (5.129), and thus the bounds on the rate of change of $\boldsymbol{A}(t)$ may be replaced by the bounds on the rates of change of the eigenvalues to ensure stability of the system. This was done by Rosenbrock [40], and we shall leave the details to the reader.

5.8. Relation of Liapunov stability to optimal control

In Section 3.3, the control algorithm for continuous-time linear systems with quadratic performance indices was developed. The end result was to solve the nonlinear Riccati differential equation to obtain the feedback matrix. In this section we shall show the relationship between this analysis and the Liapunov function as used for optimal control.

We shall consider the system

$$\dot{\boldsymbol{x}} = \boldsymbol{f}(\boldsymbol{x}, \boldsymbol{u}, t), \tag{5.130}$$

where $\boldsymbol{f}(\boldsymbol{0}, \boldsymbol{0}, t) = \boldsymbol{0}$. Since we shall want to differentiate the performance index with respect to time, we shall choose a slightly different form for it by considering the lower limit as variable time. Thus, we write the performance index to be minimized as

$$I\{\boldsymbol{x}(t), t, \boldsymbol{u}[\boldsymbol{x}(\lambda), \lambda]\} = \int_t^{t_f} J[\boldsymbol{x}, \boldsymbol{u}(\boldsymbol{x}, \lambda), \lambda]\, d\lambda, \tag{5.131}$$

where J is chosen so that

$$J \begin{cases} = 0 & \text{if and only if} \quad \|\boldsymbol{x}\| \text{ and } \|\boldsymbol{u}\| = 0, \\ > 0 & \text{if} \quad \|\boldsymbol{x}\| \text{ or } \|\boldsymbol{u}\| \neq 0, \\ \to \infty & \text{if and only if} \quad \|\boldsymbol{x}\| \text{ or } \|\boldsymbol{u}\| \to \infty. \end{cases}$$

We shall follow the treatment of this problem as given by Kopp [27] and choose the optimal performance index (that is, the performance index when optimal control is used) to be a Liapunov function

$$V(\boldsymbol{x}, t) = I^0[\boldsymbol{x}(t), t, \boldsymbol{u}^0(\boldsymbol{x}(\lambda), \lambda)] = \int_t^{t_f} J[\boldsymbol{x}, \boldsymbol{u}^0(\boldsymbol{x}, \lambda), \lambda] \, d\lambda. \tag{5.132}$$

It is at once clear that $V(\boldsymbol{x}, t)$ is positive-definite since time is monotonically increasing and $t_f > t$; also from Equation (5.132), we note that the derivative

$$dV(\boldsymbol{x}, t)/dt = -J(\boldsymbol{x}, \boldsymbol{u}^0, t), \tag{5.133}$$

and since J is positive-definite, $V(\boldsymbol{x}, t)$ is a Liapunov function for this system.

From the definition of the time derivative, Equation (5.133) may be written as

$$[\partial V(\boldsymbol{x}, t)]/\partial t + (\nabla V)'\boldsymbol{f}(\boldsymbol{x}, \boldsymbol{u}^0, t) = -J(\boldsymbol{x}, \boldsymbol{u}^0, t),$$

which gives

$$\partial V/\partial t = -(\nabla V)'\boldsymbol{f}(\boldsymbol{x}, \boldsymbol{u}^0, t) - J(\boldsymbol{x}, \boldsymbol{u}^0, t). \tag{5.134}$$

We can also evaluate the derivative of V along a general trajectory where $\boldsymbol{u} \neq \boldsymbol{u}^0$. Then

$$dV/dt = (\partial V/\partial t) + (\nabla V)'\boldsymbol{f}(\boldsymbol{x}, \boldsymbol{u}, t). \tag{5.135}$$

Now substitute Equation (5.134) into (5.135) to give

$$dV/dt = (\nabla V)'[\boldsymbol{f}(\boldsymbol{x}, \boldsymbol{u}, t) - \boldsymbol{f}(\boldsymbol{x}, \boldsymbol{u}^0, t)] - J(\boldsymbol{x}, \boldsymbol{u}^0, t). \tag{5.136}$$

From Equation (5.132), with any control,

$$dI/dt = -J(\boldsymbol{x}, \boldsymbol{u}, t). \tag{5.137}$$

Therefore, combining Equations (5.136) and (5.137) gives

$$(dV/dt) - (dI/dt) = (\nabla V)'[\boldsymbol{f}(\boldsymbol{x}, \boldsymbol{u}, t) - \boldsymbol{f}(\boldsymbol{x}, \boldsymbol{u}^0, t)] - J(\boldsymbol{x}, \boldsymbol{u}^0, t) + J(\boldsymbol{x}, \boldsymbol{u}, t), \tag{5.138}$$

and integration from t to t_f yields

$$V[\boldsymbol{x}(t_f), t_f] - I[\boldsymbol{x}(t_f), \boldsymbol{u}(t_f), t_f] + I[\boldsymbol{x}(t), \boldsymbol{u}(t), t] - V[\boldsymbol{x}(t), t]$$
$$= \int_t^{t_f} \{(\nabla V)'[\boldsymbol{f}(\boldsymbol{x}, \boldsymbol{u}, \lambda) - \boldsymbol{f}(\boldsymbol{x}, \boldsymbol{u}^0, \lambda)] + [J(\boldsymbol{x}, \boldsymbol{u}, \lambda) - J(\boldsymbol{x}, \boldsymbol{u}^0, \lambda)]\} \, d\lambda.$$

Assume that at the terminal time t_f the steady state has been reached, so that $\|x(t_f)\| = 0$ and $\|u(t_f)\| = 0$. Then

$$I[x(t), u(t), t] - V[x(t), t] = \int_t^{t_f} \{(\nabla V)'[f(x, u, \lambda) - f(x, u^0, \lambda)] + [J(x, u, \lambda) - J(x, u^0, \lambda)]\} \, d\lambda. \quad (5.139)$$

Let

$$\Delta u(t) = u(t) - u^0(t)$$

and note that

$$V[x(t), t] = I^0[x(t), u^0(t), t].$$

If the trajectory resulting from the application of $u(t)$ is sufficiently close to the optimal, then Δu is small and Equation (5.139) can be written as a partial differential equation

$$\frac{\partial I}{\partial u} = \int_t^{t_f} \left\{ \frac{\partial}{\partial u} [\nabla(V)'f] + \frac{\partial J}{\partial u} \right\} d\lambda. \quad (5.140)$$

In order that I be an extremum (minimum in this case), it is necessary that $\partial I/\partial u$ be zero. Therefore,

$$(\partial/\partial u)[\nabla(V)'f] + \partial J/\partial u = 0 \quad (5.141)$$

at $u = u^0$. Equation (5.141) thus provides a means of obtaining the optimal control.

To illustrate the application of these ideas, let us consider a linear autonomous system of the form

$$\dot{x} = Ax + Bu \quad (5.142)$$

and the performance index as given by

$$I = \int_t^{t_f} (x'Qx + u'Ru) \, d\lambda. \quad (5.143)$$

For this system we shall select a Liapunov function of a quadratic form

$$V = x'Px, \quad (5.144)$$

where we assume that the matrices Q, R, and P are symmetric and positive-definite.

From Equation (5.144)

$$\nabla V = 2Px, \quad (5.145)$$

so that

$$(\nabla V)' = 2x'P, \quad (5.146)$$

since P is symmetric. Furthermore,

$$(\nabla V)'f = (2x'P)(Ax + Bu) = 2x'PAx + 2x'PBu. \quad (5.147)$$

Therefore

$$(\partial/\partial \boldsymbol{u})[(\nabla V)'\boldsymbol{f}] = 2\boldsymbol{B}'\boldsymbol{P}\dot{\boldsymbol{x}}. \tag{5.148}$$

Since the last step might not be self-evident to the reader, we shall briefly outline the method of obtaining Equation (5.148). The problem is really one of determining

$$\left(\frac{\partial}{\partial \boldsymbol{u}}\right)(\boldsymbol{c}'\boldsymbol{u}) = \begin{bmatrix} \dfrac{\partial}{\partial u_1} \\ \vdots \\ \dfrac{\partial}{\partial u_r} \end{bmatrix} [c_1 u_1 + c_2 u_2 + \cdots + c_r u_r] = \begin{bmatrix} c_1 \\ c_2 \\ \vdots \\ c_r \end{bmatrix} = \boldsymbol{c} = (\boldsymbol{c}')'$$

and in Equation (5.147)

$$\boldsymbol{c}' = 2\boldsymbol{x}'\boldsymbol{P}\boldsymbol{B}$$

or

$$\boldsymbol{c} = 2\boldsymbol{B}'\boldsymbol{P}\boldsymbol{x},$$

which is Equation (5.148).

In the above illustration

$$J = \boldsymbol{x}'\boldsymbol{Q}\boldsymbol{x} + \boldsymbol{u}'\boldsymbol{R}\boldsymbol{u}$$

so that

$$\partial J/\partial \boldsymbol{u} = 2\boldsymbol{R}\boldsymbol{u}. \tag{5.149}$$

Now substituting Equations (5.148) and (5.149) into (5.141) yields

$$2\boldsymbol{B}'\boldsymbol{P}\boldsymbol{x} + 2\boldsymbol{R}\boldsymbol{u}^0 = \boldsymbol{0},$$

and thus the optimal control law is given by

$$\boldsymbol{u}^0 = -\boldsymbol{R}^{-1}\boldsymbol{B}'\boldsymbol{P}\boldsymbol{x}. \tag{5.150}$$

Note the correspondance of this optimal control law to Equation (3.49). Now all that remains for the unique determination of this control law is to express $\boldsymbol{P}$ in terms of the known matrices. From Equation (5.144) it is noted that

$$dV/dt = \dot{\boldsymbol{x}}'\boldsymbol{P}\boldsymbol{x} + \boldsymbol{x}'\boldsymbol{P}\dot{\boldsymbol{x}},$$

and substituting from Equation (5.142), this becomes

$$dV/dt = \boldsymbol{x}'[\boldsymbol{A}'\boldsymbol{P} + \boldsymbol{P}\boldsymbol{A}]\boldsymbol{x} + \boldsymbol{u}^{0\prime}\boldsymbol{B}'\boldsymbol{P}\boldsymbol{x} + \boldsymbol{x}'\boldsymbol{P}\boldsymbol{B}\boldsymbol{u}^0, \tag{5.151}$$

when the optimal control, $\boldsymbol{u} = \boldsymbol{u}^0$, is used. However, with optimal control, Equation (5.136) becomes

$$dV/dt = -J(\boldsymbol{x}, \boldsymbol{u}^0, t),$$

that is,

$$dV/dt = -\boldsymbol{x}'\boldsymbol{Q}\boldsymbol{x} - \boldsymbol{u}^{0\prime}\boldsymbol{R}\boldsymbol{u}^0.$$

Therefore, equating this to Equation (5.151) and substituting from Equation (5.150), we get

$$\boldsymbol{x}'(\boldsymbol{PA} + \boldsymbol{A}'\boldsymbol{P} + \boldsymbol{Q} - \boldsymbol{PBR}^{-1}\boldsymbol{B}'\boldsymbol{P})\boldsymbol{x} = 0,$$

which gives the steady-state Riccati equation similar to Equation (3.55) obtained by the use of maximum principle except that it applies for the steady-state case

$$\boldsymbol{PA} + \boldsymbol{A}'\boldsymbol{P} + \boldsymbol{Q} - \boldsymbol{PBR}^{-1}\boldsymbol{B}'\boldsymbol{P} = \boldsymbol{0}. \tag{5.152}$$

If the system is completely controllable, any state can be reached in a finite time, and this assures the existence of the optimal control.

In the above illustration, the optimal law was easily evaluated since $\boldsymbol{f}$ was purposely chosen to be linear. If $\boldsymbol{f}$ is nonlinear, an iteration scheme as developed by Vaisbord [47] may be used. To start the iteration a reasonable value for $\boldsymbol{u}$ is chosen; let us denote this by $\boldsymbol{u}^{(0)}$.

With this value of control, the differential equation describing the system is

$$\dot{\boldsymbol{x}} = \boldsymbol{f}(\boldsymbol{x}, \boldsymbol{u}^{(0)}), \tag{5.153}$$

where again at steady state, $\boldsymbol{f}(\boldsymbol{0}, \boldsymbol{0}) = \boldsymbol{0}$.

A Liapunov function may now be defined by

$$V_0 = \int_t^{t_f} J\{\boldsymbol{x}, \boldsymbol{u}^{(0)}[\boldsymbol{x}(\lambda)]\}\, d\lambda, \tag{5.154}$$

so that

$$dV_0/dt = -J[\boldsymbol{x}, \boldsymbol{u}^{(0)}(\boldsymbol{x})]. \tag{5.155}$$

Going through a similar argument as before, we try to find a control $\boldsymbol{u}$ so that

$$(\nabla V_0)'\boldsymbol{f}(\boldsymbol{x}, \boldsymbol{u}) + J(\boldsymbol{x}, \boldsymbol{u}) \tag{5.156}$$

will be minimized. For this minimization,

$$(\partial/\partial \boldsymbol{u})[(\nabla V_0)'\boldsymbol{f}(\boldsymbol{x}, \boldsymbol{u})] + (\partial/\partial \boldsymbol{u})J(\boldsymbol{x}, \boldsymbol{u}) = \boldsymbol{0} \tag{5.157}$$

and we shall call the control $\boldsymbol{u}$, which minimizes expression (5.156) and hence satisfies equation (5.157), $\boldsymbol{u}^{(1)}$. It is clear that

$$(\nabla V_0)'\boldsymbol{f}(\boldsymbol{x}, \boldsymbol{u}^{(1)}) + J(\boldsymbol{x}, \boldsymbol{u}^{(1)}) \leq (\nabla V_0)'\boldsymbol{f}(\boldsymbol{x}, \boldsymbol{u}^{(0)}) + J(\boldsymbol{x}, \boldsymbol{u}^{(0)}), \tag{5.158}$$

since $\boldsymbol{u}^{(1)}$ minimizes the expression. But the right-hand side of inequality (5.158) is zero since V_0 is not an explicit function of t (V_0 is a function of $\boldsymbol{x}$ only), and thus from Equation (5.155)

$$dV_0/dt = (\nabla V_0)'\boldsymbol{f}(\boldsymbol{x}, \boldsymbol{u}^{(0)}),$$

that is,

$$(\nabla V_0)'\boldsymbol{f}(\boldsymbol{x}, \boldsymbol{u}^{(0)}) = -J(\boldsymbol{x}, \boldsymbol{u}^{(0)}).$$

Therefore,

$$(\nabla V_0)'\boldsymbol{f}(\boldsymbol{x}, \boldsymbol{u}^{(1)}) \le -J(\boldsymbol{x}, \boldsymbol{u}^{(1)}) < 0$$

or

$$J(\boldsymbol{x}, \boldsymbol{u}^{(1)}) \le -(\nabla V_0)'\boldsymbol{f}(\boldsymbol{x}, \boldsymbol{u}^{(1)}). \tag{5.159}$$

As a result,

$$V_0(\boldsymbol{x}) = \int_t^{t_f} - \{(\nabla V_0)'\boldsymbol{f}(\boldsymbol{x}, \boldsymbol{u}^{(1)})\}\, d\lambda$$

is a Liapunov function for the system

$$\dot{\boldsymbol{x}} = \boldsymbol{f}[\boldsymbol{x}, \boldsymbol{u}^{(1)}(\boldsymbol{x})], \tag{5.160}$$

and we can construct another Liapunov function for this system, which we shall write as

$$V_1(\boldsymbol{x}) = \int_t^{t_f} J[\boldsymbol{x}, \boldsymbol{u}^{(1)}(\boldsymbol{x})]\, d\lambda. \tag{5.161}$$

Thus, we have two Liapunov functions for system (5.160), but with the help of Equation (5.159) it is seen that

$$V_1(\boldsymbol{x}) \le V_0(\boldsymbol{x}).$$

As before, we find $\boldsymbol{u}^{(2)}(\boldsymbol{x})$ to minimize the expression

$$(\nabla V_1)'\boldsymbol{f}(\boldsymbol{x}, \boldsymbol{u}) + J(\boldsymbol{x}, \boldsymbol{u}), \tag{5.162}$$

and continue the process to yield a sequence of functions $V_0, V_1, V_2, \ldots, V_k, \ldots$.

Since

$$J(\boldsymbol{x}, \boldsymbol{u}^{(k+1)}) \le -(\nabla V_k)'\boldsymbol{f}(\boldsymbol{x}, \boldsymbol{u}^{(k+1)}),$$

then

$$V_{k+1}(\boldsymbol{x}) = \int_t^{t_f} J(\boldsymbol{x}, \boldsymbol{u}^{(k+1)})\, dt \le \int_t^{t_f} -(\nabla V_k)'\boldsymbol{f}(\boldsymbol{x}, \boldsymbol{u}^{(k+1)})\, dt = V_k(\boldsymbol{x}), \tag{5.163}$$

and the sequence is monotonically decreasing. Through this iteration, we can obtain a control $\boldsymbol{u}^{(k)}$ as close to the optimal as we desire, since the Liapunov function can be thought of as a performance index which is to be minimized.

Constraints on the control do not present any difficulties, since we can always search for the appropriate control in bounded space.

For illustration purposes, we reconsider the linear system (5.142), that is,

$$\dot{\boldsymbol{x}} = \boldsymbol{A}\boldsymbol{x} + \boldsymbol{B}\boldsymbol{u} \tag{5.164}$$

and the performance index

$$I(\boldsymbol{x}, \boldsymbol{u}) = \int_0^{t_f} (\boldsymbol{x}'\boldsymbol{Q}\boldsymbol{x} + \boldsymbol{u}'\boldsymbol{R}\boldsymbol{u})\, dt. \tag{5.165}$$

If the system (5.164) is asymptotically stable when there is no control applied (that is, when $\|\boldsymbol{u}\| = 0$), the initial value for $\boldsymbol{u}$ can be taken as $\boldsymbol{0}$, namely $\boldsymbol{u}^{(0)} = \boldsymbol{0}$, for the first approximation.

Then

$$V_0(\boldsymbol{x}) = \int_0^{t_f} \boldsymbol{x}'\boldsymbol{Q}\boldsymbol{x}\, dt. \tag{5.166}$$

We can find $V_0(\boldsymbol{x})$ as the unique positive solution for the partial differential equation

$$(\nabla V_0)'(\boldsymbol{A}\boldsymbol{x}) = -\boldsymbol{x}'\boldsymbol{Q}\boldsymbol{x}. \tag{5.167}$$

Since Equation (5.167) satisfies a positive-definite quadratic form, we may write the solution as

$$V_0(\boldsymbol{x}) = \boldsymbol{x}'\boldsymbol{P}_0\boldsymbol{x}, \tag{5.168}$$

where $\boldsymbol{P}_0$ is symmetric and positive-definite. This is easily seen from Section 5.3.

Now $\boldsymbol{u}^{(1)}(\boldsymbol{x})$ may be found from the condition leading to the minimization of the expression

$$\{(\nabla V_0)'[\boldsymbol{A}\boldsymbol{x} + \boldsymbol{B}\boldsymbol{u}] + \boldsymbol{x}'\boldsymbol{Q}\boldsymbol{x} + \boldsymbol{u}'\boldsymbol{R}\boldsymbol{u}\}. \tag{5.169}$$

Differentiation of expression (5.169) with respect to $\boldsymbol{u}$ gives

$$\boldsymbol{B}'\nabla V_0 + 2\boldsymbol{R}\boldsymbol{u} = \boldsymbol{B}'2\boldsymbol{P}_0\boldsymbol{x} + 2\boldsymbol{R}\boldsymbol{u}.$$

So for the minimum of (5.169), the value of control is

$$\boldsymbol{u}^{(1)} = -\boldsymbol{R}^{-1}\boldsymbol{B}'\boldsymbol{P}_0\boldsymbol{x}, \tag{5.170}$$

and we shall note the similarity of Equation (5.170) to Equation (5.150). We shall write Equation (5.170) as

$$\boldsymbol{u}^{(1)}(\boldsymbol{x}) = -\boldsymbol{K}_1\boldsymbol{x}, \tag{5.171}$$

where

$$\boldsymbol{K}_1 = \boldsymbol{R}^{-1}\boldsymbol{B}'\boldsymbol{P}_0.$$

Substituting Equation (5.171) into (5.164) gives

$$\dot{\boldsymbol{x}} = \boldsymbol{A}\boldsymbol{x} - \boldsymbol{B}\boldsymbol{K}_1\boldsymbol{x}, \tag{5.172}$$

and we are ready to continue the iteration. We find $V_1(\boldsymbol{x})$ as a solution to the linear partial differential equation

$$(\nabla V_1)'[(\boldsymbol{A} - \boldsymbol{B}\boldsymbol{K}_1)\boldsymbol{x}] = -(\boldsymbol{x}'\boldsymbol{Q}\boldsymbol{x} + \boldsymbol{x}'\boldsymbol{K}_1'\boldsymbol{R}\boldsymbol{K}_1\boldsymbol{x}) = -\boldsymbol{x}'(\boldsymbol{Q} + \boldsymbol{K}_1'\boldsymbol{R}\boldsymbol{K}_1)\boldsymbol{x}. \quad (5.173)$$

Let the solution of Equation (5.173) be

$$V_1(\boldsymbol{x}) = \boldsymbol{x}'\boldsymbol{P}_1\boldsymbol{x}. \quad (5.174)$$

Then $\boldsymbol{u}^{(2)}(\boldsymbol{x})$ can be found by means of the condition leading to the minimization of the expression

$$\{(\nabla V_1)'(\boldsymbol{A}\boldsymbol{x} + \boldsymbol{B}\boldsymbol{x}) + \boldsymbol{x}'\boldsymbol{Q}\boldsymbol{x} + \boldsymbol{u}'\boldsymbol{R}\boldsymbol{u}\}. \quad (5.175)$$

Differentiation of (5.175) with respect to $\boldsymbol{u}$ and equating the result to zero, as before, gives

$$\boldsymbol{u}^{(2)}(\boldsymbol{x}) = -\boldsymbol{R}^{-1}\boldsymbol{B}'\boldsymbol{P}_1\boldsymbol{x} = -\boldsymbol{K}_2\boldsymbol{x}.$$

By continuing the argument, we obtain a convergent sequence of positive-definite quadratic forms

$$V_k(\boldsymbol{x}) = \boldsymbol{x}'\boldsymbol{P}_k\boldsymbol{x} \quad (5.176)$$

and a sequence of controls

$$\boldsymbol{u}^{(k)}(\boldsymbol{x}) = -\boldsymbol{K}_k\boldsymbol{x}.$$

Since the sequence V_k converges, the matrix $\boldsymbol{P}_k$ converges to a certain matrix $\boldsymbol{P}$. Also $\boldsymbol{u}^{(k)}(\boldsymbol{x})$ converges uniformly in every bounded domain of the variables x_i. Therefore, in the limit

$$\boldsymbol{u}^0(\boldsymbol{x}) = -\boldsymbol{R}^{-1}\boldsymbol{B}'\boldsymbol{P}\boldsymbol{x} = -\boldsymbol{K}\boldsymbol{x}$$

will be optimal. This corresponds to the optimal control law as given by Equation (5.150), which leads to the Riccati equation. But the iteration scheme is more general by being applicable to nonlinear systems as well. Thus, finding an optimal control is reduced to successive solution of systems of linear equations for the coefficients of a sequence of quadratic forms.

We can say one more word about starting the iteration. If the system (5.164) is unstable when $\|\boldsymbol{u}\| = 0$, we may take as a first choice of control any reasonable value, let us say, $\boldsymbol{u}^{(0)} = -\boldsymbol{K}_0\boldsymbol{x}$, so that

$$\dot{\boldsymbol{x}} = \boldsymbol{A}\boldsymbol{x} - \boldsymbol{B}\boldsymbol{K}_0\boldsymbol{x}$$

will be asymptotically stable, that is, such that the eigenvalues of $(\boldsymbol{A} - \boldsymbol{B}\boldsymbol{K}_0)$ are negative. This will guarantee that $\boldsymbol{P}_k$ will be positive-definite for $k = 0, 1, 2, \ldots$. With this choice of the starting point, the iteration scheme is the same as outlined above and leads to the optimal control.

As mentioned earlier, this method works well even if the control is constrained. In the actual iteration, it is not necessary to differentiate the expressions with respect to $\boldsymbol{u}$ to obtain the best value of $\boldsymbol{u}$. Instead, different discrete values for $\boldsymbol{u}$ may be scanned, and that one which gives the minimum value to the expression can be retained.

5.9 Numerical examples

EXAMPLE 5.1 ▪ As a first example, we shall consider the time optimal control of a train of six liquid–liquid countercurrent extraction units with a secondary feed to one of the middle stages (third stage). The system has been described in detail in Section 1.11, and the strategy for control has been discussed in Section 5.4 and 5.5.

The system dynamics equation is given by Equation (1.122), namely

$$\mathbf{z}(k+1) = \boldsymbol{\Phi}(k)\mathbf{z}(k) + \boldsymbol{\Delta}(k), \tag{5.177}$$

where

$$\mathbf{z}(0) = \begin{bmatrix} -.008782 \\ -.009584 \\ -.007975 \\ -.008937 \\ -.007774 \\ -.004741 \end{bmatrix}, \tag{5.178}$$

and we wish to pick the controls u_1 and u_2 which are bounded by

$$-1 \leq u_1 \leq 2, \qquad -1 \leq u_2 \leq 2$$

such that $\mathbf{z} = \mathbf{0}$ will be reached as fast as possible through some choice of the Liapunov function. In other words, we shall want to select u_1 and u_2 such that $|z_m| < 0.0001$ as fast as possible for $m = 1, 2, \ldots, 6$. This will be done by choosing u_1 and u_2 so that ΔV will be minimized.

To start the computations, let us write out the variables explicitly:

$$\mathbf{D} = [1.32\mathbf{A} + 1.0\mathbf{B} + 0.5\mathbf{C}] + u_1\mathbf{B} + u_2\mathbf{C}, \tag{5.179}$$

where

$$\mathbf{A} = \begin{bmatrix} -1.0 & 1.0 & & \cdots & & 0 \\ & -1.0 & 1.0 & & & \\ & & -1.0 & 1.0 & & \vdots \\ \vdots & & & -1.0 & 1.0 & \\ & & & & -1.0 & 1.0 \\ 0 & & \cdots & & -1.0 & 1.0 \end{bmatrix},$$

$$B = \begin{bmatrix} -1 & & \cdots & & 0 \\ 1 & -1 & & & \\ & 1 & & & \vdots \\ \vdots & & \ddots & & \\ & & & & \\ 0 & & \cdots & 1 & -1 \end{bmatrix}, \quad C = \begin{bmatrix} 0 & 0 & & \cdots & & 0 \\ 0 & 0 & & & & \\ & 0 & -1 & & & \vdots \\ \vdots & & 1 & -1 & & \\ & & & 1 & -1 & \\ 0 & & \cdots & & 1 & -1 \end{bmatrix},$$

$$d_3 = B\begin{bmatrix} .033335 \\ .028285 \\ .024460 \\ .019463 \\ .013785 \\ .007332 \end{bmatrix} + \begin{bmatrix} .04 \\ 0 \\ 0 \\ 0 \\ 0 \\ 0 \end{bmatrix}, \tag{5.180}$$

$$d_4 = C\begin{bmatrix} .033335 \\ .028285 \\ .024460 \\ .019463 \\ .013785 \\ .007332 \end{bmatrix} + \begin{bmatrix} 0 \\ 0 \\ .03 \\ 0 \\ 0 \\ 0 \end{bmatrix}, \tag{5.181}$$

$$\Phi = I + DT + \frac{D^2T^2}{2!} + \cdots + \frac{D^9T^9}{9!}, \tag{5.182}$$

$$\theta = \left(I + \frac{DT}{2} + \frac{D^2T^2}{3!} + \cdots + \frac{D^9T^9}{10!}\right)T, \tag{5.183}$$

$$\Delta = \theta(u_1 d_3 + u_2 d_4). \tag{5.184}$$

The equations (5.179) through (5.184) allow $z(k+1)$ to be evaluated from the knowledge of $z(k)$. In addition, we would like to write out explicitly the change in Liapunov function. For the matrix Q we must choose some appropriate positive-definite matrix. Since we want to weight each z_m equally to find a condition under which each $|z_m| < 0.0001$, we shall choose Q to be an identity matrix,

$$Q = I. \tag{5.185}$$

Now, knowing $\boldsymbol{\Phi}$, $\boldsymbol{Q}$ and Δ, we can calculate [see Equations (5.91)]

$$\boldsymbol{P} = \boldsymbol{\Phi}'\boldsymbol{Q}\boldsymbol{\Phi} - \boldsymbol{Q}, \qquad \boldsymbol{s} = 2\boldsymbol{\Phi}'\boldsymbol{Q}\Delta, \qquad R = \Delta'\boldsymbol{Q}\Delta, \tag{5.186}$$

and from Equations (5.186) evaluate $\Delta V[\boldsymbol{z}(k)]$, as given by Equation (5.92),

$$\Delta V[\boldsymbol{z}(k)] = [\boldsymbol{P}\boldsymbol{z}(k) + \boldsymbol{s}]'\boldsymbol{z}(k) + R. \tag{5.187}$$

Although the expressions for $\boldsymbol{\Phi}$ and $\boldsymbol{\theta}$ require infinite series, 10 terms were found to be sufficient in the present case for $T = 0.05$, 0.10, and 0.20.

To start the computations, a time interval of 0.10 is chosen, that is, $T = 0.10$ and six levels for u_1 and u_2 are chosen, namely $+2.0$, 1.0, 0.5, 0.0, -0.5, -1.0. This gives 36 different combinations of u_1 and u_2 to scan and 36 different ΔV's to be evaluated at each step. For $u_1 = 2.0$ and $u_2 = 2.0$, the following results are obtained:

$$\boldsymbol{\Phi}' = \begin{bmatrix} .66215 & .19727 & .02726 & .00479 & .00064 & .00007 \\ .08680 & .67414 & .17666 & .04627 & .00827 & .00112 \\ .00528 & .07773 & .53529 & .28686 & .07814 & .01420 \\ .00022 & .00489 & .06885 & .54293 & .28828 & .07787 \\ .00001 & .00021 & .00450 & .06919 & .54287 & .28487 \\ .00000 & .00001 & .00020 & .00449 & .06837 & .52418 \end{bmatrix},$$

$$\boldsymbol{\theta}' = \begin{bmatrix} .08168 & .01137 & .00103 & .00013 & .00001 & .00000 \\ .00500 & .08214 & .01057 & .00179 & .00023 & .00002 \\ .00020 & .00465 & .07366 & .01794 & .00309 & .00041 \\ .00001 & .00019 & .00431 & .07397 & .01798 & .00308 \\ .00000 & .00001 & .00018 & .00432 & .07397 & .01788 \\ .00000 & .00000 & .00001 & .00018 & .00429 & .07323 \end{bmatrix},$$

$$\Delta' = [.00114 \quad .00107 \quad .00159 \quad .00194 \quad .00221 \quad .00237],$$

and for the calculation of the change in Liapunov function, we find

$$\boldsymbol{P} = \begin{bmatrix} -.52188 & .19550 & .03484 & .00578 & .00087 & .00011 \\ .19550 & -.50458 & .16136 & .04307 & .00895 & .00140 \\ .03484 & .16136 & -.61880 & .21661 & .06874 & .01418 \\ .00578 & .04307 & .21661 & -.61129 & .21656 & .06298 \\ .00087 & .00895 & .06874 & .21656 & -.61933 & .18675 \\ .00011 & .00140 & .01418 & .06298 & .18675 & -.72054 \end{bmatrix},$$

$$\mathbf{s}' = [.0020455 \quad .0024272 \quad .0034054 \quad .0039761 \quad .0040307 \quad .0028003],$$

$$R = .00001922, \qquad \Delta V = -1.9572 \times 10^{-4},$$

$$\mathbf{z}'(1) = [-.0055478 \ -.0077865 \ -.0052621 \ -.0062478 \ -.0056183 \ -.0031548].$$

For the other 35 pairs of u_1, u_2 we have the following values for ΔV.

u_1	u_2	$\Delta V(\times 10^{-4})$
2.0	1.0	−1.6635
2.0	.5	−1.5012
2.0	0	−1.3280
2.0	− .5	−1.1434
2.0	−1.0	− .9471
1.0	2.0	−1.5226
1.0	1.0	−1.2034
1.0	.5	−1.0278
1.0	− 0	− .8409
1.0	− .5	− .6421
1.0	−1.0	− .4310
.5	2.0	−1.2836
.5	1.0	− .9519
.5	.5	− .7697
.5	0	− .5761
.5	− .5	− .3703
.5	−1.0	− .1519
0	2.0	−1.0290
0	1.0	− .6850
0	.5	− .4964
0	0	− .2960
0	− .5	− .0834
0	−1.0	.1422
− .5	2.0	− .7580
− .5	1.0	− .4019
− .5	.5	− .2069
− .5	0	− .0000
− .5	− .5	.2194
− .5	−1.0	.4522
−1.0	2.0	− .4697
−1.0	1.0	− .1015
−1.0	5	.0997
−1.0	0	.3130
−1.0	− .5	.5392
−1.0	−1.0	.7789

To choose the best allowed control values for this interval, we wish to choose the controls which minimize ΔV for this interval. It is obvious from the above that the minimum values of ΔV is given by $u_1 = 2, u_2 = 2$ with $\Delta V = -1.9572 \times 10^{-4}$. This is the largest negative value for ΔV, and it ensures that the largest step is taken toward the origin. Therefore, this set of control values is chosen to be the best for this time interval, that is, from $t = 0$ to $t = 0.10$. In other words, initially the best choice of controls is the maximum allowed by the constraints. The reader will have no trouble in seeing the similarity to the bang-bang control for minimum time in the initial stage of the calculations.

The calculations are now continued for the next time interval, using the above optimal value of $\mathbf{z}(1)$ resulting from the application of full control as the initial value, that is,

$$\mathbf{z}'(1) = [-.0055478 - .0077865 - .0052621 - .0062478 - .0056183 - .0031548],$$

and another set of 36 ΔV's is generated for this time interval. Again the minimum ΔV is chosen, and the corresponding $\mathbf{z}(2)$ serves as the initial condition for the following time interval. Calculations are thus performed, step by step, until the state is sufficiently close to the origin.

At the time of switching, where u_1 and u_2 are at some intermediate value, the time interval can be decreased and the intermediate values of u_1 and u_2 refined by considering the set of u_1 and u_2 of 0.50, 0.25, 0.10, 0.0, -0.10, -0.25, for example. Afterward, the time interval can again be increased once the control values are very close to zero, and the calculations are continued until $|z_m| < 0.0001$ for all m. Table 5.1 illustrates the manner of approach and also gives the solution to this problem. We see that at $t = 2.20$ all the $|z_m| < 0.0001$ and also remain less than 0.0001, so that the state is sufficiently close to the steady state.

Although for a problem like this, bang-bang control is predicted (see Section 5.5), we must emphasize that by considering finite intervals of time, sufficient approximations are introduced to necessitate intermediate control action. We thus have suboptimal control which is close to the optimal, but not the time-optimal control. However, the approach toward the origin is considerably faster than the transient response.

When only one control variable (let us say u_1) is used, the overshoot of the sixth stage concentration is smaller, but the over-all approach to the steady state is considerably slower. The approach to the steady state is given in Table 5.2 where for control we have chosen the possible values for u_1 to be 2, 1.5, 1.0, 0.5, 0.1, 0.0, -0.1, -0.5, -1.0, and u_2 is zero throughout.

To give a visual picture of the approach to steady state, the concentration of solute in the sixth stage is plotted as a function of time in Figure 5.2 (p. 361). It should be emphasized that we wanted each stage to approach steady state as fast as possible, and not only the sixth stage. Therefore, as we see from Tables 5.1 and 5.2, the system with two controls approaches the steady state faster than with

TABLE 5.1

Two Controls

t	u_1	u_2	Stage 1	Stage 2	Stage 3	Stage 4	Stage 5	Stage 6
0	0	0	−.0087822	−.0095841	−.0079750	−.0089374	−.0077737	−.0047414
.1	2.0*	2.0	−.0055478	−.0077865	−.0052621	−.0062478	−.0056183	−.0031548
.2	2.0	2.0	−.0032352	−.0057122	−.0032091	−.0037544	−.0033355	−.0014589
.3	2.0	2.0	−.0015125	−.0036853	−.0014983	−.0015392	−.0010823	.0003062
.35	2.0	2.0	−.0008085	−.0027342	−.0007317	−.0005297	.0000028	.0011933
.40	2.0	−1.0	−.0001869	−.0018614	−.0008434	−.0002124	.0002896	.0012968
.45	1.75	−1.0	.0002860	−.0011624	−.0008537	−.0001374	.0004954	.0013473
.50	.75	−1.0	.0004160	−.0008489	−.0009687	−.0002043	.0004357	.0011365
.55	.10	− .25	.0003498	−.0007683	−.0009502	−.0002489	.0003920	.0009753
.60	.25	− .25	.0003419	−.0006535	−.0009021	−.0002571	.0003795	.0008740
.70	.10	− .10	.0002583	−.0005375	−.0007820	−.0002619	.0003422	.0007064
.80	.10	− .10	.0002051	−.0004402	−.0006811	−.0002560	.0002972	.0005745
.90	.10	0	.0001740	−.0003534	−.0005389	−.0001974	.0003026	.0005266
1.00	.10	− .10	.0001592	−.0002755	−.0004731	−.0001826	.0002582	.0004337
1.20	0	0	.0000457	−.0002423	−.0003419	−.0001516	.0001803	.0002959
1.40	.10	− .10	.0000974	−.0001208	−.0002776	−.0001271	.0001198	.0002018
1.60	0	0	.0000363	−.0001151	−.0001994	−.0001065	.0000747	.0001364
1.80	0	0	−.0000005	−.0001061	−.0001497	−.0000883	.0000426	.0000905
2.00	0	0	−.0000216	−.0000964	−.0001168	−.0000742	.0000204	.0000583
2.20	0	0	−.0000329	−.0000871	−.0000942	−.0000637	.0000051	.0000358

* The control (2.0, 2.0) is used from $t = 0$ to $t = 0.1$; in all cases the control as shown is used in the interval from the previous to the present time.

TABLE 5.2

One Control

t	u_1	Stage 1	Stage 2	Stage 3	Stage 4	Stage 5	Stage 6
0	0	−.0087822	−.0095841	−.0079750	−.0089374	−.0077737	−.0047414
.1	2.0	−.0055532	−.0079123	−.0072487	−.0075891	−.0066223	−.0038909
.2	2.0	−.0032656	−.0060771	−.0062437	−.0063896	−.0054742	−.0030453
.3	2.0	−.0015855	−.0042943	−.0050671	−.0052229	−.0043505	−.0022079
.4	2.0	−.0003113	−.0026523	−.0038106	−.0040451	−.0032442	−.0013815
.5	2.0	+.0006822	−.0011787	−.0025409	−.0028503	−.0021454	−.0005653
.55	2.0	.0011010	−.0005054	−.0019156	−.0022494	−.0015968	−.0001601
.60	2.0	.0014755	.0001272	−.0013021	−.0016487	−.0010485	.0002436
.65	1.5	.0016954	.0005671	−.0008345	−.0011835	−.0006288	.0005194
.70	0	.0015439	.0005314	−.0007701	−.0011216	−.0005983	.0004082
.75	.1	.0014322	.0005264	−.0006868	−.0010352	−.0005479	.0003402
.80	0	.0013071	.0004922	−.0006347	−.0009783	−.0005279	.0002579
.90	.10	.0011426	.0004845	−.0004966	−.0008204	−.0004445	.0001815
1.00	0	.0009593	.0004235	−.0004239	−.0007283	−.0004216	.0000804
1.20	0	.0006802	.0003180	−.0003152	−.0005782	−.0003863	−.0000464
1.40	.10	.0005935	.0003386	−.0001545	−.0003629	−.0002450	−.0000029
1.60	0	.0004363	.0002668	−.0001062	−.0002819	−.0002189	−.0000545
1.80	0	.0003239	.0002088	−.0000746	−.0002221	−.0001953	−.0000782
2.00	0	.0002423	.0001625	−.0000542	−.0001777	−.0001731	−.0000865
2.20	0	.0001823	.0001257	−.0000412	−.0001444	−.0001524	−.0000863
2.40	0	.0001377	.0000965	−.0000330	−.0001191	−.0001335	−.0000816
2.60	0	.0001042	.0000734	−.0000278	−.0000997	−.0001165	−.0000749
2.80	0	.0000789	.0000551	−.0000246	−.0000845	−.0001015	−.0000674
3.00	0	.0000595	.0000406	−.0000225	−.0000724	−.0000883	−.0000599

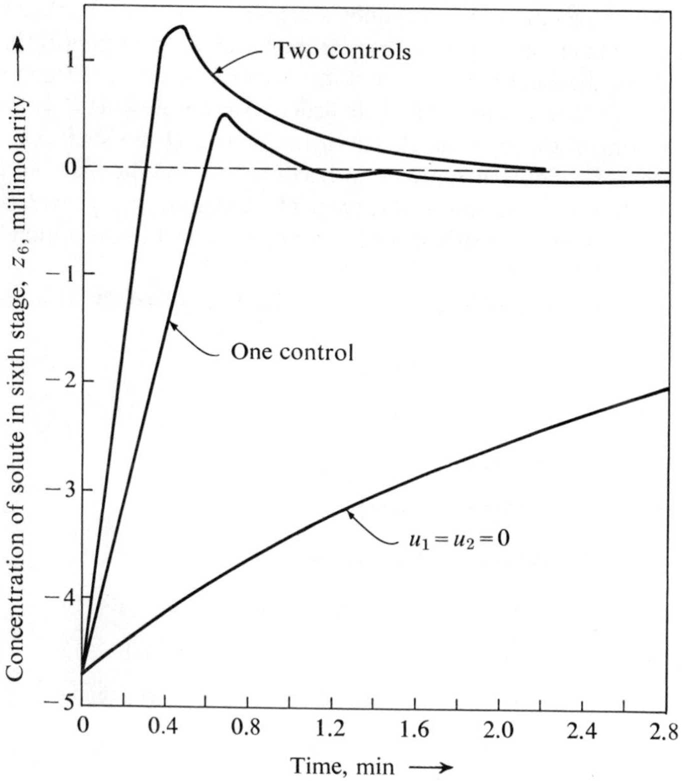

FIGURE 5.2. Control of extraction train, using Liapunov's direct method; $\mathbf{Q} = \mathbf{I}$

one control only. Both of these are considerably better than without control, where the steady state is reached after over 13.9 min.

If it had been desired to get the sixth stage concentration to its steady-state value as fast as possible, then instead of the unit matrix for $\boldsymbol{Q}$, we could have used something like

$$\boldsymbol{Q} = \begin{bmatrix} 1 & & & \cdots & & 0 \\ & 1 & & & & \\ \vdots & & 1 & & & \vdots \\ & & & 1 & & \\ & & & & 1 & \\ 0 & & & \cdots & & 10 \end{bmatrix}$$

for example, where the last stage is more heavily weighted. This concept is also detailed in Example 3.1 of Chapter 3, and arises again in the next example.

EXAMPLE 5.2 ▪ In Example 5.1 Liapunov's second method was applied to establish control for the extraction train. As can be recalled, the weighting matrix $\boldsymbol{Q}$ was chosen to be the identity matrix, and it was merely mentioned that by choosing a different $\boldsymbol{Q}$, a different control sequence may be obtained. To show the flexibility of control through the choice of the matrix $\boldsymbol{Q}$, we shall consider the six-plate absorber which was outlined in Section 1.11 and discussed in detail in Section 3.8. The consideration of this particular example also provides a direct comparison of Liapunov's method for establishing control to the optimal control as described in Chapter 3.

We shall restate the problem as follows. The normalized gas absorber equations are

$$\dot{\boldsymbol{x}} = \boldsymbol{A}\boldsymbol{x} + \boldsymbol{B}\boldsymbol{u}, \tag{5.188}$$

where the values of $\boldsymbol{A}$ and $\boldsymbol{B}$ have been given in Section 3.8 as

$$\boldsymbol{A} = \begin{bmatrix} -1.173113 & .634115 & 0 & & \cdots & 0 \\ .538998 & -1.173113 & .634115 & 0 & & \vdots \\ 0 & .538998 & -1.173113 & .634115 & & \\ 0 & 0 & .538998 & -1.173113 & .634115 & 0 \\ 0 & 0 & & .538998 & -1.173113 & .634115 \\ 0 & 0 & \cdots & 0 & 0.538998 & -1.173113 \end{bmatrix}$$

and

$$\boldsymbol{B} = \begin{bmatrix} .538998 & 0 \\ 0 & 0 \\ 0 & 0 \\ 0 & 0 \\ 0 & 0 \\ 0 & .634115 \end{bmatrix}.$$

The initial value of $\boldsymbol{x}$ is

$$\boldsymbol{x}(0) = \begin{bmatrix} -.0306632 \\ -.0567271 \\ -.0788812 \\ -.0977124 \\ -.1137188 \\ -.1273242 \end{bmatrix},$$

and the control vector $\boldsymbol{u}$ is bounded from below so that

$$0 \le u_1, \qquad -0.4167 \le u_2.$$

The problem is to find the controls u_1 and u_2 as functions of time so that the system reaches the origin (that is, $\boldsymbol{x} = \boldsymbol{0}$) as fast as possible. We shall consider the system to be sufficiently close to the origin if $|x_i| < 0.001$ for $i = 1, 2, \ldots, 6$.

We shall use the same method of approach as outlined in detail in Example 5.1. First, however, integrate Equation (5.188) over a time interval T to give

$$\boldsymbol{x}(k+1) = \boldsymbol{\Phi}\boldsymbol{x}(k) + \boldsymbol{\Delta}, \tag{5.189}$$

where $\boldsymbol{\Phi} = \exp(\boldsymbol{A}T)$ and

$$\boldsymbol{\Delta} = \left[\int_0^T \exp(\boldsymbol{A}\lambda)\, d\lambda\right]\boldsymbol{B}\boldsymbol{u}(k).$$

It should be noted that the current problem is somewhat easier than the problem considered in Example 5.1 since the coefficient matrix, $\boldsymbol{A}$, is constant, and therefore $\boldsymbol{\Phi}$ is a constant in this problem.

As before, we shall choose a Liapunov function of the positive-definite form

$$V[\boldsymbol{x}(k)] = \boldsymbol{x}(k)\boldsymbol{Q}\boldsymbol{x}(k), \tag{5.190}$$

so that

$$\Delta V[\boldsymbol{x}(k)] = [\boldsymbol{P}\boldsymbol{x}(k) + \boldsymbol{s}]'\boldsymbol{x}(k) + R, \tag{5.191}$$

where

$$\boldsymbol{P} = \boldsymbol{\Phi}'\boldsymbol{Q}\boldsymbol{\Phi} - \boldsymbol{Q}, \qquad \boldsymbol{s} = 2\boldsymbol{\Phi}'\boldsymbol{Q}\boldsymbol{\Delta}, \qquad R = \boldsymbol{\Delta}'\boldsymbol{Q}\boldsymbol{\Delta},$$

and in this example we shall use two forms for $\boldsymbol{Q}$ to show the effect of the choice of Liapunov function on the resulting trajectory. In selecting the controls, we shall use the same criterion as before, namely to choose u_1 and u_2 from a discretized set to satisfy the constraints and to minimize $\Delta V[\boldsymbol{x}(k)]$ at each time interval k. To show the improvement of using control, the uncontrolled response ($u_1 = u_2 = 0$) is plotted in Figure 5.3 (p. 364). By choosing the third and the sixth trays an idea is obtained about the behavior of the entire system. The approach to the origin is rather slow and the criterion that all $|x_i| < .001$ is met after 39 minutes have passed when no control action is used.

Now let us consider the response of the absorber to the applied controls u_1 and u_2 chosen in such a way as to minimize $\Delta V[\boldsymbol{x}(k)]$ at each interval of time.

(a) $$\boldsymbol{Q} = \boldsymbol{I}.$$

In this part of the problem, we shall weight each absorption tray evenly. The results are tabulated in part in Table 5.3 and shown graphically in Figure 5.4, (p. 364) where again the concentrations from the third and sixth trays have been plotted as a function of time. It is noticed at once that the approach to

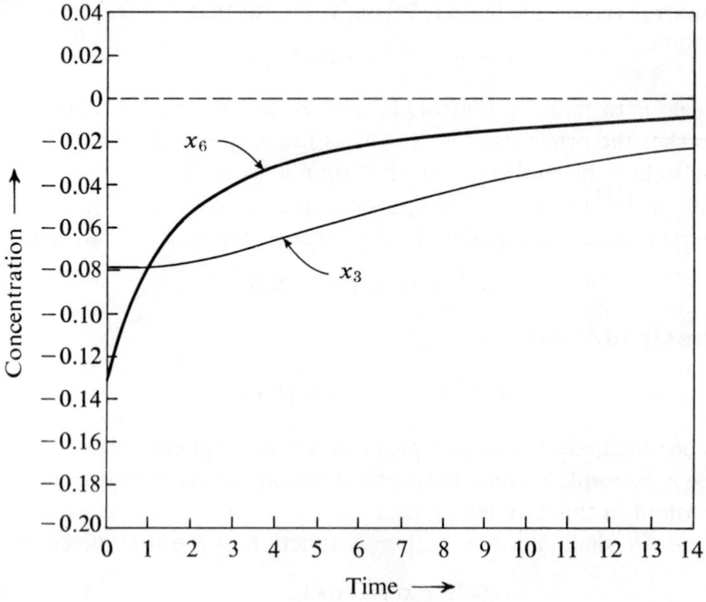

FIGURE 5.3. Uncontrolled response of the absorber system

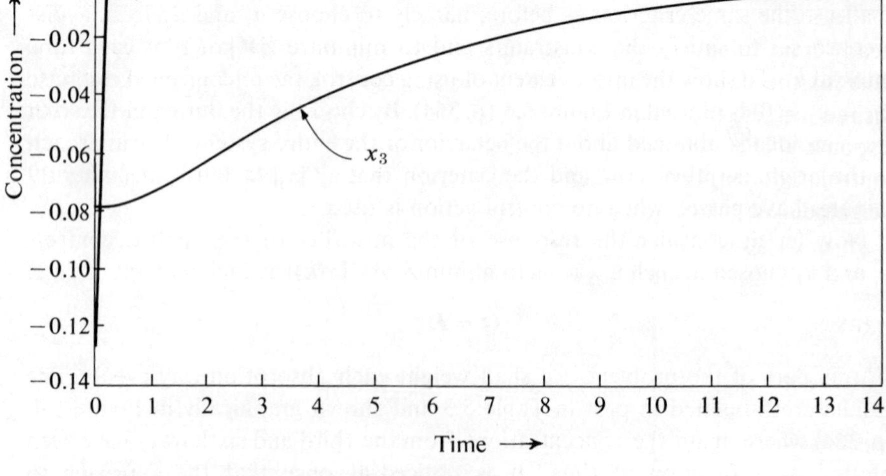

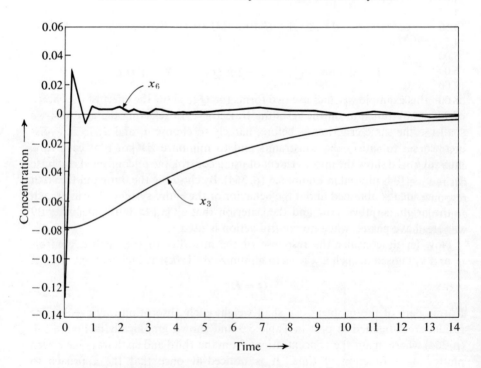

FIGURE 5.4. Control of the absorber system; $\boldsymbol{Q} = \boldsymbol{I}$

TABLE 5.3

$Q = I$

Time	u_1	u_2	x_1	x_2	x_3	x_4	x_5	x_6
0	—	—	−.03066	−.05673	−.07888	−.09771	−.11372	−.12732
.25	.5	1.0	.02792	−.05297	−.07869	−.09710	−.10188	.02967
.50	0	0	.01395	−.04790	−.07769	−.09421	−.08450	.01137
.75	0	0	.00403	−.04529	−.07601	−.08998	−.07313	−.00065
1.00	.05	.10	.00274	−.04369	−.07390	−.08527	−.06442	.00526
1.25	.05	.05	.00198	−.04230	−.07140	−.08038	−.05711	.00373
1.50	.05	.05	.00160	−.04098	−.06888	−.07555	−.05121	.00336
1.75	.05	.05	.00150	−.03965	−.06612	−.07089	−.04625	.00370
2.00	.05	.05	.00161	−.03827	−.06328	−.06646	−.04194	.00450
2.25	.05	.02	.00188	−.03683	−.06040	−.06228	−.03840	.00143
2.50	.05	.05	.00229	−.03531	−.05753	−.05838	−.03531	.00364
2.75	.05	.02	.00281	−.03374	−.05469	−.05473	−.03259	.00151
3.00	.05	.02	.00342	−.03211	−.05190	−.05135	−.03038	.00021
3.25	.02	.05	.00058	−.03067	−.04920	−.04821	−.02818	.00361
3.50	.05	.02	.00216	−.02928	−.04660	−.04526	−.02607	.00228
3.75	.05	.02	.00354	−.02772	−.04410	−.04249	−.02431	.00152
4.00	.02	.02	.00127	−.02629	−.04169	−.03992	−.02275	.00114
4.25	.05	.02	.00327	−.02489	−.03939	−.03752	−.02134	.00103
4.50	.02	.02	.00146	−.02356	−.03719	−.03528	−.02001	.00110
4.75	.02	.02	.00027	−.02243	−.03511	−.03319	−.01875	.00131
5.00	.05	.02	.00304	−.02121	−.03315	−.03122	−.01754	.00161
6.00	.02	.02	.00035	−.01704	−.02624	−.02437	−.01305	.00326
7.00	.02	.02	.00086	−.01363	−.02069	−.01876	−.00905	.00510
8.00	.02	.01	.00225	−.01036	−.01607	−.01425	−.00655	.00296
9.00	.01	.01	.00055	−.00803	−.01232	−.01083	−.00482	.00290

steady-state values is considerably faster. As a matter of fact, x_6 remains very close to the desired value. However, since x_1 and x_6 are kept very close to the desired values, the freedom of using u_1 and u_2 is lost to some extent since the response of the trays 2 to 5 is the same as for a four-tray absorber without control. Greater benefit is therefore expected if the inner trays are more heavily weighted. We therefore turn to the second part of the problem.

(b)
$$Q = \begin{bmatrix} 1.0 & 0 & & \cdots & & 0 \\ 0 & 7.39 & 0 & & & \\ & 0 & 230.0 & 0 & & \vdots \\ \vdots & & 0 & 230.0 & 0 & \\ & & & 0 & 7.39 & 0 \\ 0 & & \cdots & & 0 & 1.0 \end{bmatrix}.$$

Since the effect of one tray on the next is related approximately logarithmically, we have chosen $\boldsymbol{Q}$ so that the second tray is weighted as $e^2(=7.39)$ and the third tray as $(e^e)^2 = 230$. The effect is squared, since $\boldsymbol{Q}$ weights the square of $\boldsymbol{x}$.

TABLE 5.4

Weighted $\boldsymbol{Q}$

Time	u_1	u_2	x_1	x_2	x_3	x_4	x_5	x_6
0	—	—	−.03066	−.05673	−.07888	−.09771	−.11372	−.12732
.25	1.0	2.0	.08651	−.04922	−.07851	−.09656	−.09149	.16753
.50	.05	0	.06442	−.03870	−.07652	−.09120	−.06010	.11634
.75	.20	.10	.06662	−.03149	−.07313	−.08352	−.04069	.09476
1.00	.10	.10	.05746	−.02604	−.06874	−.07517	−.02767	.08050
1.25	.10	.10	.05124	−.02221	−.06379	−.06690	−.01856	.07114
1.50	.10	.10	.04707	−.01924	−.05860	−.05908	−.01187	.06505
1.75	.10	.05	.04432	−.01671	−.05339	−.05185	−.00718	.05431
2.00	.05	.05	.03675	−.01474	−.04829	−.04535	−.00412	.04674
2.25	.10	.05	.03719	−.01296	−.04343	−.03956	−.00199	.04138
2.50	.05	0	.03192	−.01130	−.03886	−.03448	−.00091	.03071
2.75	.05	.05	.02819	−.00997	−.03463	−.03007	−.00029	.02971
3.00	.05	0	.02558	−.00879	−.03077	−.02624	.00003	.02215
3.25	.05	.05	.02379	−.00765	−.02727	−.02293	.00030	.02340
3.50	0	0	.01676	−.00690	−.02411	−.02003	.00050	.01751
4.00	.10	.10	.02836	−.00408	−.01869	−.01504	.00331	.03406
4.50	.10	.05	.03578	.00057	−.01370	−.01028	.00718	.03207
5.00	0	0	.02045	.00307	−.00905	−.00605	.00827	.01948
5.50	0	−.05	.01215	.00320	−.00540	−.00307	.00567	.00030
6.00	0	.01	.00747	.00275	−.00291	−.00152	.00325	.00340
6.50	0	0	.00475	.00224	−.00135	−.00061	.00229	.00244
7.00	0	0	.00312	.00183	−.00041	−.00004	.00171	.00175
7.50	0	0	.00213	.00152	.00015	.00032	.00134	.00128
8.00	0	0	.00152	.00129	.00047	.00054	.00110	.00096
8.50	0	0	.00113	.00112	.00065	.00066	.00093	.00074
9.00*	0	0	.00088	.00099	.00074	.00072	.00082	.00059

* After this time all $|x_i| < 0.001$ simply by keeping the control variables zero.

Table 5.4 shows that the response is considerably better than by using the identity matrix for $\boldsymbol{Q}$ and is comparable to the minimum time response as obtained by linear programming, or dynamic programming in Chapter 3. Figure 5.5 shows the concentrations on the third and sixth trays as functions of time. The criterion that all $|x_i| < 0.001$ is met in 9 min which, compared to 39 min for the uncontrolled case, is a considerable improvement.

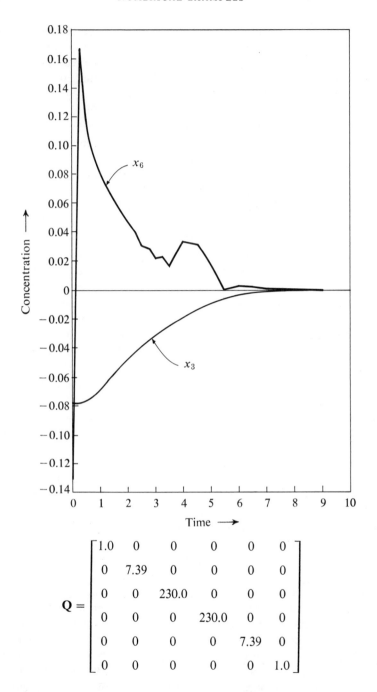

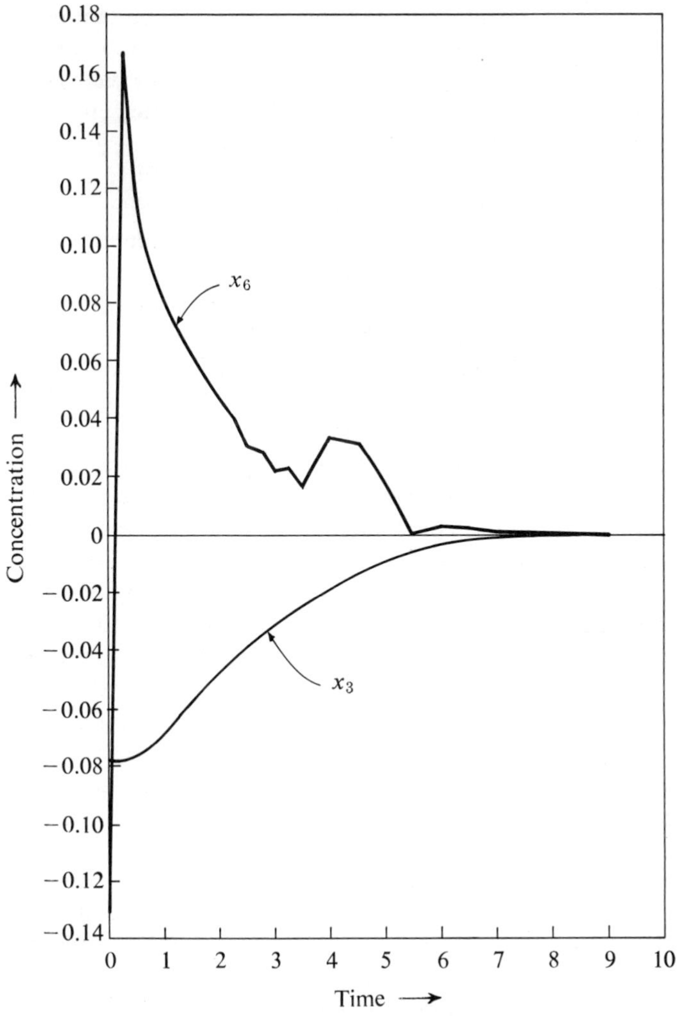

$$
\mathbf{Q} = \begin{bmatrix} 1.0 & 0 & 0 & 0 & 0 & 0 \\ 0 & 7.39 & 0 & 0 & 0 & 0 \\ 0 & 0 & 230.0 & 0 & 0 & 0 \\ 0 & 0 & 0 & 230.0 & 0 & 0 \\ 0 & 0 & 0 & 0 & 7.39 & 0 \\ 0 & 0 & 0 & 0 & 0 & 1.0 \end{bmatrix}
$$

FIGURE 5.5. Control of the absorber system

While we are still considering this example, a very important point should be noted about the nature of ΔV. It is sometimes misunderstood that if ΔV and V are both positive, the system is unstable. Both ΔV and V may be positive in a *finite* interval of time and the system can still be asymptotically stable. This is illustrated by looking at the changes in Liapunov's functions for the time interval (7.50, 8.00). The changes in Liapunov function are tabulated as functions of the control variables in Table 5.5. As usual, the minimum value for ΔV determines the control to be used for this interval. Here the minimum value for ΔV is 0.000077 as given by $u_1 = 0$, $u_2 = 0$, so with these values for control, the vector $\boldsymbol{x}(8.00)$ is evaluated and the calculation continued until all $|x_i|$ are less than 0.001 and also remain less than 0.001. This condition is met at $t = 9.0$. Hence, the system is asymptotically stable in spite of the fact that ΔV and V are both positive for some intervals of time. The ΔV, of course, becomes negative again later.

We mentioned earlier that with Liapunov's method constraints can be placed on *both* the control and the state variables. Let us consider the constraints on the state variables and use the example for illustration. Suppose that we use the weighted $\boldsymbol{Q}$ as was used to construct Table 5.4, but demand that no x_i should exceed some value, let us say, 0.10. Then, even though $u_1 = 1.0$ and $u_2 = 2.0$ give the minimum value for ΔV, the resulting value of x_6, namely 0.16753, is outside the state constraint. Thus, the minimum value for ΔV is sought in the range where the resulting state variables lie inside to constraint bounds. For example, here the controls $u_1 = 1.0$, $u_2 = 1.0$ give a value of 0.02967 for x_6 and a ΔV of -7.41×10^{-2}. Again, the constraints on the state variables simplify the problem since a smaller range of controls has to be considered. Since $u_2 = 2.0$ produces a response which lies outside bounds, it is not necessary to try values of u_2 which are greater than 2.0 for this interval of time, or the other interval for that matter.

These two examples illustrate the virtues of Liapunov's second method as used to establish the control of some linear process. First of all, constraints can be placed on *both* the control and the state variables, and actually aid the calculations by reducing the range of variables to be scanned by the computer. This is equivalent to dynamic programming numerically. Second, the dimension of the state does not matter; the problem of 10 stages instead of 6 can be handled just as easily. This is very important and quite different from the effect in dynamic programming, where the state dimension is usually more important than the number of control variables. Here, as in dynamic programming, the addition of an extra control variable complicates the problem considerably by increasing the permutations of control variables to be scanned. However, the problem can still be handled. Third, the size of time interval that is used does not really matter so long as enough terms are used in the series expansion of the exponential. Finally, the programming on a digital computer is straightforward since only matrix multiplication and addition is involved, that is, no inverse matrices need be calculated. Also, the computation time is small.

TABLE 5.5

Changes in Liapunov Function at Time Interval from 7.50 to 8.00

u_1	u_2	ΔV
.10	.10	.001628
.05	.10	.001183
.02	.10	.001031
.01	.10	.001000
.00	.10	.000979
.10	.05	.000998
.05	.05	.000554
.02	.05	.000403
.01	.05	.000372
.00	.05	.000351
.10	.02	.000789
.05	.02	.000346
.02	.02	.000196
.01	.02	.000165
.00	.02	.000144
.10	.01	.000748
.05	.01	.000345
.02	.01	.000155
.01	.01	.000124
.00	.01	.000103
.10	.00	.000721
.05	.00	.000278
.02	.00	.000128
.01	.00	.000098
.00	.00	.000077
.10	−.05	.000798
.05	−.05	.000356
.02	−.05	.000207
.01	−.05	.000177
.00	−.05	.000156
.10	−.10	.001228
.05	−.10	.000788
.02	−.10	.000640
.01	−.10	.000610
.00	−.10	.000589

We have not mentioned the effect of sampling time on the rate of approach to the origin. This can be rather important, especially when a nonidentity weighting matrix is used for the Liapunov function.

References

BOOKS

1. A. A. ANDRONOV and C. E. CHAIKIN, *Theory of Oscillations*, Princeton University Press, Princeton, N.J., 1949.
2. D. R. COUGHANOWR and B. K. LOWELL, *Process Systems Analysis and Control*, McGraw-Hill, New York, 1965.
3. W. J. CUNNINGHAM, *Nonlinear Analysis*, McGraw-Hill, New York, 1958.
4. F. R. GANTMACHER, *The Theory of Matrices*, Vols. I and II, Chelsea Publishing Co., New York, 1959.
5. J. E. GIBSON, *Nonlinear Automatic Control*, McGraw-Hill, New York, 1963.
6. W. HAHN, *Theory and Application of Liapunov's Direct Method*, Prentice-Hall, Englewood Cliffs, N.J., 1963.
7. J. IRVING and N. MALLINEUX, *Mathematics in Physics and Engineering*, Academic Press, New York, 1959.
8. Y. H. KU, *Analysis and Control of Nonlinear Systems*, Ronald Press, New York, 1958.
9. J. P. LASALLE and S. LEFSCHETZ, *Stability by Liapunov's Second Method with Applications*, Academic Press, New York, 1961.
10. J. G. MALKIN, *Theory of Stability of Motion*, U.S. AEC Translation 3352, Washington, D. C., 1958.
11. N. MINORSKY, *Nonlinear Oscillations*, D. Van Nostrand Co., Inc., Princeton, N.J., 1962.
12. T. L. SAATY and J. BRAM, *Nonlinear Mathematics*, McGraw-Hill, New York, 1964.
13. L. A. ZADEH and C. A. DESOER, *Linear System Theory*, McGraw-Hill, New York, 1963.

ARTICLES

14. R. BELLMAN, *Math. Nachr.*, *20*, 17 (1959).
15. J. S. BERGER and D. D. PERLMUTTER, *A. I. Ch. E. Jrn.*, *10*, 233 (1964); *Chem. Eng. Sci.*, *20*, 147 (1965).
16. R. W. BROCKETT, *IEEE Trans. Auto Control*, *AC-11*, 596 (1966).
17. R. C. DURBECK, *IEEE Trans. Auto. Control*, *AC-10*, 144 (1965).
18. R. M. GOLDWYN and K. J. COX, *IEEE Trans. Auto. Control*, *AC-10*, 97 (1965).
19. L. P. GRAYSON, *Automatica*, *3*, 91 (1965).
20. I. A. GURA and D. D. PERLMUTTER, *A.I.Ch.E. Jrn.*, *11*, 474 (1965).
21. W. HAHN, *Math. Nachr.*, *14*, 349 (1955).
22. A. HURWITZ, *Math. Ann.*, *46*, 273 (1895).
23. D. R. INGWERSON, *IRE Trans.*, *AC-6*, 199 (1961).
24. G. W. JOHNSON, *IEEE Trans. Auto. Control*, *AC-9*, 270 (1964).

25. R. E. Kalman and J. E. Bertram, *J. Basic Eng.*, *82*, 371, 394 (1960).
26. R. Koepcke and L. Lapidus, *Chem. Eng. Sci.*, *16*, 252 (1961).
27. R. E. Kopp, "Liapunov Stability and Optimal Control" in Appendix VI of G. R. Geiss, "The Analysis and Design of Nonlinear Control Systems Via Liapunov's Direct Method," *Grumman Aircraft Co. Report RTD-TDR-63-4076* (1964).
28. Y. H. Ku, and N. N. Puri, *J. Franklin Inst.*, *276*, 349 (1963).
29. J. P. LaSalle, *J. SIAM Control*, *Ser. A*, *1*, 3 (1962).
30. J. P. LaSalle, *SIAM Review*, *6*, 1 (1964).
31. E. J. Lefferts, "A Guide of the Application of the Liapunov Direct Method to Flight Control Systems," *NASA Report CR-209* (1965).
32. S. Lefschetz, *SIAM Review*, *7*, 1 (1965).
33. S. A. Margolis and W. G. Vogt, *IEEE Trans. Auto. Control*, *AC-8*, 104 (1963).
34. G. N. Mil'shtein, *Automatic and Remote Control*, *25*, 298 (1964).
35. R. A. Nelepin, *Eng. Cybernetics*, *6*, 114 (1964).
36. R. A. Nesbit, "Several Applications of Direct Method of Liapunov," Chapter in *Advances in Control Systems*, Vol. 2, Edited by C. T. Leondes, Academic Press, 1965.
37. W. Regenass and R. Aris, *Chem. Eng. Sci.*, *20*, 60 (1965).
38. Z. V. Rekasius and J. E. Gibson, *IRE Trans.*, *AC-7*, 3 (1962).
39. H. H. Rosenbrock, *Automatica*, *1*, 97 (1963).
40. H. H. Rosenbrock, *J. Electronics and Control*, *15*, 73 (1963).
41. M. V. Rybushov and Y. Y. Dudnikov, *Eng. Cybernetics*, *6*, 108 (1964).
42. D. G. Schultz, "The Generation of Liapunov Functions," Chapter in *Advances in Control Systems*, Vol. 2, Edited by C. T. Leondes, Academic Press, 1965.
43. D. G. Schultz and J. E. Gibson, *Trans, AIEE*, *81*, 203 (1962).
44. W. F. Stevens and L. A. Wanninger, *Canad. Jrn. of Chem. Eng.*, *44*, 158 (1966)
45. G. P. Szego, *J. Basic Eng.*, *85*, 137 (1963).
46. G. P. Szego, *Appl. Mech. Review*, *19*, 833 (1966).
47. E. M. Vaisbord, *Automatic and Remote Control*, *24*, 1482 (1963).
48. R. B. Warden, R. Aris and N. R. Amundson, *Chem. Eng. Sci.*, *19*, 149, 173 (1964).
49. J. Wei, *Chem. Eng. Sci.*, *20*, 729 (1965).

6

Stability of Nonlinear Lumped-Parameter Systems

In Chapter 5, the emphasis was on the consideration of linear systems, although the control of nonlinear systems was briefly mentioned in Section 5.8. We have seen that a set of linear equations could arise either from the inherent linearity of the system or by the process of linearization of a truly nonlinear system. Since most physical systems are nonlinear, linearization could lead to over-simplification which consequently might give misleading results, even to a simple physical system such as an exothermic irreversible reaction in a continuous stirred tank reactor. In such cases, it is essential that the nonlinearities be considered to investigate the stability and the over-all behavior.

Since there is no general method of solving nonlinear differential equations, some ingenuity must be used to extract as much information as possible from these equations in order to predict the operational characteristics of the system under consideration. Although the differential equations can be readily integrated numerically with a digital computer, the process may be tedious and time-consuming when a series of different integrations are required, as is the case when parameter variations are considered. Therefore, wherever possible, one would like to use an analytical approach, even if the procedure is approximate, to investigate the system behavior.

Quite frequently the nonlinearity in the system is not dominant, but yet its linearization could lead to significant error. Usually under this condition the descriptive differential equation(s) can be written so that the main effect is determined by the linear part and the correction to this is obtained by the nonlinear part; the solution may then be constructed in the form of asymptotic series. This approach is used in the perturbation, asymptotic, and stroboscopic methods, to be discussed shortly. The questions concerning the identification of small parameters and the number of terms to use in the series sometimes present considerable difficulties. Also, if the nonlinearity is small, it can be replaced by its average value over an interval, as has been outlined by the method of averaging by Krylov and Bogoliubov.

At other times the nonlinearity can be very important and will not be merely a correction to linear behavior. Then one might use graphical analysis, in which the trajectories are mapped on the phase plane; the Liapunov direct method, in which the system behavior is predicted by some sign-definite functions; or the newly-developed averaging technique, in which an approximate solution is constructed to the system equations. Afterward, to substantiate the results so obtained, the digital computer can be used to integrate the differential equations numerically. The purpose of this chapter is to acquaint the reader with the various methods available to approach the nonlinear systems. In this chapter, we shall not be concerned with control explicitly, although the more complicated system models will be in a form suitable for control analysis.

6.1. Perturbation and asymptotic methods of analysis

When the system contains a small parameter, it is quite natural to neglect the small term as a first approximation and then construct correction terms; in other words, we shall be searching for a solution in the form of an asymptotic series. To illustrate this *perturbation method*, let us consider the familiar electric circuit equation

$$V(t) = RI(t) + L\dot{I}(t), \tag{6.1}$$

where the voltage $V(t)$ is an imposed function of time, the current $I(t)$ is to be found, and the resistance R and the inductance L are positive constants. We shall assume that the initial condition $I(0)$ is given. Let us propose to examine the solution in the limit as the resistance R tends to zero.

Here, immediately R is identified as a small parameter and the solution to Equation (6.1) is assumed as a power series in R. We therefore write

$$I(t) = I_0(t) + RI_1(t) + R^2I_2(t) + \cdots, \tag{6.2}$$

where $I(t)$ is the desired current and $I_0, I_1, I_2, \ldots$ are some functions of time to be determined. Substitution of Equation (6.2) into Equation (6.1) yields

$$V(t) = R[I_0 + RI_1 + R^2I_2 + \cdots] + L[\dot{I}_0 + R\dot{I}_1 + R^2\dot{I}_2 + \cdots]. \tag{6.3}$$

The terms in Equation (6.3) may be regrouped to give

$$V(t) = L\dot{I}_0 + R[I_0 + L\dot{I}_1] + R^2[I_1 + L\dot{I}_2] + \cdots. \tag{6.4}$$

Here R is assumed to be small (since we are considering the case where R tends to zero), and therefore the power on R will determine the order of magnitude. Since the terms of the same order of magnitude must balance, the terms of the same powers of R can be equated, with the result that

$$V(t) = L\dot{I}_0, \tag{6.5}$$

$$0 = I_0 + L\dot{I}_1, \tag{6.6}$$

$$0 = I_1 + L\dot{I}_2, \tag{6.7}$$

$$\vdots$$

Integration of Equation (6.5) gives

$$I_0(t) = I(0) + \int_0^t \frac{V(\lambda)}{L}\, d\lambda, \tag{6.8}$$

and $I_0(t)$ can be evaluated from the given $V(\lambda)$. Then immediately Equation (6.6) gives

$$I_1(t) = -\int_0^t \frac{I_0(\lambda)}{L}\, d\lambda, \tag{6.9}$$

and once we have I_1, Equation (6.7) gives

$$I_2(t) = -\int_0^t \frac{I_1(\lambda)}{L}\, d\lambda, \tag{6.10}$$

and the process can be continued to obtain higher-order terms in the series to give the current $I(t)$ to the desired degree of accuracy. The iteration is straightforward, and at once we have

$$I(t) = I(0) + \int_0^t \frac{V(\lambda)}{L}\, d\lambda - \frac{R}{L}\int_0^t \left(I(0) + \int_0^\tau \frac{V(\lambda)}{L}\, d\lambda \right) d\tau + \cdots. \tag{6.11}$$

It should be noted that in the above development we have assumed that the derivative of the function is of the same order of magnitude as the function itself. This is, of course, not true in general, and we shall discuss this in some detail later in this section. Before this, however, let us choose to examine the solution when the other parameter is very small.

Let us consider the problem in the limit $L \to 0$. We note at once that the inductance term must be kept to satisfy the initial condition. As before, the current is expressed as a power series in the small parameter (L instead of R in this case)

$$I(t) = I_0(t) + LI_1(t) + L^2 I_2(t) + \cdots, \tag{6.12}$$

and we wish to determine the current $I(t)$ when the voltage $V(t)$ is imposed on the system with given $I(0)$. As before, we substitute the series expression into the system equation [Equation (6.1)]. This yields

$$V(t) = R[I_0 + LI_1 + \cdots] + L[I_0 + LI_1 + \cdots]^{\cdot}. \tag{6.13}$$

Balancing the terms of the same order of magnitude gives

$$V(t) = RI_0, \tag{6.14}$$

$$0 = RI_1 + \dot{I}_0, \tag{6.15}$$

$$0 = RI_2 + \dot{I}_1, \tag{6.16}$$

$$\vdots$$

Therefore, we have

$$I_0(t) = \frac{V(t)}{R}, \tag{6.17}$$

$$I_1(t) = -\frac{1}{R}\dot{I}_0(t) = -\frac{1}{R}\left(\frac{V}{R}\right)^{\cdot}, \tag{6.18}$$

$$I_2(t) = -\frac{1}{R}\dot{I}_1(t) = \frac{1}{R^2}\left(\frac{V}{R}\right)^{\cdot\cdot}, \tag{6.19}$$

and higher terms can be similarly evaluated. The solution is then given by

$$I(t) = \frac{V(t)}{R} - \frac{L}{R^2}\dot{V}(t) + \frac{L^2}{R^3}\ddot{V}(t) - \frac{L^3}{R^4}\dddot{V}(t) + \cdots. \tag{6.20}$$

However, we see at once that here we have lost the freedom to choose the initial condition $I(0)$ at will. Before showing how to account for the given initial condition, we shall show how the same result is obtained asymptotically.

According to the *principle of recursion* [22], the nondominant terms can be treated as if they were known, even though they involve the unknown solution. Therefore, in the above case where L is small, if $\dot{I}$ is of the same order of magnitude as I, we can treat $L\dot{I}$ as a known quantity since it will constitute the nondominant term of Equation (6.1). We shall rewrite Equation (6.1) as

$$I(t) = (1/R)[V(t) - L\dot{I}(t)]. \tag{6.21}$$

In this equation, the current I appears on both sides of the equation (on the right-hand side it appears as $\dot{I}$). Since $L\dot{I}$ is nondominant for small L, we can use Equation (6.21) itself to form an iteration scheme because $L\dot{I}$ is considered known; we shall have

$$I(t) = \frac{1}{R}\left[V - L\left\{\frac{1}{R}\left[V - L\dot{I}\right]\right\}^{\cdot}\right], \tag{6.22}$$

and continuing the process another step, we obtain

$$I(t) = \frac{1}{R}\left[V - L\left\{\frac{1}{R}\left[V - L\left(\frac{1}{R}[V - L\dot{I}]\right)^{\cdot}\right]\right\}^{\cdot}\right]. \tag{6.23}$$

Therefore, we have

$$I = \frac{1}{R}\left[V - \frac{L}{R}\dot{V} + \frac{L^2}{R^2}\ddot{V} - \frac{L^3}{R^3}\dddot{V} + \cdots\right], \tag{6.24}$$

which is identical to Equation (6.20).

Now let us examine how we have lost the freedom to choose the initial condition. We have assumed in the above treatment that $\dot{I}$ is of the same order of magnitude as I. Intuition tells us that this is not necessarily true in the beginning, where a large change in I can take place in a very short interval of time. In fact, the change of I with respect to time can be very large initially. To investigate this initial region, we shall change the time scale by putting

$$t = L\tau, \tag{6.25}$$

where τ is the rescaled time. Equation (6.1) then becomes

$$V(L\tau) = RI + dI/d\tau. \tag{6.26}$$

However, by Taylor's series,

$$V(L\tau) = V(0) + L\tau\,\dot{V}(0) + \frac{L^2\tau^2}{2!}\,\ddot{V}(0) + \cdots. \tag{6.27}$$

Also, we shall use the series expansion for I as given by Equation (6.12), namely,

$$I(L\tau) = I_0(L\tau) + LI_1(L\tau) + L^2I_2(L\tau) + \cdots. \tag{6.28}$$

Substitution of Equations (6.27) and (6.28) into Equation (6.26) yields

$$V(0) + L\tau\,\dot{V}(0) + \cdots = R[I_0 + LI_1 + \cdots] + (d/d\tau)[I_0 + LI_1 + \cdots]. \tag{6.29}$$

Then, again balancing terms of the same order of magnitude gives

$$V(0) = RI_0 + \frac{dI_0}{d\tau}, \tag{6.30}$$

$$\tau\,\dot{V}(0) = RI_1 + \frac{dI_1}{d\tau}, \tag{6.31}$$

$$\vdots$$

Equation (6.30) can be integrated to give

$$I_0(t) = \frac{1}{R}V(0) + e^{-(Rt/L)}\left[I_0(0) - \frac{1}{R}V(0)\right] = \frac{1}{R}V(0) + e^{-(Rt/L)}\left[I(0) - \frac{1}{R}V(0)\right], \tag{6.32}$$

since $I_0(0) = I(0)$ and $I_i(0) = 0$ for $i = 1, 2, \ldots$. There is no problem in going to higher-order terms, and this extension is left to the reader.

In solving problems like this one, the over-all region is divided into two separate regions: the *initial* region and the *main* region. For the above problem, the first term of the series describing the initial region is given by Equation (6.32) and the main region is given by Equation (6.20) [or Equation (6.24)]. These two regions are fitted together smoothly. No doubt, the reader is already familiar with this procedure in fluid mechanics, where the solution is separated into two parts, one dealing with the bulk of the fluid and the other with the fluid very close to the solid [6].

The same procedures are easily carried over to higher-order ordinary differential equations. We could, for example, consider a second-order ordinary differential equation

$$\frac{d^2y}{dx^2} = f\left(x, y, \frac{dy}{dx}, \varepsilon\right), \tag{6.33}$$

where ε is a small parameter.

As before, we try to construct a solution in the form of an asymptotic series in the small parameter ε

$$y(x) = y_0(x) + \varepsilon y_1(x) + \varepsilon^2 y_2(x) + \cdots \tag{6.34}$$

by substituting this series into Equation (6.33) and balancing the terms of the same order of magnitude. This gives

$$\frac{d^2y_0}{dx^2} = f\left(x, y_0, \frac{dy_0}{dx}, 0\right), \tag{6.35}$$

$$\frac{d^2y_1}{dx^2} = \frac{\partial}{\partial\varepsilon}\left\{f\left(x, y_0, \frac{dy_0}{dx}, 0\right)\right\} + \left\{\frac{\partial}{\partial y} f\left(x, y_0, \frac{dy_0}{dx}, 0\right)\right\} y_1 + \left\{\frac{\partial}{\partial y_0'} f\left(x, y_0, \frac{dy_0}{dx}, 0\right)\right\} y_1', \tag{6.36}$$

where $y_0' = dy_0/dx$ and $y_1' = dy_1/dx$, etc. These perturbation equations are linear (but not homogeneous in general), and so we can solve for $y_0, y_1, \ldots$ and then have the solution to the problem.

An interesting situation arises if the second derivative itself is small, that is, if we have an equation of the form

$$\varepsilon\frac{d^2y}{dx^2} = f\left(x, y, \frac{dy}{dx}, \varepsilon\right), \tag{6.37}$$

where ε is a small parameter. The first approximation is

$$0 = f\left(x, y_0, \frac{dy_0}{dx}, 0\right), \tag{6.38}$$

which is a differential equation of the *first order*, and we cannot use so many boundary conditions. To illustrate the problem that we are facing, let us suppose that the boundary conditions for Equation (6.37) are

$$y = a \quad \text{at} \quad x = 0, \qquad y = b \quad \text{at} \quad x = 1. \tag{6.39}$$

Equation (6.38) can satisfy only one of these . . . but which one? To answer this question, it must be considered that there is at least one place where $\varepsilon(d^2y/dx^2)$ is not small. This enables the other boundary condition to be picked up. *A priori*, we do not know at which boundary we have this rapid change of y with respect to x.

To illustrate the means of determining at which boundary this region lies, we consider the following equation

$$\varepsilon \frac{d^2y}{dx^2} = x \frac{dy}{dx}, \tag{6.40}$$

and call the region where $\varepsilon(d^2y/dx^2)$ is not small the boundary layer. Let us assume that the boundary layer lies near $x = 0$. Then rescale the independent variable x by the substitution

$$\xi = (1/\sqrt{\varepsilon})x \tag{6.41}$$

to remove ε from the left-hand side of Equation (6.40). Then Equation (6.40) becomes

$$d^2y/d\xi^2 = \xi(dy/d\xi), \tag{6.42}$$

which can be integrated immediately to give

$$y = C_1 \int_0^x \exp\left(\frac{x^2}{2\varepsilon}\right) dx + C_2, \tag{6.43}$$

where C_1 and C_2 are constants of integration. However, the first term on the right-hand side of Equation (6.43) diverges as x increases. Thus, we conclude that for the system described by Equation (6.40) the boundary layer cannot exist near $x = 0$.

This leaves us to examine the system near $x = 1$. At $x = 1$,

$$\varepsilon(d^2y/dx^2) = dy/dx \tag{6.44}$$

and

$$y \sim e^{x/\varepsilon}, \tag{6.45}$$

which decays into the origin since x moves in the negative *direction*. We therefore conclude that in this particular example the boundary layer is at $x = 1$.

When we use the perturbation method to study equations having periodic solutions, often some nonperiodic terms, referred to as *secular* terms, appear. Consider the expansion

$$\sin t \equiv t - \frac{t^3}{3!} + \frac{t^5}{5!} - \frac{t^7}{7!} + \cdots. \tag{6.46}$$

If a finite number of terms is used and t is allowed to approach infinity, the right-hand side of Equation (6.46) will approach $+\infty$ or $-\infty$, depending on whether an odd number or an even number of terms is used in the series. Therefore, when series solutions are sought, the secular terms must be eliminated. Frequently recursive integrations are involved so the constants of integration can be chosen to satisfy this condition of elimination of the nonperiodic terms. We shall illustrate this by considering the van der Pol equation

$$\ddot{x} + \varepsilon(x^2 - 1)\dot{x} + x = 0, \tag{6.47}$$

where ε is a small parameter greater than zero. It is noted that if $\varepsilon = 0$, the solution to Equation (6.47) is given by $x = A \sin t$, where A is an arbitrary constant determined by the initial conditions.

Therefore if $\varepsilon > 0$, let us expand $x(t)$ in a power series of ε:

$$x(t) = x_0(t) + \varepsilon x_1(t) + \varepsilon^2 x_2(t) + \cdots, \tag{6.48}$$

where the functions $x_0, x_1, x_2, \ldots$ are to be determined. Substituting Equation (6.48) into Equation (6.47) gives

$$(\ddot{x}_0 + \varepsilon\ddot{x}_1 + \cdots) + \varepsilon[(x_0 + \varepsilon x_1 + \cdots)^2 - 1][\dot{x}_0 + \varepsilon\dot{x}_1 + \cdots] + [x_0 + \varepsilon x_1 + \cdots] = 0. \tag{6.49}$$

Balancing the terms of equal magnitude (that is, equal powers of ε) gives

$$\ddot{x}_0 + x_0 = 0, \tag{6.50}$$

$$\ddot{x}_1 + x_1 = (1 - x_0)\dot{x}_0, \tag{6.51}$$

$$\vdots$$

From Equation (6.50), we have

$$x_0 = A \sin(t + \alpha), \tag{6.52}$$

where we shall choose α to be zero since the system (6.47) is autonomous and the phase shift does not change the over-all solution. Substitution of (6.52) into Equation (6.51) gives

$$\ddot{x}_1 + x_1 = (1 - A^2 \sin^2 t)A \cos t, \tag{6.53}$$

and thus

$$x_1 = \int_0^t \sin(t - \lambda)(1 - A^2 \sin^2 \lambda)A \cos \lambda \, d\lambda,$$

which can be integrated to give

$$x_1 = \left(\frac{A}{2} - \frac{A^3}{8}\right) t \sin t + \tfrac{1}{4} A \sin t \sin 2t - A \cos t \sin^2 t$$
$$+ \frac{A^2}{32} \sin t \sin 4t + \frac{A^3}{4} \cos t \sin 4t. \tag{6.54}$$

The first term on the right-hand side of Equation (6.54) is a secular term. To put this equal to zero, we choose

$$A = \pm 2. \tag{6.55}$$

Since the negative value is equivalent to phase shift, we select $A = 2$, and therefore to the first-order terms in ε

$$x(t) = 2 \sin t + \varepsilon[\tfrac{1}{2} \sin t \sin 2t - 2 \cos t \sin^2 t + \tfrac{1}{4} \sin t \sin 4t + 2 \cos t \sin 4t], \tag{6.56}$$

and we can proceed to higher terms in similar fashion.

As a closing remark, we wish to emphasize that the asymptotic series obtained by using the perturbation method does not have to be convergent. Experience will usually tell how many terms are sufficient, and when to stop. In most cases, the first two terms in the asymptotic series describe the system containing a small parameter quite well. The perturbation method, therefore, gives a physical insight into the behavior of the system without really discarding the nonlinear terms. However, even for a simple system the calculations are long and tedious, and a moderately hard problem can rarely be solved satisfactorily by the perturbation method.

6.2. Method of averaging

Since nonautonomous systems are more difficult to analyze than autonomous systems, considerable effort has gone into devising schemes to convert nonautonomous systems to autonomous systems by removing the explicit time dependence. One such method is the *method of averaging*, first formulated by Krylov and Bogoliubov in 1937 [5]. This method has been found especially useful in simplifying equations that describe a system of many degrees of freedom, and contain a small parameter. An improved version of this important development can be found in a recent text by Bogoliubov and Mitropolsky [2]. They consider a system of differential equations of the form

$$\dot{\boldsymbol{x}} = \varepsilon \boldsymbol{g}(t, \boldsymbol{x}), \tag{6.57}$$

where $\boldsymbol{x}$ and $\boldsymbol{g}$ are n-dimensional vectors. If ε is small enough,

$$\dot{\boldsymbol{x}} \doteq \varepsilon \boldsymbol{g}_0(\boldsymbol{x}), \tag{6.58}$$

where

$$\boldsymbol{g}_0 = \lim_{T \to \infty} \frac{1}{T} \int_0^T \boldsymbol{g}(t, \boldsymbol{x})\, dt, \tag{6.59}$$

provided that this limit exists. During the integration, the vector $\boldsymbol{x}$ is held constant. In other words, $\boldsymbol{g}$ is replaced by its average value, $\boldsymbol{g}_0$, if ε is sufficiently small.

To illustrate the ease of applying this method of averaging, let us consider the following system,

$$\dot{x}_1 = x_2, \qquad \dot{x}_2 = -x_1 + \varepsilon[1 - (x_1 + B \sin \omega t)^2]x_2, \tag{6.60}$$

for which the averaged equations are

$$\dot{x}_1 = x_2, \qquad \dot{x}_2 = -x_1 + \varepsilon\left(1 - x_1^2 - \frac{B^2}{2}\right)x_2, \tag{6.61}$$

since the average value of $\sin \omega t$ is zero and of $\sin^2 \omega t$ is $\frac{1}{2}$. This method was successfully used by Hale [4], who studied the quenching of the van der Pol equation.

In many cases, however, the approximate autonomous system fails to describe the behavior of the original system altogether. To emphasize this point, it is sufficient to consider the linear Mathieu equation:

$$\dot{x} = y, \qquad \dot{y} = -by - x - ax \cos 2t, \tag{6.62}$$

where a and b are small constants. For this system, the averaged equations are

$$\dot{x} = y, \qquad \dot{y} = -by - x, \tag{6.63}$$

and it might be concluded erroneously that the system is always stable for $b > 0$ regardless of the value of a, whereas in reality b must be greater than $a/2$ for stability [24].

6.3. Stroboscopic method

Minorsky [27] developed a means of converting a nonautonomous system to an autonomous one by constructing the so-called *stroboscopic differential equations*, which have the property that the existence as well as stability of a singular point in the auxiliary system is the criterion for the existence and stability of a *periodic* solution of the original system. For a detailed development of this method with geometric representation and numerous applications, the reader should consult the text by Minorsky [9]. We shall briefly outline the derivation of the stroboscopic equations.

Consider a *nearly linear* nonautonomous second-order system of the form

$$\dot{x} = f(x, y, t), \qquad \dot{y} = g(x, y, t), \tag{6.64}$$

where f and g are linear functions of x, y, and t. We shall write these in polar coordinates for convenience,

$$d\rho/dt = F(\rho, \psi, t), \qquad d\psi/dt = G(\rho, \psi, t), \tag{6.65}$$

where $\rho = x^2 + y^2$ and $\psi = \tan^{-1}(y/x)$. Here F and G are periodic functions with period 2π in t.

Since the system is nearly linear, its behavior is close to that of a harmonic oscillator and the differential equations (6.65) can be put in the form

$$d\rho/dt = \varepsilon f(\rho, \psi, t), \qquad d\psi/dt = -1 + \varepsilon g(\rho, \psi, t), \tag{6.66}$$

where ε is a small parameter. Note that for $\varepsilon = 0$, we have the conditions for a harmonic oscillator.

A solution to (6.66) is sought in the form of two series

$$\rho(t) = \rho_0(t) + \varepsilon\rho_1(t) + \cdots, \qquad \psi(t) = \psi_0(t) + \varepsilon\psi_1(t) + \cdots. \tag{6.67}$$

These series are substituted into Equations (6.66) and the terms of the same order of magnitude are balanced. Thus, equating the coefficients of like powers of ε gives

$$\rho_0(t) = \rho_0 = \text{const}, \qquad \psi_0(t) = \phi_0 - t, \tag{6.68}$$

where $\rho(0) = \rho_0$; $\psi(0) = \phi_0 = \text{const}$. The first-order correction terms are

$$\rho_1(t) = \int_0^t f(\rho_0, \phi_0 - \lambda, \lambda)\, d\lambda, \qquad \psi_1(t) = \int_0^t g(\rho_0, \phi_0 - \lambda, \lambda)\, d\lambda. \tag{6.69}$$

And therefore we can write the solution in the first approximation as

$$\rho(t) = \rho_0 + \varepsilon\rho_1(t), \qquad \psi(t) = \phi_0 - t + \varepsilon\psi_1(t). \tag{6.70}$$

These expressions can be used to evaluate $\rho(t)$ and $\psi(t)$ for $t = 2\pi, 4\pi, \ldots$; but this cannot be done as $t \to \infty$, inasmuch as the higher-order terms which have been neglected may impair the accuracy of the approximation in the long run. To avoid this problem of taking on large values of t, t is varied only during an interval 2π and the variations $\rho_1(2\pi)$ and $\psi_1(2\pi)$ are calculated during one interval 2π. With the new values of $\rho(2\pi)$ and $\psi(2\pi)$, which are considered for the second interval as $\rho(0)$ and $\psi(0)$, the new values of ρ and ψ at the end of the second interval are calculated, and so on. In this manner t is varied only by finite intervals 2π in each interval, and the initial conditions are adjusted so that the terminal conditions of the $(n-1)$st interval become the initial conditions for the nth interval.

Therefore, after a certain interval the following equations can be written:

$$\rho(2n\pi) = \rho(2(n-1)\pi) + \varepsilon\rho_1(2n\pi), \qquad \phi(2n\pi) = \phi(2(n-1)\pi) + \varepsilon\psi_1(2n\pi). \quad (6.71)$$

These equations may be put into the form

$$\begin{aligned} \Delta\rho &= \rho(2n\pi) - \rho(2(n-1)\pi) = 2\pi\varepsilon K(\rho_0, \phi_0), \\ \Delta\phi &= \phi(2n\pi) - \phi(2(n-1)\pi) = 2\pi\varepsilon L(\rho_0, \phi_0). \end{aligned} \quad (6.72)$$

It is obvious that, if the transformation leads ultimately to a fixed point,

$$\Delta\rho = \Delta\phi = 0.$$

For convenience, the time element that was lost in the integration of Equations (6.69) between 0 and 2π is introduced by defining a new "stroboscopic" time, τ, by the expression

$$\Delta\tau = 2\pi\varepsilon. \quad (6.73)$$

Then Equations (6.72) can be rewritten as

$$\frac{\Delta\rho}{\Delta\tau} = K(\rho_0, \phi_0), \qquad \frac{\Delta\phi}{\Delta\tau} = L(\rho_0, \phi_0). \quad (6.74)$$

These difference equations can be written as differential equations if $\Delta\tau$ is sufficiently small and if the total duration of the process is long as compared to one period 2π. Under these conditions, we have the stroboscopic autonomous differential equations

$$\frac{d\rho}{d\tau} = K(\rho, \phi), \qquad \frac{d\phi}{d\tau} = L(\rho, \phi). \quad (6.75)$$

The problem of establishing the existence of a periodic solution of the original nonautonomous system (6.64) is thus reduced to ascertaining the existence of a singular point of the autonomous system (6.75). Likewise the question of stability of the periodic solution of (6.64) is reduced to the investigation of stability of the singular point of (6.75).

According to the knowledge of the authors, the stroboscopic method has been used successfully only in some particular problems in physics and electrical engineering. Its use in chemical engineering has not been reported, and the reasons seem apparent. First of all, there is the difficulty of identifying a small parameter in systems like the continuous stirred tank reactor. Secondly, the requirement that the duration of the process is long as compared to one period, 2π, is too demanding for useful control design. Also, most of the systems are multidimensional, and it is not clear how the stroboscopic method could be extended to higher dimensions. In this book, therefore, we introduce the *averaging technique*, which overcomes the problems of small parameter identification and the time of duration. We shall discuss this in detail in Section 6.6.

6.4. Graphical analysis of nonlinear systems

6.4.1. PHASE-PLANE REPRESENTATION

To analyze a physical system whose behavior can be represented by two simultaneous autonomous (i.e., time does not appear explicitly) differential equations, a phase-plane representation is convenient. This allows one to visualize the system behavior "in the large," as the trajectories are mapped on the plane. Even for nonautonomous systems, the phase plane can be useful for recording data and interpreting the results of numerical integrations, but the representation is not so clear since the paths (which now are really projections of the trajectories) may intersect.

Consider a pair of simultaneous differential equations in the form

$$\dot{x} = ax + by + P_2(x, y), \qquad \dot{y} = cx + dy + Q_2(x, y), \tag{6.76}$$

where P_2 and Q_2 are of second degree or higher. The coordinates are chosen so that the origin is at the singularity. There may be other singularities in the vicinity of the origin, but we shall consider only the singularity at the origin. According to Liapunov [8], the nature of this singularity can be determined from the simplified equations, where the nonlinear parts are omitted,

$$\dot{x} = ax + by, \qquad \dot{y} = cx + dy. \tag{6.77}$$

Equations (6.77) have been discussed in detail in Section 5.2. We shall merely add that once the type of singularity is determined from Equations (6.77), Equations (6.76) can be integrated by a digital or analog computer to determine the over-all phase portrait. This will then give a clear picture of what is happening in the two-dimensional system. For higher-dimension systems, projections can be used to obtain phase-plane plots and instead of a single phase plane, there will be a number of them to describe the system behavior.

6.4.2. LIMIT CYCLES

In a nonlinear system, it is possible to have a self-sustained oscillation with the amplitude of oscillation being independent of its initial value. In the phase plane, where one dependent variable is plotted against another, this can be represented as an isolated closed trajectory. Such a free oscillation is called a limit cycle. Under some conditions a constant input into a continuous stirred tank reactor (CSTR) can produce a limit cycle in the temperature-concentration phase plane. This oscillation can be large enough to make the product undesirable or to surpass the temperature limitations of the reactor. It is thus important, from both a theoretical and an applied point of view, to detect the presence of such limit cycles.

From the theoretical point of view, it is hard to formulate the necessary and sufficient conditions on the form of the differential equations to guarantee the existence of a limit cycle in a given region. On the other hand, we have the Bendixon's First Theorem, which provides conditions under which limit cycles *cannot* exist in a given region. Let us consider two autonomous differential equations in the form

$$\dot{x} = P(x, y), \qquad \dot{y} = Q(x, y), \tag{6.78}$$

where P and Q are some functions of x and y, and $P(0, 0) = Q(0, 0) = 0$. The Equations (6.78) can be combined to give

$$\frac{dy}{dx} = \frac{Q(x, y)}{P(x, y)} \tag{6.79}$$

or

$$P(x, y)\, dy - Q(x, y)\, dx = 0. \tag{6.80}$$

If there is a closed solution curve (that is, a limit cycle) we may integrate the left-hand side of (6.80) along this contour. The line integral can be expressed as a surface integral where the surface, S, is the part inside the closed curve. We shall have

$$\int_C [P(x, y)\, dy - Q(x, y)\, dx] = \iint_S \left(\frac{\partial P}{\partial x} + \frac{\partial Q}{\partial y}\right) dx\, dy. \tag{6.81}$$

However, since the left-hand side is zero everywhere,

$$\iint_S \left(\frac{\partial P}{\partial x} + \frac{\partial Q}{\partial y}\right) dx\, dy = 0, \tag{6.82}$$

if there is a limit cycle. In order to satisfy Equation (6.82), $[(\partial P/\partial x) + (\partial Q/\partial y)]$ must be zero somewhere in the region. If $[(\partial P/\partial x) + (\partial Q/\partial y)]$ is sign definite everywhere in the region, a limit cycle *cannot* exist in that region.

As an example, consider the autonomous van der Pol equation, which we shall write as

$$\dot{x} = y, \qquad \dot{y} = \varepsilon(1 - x^2)y - x, \tag{6.83}$$

where

$$(\partial P/\partial x + \partial Q/\partial y) = \varepsilon(1 - x^2). \tag{6.84}$$

Hence $(\partial P/\partial x + \partial Q/\partial y)$ is positive when $|x| < 1$, and it can be concluded that no limit cycle can exist inside this region. When $|x| > 1$, $(\partial P/\partial x + \partial Q/\partial y)$ becomes negative, indicating the possibility of a limit cycle.

For general application, it is found that the above condition is too restrictive and is of little practical value in determining the existence of limit cycles [24]. This point will be illustrated in Example 6.2.

6.5. Application of Liapunov's second method to determine stability of nonlinear systems

In Chapter 5 we saw that to determine the stability of a linear system the procedure is fairly straightforward, and in the case of a constant coefficient matrix it is necessary and sufficient that all eigenvalues have only negative real parts. Even with a time-varying coefficient matrix, the stability can be readily determined, although negative real parts of the eigenvalues do not ensure stability unless the time variation is sufficiently slow. For a nonlinear system, however, a significant difficulty arises, namely the estimation of the region of asymptotic stability. To find that a particular equilibrium point is asymptotically stable is insufficient without the knowledge of the size of the region. In many instances, the extent of asymptotic stability could be so small that, for all practical purposes, the system could be considered unstable. The following two theorems, due to LaSalle [23], help us to determine the extent of the region of asymptotic stability.

▶ THEOREM 6.1. *Let Ω denote the closed region defined by $V(\boldsymbol{x}) < l$ and suppose that $V(\boldsymbol{x})$ has continuous first partials in Ω. Assume that Ω is bounded and that within Ω*

$$V(\boldsymbol{x}) > 0 \qquad \text{for} \qquad \boldsymbol{x} \neq \boldsymbol{0}, \qquad \dot{V}(\boldsymbol{x}) \leq 0.$$

Let R be the set of all points within Ω where $\dot{V}(\boldsymbol{x}) = 0$ and, let M be the largest invariant set in R. Then every solution $\boldsymbol{x}(t)$ in Ω tends to M as $t \to \infty$.

▶ THEOREM 6.2. *If $\dot{V}(\boldsymbol{x}) < 0$ for $\boldsymbol{x} \neq \boldsymbol{0}$ and the other conditions hold as stated above, then the origin is* asymptotically *stable and every solution in Ω tends to the origin as $t \to \infty$.*

For the proofs of these theorems, we refer the reader to the work of LaSalle [23]. We shall, however, illustrate the application by considering the autonomous van der Pol equation

$$\ddot{x} + \varepsilon(x^2 - 1)\dot{x} + x = 0, \tag{6.85}$$

which, we know, has a unique stable limit cycle for all $\varepsilon > 0$. This means that the region inside the limit cycle is unstable. If we can determine the size of this region of instability, we shall know the size of the limit cycle, or really the lower bound on the limit cycle. We shall, therefore, study the behavior of the system in reverse time by replacing t by $-\tau$ and determine the region of *stability* for the new system, since the time scale will be now reversed. With this substitution, Equation (6.85) becomes

$$\frac{d^2x}{d\tau^2} + \varepsilon(1 - x^2)\frac{dx}{d\tau} + x = 0. \tag{6.86}$$

We shall write this second-order differential equation as a set of two first-order differential equations by introducing the variable y so that

$$\frac{dx}{d\tau} = y - \varepsilon\left(x - \frac{x^3}{3}\right), \qquad \frac{dy}{d\tau} = -x. \tag{6.87}$$

Now the system is in standard form, and we shall choose a Liapunov function of the form

$$V = \tfrac{1}{2}(x^2 + y^2). \tag{6.88}$$

Then

$$\frac{dV}{d\tau} = x\frac{dx}{d\tau} + y\frac{dy}{d\tau} = -\varepsilon x^2\left(1 - \frac{x^2}{3}\right), \tag{6.89}$$

and it is evident that if $x^2 < 3$, $dV/d\tau < 0$. Then, according to Theorem 6.2, inside the closed region defined by $V(x, y) < \frac{3}{2}$, $dV/d\tau < 0$ and every solution inside the circle $x^2 + y^2 < 3$ approaches the origin as $\tau \to \infty$. The limit cycle must therefore lie outside this circle.

For nonlinear systems, the size of the region of asymptotic stability as determined by Liapunov's method is frequently greatly underestimated, and much effort is usually spent in constructing "better" Liapunov functions, that is, those which indicate larger regions of asymptotic stability. Furthermore, frequently the size of the region is also affected by the manner in which the set of first-order differential equations are chosen. Let us illustrate this point by introducing the variable z such that

$$\frac{dx}{d\tau} = z, \qquad \frac{dz}{d\tau} = -\varepsilon(1 - x^2)z - x. \tag{6.90}$$

At once it is seen that Equations (6.90) are equivalent to Equation (6.86) in the sense that z can be eliminated from (6.90) to yield (6.86). In the same sense, Equations (6.87) are equivalent to Equation (6.86). However, Equations (6.87) are not equivalent to Equations (6.90) in the sense of stability-domain determination.

Choosing a Liapunov function for Equations (6.90) as before, we shall have

$$V(x, z) = \tfrac{1}{2}(x^2 + z^2) \tag{6.91}$$

and

$$dV/d\tau = -\varepsilon(1 - x^2)z^2, \tag{6.92}$$

and the region of asymptotic stability is contained in the circle $x^2 + z^2 < 1$. At once it is seen that the region so described is *smaller* than the region inside the circle $x^2 + y^2 < 3$, since $z = y - \varepsilon[x - (x^3/3)]$. We could have obtained the same region of asymptotic stability if we had taken, instead of Equation (6.91), the following expression for the Liapunov function:

$$V(x, z) = \frac{1}{2}\left\{x^2 + \left[z + \varepsilon\left(x - \frac{x^3}{3}\right)\right]^2\right\}. \tag{6.93}$$

Although for nonlinear systems there is no systematic straightforward method of constructing a Liapunov function, there are some ways one may conduct the search, and it is the goal of this section to acquaint the reader with the more common methods. Even if these might not give an appropriate Liapunov function for some cases, they still provide a starting point to the solution of some particular problem. As was mentioned earlier, for most nonlinear systems the search for a suitable Liapunov function turns out to be a trial-and-error struggle, but yet it is useful to know some of the standard approaches for guidance in constructing trial functions.

We shall be interested in investigating the stability of the equilibrium point ($\boldsymbol{x} = \boldsymbol{0}$) of the autonomous unforced differential equation

$$\dot{\boldsymbol{x}} = \boldsymbol{f}(\boldsymbol{x}), \tag{6.94}$$

where $\boldsymbol{f}(\boldsymbol{0}) = \boldsymbol{0}$; here $\boldsymbol{x}$ and $\boldsymbol{f}$ are n-dimensional vectors. There are various means of constructing Liapunov functions, but we shall discuss and illustrate only three of them. For the interested reader, the papers of Perlmutter [13, 21, 28] and Warden [37] are instructive in terms of constructing Liapunov functions for engineering systems.

6.5.1. ZUBOV'S METHOD OF CONSTRUCTION

Since for an autonomous system $\partial V/\partial t$ is zero,

$$\dot{V} = \nabla V \cdot \dot{\boldsymbol{x}} = \sum_{i=1}^{n} \frac{\partial V}{\partial x_i} f_i(\boldsymbol{x}), \tag{6.95}$$

where $f_i(\boldsymbol{x})$ are the elements of $\boldsymbol{f}$ as given by Equation (6.94). The solution of the partial differential equation

$$\frac{\partial V}{\partial x_1} f_1(\boldsymbol{x}) + \frac{\partial V}{\partial x_2} f_2(\boldsymbol{x}) + \cdots + \frac{\partial V}{\partial x_n} f_n(\boldsymbol{x}) = -\phi(\boldsymbol{x}), \tag{6.96}$$

where $\phi(\boldsymbol{x})$ is positive-definite, will therefore furnish the Liapunov function $V(\boldsymbol{x})$ if $V(\boldsymbol{x})$ is also positive-definite. If the construction of V can be carried out exactly, then the boundary of the stability region is precisely defined. The methods of construction with examples is well presented by Margolis and Vogt [26], and we shall only briefly outline the method by considering the two-dimensional case

$$\dot{x}_1 = f_1(x_1, x_2), \qquad \dot{x}_2 = f_2(x_1, x_2). \tag{6.97}$$

For this two-dimensional system, Equation (6.96) reduces to

$$\frac{\partial V}{\partial x_1} f_1(x_1, x_2) + \frac{\partial V}{\partial x_2} f_2(x_1, x_2) = -\phi(x_1, x_2). \tag{6.98}$$

Let us now transform the Liapunov function by defining

$$V(x_1, x_2) = -\ln\,[1 - v(x_1, x_2)], \tag{6.99}$$

where $v(x_1, x_2)$ is a transformation variable. If we can find such a $v(x_1, x_2)$ that lies in the range $0 \leq v < 1$, then $V(x_1, x_2)$ as defined by Equation (6.99) is positive-definite.

From Equation (6.99), we see that

$$dV = \frac{1}{1 - v}\, dv, \tag{6.100}$$

which substituted into Equation (6.98) gives

$$\frac{\partial v}{\partial x_1} f_1(x_1, x_2) + \frac{\partial v}{\partial x_2} f_2(x_1, x_2) = -\phi(x_1, x_2)[1 - v(x_1, x_2)]. \tag{6.101}$$

If Equation (6.101) can be solved for v, and if $0 \leq v(x_1, x_2) < 1$, v is a Liapunov function and we have the necessary and sufficient condition for the complete stability of the origin, $x_1 = x_2 = 0$. Furthermore, if $v(x_1, x_2) = 1$, this defines the exact boundary of the region of asymptotic stability. Unfortunately, this partial differential equation 6.101 can seldom be solved in closed form.

We shall, however, consider an example as given by Hahn [3] in which the corresponding partial differential equation can be solved. Consider, thus, the system

$$\dot{x}_1 = -x_1 + 2x_1^2 x_2, \qquad \dot{x}_2 = -x_2, \tag{6.102}$$

and let

$$\phi(x_1, x_2) = x_1^2 + x_2^2. \tag{6.103}$$

Then Equation (6.101) becomes

$$\frac{\partial v}{\partial x_1}(-x_1 + 2x_1^2 x_2) + \frac{\partial v}{\partial x_2}(-x_2) = -(x_1^2 + x_2^2)(1 - v),$$

which has the solution

$$v(x_1, x_2) = 1 - \exp\left\{\frac{-x_2^2}{2} - \frac{x_1^2}{2(1 - x_1 x_2)}\right\}. \tag{6.104}$$

It is noted that v as given by Equation (6.104) vanishes only at the origin and is positive outside it; so it fulfills the requirements to be a Liapunov function. Also, when $x_1x_2 = 1$, $v(x_1, x_2) = 1$, and therefore we obtain $x_1x_2 = 1$ as the boundary of stability; that is, when $x_1x_2 < 1$, the system is asymptotically stable.

In spite of the freedom to choose $\phi(x_1, x_2)$, in general it will not be possible to obtain a solution to the partial differential equation in closed form. Then the region of asymptotic stability can be estimated only approximately. But the above method still provides a powerful approach.

6.5.2. THE VARIABLE-GRADIENT METHOD

The variable-gradient method is outlined and illustrated in detail by Schultz and Gibson [33]. We shall briefly outline the method and illustrate it with an example from that paper.

A variable gradient function is chosen in the form

$$\nabla V = \begin{bmatrix} \alpha_{11}x_1 + \alpha_{12}x_2 + \cdots + \alpha_{1n}x_n \\ \alpha_{21}x_1 + \alpha_{22}x_2 + \cdots + \alpha_{2n}x_n \\ \vdots \qquad\qquad\qquad \vdots \\ \alpha_{n1}x_1 + \alpha_{n2}x_2 + \cdots + \alpha_{nn}x_n \end{bmatrix}, \tag{6.105}$$

where α_{ij} is equal to a constant plus a function of $x_1, x_2, \ldots, x_{n-1}$; that is, we can write

$$\alpha_{ij} = c_{ij} + v_{ij}(x_1, x_2, \ldots, x_{n-1}). \tag{6.106}$$

The α_{ii} are chosen to be positive, and to be a sum of a constant and a variable of x_i only

$$\alpha_{ii} = c_{ii} + v_{ii}(x_i) > 0 \qquad (i \neq n), \qquad \alpha_{nn} = 2, \tag{6.107}$$

From the gradient, the derivative of V with respect to time is immediately obtained since

$$\dot{V} = (\nabla V) \cdot \boldsymbol{f}(\boldsymbol{x}), \tag{6.108}$$

and $\dot{V}$ is constrained to be at least semidefinite.

Since the Liapunov function is to be calculated from the line integral

$$V = \int \nabla V \cdot d\boldsymbol{x}, \tag{6.109}$$

it must be ensured that V is uniquely determined. In other words, the path of integration should not affect the value of V. This will be so if the curl of the gradient of V vanishes, that is,

$$\nabla \times \nabla V = \boldsymbol{0}, \tag{6.110}$$

which may be written as

$$\partial(\nabla V)_i/\partial x_j = \partial(\nabla V)_j/\partial x_i \tag{6.111}$$

for $i, j = 1, 2, \ldots n$; here $(\nabla V)_i$ is the ith component of ∇V.

The variables in (∇V) are thus determined from Equations (6.111) and (6.108) with the requirement that $\dot{V}$ be at least semidefinite (that is, $\dot{V} \leq 0$). Then with the known (∇V), we can evaluate V from Equation (6.109). This provides a logical and systematic method of generating Liapunov functions. In general, there is much freedom in choosing the c_{ij} and v_{ij}, so that experience is essential in using this method. Let us consider one of the examples presented by Schultz and Gibson [33] to illustrate the method.

For the illustration we consider the two-dimensional system given by

$$\dot{x}_1 = x_2, \qquad \dot{x}_2 = -x_1^3 - x_2. \tag{6.112}$$

The gradient of V is chosen to be

$$\nabla V = \begin{bmatrix} [c_{11} + v_{11}(x_1)]x_1 + [c_{12} + v_{12}(x_1)]x_2 \\ [c_{21} + v_{21}(x_1)]x_1 + 2x_2 \end{bmatrix}. \tag{6.113}$$

Substituting Equations (6.112) and (6.113) into Equation (6.108) gives

$$\begin{aligned} \dot{V} &= (\nabla V) \cdot \boldsymbol{f}(\boldsymbol{x}) \\ &= x_1 x_2[c_{11} + v_{11} - c_{21} - v_{21} - 2x_1^2] + (c_{12} + v_{12} - 2)x_2^2 - (c_{21} + v_{21})x_1^4. \end{aligned} \tag{6.114}$$

In order that $\dot{V}$ be negative-definite, let

$$\begin{aligned} c_{11} + v_{11} - c_{21} - v_{21} - 2x_1^2 &= 0, \\ c_{12} + v_{12} - 2 &< 0, \\ c_{21} + v_{21} &> 0. \end{aligned} \tag{6.115}$$

We note that both of the inequalities in (6.115) are satisfied if we choose

$$c_{12} + v_{12} = 1, \qquad c_{21} + v_{21} = 1. \tag{6.116}$$

With this choice,

$$\partial(\nabla V)_1/\partial x_2 = c_{12} + v_{12} = 1. \tag{6.117}$$

In addition,

$$\partial(\nabla V)_2/\partial x_1 = c_{21} + v_{21} + dv_{21}/dx_1. \tag{6.118}$$

Now to satisfy Equation (6.111),

$$c_{21} + v_{21} + (dv_{21}/dx_1) = 1. \tag{6.119}$$

To satisfy Equation (6.119) and also the first equation in (6.115), we can choose $c_{21} = 1$, $v_{21} = 0$, $c_{11} = 1$, and $v_{11} = 2x_1^2$. This gives

$$\dot{V} = -x^2 - x_1^4 \tag{6.120}$$

and

$$\nabla V = \begin{bmatrix} x_1 + 2x_1^3 + x_2 \\ x_1 + 2x_2 \end{bmatrix}. \tag{6.121}$$

To evaluate V, we shall take the path from $(0, 0)$ to $(x_1, 0)$ and from $(x_1, 0)$ to (x_1, x_2) and integrate Equation (6.109):

$$\begin{aligned} V = \int_{(0,0)}^{(x_1,0)} (x_1 + 2x_1^3)\, dx_1 + \int_{(x_1,0)}^{(x_1,x_2)} (x_1 + 2x_2)\, dx_2 &= \frac{x_1^2}{2} + \frac{x_1^4}{2} + x_1x_2 + x_2^2 \\ &= \tfrac{1}{2}(x_1 + x_2)^2 + \tfrac{1}{2}x_2^2 + \tfrac{1}{2}x_1^4, \end{aligned} \tag{6.122}$$

so that V is positive-definite and the system is completely stable. For further examples of this method and illustration of its flexibility, the reader is referred to the above-mentioned paper. It should be emphasized that whenever possible the constants and variables should be kept as simple as possible and that in this method there is a considerable amount of freedom to use one's experience to choose functions and constants.

6.5.3. THE USE OF INTEGRATION BY PARTS

Quite frequently a Liapunov function can be constructed and improved by the use of integration by parts. The following example from Geiss [19] illustrates the procedure.

Let us consider the equation

$$\ddot{x} + b\dot{x} + x + cx^3 = 0, \tag{6.123}$$

where b and c are positive constants; this may be thought of as a simplified form of the nonlinear Mathieu equation

$$\ddot{x} + b\dot{x} + (1 + a \cos 2t)x + cx^3 = 0, \tag{6.124}$$

where the constant, a, is taken to be zero. Equation (6.124) will be discussed in Section 6.6, where the averaging technique is used to study its behavior.

We shall rewrite Equation (6.123) as a set of two first-order differential equations

$$\dot{x}_1 = x_2, \qquad \dot{x}_2 = -bx_2 - x_1 - cx^3. \tag{6.125}$$

Let the first choice of a Liapunov function be

$$V_1 = \tfrac{1}{2}(x_1^2 + x_2^2), \tag{6.126}$$

which results in

$$\dot{V}_1 = x_1\dot{x}_1 + x_2\dot{x}_2 = -bx_2^2 - cx_1^3x_2. \tag{6.127}$$

To make $\dot{V}_1$ at least semidefinite, we must remove the last term in Equation (6.127), which may be either positive or negative, depending on the sign of x_1x_2. Therefore consider

$$\dot{V}_2 = cx_1^3x_2, \tag{6.128}$$

which may be integrated to give

$$V_2 = \int cx_1^3 \frac{dx_1}{dt}\, dt = \frac{cx_1^4}{4}, \tag{6.129}$$

where the constant of integration is always put equal to zero. Now we may combine V_1 and V_2 to give

$$V_3 = V_1 + V_2 = \frac{x_1^2}{2} + \frac{x_2^2}{2} + \frac{cx_1^4}{4}, \tag{6.130}$$

where

$$\dot{V}_3 = \dot{V}_1 - \dot{V}_2 = -bx_2^2. \tag{6.131}$$

We would like to improve the Liapunov function further by making the derivative definite and not only semidefinite, as given by Equation (6.131). Thus, let us suppose that there exists a $\dot{V}_4$ such that

$$\dot{V}_4 = -bx_2^2 - x_1^2. \tag{6.132}$$

Then

$$V_4 = \int \dot{V}_4\, dt = -\int (bx_2^2 + x_1^2)\, dt,$$

and

$$V_4 = V_3 - \int x_1^2\, dt. \tag{6.133}$$

In evaluating the last term of Equation (6.133), we observe from Equation (6.125) that

$$x_1 = (-bx_2 - cx_1^3 - \dot{x}_2). \tag{6.134}$$

Therefore,

$$\int x_1^2\, dt = \int x_1(-bx_2 - cx_1^3 - \dot{x}_2)\, dt = -b\int x_1\dot{x}_1\, dt - c\int x_1^4\, dt - \int x_1\dot{x}_2\, dt$$

$$= -\frac{bx_1^2}{2} - c\int x_1^4\, dt - \int x_1\dot{x}_2\, dt. \tag{6.135}$$

Now we shall use integration by parts to integrate the last term in Equation (6.135):

$$\int x_1\dot{x}_2\,dt = x_1x_2 - \int \dot{x}_1x_2\,dt = x_1x_2 - \int \dot{x}_1\frac{1}{b}(\dot{x}_2 + x_1 + cx_1^3)\,dt$$

$$= x_1x_2 + \frac{x_2^2}{2b} + \frac{1}{2b}x_1^2 + \frac{cx_1^4}{4b}. \tag{6.136}$$

Hence, we have

$$V_4 = \frac{1}{2}(x_1 + x_2)^2 + \left(b + \frac{1}{b}\right)\frac{x_1^2}{2} + \frac{c}{b}(1 + b)\frac{x_1^4}{4} + \frac{x_2^2}{2b} + c\int x_1^4\,dt. \tag{6.137}$$

It is observed that subtracting the integral from V_4 will result in subtracting the integrand from $\dot{V}_4$. Therefore, let

$$V = \frac{1}{2}(x_1 + x_2)^2 + \left(b + \frac{1}{b}\right)\frac{x_1^2}{2} + \frac{c}{b}(1 + b)\frac{x_1^4}{4} + \frac{x_2^2}{2b}, \tag{6.138}$$

whose derivative is

$$\dot{V} = -bx_2^2 - x_1^2 - cx_1^4. \tag{6.139}$$

Since now V is positive-definite and $\dot{V}$ is negative-definite, V is a Liapunov function, and the system as described by Equation (6.123) or by Equations (6.125) is asymptotically stable.

The reader has, no doubt, seen that in most cases the size of the region of asymptotic stability as determined by Liapunov's second method tends to be rather conservative. There are various methods of constructing Liapunov functions for a set of first-order differential equations. Also, there is more than one way of reducing a high-order differential equation to a set of first-order differential equations. To illustrate this point, let us consider the Liénard's equation

$$\ddot{x} + f(x)\dot{x} + g(x) = 0. \tag{6.140}$$

We could write Equation (6.140) either as

$$\dot{x} = y, \qquad \dot{y} = -f(x)y - g(x) \tag{6.141}$$

or as

$$\dot{x} = z - \int_0^x f(\lambda)\,d\lambda, \qquad \dot{z} = -g(x). \tag{6.142}$$

If Equation (6.140) is written as Equation (6.142) LaSalle [23] has found that a suitable Liapunov function is

$$V = \tfrac{1}{2}z^2 + \int_0^x g(\lambda)\,d\lambda. \tag{6.143}$$

Here the derivative is

$$\dot{V} = z\dot{z} + g(x)\dot{x} = -g(x)\int_0^x f(\lambda)\,d\lambda, \tag{6.144}$$

and if, within some region $0 < |x| < a$, the following conditions hold:

$$\begin{aligned} &\text{(i)} \quad g(x)\int_0^x f(\lambda)\,d\lambda > 0, \\ &\text{(ii)} \quad 0 < \int_0^x g(\lambda)\,d\lambda < l, \end{aligned} \tag{6.145}$$

where a and l are some constants, then the region Ω defined by

$$\tfrac{1}{2}z^2 + \int_0^x g(\lambda)\,d\lambda < l \tag{6.146}$$

is bounded and, inside Ω, $\dot{V} \leq 0$. The inequality (6.146) defines the region of asymptotic stability since $\dot{V} = 0$ only when $x = 0$. We can take l to be the smaller of the two numbers $\int_0^a g(\lambda)\,d\lambda$ or $\int_0^{-a} g(\lambda)\,d\lambda$, and we shall have an idea of the size of the region of asymptotic stability.

In this section we have considered only autonomous differential equations and have drawn the illustrations for only second-order systems. There has been no effort made to go too deeply into the applications of Liapunov's second method since some excellent books on Liapunov's second method are available for the interested reader [1, 3, 7, 10, 19].

6.6. Averaging technique

In Section 6.2 we outlined in some detail the method of averaging as developed by Krylov and Bogoliubov. The present method, which we have called the *averaging technique*, embodies a different type of averaging altogether, and really goes beyond just averaging. It is felt, however, that the chosen title describes the technique quite well, and no confusion is anticipated. The following development is based on the work of Luus [24, 25]. To aid in the visualization of the method, we shall present initially the qualitative ideas which we shall follow up with mathematical formulation.

6.6.1. QUALITATIVE IDEAS

Let us consider a second-order autonomous system which, for convenience, can be written in the form

$$\dot{x} = P(x, y), \qquad \dot{y} = Q(x, y). \tag{6.147}$$

The functions $P(x, y)$ and $Q(x, y)$ are assumed to be continuous, and the coordinates have been chosen to make the origin an equilibrium point; that is, $P(0, 0) = 0$ and $Q(0, 0) = 0$. When Equations (6.147) are presented in the phase plane y vs. x, a continuous nonintersecting path is obtained. To continue the discussion, it is assumed that the system represented by these equations has a trajectory as shown in Figure 6.1. The arrow indicates the direction of increasing time.

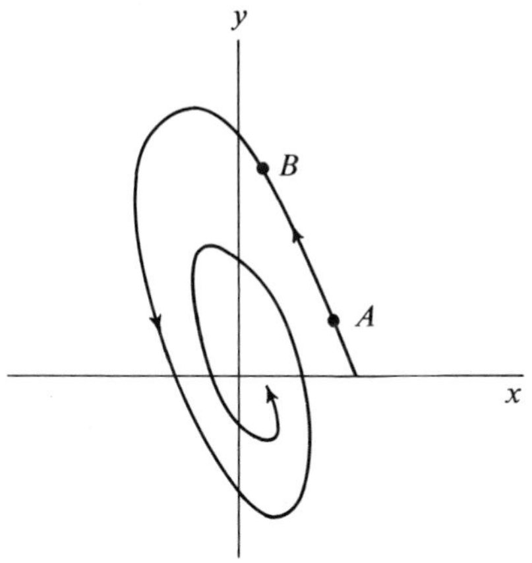

FIGURE 6.1. Phase-plane representation of a two-dimensional system trajectory

Once the trajectory is mapped on the plane, it is immediately seen that this particular system is asymptotically stable, since the origin is approached as time increases, regardless of the starting point. However, without this visual aid, it is not a simple matter to determine this stability.

For example, to construct a Liapunov function for this system, the first trial would probably be to choose

$$V = x^2 + y^2. \tag{6.148}$$

But from the diagram, we see that as the system goes from A to B, $dV/dt > 0$. Therefore, this trial function is unsuitable.

The next attempt is usually to take

$$V = \alpha_{11}x^2 + 2\alpha_{12}xy + \alpha_{22}y^2, \tag{6.149}$$

and to find conditions on $\alpha_{11}, \alpha_{12}, \alpha_{22}$ to make $\dot{V} < 0$. Even for a simple system, considerable difficulties arise.

Although in Section 6.5 we outlined certain approaches that one could use to construct a Liapunov function, there is, as yet, no straightforward way of selecting a suitable Liapunov function for an arbitrary system. Frequently the stability domain so determined is grossly underestimated, and much effort must be expended to improve the Liapunov function.

A better attempt to determine the system stability is to consider not the radius vector, but the area it sweeps out in successive cycles. We shall then have a series of areas, as shown in Figure 6.2. We shall label these areas $A_1, A_2, \ldots,$ $A_{i-1}, A_i, A_{i+1}, \ldots$. Then we can draw the following conclusions:

(1) If $A_i/A_{i+1} > 1$ for any i, the system is asymptotically stable.
(2) If $A_i/A_{i+1} < 1$ for any i, the system is unstable.
(3) If $A_{i-1}/A_i > 1$, $A_i/A_{i+1} = 1$, and $A_{j-1}/A_j < 1$, $A_j/A_{j+1} = 1$, there exists a stable limit cycle.

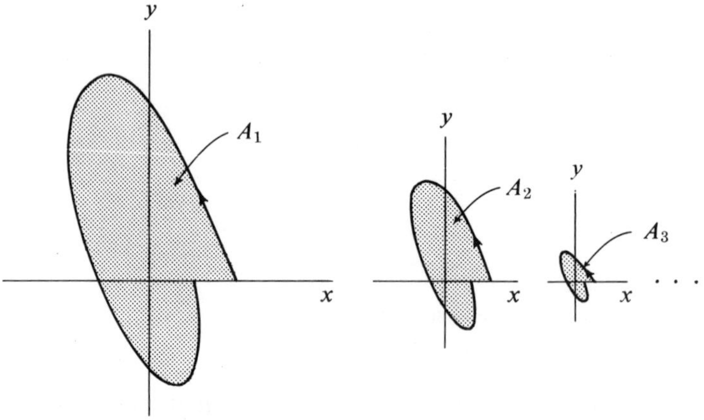

FIGURE 6.2. Consideration of the series of areas

These ideas appear simple so far. However, to apply them in this form is almost impossible. To obtain the areas by contour integration in exact form is as hard or even harder than solving the original set of differential equations. So to apply this method, certain approximations must be introduced and the technique should be extended so that the restrictive approximations are present only in the starting stage and can be removed in the final form.

We make the following two important observations:

(1) The distance from the origin to the trajectory does not generally change much after a single cycle, and the cases which are hardest to analyze are ones in which the radius is almost constant.

(2) In most realistic systems, the angle swept out by the radius vector is a single-valued function of time.

These two observations allow one to calculate and study the behavior of the average distance of the phase point from the origin, where the distance is *averaged over an entire cycle.*

6.6.2. MATHEMATICAL FORMULATION

Let us consider a second-order nonautonomous system described by the ordinary differential equations

$$\dot{x} = f(x, y, t), \qquad \dot{y} = g(x, y, t), \tag{6.150}$$

where f and g are some (nonlinear) functions of x, y, and t, and $f(0, 0, t)$ and $g(0, 0, t)$ are zero, so that $x = 0$, $y = 0$ is the origin of the system.

Let us transform Equations (6.150) into polar coordinates by letting $r^2 = x^2 + y^2$ and $\psi = \tan^{-1}(y/x)$. Then

$$\dot{r} = (1/r)(x\dot{x} + y\dot{y}) = \cos\psi f(r\cos\psi, r\sin\psi, t) + \sin\psi g(r\cos\psi, r\sin\psi, t), \tag{6.151}$$

and

$$\dot{\psi} = (1/r^2)(x\dot{y} - y\dot{x}) = (1/r)[\cos\psi g(r\cos\psi, r\sin\psi, t) - \sin\psi f(r\cos\psi, r\sin\psi, t)]. \tag{6.152}$$

Now we shall apply the above-mentioned observations to Equations (6.151) and (6.152). Since the radius does not usually change much after a cycle, we shall approximate the right-hand sides of Equations (6.151) and (6.152) by letting

$$r \doteq r_0, \tag{6.153}$$

where r_0 is taken to be some constant and not necessarily the radius at the beginning of the cycle. Any deviation from this approximation will be given by Equation (6.151). Since in most realistic systems, the angle is a single-valued function of time, we shall introduce a further approximation and assume that the angle changes *uniformly* with time and can therefore be written as

$$\psi \doteq \phi_0 - At, \tag{6.154}$$

where ϕ_0 and A are constants. Any deviation from this approximation will be given by Equation (6.152). Later on in this section, it will be shown that the approximation (6.153) is considerably better than the approximation of Equation (6.154), but let us continue the mathematical development. We shall substitute the approximations (6.153) and (6.154) into the right-hand sides of Equations (6.151) and (6.152) to get a set of approximate equations:

$$\dot{r} \doteq [\cos(\phi_0 - At)f_0 + \sin(\phi_0 - At)g_0], \tag{6.155}$$

$$\dot{\psi} \doteq \frac{1}{r_0}[\cos(\phi_0 - At)g_0 - \sin(\phi_0 - At)f_0], \tag{6.156}$$

where

$$\begin{aligned} f_0 &= f[r_0\cos(\phi_0 - At), r_0\sin(\phi_0 - At), t], \\ g_0 &= g[r_0\cos(\phi_0 - At), r_0\sin(\phi_0 - At), t]. \end{aligned} \tag{6.157}$$

If, indeed, ψ can be expressed by $\phi_0 - At$, then between $t = 0$ and $t = 2\pi/|A|$, the system will perform one cycle.

To find the differences in the values of r and ψ after an assumed cycle, we shall integrate Equations (6.155) and (6.156) between $t = 0$ and $t = 2\pi/|A| = T$:

$$r(T) - r(0) = \int_0^T [\cos(\phi_0 - At) f_0 + \sin(\phi_0 - At) g_0] \, dt, \tag{6.158}$$

$$\psi(T) - \psi(0) = \frac{1}{r_0} \int_0^T [\cos(\phi_0 - At) g_0 - \sin(\phi_0 - At) f_0] \, dt. \tag{6.159}$$

Equation (6.158) gives an expression for the difference in the radius of the path between the end and the beginning of an assumed cycle. This is expressed as a function of r_0 and ϕ_0. Similarly, Equation (6.159) gives the difference in the angle after an assumed cycle. In other words, $|\psi(T) - \psi(0)| = 2\pi$ if the angular velocity is really A, since then there is exactly the same angle ϕ_0 as at the beginning of the cycle, but the radius vector has gone once around.

We shall divide Equations (6.158) and (6.159) by the time assumed for one cycle, namely T, to give

$$\frac{r(T) - r(0)}{T} = F(r_0, \phi_0), \tag{6.160}$$

$$\frac{\psi(T) - \psi(0)}{T} = G(r_0, \phi_0). \tag{6.161}$$

But Equation (6.161) can be written as

$$\frac{\psi(T) - \psi(0)}{T} = \frac{\phi_0(T) - AT - \phi_0(0)}{T} = \frac{\phi_0(T) - \phi_0(0)}{T} - A, \tag{6.162}$$

that is,

$$\frac{\phi_0(T) - \phi_0(0)}{T} = A + G(r_0, \phi_0). \tag{6.163}$$

Equations (6.160) and (6.163) are really difference equations since T can be thought of as the difference in time following and before an assumed cycle. Thus, we may rewrite Equations (6.160) and (6.163) as

$$\Delta r/\Delta t = F(r, \phi), \tag{6.164}$$

$$\Delta\phi/\Delta t = A + G(r, \phi), \tag{6.165}$$

where the subscripts on r and ϕ are no longer necessary and have therefore been dropped. We shall now write these difference equations as differential equations since there is really no limitation on the size of Δt to give changes in Δr and $\Delta\phi$. We shall then have the *averaged* differential equations

$$dr/dt = F(r, \phi), \tag{6.166}$$

$$d\phi/dt = A + G(r, \phi). \tag{6.167}$$

Equation (6.166) is an approximation to Equation (6.151). Equation (6.167) is an approximation to Equation (6.152) and also has a transformed variable $\phi = \psi + At$. It should be noted that these equations are now autonomous and therefore should be easier to interpret or to solve than the original nonautonomous set of Equations (6.150). Furthermore, noncontributing terms have been averaged out.

Although Equations (6.166) and (6.167) are similar to the stroboscopic equations developed by Minorsky, there are some important differences:

(1) No mention has been made of a small parameter, and no series expansions have been used in some small parameters.

(2) No approximate solution is necessary beforehand; there is a complete freedom to choose A for autonomous systems. Even if a wrong sign is chosen, Equation (6.167) will show the correction to be made. For calculations of autonomous systems, therefore, A is taken to be unity for simplicity.

(3) Equation (6.166) gives the variation of the actual distance of the phase point from the singularity as a function of the real time. Although the distance is interpolated between the value at the beginning and the end of a cycle, the knowledge of this is very important, because it is possible to see immediately how close to the singular point the system has reached in a given time. Stability determination is then a simple matter of following the system as a function of time.

(4) There is no limitation concerning the length of time after which the approximate analytical solution becomes valid. In the stroboscopic method the time must be large as compared to the time required to make one cycle. The above technique gives accurate results for times less than the time required for a single cycle, as well as for times greater than a hundred cycles.

There is, however, no straightforward way of improving the final Equations (6.166) and (6.167), and there is no simple manner of improving the accuracy. One can visualize some means of iterating the answers obtained from Equations (6.166) and (6.167) to give different starting values for r_0 and $\phi_0 - At$. However, it is felt that the extra complexity resulting from this manipulation is hardly worth the effort. After all, for more precise information, computers may be used with this averaging technique as a useful guide.

In some cases $F(r, \phi)$ will be independent of ϕ. Then we can immediately integrate the differential Equation (6.166) to give

$$\int_{r_0}^{r} \frac{dr}{F(r)} = t - t_0, \tag{6.168}$$

where $r = r_0$ at $t = t_0$. The integration gives directly $r = \sqrt{x^2 + y^2}$ as a function of time. For stability determination, all that is necessary is to let t approach a large number and to observe the effect of this on r.

Similarly, often $G(r, \phi)$ will be independent of r. Then we can integrate Equation (6.167) immediately to give

$$\int_0^\phi \frac{d\phi}{A + G(\phi)} = t, \tag{6.169}$$

since we can always select $\phi = 0$ at $t = 0$ without any loss of generality. Once ϕ is obtained by integration, this value of ϕ can be substituted into Equation (6.166) to give r. An example of this can be found in the analysis of the Mathieu equation, and is presented here for the illustration of this point. In the analysis of CSTR the angular variation is very nonuniform, and the linear approximations to the system nonlinear equations will be used to obtain greater accuracy for the determination of the frequency of oscillation.

This averaging technique can be used to analyze systems with more than one singularity, but care must be taken in the interpretation of the region of asymptotic stability. In other words, the resulting equations might indicate that a particular singular point is asymptotically stable in the large, whereas in reality the existence of multiple singular points can make this impossible. Therefore, in applying this technique to such systems, we must interpret results obtained as local behavior where only a single singular point influences the trajectory.

Furthermore, one should not use this technique blindly. It must be ensured that the trajectory goes around the origin; that is, it must be ensured that the equilibrium point is not a saddle point. This is accomplished readily by linearizing the equation near the singularity and asking that $ad - bc > 0$ be satisfied (see Section 5.2). A number of examples will illustrate this method and will also give a feeling for this averaging technique to the reader.

To illustrate the averaging technique, we shall consider first the autonomous van der Pol equation, which can be written as

$$\ddot{x} + \varepsilon(x^2 - 1)\dot{x} + x = 0. \tag{6.170}$$

This can be readily transformed into two first-order differential equations by simple substitution:

$$\dot{x} = y, \qquad \dot{y} = \varepsilon(1 - x^2)y - x. \tag{6.171}$$

If we look at the equations (6.171), we can write the linear parts as

$$\dot{x} = 0x + y, \qquad \dot{y} = -x + \varepsilon y. \tag{6.172}$$

Here $a = 0$, $b = 1$, $c = -1$, $d = \varepsilon$, and

$$ad - bc = 0 + 1 = 1 > 0. \tag{6.173}$$

Now we are ensured that the singular point $x = 0$, $y = 0$ is not a saddle point, and we may proceed to apply the averaging technique to Equations (6.171).

Let $r = \sqrt{x^2 + y^2}$ and $\psi = \tan^{-1}(y/x)$ to transform the system to polar coordinates. In polar coordinates, Equations (6.171) give

$$\dot{r} = \varepsilon\left(r \sin^2 \psi - \frac{r^3}{4} \sin^2 2\psi\right), \tag{6.174}$$

$$\dot{\psi} = -1 + \varepsilon(\sin \psi \cos \psi - r^2 \cos^3 \psi \sin \psi). \tag{6.175}$$

Now we shall let $r = r_0$ and $\psi = \phi_0 - t$ on the right-hand sides of Equations (6.174) and (6.175) to give the set of approximate equations

$$\dot{r} \doteq \varepsilon\left\{r_0 \sin^2 (\phi_0 - t) - \frac{r_0^3}{4} \sin^2 [2(\phi_0 - t)]\right\}, \tag{6.176}$$

$$\dot{\psi} \doteq -1 + \varepsilon\{\sin (\phi_0 - t) \cos (\phi_0 - t) - r_0^2 \cos^3 (\phi_0 - t) \sin (\phi_0 - t)\}. \tag{6.177}$$

These equations can now be integrated over a cycle to give

$$\frac{\Delta r}{\Delta t} = \frac{\varepsilon}{2\pi} \int_0^{2\pi} \left[r_0 \sin 2(\phi_0 - t) - \frac{r_0^3}{4} \sin^2 2(\phi_0 - t)\right] dt \tag{6.178}$$

and

$$\frac{\Delta \phi}{\Delta t} = 1 - 1 + \frac{\varepsilon}{2\pi} \int_0^{2\pi} \left[\frac{\sin^2 (\phi_0 - t)}{2} - r_0^2 \cos^3 (\phi_0 - t) \sin (\phi_0 - t)\right] dt. \tag{6.179}$$

These yield, after integration,

$$\frac{\Delta r}{\Delta t} = \frac{\varepsilon}{2\pi}\left[\frac{r_0}{2} - \frac{r_0^3}{8}\right] 2\pi, \tag{6.180}$$

$$\frac{\Delta \phi}{\Delta t} = 0. \tag{6.181}$$

Therefore, we have the averaged differential equations

$$dr/dt = (\varepsilon/2)r[1 - (r^2/4)] \tag{6.182}$$

and

$$d\phi/dt = 0. \tag{6.183}$$

Equation (6.182) can be immediately integrated to give

$$r^2 = \frac{4r_0^2}{4 \exp(-\varepsilon t) + r_0^2[1 - \exp(-\varepsilon t)]}, \tag{6.184}$$

where $r = r_0$ at $t = 0$. Equation (6.183) gives

$$\phi = \phi_0, \qquad \text{a constant}, \tag{6.185}$$

that is,

$$\psi = \phi_0 - t,$$

and a point on the trajectory is expected to move clockwise at a natural frequency of one radian per unit time.

Looking at Equation (6.184), we see that there are three cases to consider.

CASE 1. $\varepsilon > 0$

$$\lim_{t \to \infty} r^2 = 4r_0^2/r_0^2 = 4, \tag{6.186}$$

that is, regardless of the starting point, r^2 will always approach the value 4 as t becomes large. This means that there exists a *stable limit cycle* of an average radius of 2. Furthermore, the approach to the limit cycle is exponential, as shown by Equation (6.184).

By integrating the original van der Pol equation on a digital computer, it can be seen that the radial dependence is given quite accurately. However, for large values of ε (greater than 1), the actual frequency is considerably smaller than the expected value of 1.0 rad/unit time [24].

CASE 2. $\varepsilon = 0$

$$r^2 = \frac{4r_0^2}{4} = r_0^2. \tag{6.187}$$

This means that the system neither converges nor diverges, but retains its original distance from the equilibrium point. This is an example of a center, which is a singular point possessing the property that all trajectories turn around it without either approaching it or receding indefinitely. This is, of course, just an undamped harmonic oscillator.

CASE 3. $\varepsilon < 0$

$$\lim_{t \to \infty} r^2 = \begin{cases} 0 & \text{if} \quad r_0^2 < 4, \\ 4 & \text{if} \quad r_0^2 = 4. \end{cases} \tag{6.188}$$

It is not immediately obvious what happens when $r_0^2 > 4$. Let us, therefore, let $\varepsilon = -\delta$, where $\delta > 0$, and $r_0^2 = 4 + \eta$, where $\eta > 0$. Equation (6.184) then becomes

$$r^2 = \frac{4(4+\eta)}{4\exp(\delta t) + (4+\eta)[1 - \exp(\delta t)]} = \frac{4(4+\eta)}{4 + \eta - \eta\exp(\delta t)}. \tag{6.189}$$

From Equation (6.189), it is seen that as soon as

$$t = \frac{1}{\delta}\ln\left(\frac{4+\eta}{\eta}\right) \tag{6.190}$$

the radius will reach infinity. In other words, one does not have to wait long for the system to blow up.

Therefore, if $\varepsilon < 0$, an unstable limit cycle of average radius equal to 2 will be encountered.

In the application of the averaging technique, it is not necessary to write down all the intermediate steps. This has been done in this instance mainly for clarity and to illustrate the approximations in some detail.

We mentioned before that for some systems, Equation (6.167) will not involve r explicitly, so that it can be integrated immediately to give the angular dependence, and once this is known, we can solve for r. We shall illustrate this here, using the Mathieu equation written as

$$\ddot{x} + b\dot{x} + (1 + a\cos 2t)x + cx^3 = 0, \qquad (6.191)$$

where a, b, and c are positive constants, not necessarily small or of the same order of magnitude. As before, we shall write the second-order equation as two first-order equations by a simple substitution,

$$\dot{x} = y, \qquad \dot{y} = -by - (1 + a\cos 2t)x - cx^3. \qquad (6.192)$$

Now, letting $\rho = x^2 + y^2$ and $\psi = \tan^{-1}(y/x)$ to convert these to polar coordinates, we obtain

$$d\rho/dt = -2b\rho\sin^2\psi - a\rho\sin 2\psi\cos 2t - 2c\rho^2\cos^3\psi\sin\psi, \qquad (6.193)$$

and

$$d\psi/dt = -1 - \tfrac{1}{2}b\sin 2\psi - a\cos^2\psi\cos 2t - c\rho\cos^4\psi. \qquad (6.194)$$

For the van der Pol equation, we showed the step-by-step development. Since the intermediate steps are straightforward, we shall omit them for the present and simply write the resulting equations after the averaging technique has been applied. We get

$$d\rho/dt = -\tfrac{1}{2}\rho(2b + a\sin 2\phi), \qquad (6.195)$$

$$d\phi/dt = -\tfrac{1}{4}(a\cos 2\phi + \tfrac{3}{2}c\rho), \qquad (6.196)$$

where

$$\phi = \psi + t.$$

CASE 1. $c = 0$.

This condition allows Equation (6.196) to be integrated to give

$$\sin 2\phi = \frac{2\exp(-at)}{1 + \exp(-at)} - 1. \qquad (6.197)$$

Now substituting Equation (6.197) into (6.195), we get

$$\frac{d\rho}{dt} = \rho\left\{\frac{(a-2b)}{2} - \frac{a\exp(-at)}{1+\exp(-at)}\right\}, \tag{6.198}$$

which can be immediately integrated to give

$$\rho = \rho_0 \cosh(\tfrac{1}{2}at)\exp(-bt), \tag{6.199}$$

where ρ_0 is the value of ρ at time $t = 0$.

From Equation (6.199) we see that the necessary and sufficient condition for asymptotic stability is that

$$b > \tfrac{1}{2}a. \tag{6.200}$$

When condition (6.200) is met then, $\lim_{t\to\infty} \rho = 0$. It is interesting to note that when $b = a/2$, the square of the radius of the cycle approaches a constant value which is one-half of its initial value. It has been found that Equation (6.199) describes this system very well when a and b are small. Even when a and b are large, Equation (6.199) describes the system behavior quite well [24]. By small we mean a, $b < 0.1$, and by large we mean values close to unity.

CASE 2. $c \neq 0$.

(a) If $b \geq a/2$, it is immediately seen that the system is asymptotically stable.

(b) If $b < a/2$, it is seen from Equations (6.195) and (6.196) that at some values of ρ and ϕ, both

$$d\rho/dt = 0 \qquad \text{and} \qquad d\phi/dt = 0 \tag{6.201}$$

simultaneously. We shall denote this condition by $\rho = \rho_0$ and $\phi = \phi_0$. Now let us suppose that $\rho > \rho_0$. Then from Equation (6.196) it is seen that $d\phi/dt < 0$; that is, $\sin 2\phi$ will decrease, and from Equation (6.195) it follows that $d\rho/dt < 0$. Now suppose that $\rho < \rho_0$. Then $d\phi/dt > 0$ and $d\rho/dt > 0$. Similarly, if $\phi > \phi_0$, from Equation (6.195) $d\rho/dt < 0$, and from Equation (6.195) it follows that $d\phi/dt < 0$; and if $\phi < \phi_0$, $d\rho/dt > 0$, which in turn makes $d\phi/dt > 0$.

Thus, it follows that $\rho = \rho_0$ and $\phi = \phi_0$ describe a stable limit cycle. To obtain a value for ρ_0 we note that when $d\rho/dt = 0$ and $d\phi/dt = 0$,

$$\sin 2\phi_0 = -2b/a \tag{6.202}$$

and

$$\cos 2\phi_0 = -\tfrac{3}{2}c\rho_0/a \tag{6.203}$$

Since $\sin^2 2\phi_0 + \cos^2 2\phi_0 = 1$, squaring Equations (6.202) and (6.203) and adding gives

$$1 = \frac{4b^2}{a^2} + \frac{9}{4}\frac{c^2\rho_0^2}{a^2}, \tag{6.204}$$

so that

$$\rho_0 = \frac{2\sqrt{a^2 - 4b^2}}{3c}, \tag{6.205}$$

which is a real quantity since $b < a/2$. Therefore, if $c \neq 0$ and $b < \frac{1}{2}a$, there will be a stable limit cycle whose radius is given by

$$r_0 = \sqrt{(2/3c)\sqrt{a^2 - 4b^2}}. \tag{2.606}$$

The limit cycle is stable since we have shown that the radius is approached regardless of the initial conditions.

The simplicity with which these results are obtained with the averaging technique should be appreciated. Especially, when stability is to be determined, it is seen that this information is inherent in the answer. There is no need to consider the variational differential equations or to determine the characteristic equation.

These two examples allow the reader to become acquainted with the averaging technique. As was seen, an approximate analytical solution could be obtained readily without extensive calculations, and stability information is inherent in the solution. Although the systems considered contained parameters which may be small, it is important to note that these parameters did not have to be identified as such. However, there are some disadvantages and limitations, which we shall discuss presently.

To fully demonstrate the limitations of this averaging technique, let us consider two coupled linear differential equations of the form

$$\dot{x} = ax + by, \qquad \dot{y} = cx + dy, \tag{6.207}$$

and compare the results obtained by the averaging technique with the actual integration as carried out in Section 5.2. In Equations (6.207), it is assumed that

$$ad - bc > 0, \tag{6.208}$$

so that the singularity $x = 0$, $y = 0$ will not be a saddle point.

Writing the system in polar coordinates, we get

$$\dot{\rho} = 2a\rho \cos^2\psi + 2d\rho \sin^2\psi + (b + c)\rho \sin 2\psi, \tag{6.209}$$

$$\dot{\psi} = c \cos^2\psi - b \sin^2\psi + (d - a) \sin \psi \cos \psi, \tag{6.210}$$

where

$$\rho = x^2 + y^2 \qquad \text{and} \qquad \psi = \tan^{-1}(y/x).$$

Immediately, the averaged equations become

$$d\rho/dt = (a + d)\rho, \tag{6.211}$$

$$d\phi/dt = 1 + \tfrac{1}{2}(c - b), \tag{6.212}$$

where

$$\phi = \psi + t.$$

Equations (6.211) and (6.212) can be integrated to yield

$$\rho = \rho_0 \exp [(a + d)t], \tag{6.213}$$

where $\rho = \rho_0$ at $t = 0$. For the angular equation, we get from Equation (6.212)

$$\phi = \phi_0 + [1 + \tfrac{1}{2}(c - b)]t, \tag{6.214}$$

or in terms of the original angle

$$\psi = \phi_0 + \tfrac{1}{2}(c - b)t. \tag{6.215}$$

By integrating Equations (6.207) directly with the initial conditions

$$x = 1, \qquad y = 0 \qquad \text{at } t = 0,$$

we obtained the following expressions for x and y in Section 5.2:

$$x = \frac{\exp [\frac{1}{2}(a + d)t]}{\alpha} [(a - d) \sinh (\tfrac{1}{2}\alpha t) + \alpha \cosh (\tfrac{1}{2}\alpha t)],$$

$$y = \frac{2c}{\alpha} \exp [\tfrac{1}{2}(a + d)t] \sinh (\tfrac{1}{2}\alpha t),$$

which are Equations (5.52) and (5.53), respectively. Here, as before,

$$\alpha = \sqrt{(a - d)^2 + 4bc}.$$

Squaring these equations and adding, we find that

$$\rho = \left[\frac{\exp (a + d)t}{(a - d)^2 + 4bc}\right][2c(b - c) + (a - d)^2 + 2c(b + c) \cos \beta t - \beta(a - d) \sin \beta t], \tag{6.216}$$

where

$$\beta = -i\sqrt{(a - d)^2 + 4bc}. \tag{6.217}$$

It is noted that if $b = -c$ and $a = d$, then Equation (6.216) becomes

$$\rho = \exp [(a + d)t], \tag{6.218}$$

which corresponds identically to Equation (6.213) with $\rho_0 = 1$. Also, the angular dependence is then exact. In other words, the averaging technique will give the exact solution to the linear problem under these conditions. The coordinate axes can be rescaled and rotated to accomplish the above conditions. Usually, however, the results obtained without the improvement are sufficiently good for the radial dependence. Only the angular dependence requires adjustment.

Since a general second-order autonomous nonlinear system can always be written in the form

$$\dot{x} = ax + by + P_2(x, y), \qquad \dot{y} = cx + dy + Q_2(x, y), \tag{6.219}$$

where $P_2(x, y)$ and $Q_2(x, y)$ are functions of degree 2 or higher, in a control system where the system should be maintained close to the origin, a good approximation to the angular relationship is then

$$\psi = \phi_0 + [\operatorname{sgn}(c - b)]\{\sqrt{-bc - (a - d)^2/4}\}t. \tag{6.220}$$

Therefore, in using the averaging technique to analyze highly nonlinear systems, we shall use the averaging technique as outlined above for the radial dependence. The angular dependence will be obtained from Equation (6.220), which is the exact solution to the linearized equation. Especially in the analysis of the CSTR, where the angular variation is very nonuniform, Equation (6.220) has been used successfully to determine the period of the cycle and the direction. This is outlined in detail in Section 6.7. Further reading in the areas of stability and limit-cycle analysis can be found in [16, 17, 18, 20, 28, 31, 32, 34].

6.7. Examples

In this section, we shall show in detail the application of the averaging technique in Section 6.6. Although the emphasis will be on the analysis of chemical engineering problems, we shall also consider the *forced* van der Pol equation to give the insight necessary to consider more complicated systems, such as a series of CSTR's. We shall start with the autonomous CSTR which was outlined in Section 1.11 and was considered as an illustration of the application of the maximum principle in Chapter 2; then we shall go on to the more complicated cases where the nonlinear systems are forced and thus suitable for control models.

FIRST-ORDER REACTION IN A CSTR

EXAMPLE 6.1 ▪ A first-order exothermic reaction in a CSTR as outlined in Section 1.11 is described by two first-order differential equations relating the temperature and concentration. These are expressed by Equations (1.136) and (1.135), namely,

$$\dot{T} = -2(T + 0.25) - kT(T + 0.25) + (C + 0.5)\exp\left(\frac{25T}{T + 2}\right), \tag{6.221}$$

$$\dot{C} = 0.5 - C - (C + 0.5)\exp\left(\frac{25T}{T + 2}\right), \tag{6.222}$$

where T is the deviation from the dimensionless steady state temperature and C is the deviation from the dimensionless steady-state concentration of component A; k is the proportional constant for control and is an arbitrary parameter. We wish to choose k in such a way that satisfactory control can be obtained for the reactor. It was already shown in Section 2.8, Example 2.3, that if the reaction is started at a point away from the steady state, then bang-bang control will give time optimal approach to the steady state. But once we have reached the steady state, then it is useful to use proportional control to compensate for perturbations that tend to drive the system away from the steady state. Therefore, it is important to study the behavior of the system as given by Equations (6.221) and (6.222) for different values of proportional control constant, k.

The stability of the chemical reactor was first undertaken by Bilous and Amundson [14], who accomplished the stability determination through linearization of Equations (6.221) and (6.222) with the subsequent application of the Routh-Hurwitz criterion. This problem was analyzed more thoroughly by Aris and Amundson [11], who made detailed numerical calculations to show the nature of the C-T phase plane at different values of the control proportionality constant, k, and proceeded to control the reactor at the naturally unstable steady-state. Now we shall analyze the system as described by Equations (6.221) and (6.222) by the averaging technique.

We shall be satisfied with an approximate solution to Equations (6.221) and (6.222), so we shall expand the exponential into an approximate power series:

$$\exp\left[\frac{25T}{2+T}\right] \doteq \exp(12.5T) \doteq 1 + 12.5T + 78T^2, \tag{6.223}$$

which will be a good approximation when T is small. Substituting Equation (6.223) into Equations (6.221) and (6.222), there results

$$dT/dt = (4.25 - 0.25k)T + C + (39 - k)T^2 + 12.5CT + 78CT^2, \tag{6.224}$$

$$dC/dt = -6.25T - 2C - 39T^2 - 12.5CT - 78CT^2. \tag{6.225}$$

In order not to have a saddle point, it is assumed that k has been chosen so that

$$-2(4.25 - 0.25k) + 6.25 > 0, \qquad \text{that is,} \qquad k > 4.5. \tag{6.226}$$

To express Equations (6.224) and (6.225) in polar coordinates, we shall let $T = r\cos\psi$ and $C = r\sin\psi$, which gives

$$\begin{aligned} dr/dt = [&(4.25 - 0.25k)r\cos^2\psi - 5.25r\sin\psi\cos\psi + (39 - k)r^2\cos^3\psi \\ &- 26.5r^2\sin\psi\cos^2\psi + 78r^3\sin\psi\cos^3\psi - 2r\sin^2\psi \\ &- 12.5r^2\sin^2\psi\cos\psi - 78r^3\sin^2\psi\cos^2\psi]. \end{aligned} \tag{6.227}$$

We shall not write the equation for the angular dependence since, as was pointed out in Section 6.6, the angular variation is very nonuniform and the linear parts of Equations (6.224) and (6.225) are used to determine its time dependence. From Equation (6.227), we obtain the average radius equation immediately:

$$dr/dt = r(1.125 - 0.125k - 9.75r^2), \tag{6.228}$$

where $k > 4.5$. Equation (6.228) shows that to control the reaction, k must be greater than 9 so that dr/dt would be negative. The quality of control increases as k increases but, due to time lags in practice, there will be an upper bound on k. Equation (6.228) can be integrated to give

$$r^2 = \frac{(1.125 - 0.125k)r_0^2 \exp[(2.25 - 0.25k)t]}{1.125 - 0.125k - 9.75(1 - \exp[(2.25 - 0.25k)t])r_0^2}, \tag{6.229}$$

where $r = r_0$ at $t = 0$, and $k > 4.5$.

To determine the nature of the steady state, we shall investigate the behavior of r^2 as given by Equation (6.229). Before this, however, we see that both the numerator and denominator vanish when $k = 9$. We shall therefore use L'Hospital's rule to show that

$$\lim_{k\to 9} r^2 = \frac{r_0^2}{1 + 19.5r_0^2 t}, \tag{6.230}$$

and it is seen that

$$\lim_{t\to\infty;\, k=9} r^2 = 0, \tag{6.231}$$

so that the system is asymptotically stable at $k = 9$. From Equation (6.229) we see that

$$\lim_{\substack{t\to\infty,\\ 4.5<k<9.0}} r^2 = \frac{1.125 - 0.125k}{9.75}, \tag{6.232}$$

which states that the average distance from the steady state to the trajectory becomes constant for $4.5 < k < 9.0$. This could be explained by either of the two possibilities:

(1) the trajectory reaches a stable singularity which does not coincide with the steady state or

(2) the trajectory tends to a stable limit cycle which surrounds the steady state. To determine which of these situations exists, we shall consider the angular variation. The period of the oscillation as determined from Equation (6.220) is

$$T = \frac{2\pi}{\sqrt{-bc - (a-d)^2/4}}, \tag{6.233}$$

which becomes

$$T = \frac{2\pi}{\sqrt{6.25 - (3.125 - 0.125k)^2}}, \tag{6.234}$$

and is defined for $5 < k < 45$. Since the period is not defined in the range $4.5 < k \le 5$, we conclude that for this range the trajectory approaches a stable singularity situated at a distance of $\sqrt{(1.125 - 0.125k)/9.75}$ from the steady state (which is an unstable node). In the range $5 < k < 45$, the steady state becomes a focus; this focus is unstable if $5 < k < 9$, and since a steady value of the radius, as given by Equation (6.232), is reached we may have a stable limit cycle in this range. The existence of the stable limit cycle is confirmed if no other singularity lies within $\sqrt{(1.125 - 0.125k)/9.75}$ of the origin. Therefore, the determination of the existence, the radius, and the period of the limit cycle is readily carried out analytically. Then, for greater accuracy the results can be checked by calculations on the digital computer.

We shall now turn our attention to the range $k \geq 9$. It is readily seen from Equations (6.229) and (6.230) that

$$\lim_{t \to \infty;\, k \geq 9} r^2 = 0, \tag{6.235}$$

which means that for $k \geq 9.00$, the system will always be stable.

When $9 \leq k < 45$, the period of the oscillation is given by Equation (6.234), and it is concluded that the origin is a *stable* focus. When $k \geq 45$, the origin becomes a *stable* node, for which the period is not defined.

It is further noted here that $\operatorname{sgn}(c - b) = \operatorname{sgn}(-6.25 - 1) = -1$. Therefore, the phase point moves along the trajectory clockwise. The period as given by Equation (6.234) gives good values for the true period (as computed on the IBM 7094 computer) as can be seen in Table 6.1. It is noted that the agreement is excellent near $k = 9$. This is important, since the consideration of tanks in series, to be considered later, demands the knowledge of the period of oscillation.

TABLE 6.1

Comparison of Calculated Periods of Limit Cycles and Foci with True Periods

k	Calculated period by Equation (6.234)	Computed period	Percent error
11	3.52	3.52	0
10	3.80	3.80	0
9	4.18	4.18	0
8	4.78	4.90	2
7	5.75	6.70	14
6	8.10	26.1	69

Returning to the analytical expression for the radial dependence for $k \geq 9$ as t approaches ∞, Equation (6.235) predicts that the limit cycle collapses as k approaches 9 and no cycles, either stable or unstable, exist for $k = 9$. This is a direct contradiction to the claim by Aris and Amundson [11], that for k greater than 9 but less than 9.025, an unstable limit cycle exists with radius equal to $0.0426\sqrt{k - 9}$, and a stable limit cycle surrounds this unstable one.

The reasons for computational difficulties when k is close to 9 are apparent when we look at Equation (6.228) when k is put equal to 9; namely,

$$dr/dt = -9.75r^3, \qquad \text{when } k = 9. \tag{6.236}$$

Furthermore, when the initial value of r is taken to be 0.02, the change of r with respect to time becomes

$$dr/dt = -7.8 \times 10^{-5}. \tag{6.237}$$

This means that at this value of r, in one cycle the radius is expected to decrease by only 0.00033. Unless the numerical integrations are performed very accurately, this small change might go by unnoticed, and one might conclude falsely that there is a limit cycle for $k = 9.00$. This illustrates the value of an analytical guide. Since only very small changes were anticipated, the results were carefully examined, and it was seen that, regardless of the initial conditions, at $k = 9$ the distance to the origin always decreased at a fixed value of one of the dependent variables.

To further check out this point, the limit cycles were accurately computed with k approaching the value of 9. These results are shown in Figures 6.3 and 6.4.

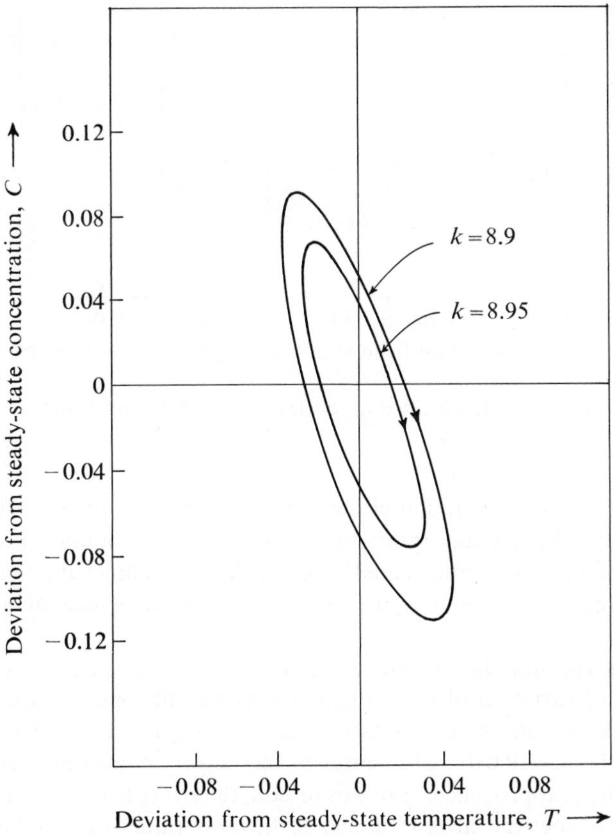

FIGURE 6.3. CSTR limit cycles for $k = 8.9$ and $k = 8.95$

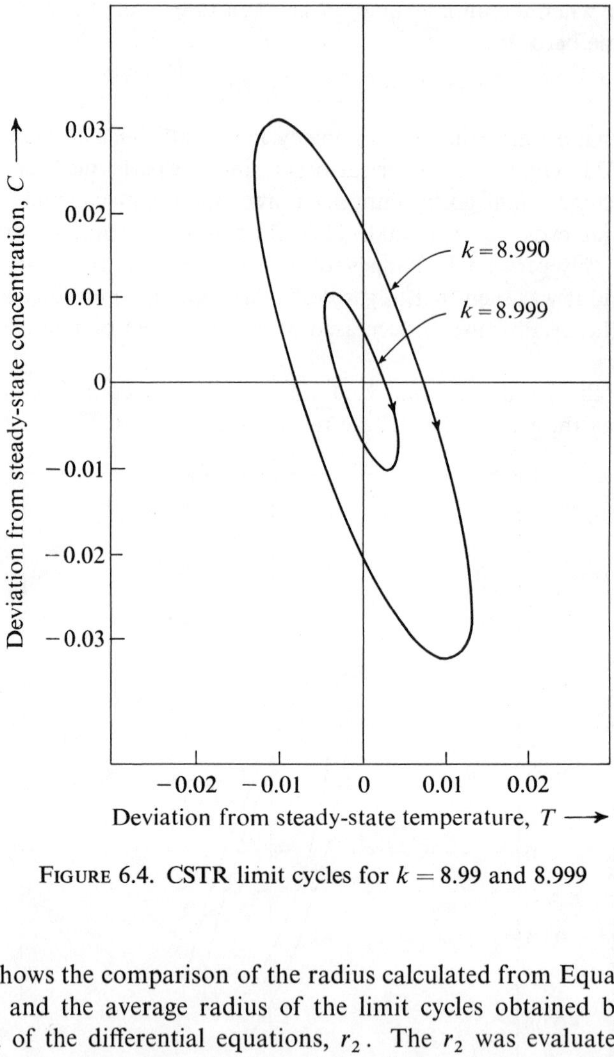

FIGURE 6.4. CSTR limit cycles for $k = 8.99$ and 8.999

Table 6.2 shows the comparison of the radius calculated from Equation (6.229), that is, r_1, and the average radius of the limit cycles obtained by numerical integration of the differential equations, r_2. The r_2 was evaluated by taking one-half the geometric mean of the major and the minor axes of the elliptical shape.

The fourth column shows that the ratio of r_1/r_2 is almost constant for the whole range of variation of the radius. Therefore, the agreement is good, and the limit cycle actually collapses as k reaches 9. Figures 6.5 and 6.6 show the phase plane for $k = 9.010$. The spiral is very slowly converging, especially as the steady state is approached. For this reason, the entire trajectory is not drawn. The position of the trajectory is shown at different values of time instead. The convergence is accurately predicted by Equation 6.229, as is shown in Table 6.3. The calculated values of the radius as determined by the linear approximation

TABLE 6.2

Comparison of Calculated Radius, r_1, with Measured Radius, r_2

k	$r_1 = 0.113\sqrt{9-k}$	$r_2 = \sqrt{\text{area of ellipse}/\pi}$	r_1/r_2
7.0	.148	.190	.78
8.2	.101	.130	.78
8.9	.036	.050	.72
8.95	.025	.035	.71
8.99	.011	.015	.74
8.999	.0036	.0053	.68

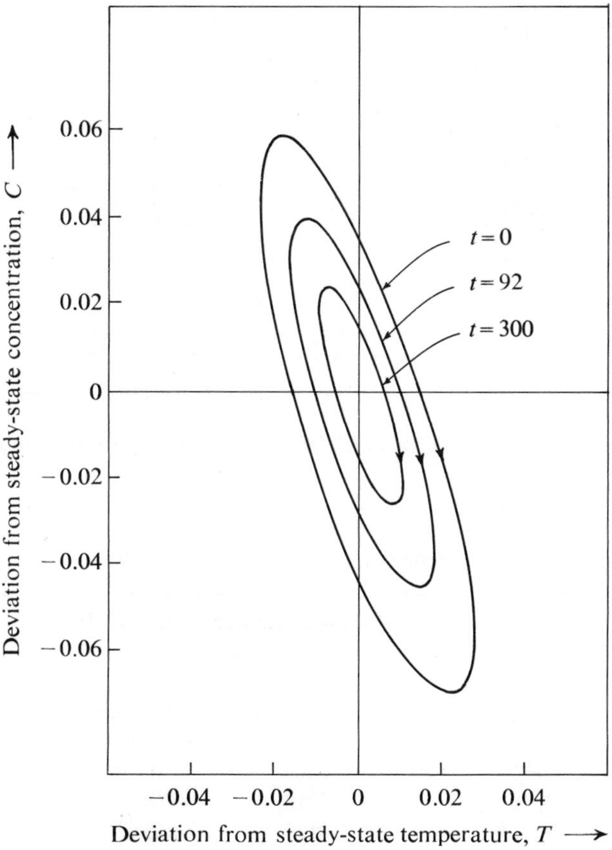

FIGURE 6.5. Convergence of CSTR system at $k = 9.010$

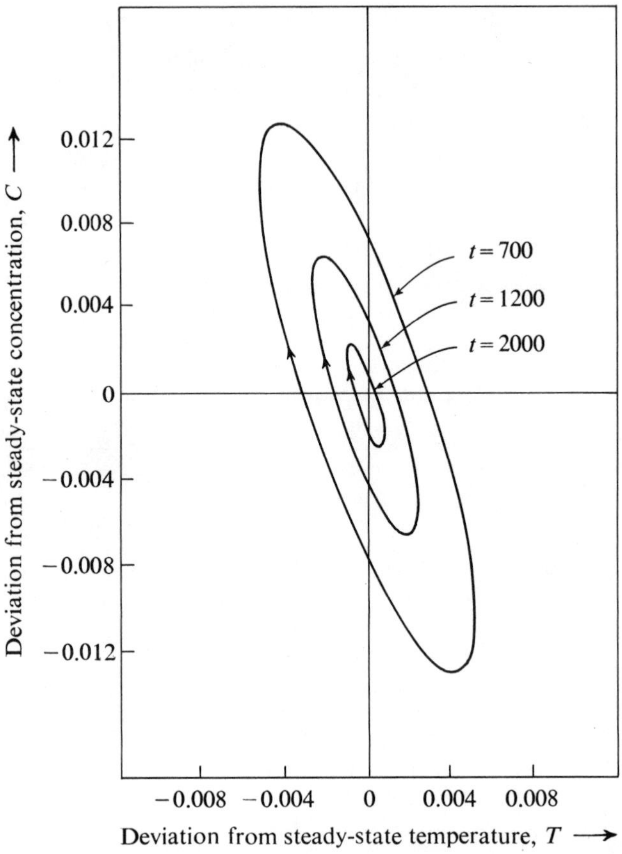

FIGURE 6.6. Convergence of CSTR system at $k = 9.010$ (continued)

TABLE 6.3

Convergence of the System at k = 9.010

Time	Radius calculated from Equation (6.229) r_1	Radius calculated from linear part r_3	Measured radius r_2	r_1/r_2	r_3/r_2
0	—	—	.0318	—	—
92	.0175	.0284	.0210	.83	1.35
300	.00961	.0218	.0120	.80	1.82
700	.00483	.0132	.00625	.78	2.11
1200	.00244	.00710	.00320	.76	2.22
2000	.000805	.00261	.00115	.70	2.28

to the exponential are also included. This is denoted by r_3. The ratios of r_1/r_2 and r_3/r_2 at once show the importance of including the square term to approximate the exponential even close to the origin. As can be seen, the ratio r_1/r_2 is within 30% of 1.0, whereas r_3/r_2 deviates by over 100%. It should also be noted that $0.0426\sqrt{9.010 - 9.000} = 0.00426$, so this value of the radius was passed without finding a stable or an unstable limit cycle.

APPLICATION OF BENDIXON'S NONEXISTENCE (FIRST) THEOREM TO DETERMINE THE EXISTENCE OF LIMIT CYCLES IN CSTR

EXAMPLE 6.2 ▪ In Section 6.4 we outlined the Bendixon's first theorem, which provides conditions under which limit cycles *cannot* exist in a given region. Its application to CSTR illustrates the difficulty of determining the existence of limit cycles. We shall consider the same CSTR as in Example 6.1, but we shall write the equations in the form

$$\dot{\eta} = -2(\eta - 1.75) - k(\eta - 2)(\eta - 1.75) + \xi \exp\left[50\left(\frac{1}{2} - \frac{1}{\eta}\right)\right] = P(\eta, \xi), \quad (6.238)$$

$$\dot{\xi} = 1 - \xi - \xi \exp\left[50\left(\frac{1}{2} - \frac{1}{\eta}\right)\right] = Q(\eta, \xi), \quad (6.239)$$

where η denotes the dimensionless temperature and ξ denotes the dimensionless concentration.

If we can find conditions under which $(\partial P/\partial\eta + \partial Q/\partial\xi)$ is sign-definite, then it is known that a limit cycle cannot exist in that region. From Equations (6.238) and (6.239), we find that

$$\frac{\partial P}{\partial \eta} + \frac{\partial Q}{\partial \xi} = -3 - 2k\eta + 3.75k + \left(\frac{50\xi}{\eta^2} - 1\right) \exp\left[50\left(\frac{1}{2} - \frac{1}{\eta}\right)\right]. \quad (6.240)$$

At the steady-state point, where $\eta = 2$, $\xi = 0.5$, Equation (6.240) becomes

$$(\partial P/\partial\eta + \partial Q/\partial\xi) = -3 - 4k + 3.75k + 5.25. \quad (6.241)$$

The expression (6.241) is zero only if $k = 2.25/0.25 = 9.0$. Therefore, the limiting value for k to produce limit cycles is 9.0.

It is not immediately apparent whether limit cycles exist for $k > 9$ or for $k < 9$. Consider, therefore, the region around the origin given by

$$\eta = 2.0 + \varepsilon, \qquad \xi = 0.5 + \delta. \quad (6.242)$$

When Equations (6.242) are substituted into Equation (6.240), there results

$$\frac{\partial P}{\partial \eta} + \frac{\partial Q}{\partial \xi} = -3 - 0.25k - 2\varepsilon k + \left[\frac{50(0.5 + \delta)}{(2.0 + \varepsilon)^2} - 1\right]\left[\exp\left(\frac{25\varepsilon}{2 + \varepsilon}\right)\right]. \quad (6.243)$$

Now suppose we arbitrarily set $\varepsilon = 0$. Equation 6.243 then becomes

$$(\partial P/\partial \eta + \partial Q/\partial \xi)_{\varepsilon=0} = 2.25 - 0.25k + 12.5\delta. \tag{6.244}$$

If $k > 9$, one can choose $\delta > 0$ to make (6.244) zero; if $k < 9$, one can choose $\delta < 0$ to make (6.244) zero. Therefore, according to Bendixon's theorem, limit cycles may exist for both $k > 9$ and $k < 9$. However, only when $k = 9$ is it possible to have a limit cycle right at the steady-state point. This is the only useful information that is obtained from Bendixon's theorem.

FORCED VAN DER POL EQUATION

EXAMPLE 6.3 ▪ Valuable insight into the behavior of nonlinear systems under the effect of forcing functions can be gained by considering a simple system such as the van der Pol equation forced by a sinusoidal forcing function. We shall write the differential equation as

$$\ddot{x} + \varepsilon(x^2 - 1)\dot{x} + x = A \sin \omega t, \tag{6.245}$$

where A is the amplitude of the forcing function and ω is the frequency.

It is known that without forcing (that is, $A = 0$), the system exhibits a stable limit cycle of radius 2, and if $\varepsilon < 1$, the frequency is close to 1. Since the maximum effect of the forcing function is expected when ω is equal to the frequency of the unforced case, we shall analyze such a situation with the averaging technique outlined in Section 6.6.

As before, the equation is written as two first-order differential equations

$$\dot{x} = y, \qquad \dot{y} = -x + \varepsilon(1 - x^2)y + A \sin \omega t. \tag{6.246}$$

In polar coordinates, the equation for the radial dependence is

$$dr/dt = (1/r)(\varepsilon y^2 - \varepsilon x^2 y^2 + Ay \sin \omega t), \tag{6.247}$$

where $r = \sqrt{x^2 + y^2}$. Assuming that ω is the same as the frequency of the unforced system, we obtain with the averaging technique

$$\frac{dr}{dt} = \frac{\varepsilon r}{2} - \frac{\varepsilon r^3}{8} + \frac{A}{2}. \tag{6.248}$$

Therefore, the radius of the resulting oscillation is given by

$$r_0^3 - 4r_0 - \frac{4A}{\varepsilon} = 0, \tag{6.249}$$

that is,

$$r_0 = \sqrt[3]{2A/\varepsilon + \sqrt{4A^2/\varepsilon^2 - 64/27}} + \sqrt[3]{2A/\varepsilon - \sqrt{4A^2/\varepsilon^2 - 64/27}}, \tag{6.250}$$

since r_0 must be real and positive (and therefore the other two values for r_0 resulting from the cubic equation are discarded). Equation (6.250) is used to evaluate r_0 when $(4A^2/\varepsilon^2 - 64/27) \geq 0$. Since ε is usually small, this condition is satisfied for most cases. If, however, $(4A^2/\varepsilon^2 - 64/27) < 0$, Equation (6.249) is used to evaluate r_0. It is also interesting to note from Equation (6.249) that if $A = 0$,

$$r_0^3 - 4r_0 = 0, \tag{6.251}$$

which gives $r_0 = 2$, the radius for the unforced system.

From Equation (6.248) we readily see that the oscillation as given by either Equation (6.249) or (6.250) is stable since when $r > r_0$, then $dr/dt < 0$, and when $r < r_0$, $dr/dt > 0$, and hence the radius approaches a constant value.

To verify the expression (6.250) for the radius of the limit cycle, its value is compared to the maximum value of x as obtained by numerical integration. Since the trajectories are nearly circular, this test is expected to be good. Although the natural frequency of the unforced system decreases slightly with increase in ε, in all cases the angular frequency of the input was taken as 1.00. Tables 6.4 and 6.5 show the good agreement between the expected and the true radius of the limit cycle.

TABLE 6.4

Expected vs. True Radius of Limit Cycle of Forced van der Pol Equation

	$A = 2.0$	$\omega = 1.0$	
ε	x_{max}	r_0	r_0/x_{max}
.001	20.0	20.0	1.00
.005	11.8	11.8	1.00
.01	9.41	9.44	1.00
.05	5.65	5.67	1.00
.10	4.60	4.62	1.00
.5	2.99	3.04	1.02
1.0	2.57	2.65	1.03

Tables 6.4 and 6.5 are of special interest since they show that the oscillations produced by a sinusoidal input at the natural frequency of the unforced system produce bounded oscillations. Instead of using the averaging technique, one could have obtained the same information by balancing the energy input and the energy dissipation terms. In steady state,

$$\varepsilon(x^2 - 1)\dot{x} \sim A. \tag{6.252}$$

TABLE 6.5

Expected vs. True Radius of Limit Cycle of Forced van der Pol Equation

$A = 10.0$		$\omega = 1.0$	
ε	x_{max}	r_0	r_0/x_{max}
.00005	92.7	92.8	1.00
.0001	73.6	73.7	1.00
.0005	43.0	43.1	1.00
.001	34.1	34.2	1.00
.005	19.9	20.0	1.00
.01	15.8	15.9	1.01
.05	9.18	9.42	1.02
.1	7.28	7.54	1.03
.5	4.33	4.62	1.06
1.0	3.53	3.81	1.08

So if x is large, we can rescale x by the equation

$$x = ay, \tag{6.253}$$

where a is a scaling factor and y is of the order of unity. Then,

$$\varepsilon a^3 \sim A,$$

and thus

$$a \sim \sqrt[3]{A/\varepsilon}. \tag{6.254}$$

This means that large forcing functions are damped out by the system. The same information is given by Equation (6.250) obtained by the averaging technique where, in addition, we also have the true expression for the radius of oscillation.

There is considerable ambiguity in the diagram presented by Hale [4, p. 49], where it is indicated that the radius of oscillation becomes very large as the frequency of the forcing function approaches the frequency of the unforced system. Furthermore, Hale stated that small forcing functions can produce large oscillations if ε is sufficiently small. For the development of the supporting equations, he used a forcing function of the order of ε. Figures 6.7 and 6.8 show that if the forcing function is of the order of ε, then the radius of the resulting oscillation is of the order of 2.5. This could also be seen very clearly from Equation (6.250) by substituting $A = \varepsilon$. Then,

$$r_0 = \sqrt[3]{2 + \sqrt{4 - 64/27}} + \sqrt[3]{2 - \sqrt{4 - 64/27}}; \tag{6.255}$$

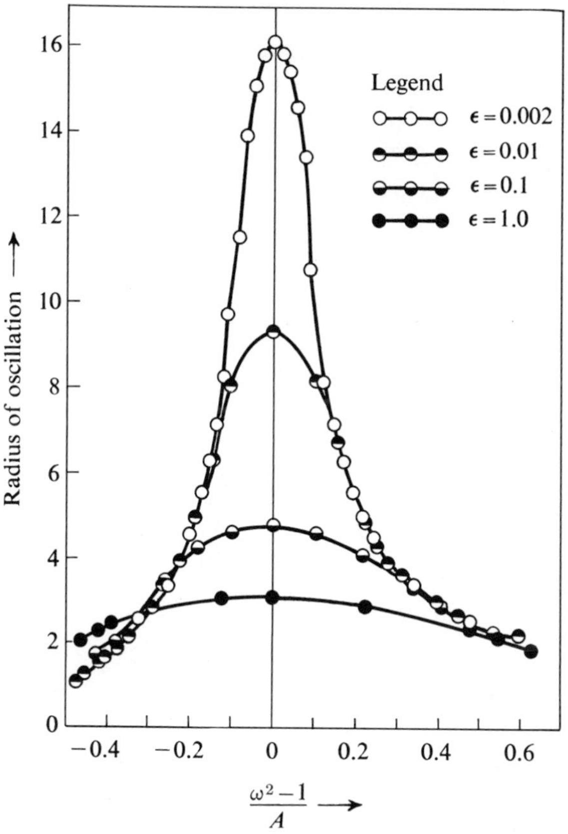

FIGURE 6.7. Entrainment of van der Pol's oscillator;
$\ddot{x} + \varepsilon(x^2 - 1)\dot{x} + x = A \sin \omega t \ (A = 2.0)$

that is, $r_0 = 2.39$, which is of the order of 2.5. It is also noted that for the forcing functions that have been used here, the maximum effect always occurs when the frequency of the input is the same as the natural frequency of the unforced system. This is not quite true for very large forcing functions. For example, when $A = 10$, the maximum effect was obtained when the frequency of the input was slightly *smaller* than the frequency of the unforced system. It appears that part of the energy, that is left over when the system acquires the same frequency as the forcing function in the process of synchronization, is used to increase the amplitude of the oscillation. There is thus amplitude-frequency coupling. However, the effect is small, and for the first approximation it can be said that the maximum effect is produced when the forcing function has the same frequency as the unforced system.

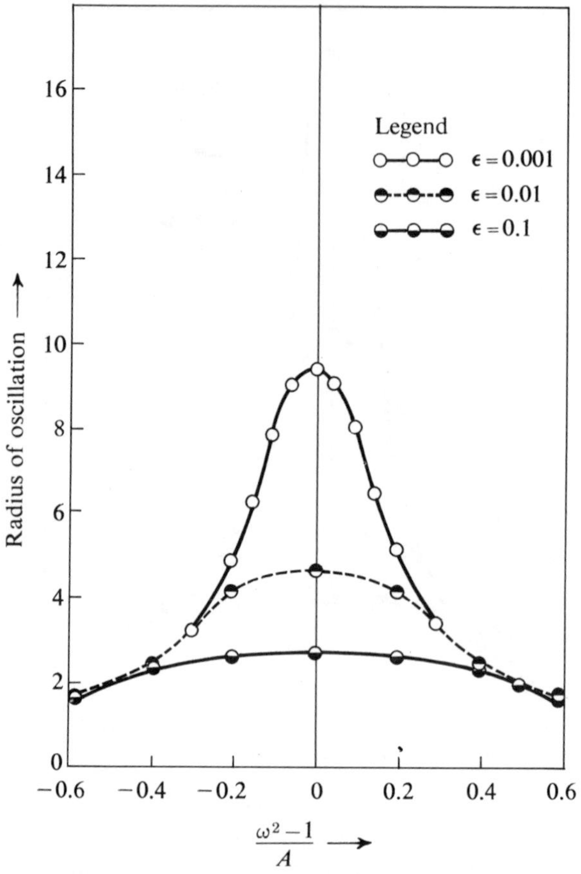

FIGURE 6.8. Entrainment of van der Pol's oscillator; $\ddot{x} + \varepsilon(x^2 - 1)\dot{x} + x = A \sin \omega t$ $(A = 0.2)$

The limit of synchronization as given by Hale [4, p. 49], that is, $|(\omega^2 - 1)/A| < 0.5$ is slightly surpassed. Also, the radius of oscillation at the limit of synchronization falls below 2.0, as is seen in Figures 6.7 and 6.8. When $|(\omega^2 - 1)/A|$ is greater than about 0.6, the autoperiodic frequency is no longer entrained by the forcing function frequency ω, and the system oscillates at both frequencies.

Interesting effects are observed when the frequency of the forcing function deviates greatly from the frequency of the unforced system. One such effect is illustrated in Figure 6.9, where the van der Pol equation is forced with a sine wave of frequency 2.5 rad/unit time. This also shows the usefulness of the phase-plane representation of nonautonomous systems to give a clear picture of what is happening.

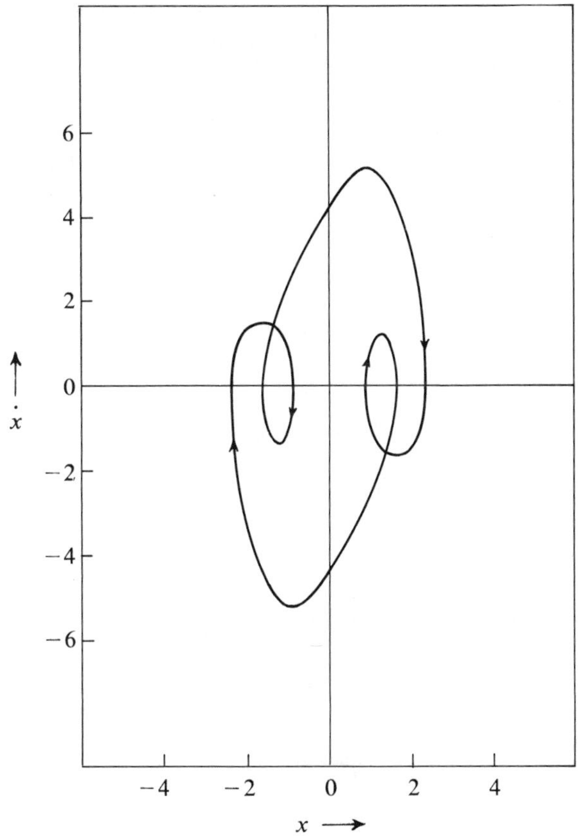

FIGURE 6.9. Forced van der Pol oscillator;
$\ddot{x} + \varepsilon(x^2 - 1)\dot{x} + x = A \sin \omega t$
$A = 5,\ \varepsilon = 1,\ \omega = 2.5$

CSTR WITH FORCING FUNCTION

EXAMPLE 6.4 ▪ In Example 6.3, where we considered the van der Pol equation with a sinusoidal forcing function, we saw that the resulting oscillations were bounded but that the amplitude was influenced by the magnitudes of ε and A and was greatest when the frequency of the forcing function was the same as the frequency of the unforced system. Also, it is well known that if a system is asymptotically stable and if a bounded constantly acting perturbation is acting on this system, the resulting fluctuations are bounded. However, in spite of boundedness, if a forcing function is introduced into a stable CSTR, the bounded temperature fluctuations might be too large, and for all practical purposes the system might be considered unstable. In addition, the output concentration might fluctuate so much that the product could be undesirable. In a real reactor system, perturbations in feed concentration or temperature might arise; thus it is of interest and importance to consider such a problem. For analysis, it is first assumed that the perturbation is a sine wave of the same frequency as the natural frequency of the unforced system.

(a) *Sinusoidal perturbation in feed temperature or concentration.* If a sinusoidal perturbation of amplitude A is introduced into the feed temperature, Equations (6.224) and (6.225) become

$$\dot{T} = (4.25 - 0.25k)T + C + (39 - k)T^2 + 12.5CT + 78CT^2 + A \sin \omega t, \quad (6.256)$$

$$\dot{C} = -6.25T - 2C - 39T^2 - 12.5CT - 78CT^2, \quad (6.257)$$

where ω is the frequency of the forcing function and is given by

$$\omega = \sqrt{6.25 - (3.125 - 0.125k)^2}. \quad (6.258)$$

By introducing $r = \sqrt{T^2 + C^2}$ and applying the averaging technique to Equations (6.256) and (6.257), we get

$$\dot{r} = \tfrac{1}{2}A + r(1.125 - 0.125k - 9.75r^2), \quad (6.259)$$

and the steady-state radius of oscillation is given by

$$r_0^3 + 0.0128(k - 9)r_0 - 0.0513A = 0, \quad (6.260)$$

which gives

$$r_0 = \sqrt[3]{0.0256A + B} + \sqrt[3]{0.0256A - B}, \quad (6.261)$$

where

$$B = \sqrt{6.56 \times 10^{-4}A^2 + 7.75 \times 10^{-8}(k - 9)^3}, \quad (6.262)$$

when the expression under the square-root sign is positive. If this condition is not fulfilled, the radius is calculated by trial and error from Equation (6.260).

It is immediately seen that if $r > r_0$, then $dr/dt < 0$, and if $r < r_0$, then $dr/dt > 0$. Thus the resulting oscillation is *stable* in the sense that a constant radius of oscillation will be reached.

At present, it is noted that if a sinusoidal perturbation of amplitude A is introduced into the feed concentration, Equations (6.224) and (6.225) become

$$\dot{T} = (4.25 - 0.25k)T + C + (39 - k)T^2 + 12.5CT + 78CT^2, \quad (6.263)$$

$$\dot{C} = -6.25T - 2C - 39T^2 - 12.5CT - 78CT^2 + A \sin \omega t, \quad (6.264)$$

and the averaging technique predicts the same radius of oscillation. In other words, it should not matter whether the perturbation is in feed temperature or in feed concentration. In either case, it is expected that the radius of oscillation is given by Equation (6.260) or (6.261). This brings up the importance of rescaling the dimensionless variables so that they are of the same order of magnitude.

Figures 6.10 and 6.11 show the oscillations produced in the asymptotically stable CSTR when a sinusoidal perturbation of amplitude equal to 0.05 is introduced into the feed temperature and concentration, respectively. It is

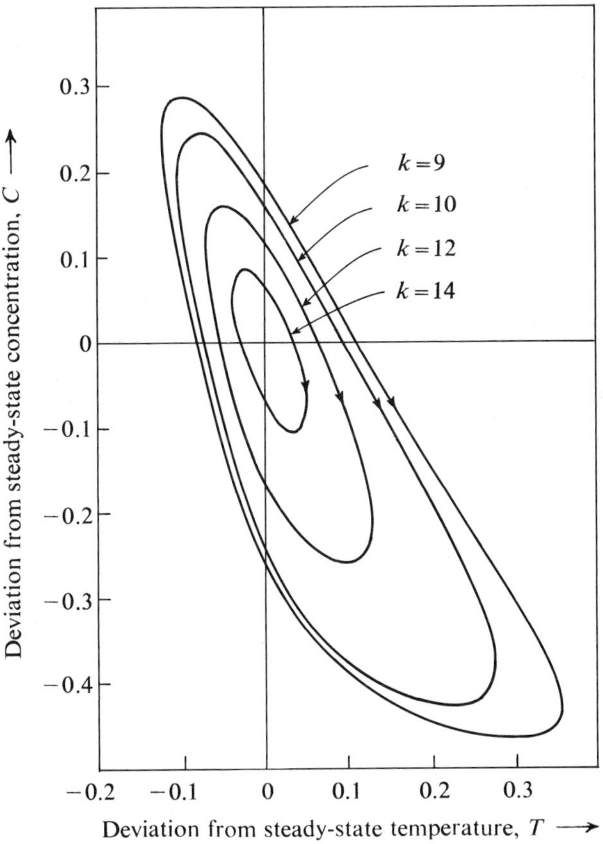

FIGURE 6.10. Sinusoidal input in temperature; $\eta_0 = 1.75 + 0.05 \sin \omega_n t$ and $\omega_n = \sqrt{6.25 - (6.25 - .25\,k)^2/4}$

apparent that temperature fluctuations in feed are of greater importance than concentration fluctuations, and that even at $k = 14$, the oscillations are still of considerable magnitude. These effects are shown in greater detail in Figure 6.12 (p. 427) where the average radius of the oscillation is plotted as a function of the

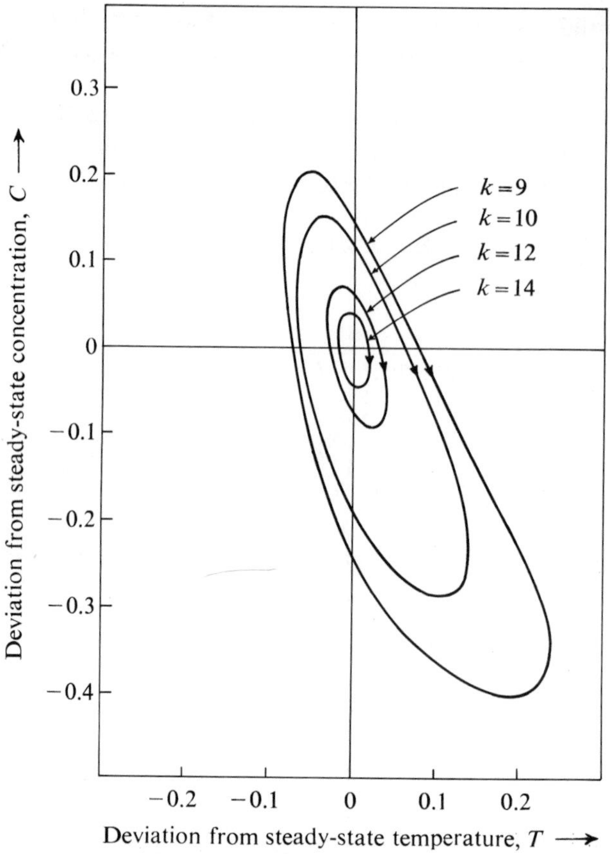

FIGURE 6.11. Sinusoidal input in concentration
$\xi_0 = 1 + 0.05 \sin \omega_n t,$
$\omega_n = \sqrt{[6.25 - (6.25 - 0.25\, k)^2]/4}$

control constant, k. Figure 6.13 shows the same type of results, but for a smaller perturbation. On these figures is also superimposed the radius as calculated from Equation (6.261). (See page 428.)

In every case, the maximum effect is obtained when the input perturbation is at the natural frequency of the unforced system. When the frequency of the forcing function is changed, the effect is decreased, as is shown in Figures 6.14 through 6.16 (pp. 429–431). At all these frequencies synchronization is obtained, that is, there is only one resulting frequency of oscillation which is equal to the input frequency. When the input frequency deviates much from the natural frequency of the unforced system, the system oscillates at both the input frequency and its own frequency. The effect is very noticeable when the input frequency is approximately one-half the natural frequency. One such result is shown in Figure 6.17

(p. 432). This also shows the importance of a detailed analysis of the system. It is not enough to consider only a part of a trajectory, since only the inner loop might be seen.

(b) *Triangular perturbation in feed temperature.* If a triangular perturbation of amplitude A is introduced into the feed temperature or the feed concentration, the equation for the radial dependence becomes

$$dr/dt = 0.406A + r(1.125 - 0.125k - 9.75r^2), \tag{6.265}$$

and

$$r_0 = \sqrt[3]{0.0208A + B^*} + \sqrt[3]{0.0208A - B^*}, \tag{6.266}$$

where

$$B^* = \sqrt{7.75 \times 10^{-8}(k - 9)^3 + 4.32 \times 10^{-4}A^2}, \tag{6.267}$$

provided that B^* is real. We shall leave the details to the reader to verify Equation (6.266).

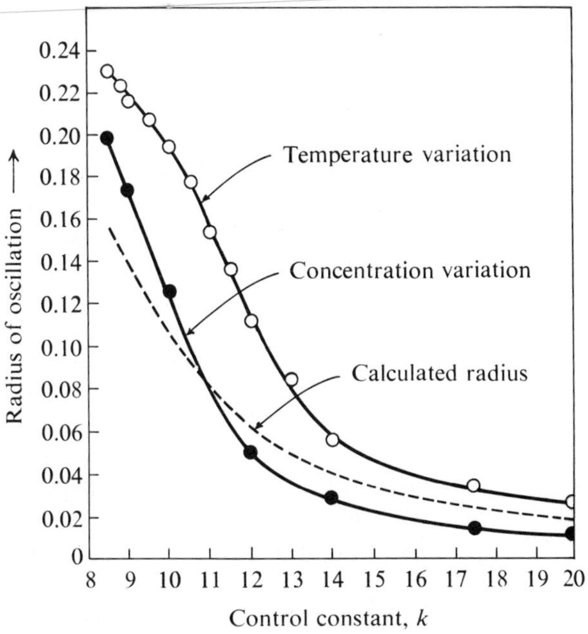

FIGURE 6.12. Production of oscillations by sinusoidal perturbations in feed of amplitude = 0.05 at natural frequency

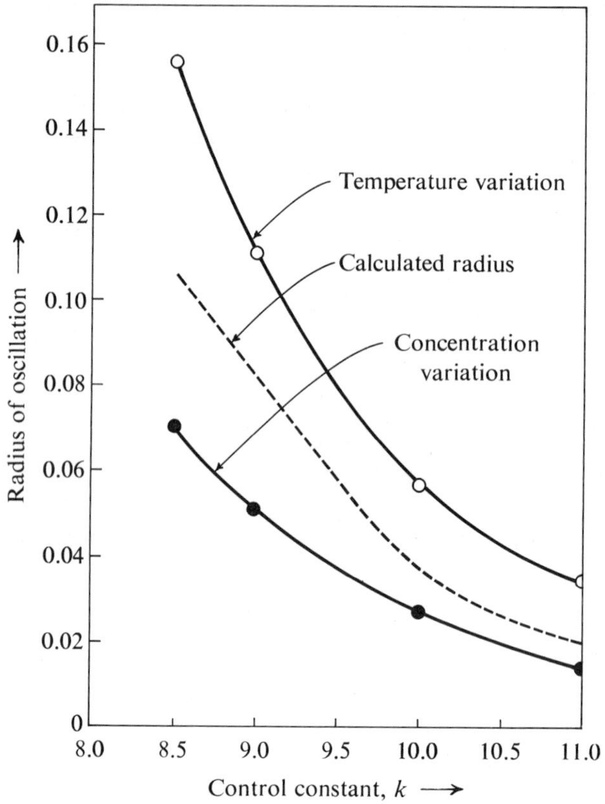

FIGURE 6.13. Production of oscillations by sinusoidal perturbations in feed of amplitude = 0.01 at natural frequency

Figure 6.18 (p. 433) shows the phase plane when the triangular perturbation of amplitude 0.05 is fed into the CSTR at its natural frequency. As was expected, the amplitude of oscillation is slightly less than when a sinusoidal perturbation of the same amplitude is used.

(c) *Step changes in feed temperature or concentration.* When step changes in the feed temperature or concentration are introduced, the result is to change both the steady state and the initial condition. The analysis, however, is the same as for the autonomous CSTR discussed in Example 6.1, and thus will not be detailed again.

(d) *Control of the CSTR.* For the CSTR to be amenable to control, it is necessary that periodic perturbations in the feed should produce smaller perturbations in the output. From Figure 6.12 we see that when k is chosen greater than 17, this requirement is achieved. This will also give good quality of control

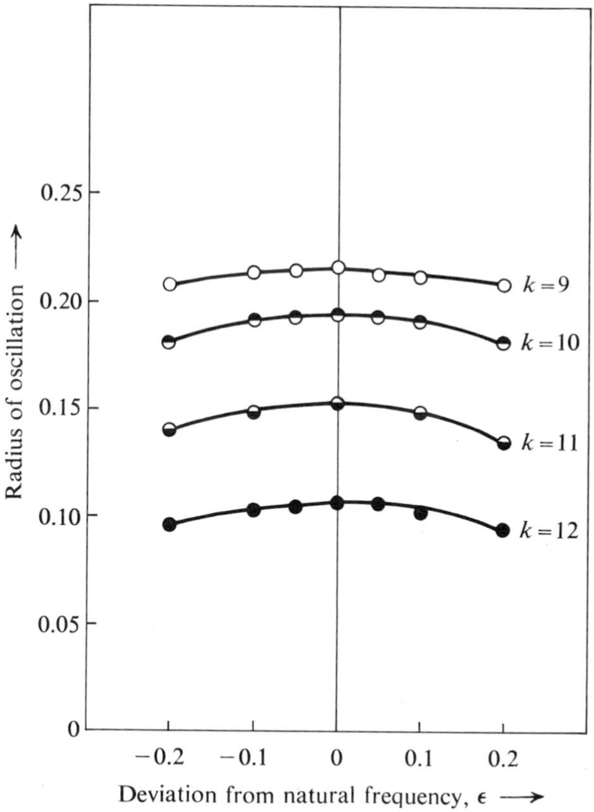

FIGURE 6.14. Oscillations produced by sinusoidal perturabtions in feed temperature; $\eta_0 = 1.75 + 0.05 \sin [(\omega_n + \varepsilon)t]$

for step changes. It is thus suggested that the control constant be kept larger than 17, but not too large, in case the time delays in the mechanical part of the system offset the benefits gained by having a large proportionality constant.

CSTR'S IN SERIES

EXAMPLE 6.5 ▪ In the previous example it was noted that a small periodic disturbance in the input temperature or concentration at the natural frequency of the reactor could produce large oscillations in the temperature and concentration in the output, even if the reactor is asymptotically stable with constant input. Since a packed-bed reactor can be approximated by a series of CSTR's [see 15], con-

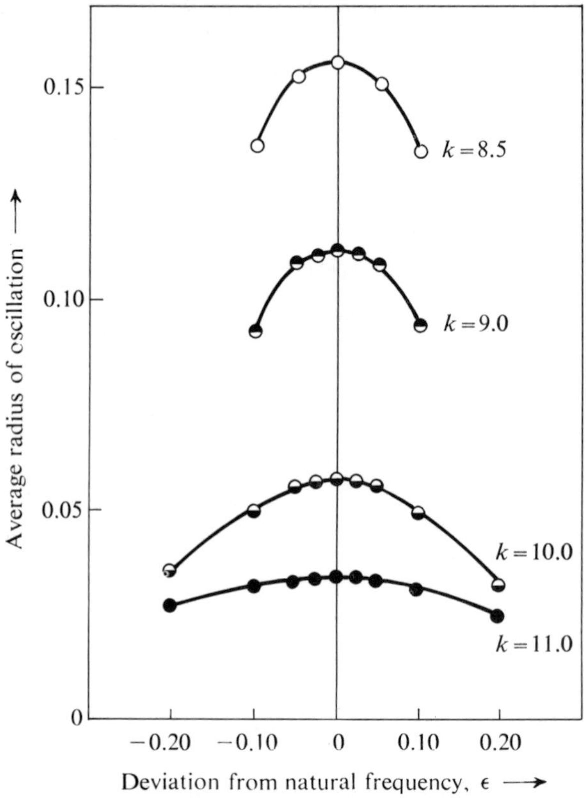

FIGURE 6.15. Oscillations produced by sinusoidal perturbations in feed temperature; $\eta_0 = 1.75 + 0.01 \sin [(\omega_n + \varepsilon)t]$

sideration of CSTR's in series may give some idea of the stability ot the packed-bed reactor. Therefore, one is faced with the problem of analyzing the effect of feeding the output from the first tank into the second tank, the output from the second tank into the third tank, and so on. It is especially interesting to see what happens if the control constant, k, is chosen so that a limit cycle is already produced in the first tank and is fed into the second tank, etc. Will the limit cycle grow or shrink in the successive tanks? This question will be answered below.

To answer these questions by straight digital computation requires an enormous amount of work, since the propagation of the disturbance must be studied for many values of k; the calculations for each value of k must be carried for various values of the initial conditions in each succeeding tank; and finally the calculations must be continued long enough to ensure that the over-all system has come to a steady state. Therefore, this problem will be approached analytically by the averaging technique, and the approximate solution will be checked by computations on the computer for only two values of k.

The calculations are straightforward. The subscript 0 will be used for the input to a tank under consideration and the subscript 1, for its output.

First tank

$$\xi_0 = 1.0, \qquad \eta_0 = 1.75; \tag{6.268}$$

$$\dot{\xi} = 1.0 - \xi - \xi Y, \qquad \dot{\eta} = -2(\eta - 1.75) - k(\eta - 2)(\eta - 1.75) + \xi Y, \tag{6.269}$$

where

$$Y = \exp\left[50\left(\frac{1}{2} - \frac{1}{\eta}\right)\right],$$
$$dr/dt = r(1.125 - 0.125k - 9.75r^2). \tag{6.270}$$

Thus if $5 < k < 9$, the output from the first tank will be

$$r_1 = 0.113\sqrt{9 - k}. \tag{6.271}$$

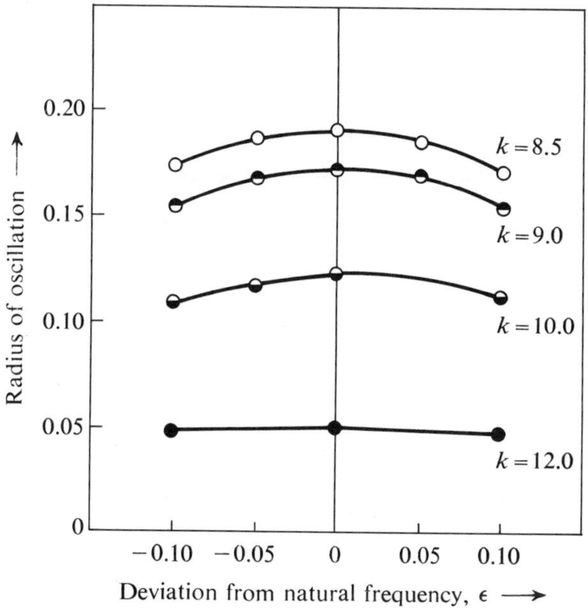

FIGURE 6.16 Oscillations produced by sinusoidal perturbations in feed concentration; $\xi_0 = 1 + 0.05 \sin [(\omega_n + \varepsilon)t]$

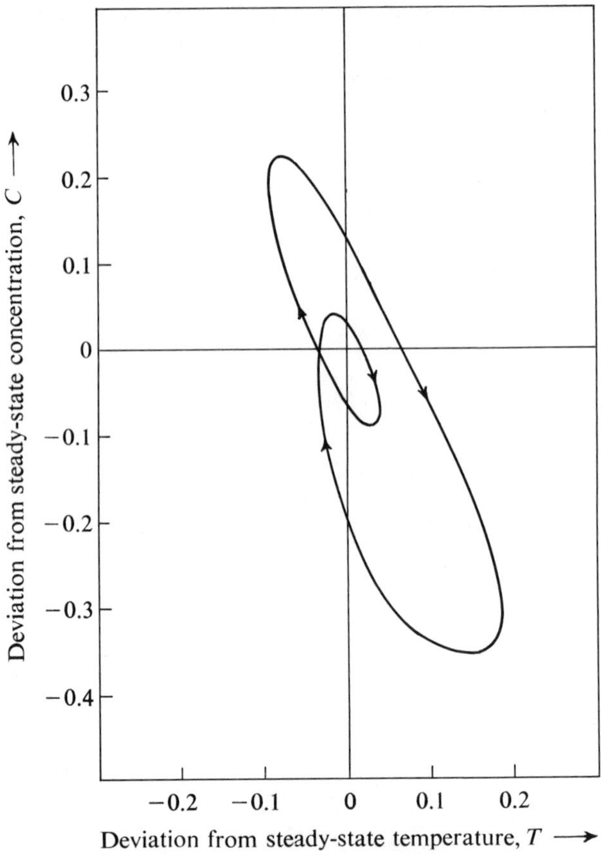

FIGURE 6.17. Response to input at half the natural frequency; $\eta_0 = 1.75 + 0.05 \sin [\omega_n t/2]$, $k = 10.0$

Second tank

$$\xi_0 = 0.5 + r_0 \sin \psi, \qquad \eta_0 = 2.0 + r_0 \cos \psi, \tag{6.272}$$

where $r_0 = 0.113\sqrt{9 - k}$. The differential equations describing the mass and heat balances are

$$\begin{aligned} \dot{\xi} &= 0.5 + r_0 \sin \psi - \xi - \xi Y, \\ \dot{\eta} &= -\,2\eta + 3.75 + r_0 \cos \psi - k(\eta - 2)(\eta - 1.75) + \xi Y. \end{aligned} \tag{6.273}$$

Immediately, one gets

$$dr/dt = r_0 - r(0.438 + 0.125k + 9.75r^2). \tag{6.274}$$

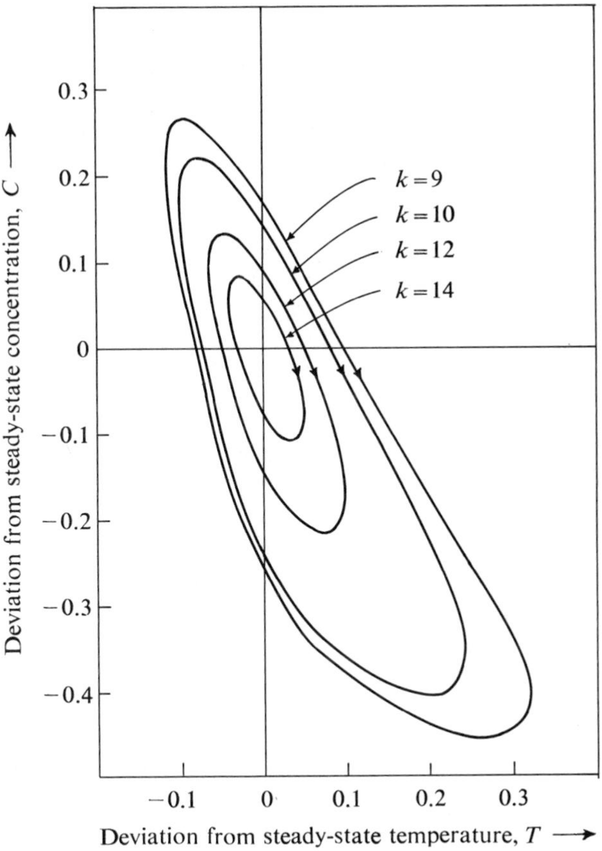

FIGURE 6.18. Response to triangular input in temperature at natural frequency and amplitude of 0.05

At this time, an important observation is made. The radius of the oscillation can be written as

$$r_1 = \frac{r_0}{0.438 + 0.125k + 9.75r_1^2}. \tag{6.275}$$

Since k is taken to be greater than 5, the denominator is always greater than unity. Therefore, the limit cycle will be smaller in the second tank.

Third tank

$$\xi_0 = 0.25 + r_0 \sin \psi, \qquad \eta_0 = 2.0 + r_0 \cos \psi, \tag{6.276}$$

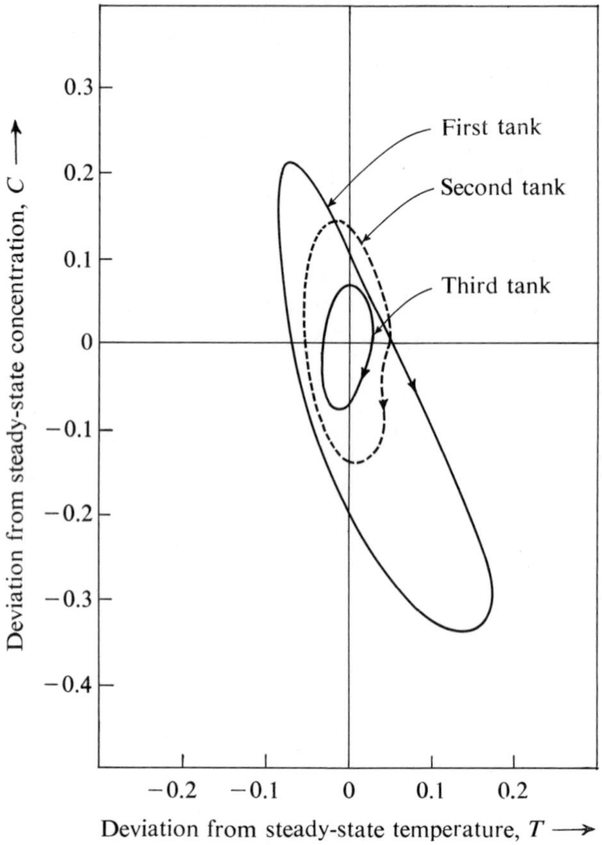

FIGURE 6.19. Consideration of CSTR's in series; $k = 8.0$

where r_0 is given by r_1 in Equation (6.275).

$$\begin{aligned}\dot{\xi} &= 0.25 + r_0 \sin \psi - \xi - \xi Y,\\ \dot{\eta} &= -2\eta + 3.75 + r_0 \cos \psi - k(\eta - 2)(\eta - 1.75) + \xi Y.\end{aligned} \tag{6.277}$$

The steady-state point is approximately (1.96, 0.167) when k is about 8. This gives

$$dr/dt = r_0 - r(0.75 + 0.085k + 0.781r^2), \tag{6.278}$$

so that

$$r_1 = \frac{r_0}{0.75 + 0.085k + 0.781r_1^2}. \tag{6.279}$$

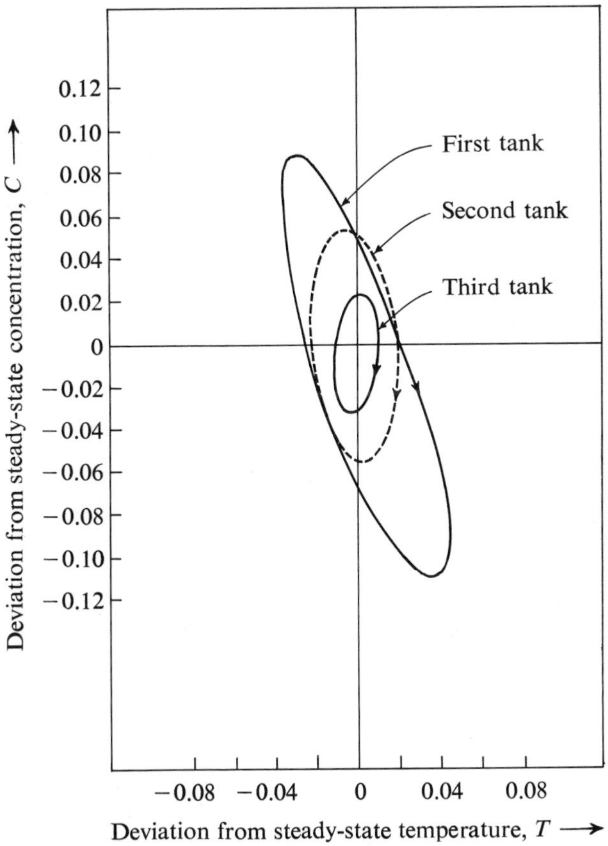

FIGURE 6.20. Consideration of CSTR's in series; $k = 8.9$

Again, we see that the denominator is always greater than unity if $k > 5$. Therefore, the limit cycle damps out.

It is concluded that under the conditions whereby limit cycles are formed in the first tank, the limit cycles become smaller in successive tanks. Since the natural frequencies of the other tanks differ from each other, the damping is expected to be even greater than predicted by the above equations.

Figures 6.19 and 6.20 show how the limit cycle shrinks in successive tanks for $k = 8$ and $k = 8.9$. The effect is close to the predicted effect, as is shown in Figure 6.21.

In the above calculations, it has been assumed that the coolant water temperature is the same for each tank. However, if the CSTR's are to represent a packed-bed reactor, it is possible that the coolant water temperature may decrease or increase in successive tanks, representing countercurrent or cocurrent cooling

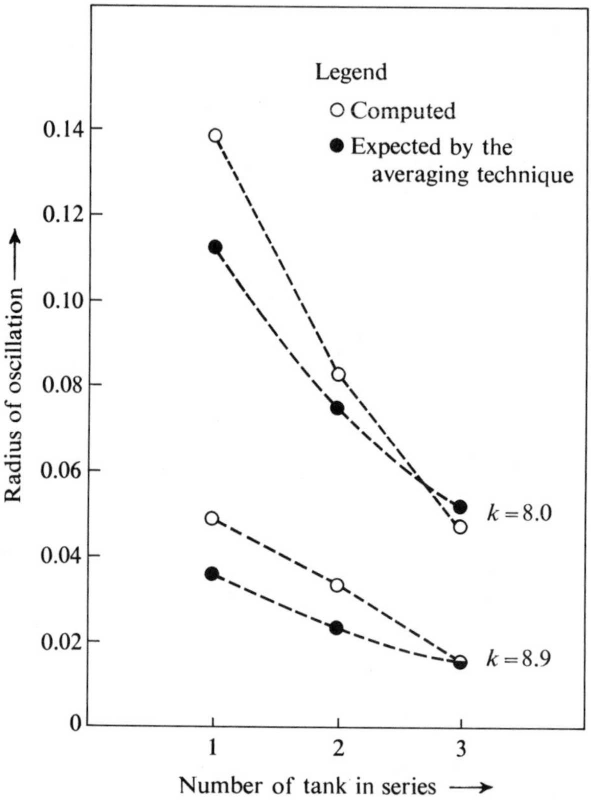

FIGURE 6.21. Comparison of predicted and computed radii of oscillations in tanks connected in series

systems, respectively. Figure 6.22 shows that the maximum oscillations are produced when the coolant water temperature is approximately the same in each tank. Here, the limit cycle from the first tank with $k = 8.9$ is fed into the second CSTR, which is identical to the first one except for the coolant water temperature, which is allowed to be different from 1.75. When the coolant water temperature is greater than 1.75, the CSTR operates at a higher temperature but the oscillation is smaller. Similarly, below 1.75 the CSTR operates at a lower temperature but the oscillation is smaller than when the coolant water temperature is 1.75. Thus in a packed-bed reactor, the oscillations in temperature and concentration are damped out for both countercurrent and cocurrent cooling systems.

These five examples illustrate the application and the usefulness of the averaging technique. In all cases, the digital computer was used to check the predicted

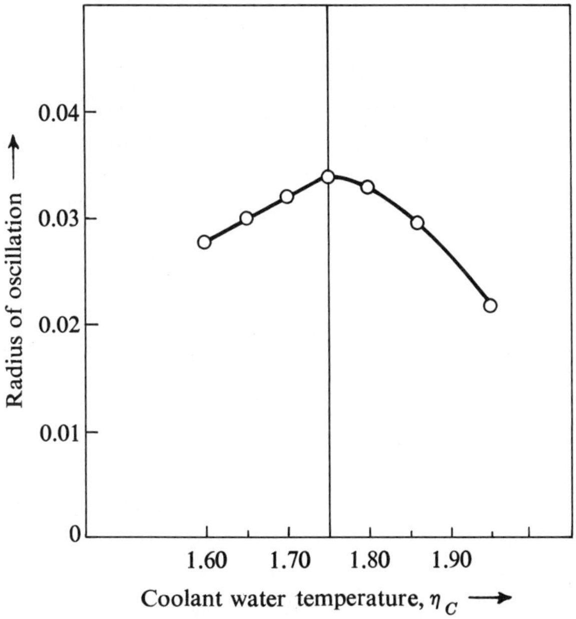

FIGURE 6.22. Effect of changing coolant water temperature in second CSTR; $k = 8.9$

behavior and to furnish additional information when required. The averaging technique has the great advantage of allowing parameters to remain as parameters in the equations, and thus gives information over the entire range of variation.

References

BOOKS

1. H. A. ANTOSIEWICZ, "A Survey of Liapunov's Second Method," in S. Lefschetz (Editor), *Contributions to Nonlinear Oscillations, IV*," *Ann. Math. Study*, pp. 141–166, Princeton University Press, Princeton, N.J., 1958.
2. N. N. BOGOLIUBOV and J. A. MITROPOLSKY, *Asymptotic Methods in the Theory of Nonlinear Oscillations*, translation, Hindustan Publishing Corp., Delhi-6, 1961.
3. W. HAHN, *Theory and Application of Liapunov's Direct Method*, translation, Prentice-Hall, Englewood Cliffs, N.J., 1963.
4. J. K. HALE, *Oscillations in Nonlinear Systems*, McGraw-Hill, New York, 1963.
5. N. KRYLOV and N. N. BOGOLIUBOV, *Introduction to Nonlinear Mechanics*, Ann. Math. Study, No. 11, Princeton University Press, Princeton, N.J., 1943.
6. H. LAMB, *Hydrodynamics*, Cambridge University Press, Cambridge, Great Britain, 1930.

7. J. P. LaSalle and S. Lefschetz, *Stability by Liapunov's Direct Method with Applications*, Academic Press, New York, 1961.
8. A. M. Liapunov, *Probléme Général de la Stabilité du Mouvement*, Ann. Math. Study, No. 17, Princeton University Press, Princeton, N.J., 1947.
9. N. Minorsky, *Nonlinear Oscillations*, D. van Nostrand Co., Princeton, N.J., 1962.
10. V. I. Zubov, *Mathematical Methods for the Study of Automatic Control Systems*, translation, Macmillan Co., New York, 1963.

ARTICLES

11. R. Aris and N. R. Amundson, *Chem. Eng. Sci.*, *7*, 121, 132, 148 (1958).
12. F. N. Bailey, *J. SIAM Control*, *3*, 443 (1966).
13. J. S. Berger and D. D. Perlmutter, *A. I. Ch. E. Jrn.*, *10*, 233, 238 (1964); *Chem. Eng. Sci.*, *20*, 147 (1965); *IEC Fund.*, *4*, 90 (1965).
14. O. Bilous and N. R. Amundson, *A. I. Ch. E. Jrn.*, *1*, 513 (1955).
15. H. Deans and L. Lapidus, *A. I. Ch. E. Jrn.*, *6*, 663 (1960).
16. J. M. Douglas and D. W. T. Rippin, *Chem. Eng. Sci.*, *21*, 305 (1966).
17. C. E. Gall and R. Aris, *Canad. Jrn. Chem. Eng.*, *43*, 16 (1965).
18. G. R. Gavales, *Chem. Eng. Sci.*, *21*, 477 (1966).
19. G. R. Geiss, "The Analysis and Design of Nonlinear Control Systems via Liapunov's Direct Method," *Grumman Aircraft Engineering Corp. Report RTD-TDR-63-4076*, Bethpage, N.Y. (1964).
20. R. P. Goldstein and N. R. Amundson, *Chem. Eng. Sci.*, *20*, 195 (1965).
21. I. A. Gura and D. D. Perlmutter, *A. I. Ch. E. Jrn.*, *11*, 474 (1965).
22. M. D. Kruskal, "Asymptotology," *AEC Res. and Dev. Report MATT-160* (1962).
23. J. P. LaSalle, *J. SIAM Control*, *A*, *1*, 3 (1962).
24. R. Luus, "The Stability of Autonomous and Nonautonomous Nonlinear Systems," *Ph. D. Dissertation, Princeton University* (1964).
25. R. Luus and L. Lapidus, *Chem. Eng. Sci.*, *21*, 159 (1966).
26. S. G. Margolis and W. G. Vogt, *IEEE Trans. Auto. Control*, *AC-8*, 104 (1963).
27. N. Minorsky, *J. Franklin Inst.*, *254*, 21 (1952).
28. W. O. Paradis and D. D. Perlmutter, *A. I. Ch. E. Jrn.*, *12*, 130 (1966).
29. T. Pavlidis, *Inform. and Control*, *9*, 298 (1966).
30. N. N. Puri and R. L. Drake, *J. Franklin Inst.* *276*, 209 (1965).
31. W. Regenass and R. Aris, *Chem. Eng. Sci.*, *20*, 60 (1965).
32. M. J. Reilly and R. A. Schmitz, *A. I. Ch. E. Jrn.*, *12*, 153 (1966).
33. D. G. Schultz and J. E. Gibson, *Trans. AIEE*, *81*, 203 (1962).
34. D. D. Siljak and M. R. Stojic, *IEEE Trans. Auto. Control*, *AC-10*, 413 (1965).
35. C. P. Szego, *Appl. Mech. Review*, *19*, 833 (1966).
36. P. K. C. Wang, *J. Franklin Inst.*, *281*, 51 (1966).
37. R. B. Warden, R. Aris, and N. R. Amundson, *Chem. Eng. Sci.*, *19*, 149, 173 (1964).

Index

Index

A B C D E F G H I J 5 4 3 2 1 7 0 6 9 8 7